Instructor's Guide with Solutions
for Moore, McCabe, Duckworth, and Alwan's

The Practice of Business Statistics
Second Edition

Ellen Gundlach
Purdue University

Lori Seward
University of Colorado at Boulder

D1511550

W.H. Freeman and Company
New York

ISBN-13: 978-0-7167-3010-1
ISBN-10: 0-7167-3010-3

Printed in the United States of America

First printing

W. H. Freeman and Company
41 Madison Avenue
New York, NY 10010
Houndmills, Basingstoke
RG21 6XS England

www.whfreeman.com

CONTENTS

Preface

This Instructor's Manual is intended to help you teach from the second edition of *The Practice of Business Statistics* (*PBS*). It is broken down into two parts. The first part contains teaching tips, suggestions for using the *Against All Odds* and *Decisions Through Data* videos, and comments on planning your course, along with individual chapter comments. The second part, and by far the longest of the two parts, contains worked out solutions to all of the exercises in the text.

Lori Seward (University of Colorado at Boulder) wrote the solutions to the original chapter exercises in the first edition. For the second edition, I picked up these solutions in the relatively small number of times when the exercises remained the same, and I used these original solutions as a framework when the data changed. I wrote the solutions to all of the new exercises, and often added SPSS output in these cases.

The authorship of the first part of this Instructor's Manual is more varied. David Moore, Darryl Nester (Bluffton University), and Lori Seward provided this instructor's material for the first edition of *PBS*. They did such a nice job that I have kept most of the original comments but updated some of the websites and made some minor changes.

If you have any suggestions or corrections to the solutions, please feel free to contact me. I am always happy to talk with other teachers who are enthusiastic about sharing the importance of statistics with students.

Ellen Gundlach
Purdue University
gundlach@stat.purdue.edu

To the Instructor

Philosophy

Here are the key ways in which *The Practice of Business Statistics* differs from more traditional texts:

- There is more attention to data analysis. Chapters 1 and 2 give quite full coverage. It is now becoming common to emphasize data in a first course, but many texts still begin with a too-brief treatment of "descriptive statistics."
- There is more attention to designing data production. It is surprising to a practicing statistician how little attention these ideas (among the most influential aspects of statistics) receive in many first courses. Chapter 3 discusses sampling and experimental design, with attention to some of the practical issues involved.
- Probability is covered in two chapters. Chapter 4 contains only the probability material that is needed to understand statistical inference. Chapter 5 includes additional probability material, such as Poisson distributions that are often used in business processes.
- There is more discussion of the ideas of inference. Chapter 6 (with the introduction to sampling distributions in Chapter 4) is the core of the presentation of inference. The ideas aren't easy but are the key to an understanding that is more than mechanical.
- The presentation of significance tests emphasizes *P*-values rather than probabilities of Type I and Type II errors and tests with fixed α. This reflects common practice and helps students understand the output of statistical software. The alternative approach appears in the optional Section 6.4.
- The discussion of the power of a significance test should also be a requirement in any complete business statistics course. It is a difficult concept for the students to grasp but seeing it at this introductory level will make it easier to understand the next time they encounter the idea of power.
- There is more attention to statistics in practice. Realism may be too much to claim in a book that is genuinely elementary. Nonetheless, Chapter 3 describes the practical difficulties of producing good data and the exposition and examples in Chapters 7 to 11 raise many issues that arise in applying inference methods to real problems.

Upon completion of a course based on *PBS*, students should be able to think critically about data, select and use graphical and numerical summaries, apply standard statistical inference procedures, and draw conclusions from such analyses. They are ready for more specialized statistics courses (such as applied regression or quality control), "research methods" courses in many fields of study, and projects, reports, or employment that require basic data analysis.

Calculators and Computers

The practice of statistics requires a good deal of graphing and numerical calculation. Doing some graphing and calculating "by hand" may build understanding of methods. On the other hand, graphics and calculations are always automated in statistical practice. Moreover, struggling with computational aspects of a procedure often interferes with a full understanding of the concepts. Students are easily frustrated by their inability to complete problems correctly. Automating the arithmetic greatly improves their ability to complete problems. We therefore favor automating calculations and graphics as much as your resources and setting allow.

All students should have a calculator that does "two-variable statistics," that is, that calculates not only x and s but the correlation r and the least-squares regression line from keyed-in data. *PBS* is written so that a student with such a calculator will not often be frustrated by the required calculations. Even if you use computer software, students should have a calculator for use during class, at home, and on exams. Two-variable statistics calculators are inexpensive (generally available for less than $20). *PBS* does not present anachronistic "computing formulas" that presuppose a four-function calculator.

Based on experience with large classes, it is almost a "must" for the students to have the same type of calculator. Business students will most likely find some type of financial calculator useful for future courses. Perhaps you might want to give your students a choice between two calculators in two different price ranges so that during class you don't have to struggle with many different types of keypads. Small classes (fewer than 30 students) can take advantage of graphing calculators.

Graphing calculators now automate almost all procedures discussed in a first statistics course, including basic graphs. Calculators have the great advantage that students own them, carry them around, and take them home. If everyone in the classroom has a graphing calculator, class discussions can take on new dimensions: pose a problem and let everyone work on it. Students who took advanced math in high school are often familiar with graphing calculators when they arrive in our classes. If your circumstances favor use of a specific type of graphing calculator, by all means do it.

Software retains some clear advantages in entering and editing data and in graphics not constrained by the small window of a graphing calculator. Almost all students now have some familiarity with personal computers, so that the learning curve for menu-driven software is short and steep. Use software, even a spreadsheet such as Excel, if you can. A good deal of computer output appears in *PBS*, from several different packages. Separate student guides keyed to *PBS* are available for most of these options. The output is deliberately varied because any statistics student should become accustomed to looking at computer output and should be able to recognize terms and results familiar from her study.

The solutions included in this manual were solved with both Excel and Minitab. SPSS now is used in some of the solutions. The emphasis is on Excel output. Although some professionals view Excel as less sophisticated and more cumbersome than other software packages, it is a great teaching tool. Many students are expected to use Excel in future course work and while interning in industry jobs. Students who can use Excel for statistical analysis are capable of learning to use more sophisticated software very quickly. Students who learn a more sophisticated software package may not be able to step back down to Excel if they need to in a future course or during their initial employment.

Using Video

One of the most effective ways to convince your students that statistics is useful is to show them real people (not professors) employing statistics in a variety of settings. Video allows you to do this in the classroom. Two related video series that contain many short documentaries of statistics in use "on location" are:

- *Against All Odds: Inside Statistics*. This telecourse, consisting of 26 half-hour programs, was prepared by COMAP for the Annenberg Corporation for Public Broadcasting Project. It is available in the United States at a subsidized price. Call 1-800-LEARNER or visit the website (http://www.learner.org) for information or to order a copy.
- *Statistics: Decisions Through Data*. This set of 21 shorter modules (5 hours total) is intended for use as a classroom supplement in secondary schools. It was prepared by COMAP for the National Science Foundation and draws on the location segments of *Against All Odds*. It is available from COMAP. Call 1-800-77-COMAP for information or visit http://www.comap.com/ . If you are outside the United States, you can obtain information about both video series from:

COMAP Inc.
Suite 210
57 Bedford Street
Lexington, MA 02173 USA
Fax 1-617-863-1202

Because David Moore was the content developer for these video series, they fit the style and sequence of *PBS* well. We do not recommend showing complete programs from *Against All Odds* in the classroom. The shorter modules from *Decisions Through Data* are more suitable for classroom use. Video is a poor medium for exposition, and it leaves viewers passive. It is therefore generally not a good substitute for a live teacher. We suggest regular showing of selected on-location stories from AAO or DTD in most classrooms, rather than full programs. If you have a very large lecture (several hundred students), however, full DTD video modules along with computer demonstrations will help hold an audience too large for personal interaction.

Video has several strengths that make short segments an ideal supplement to your own teaching. Television can bring real users of statistics and their settings into the classroom. And psychologists find that television communicates emotionally rather than rationally, so that it is a vehicle for changing attitudes. One of our goals in teaching basic statistics is to change students' attitudes about the subject. Because video helps do this, consider showing video segments regularly even if you don't think they help students learn the specific topic of that class period. You can find more discussion of the uses of video and references in Moore, 1993.

Here are some specific suggestions for excerpts from *Against All Odds* and *Decisions Through Data* that work effectively in class:

• The 14-minute video *What is Statistics?* is a good way to start a course. This collage of examples from *Against All Odds* forms part of the first unit of AAO and is the first module of DTD. It is available separately (and inexpensively) from:

The American Statistical Association
1429 Duke Street
Alexandria, VA 22314 USA
(703) 684-1221 or www.amstat.org

• *Lightning Research* from Program 2 of AAO and Module 3 of DTD. A study of lightning in Colorado discovers interesting facts from a histogram.
• *Calories in Hot Dogs* from Program 3 of AAO and Module 5 of DTD. The five-number summary and box plots compare beef, meat, and poultry hot dogs.
• *The Boston Beanstalk Club* from Program 4 of AAO, and Module 7 of DTD. This social club for tall people leads to discussion of the 68–95–99.7 rule for normal distributions.
• *Saving the Manatees* from Program 8 of AAO and Module 11 of DTD. There is a strong linear relation between the number of power boats registered in Florida and the number of manatees killed by boats.
• *Obesity and Metabolism* from Program 8 of AAO and Module 12 of DTD looks at the linear relationship between lean body mass and metabolic rate in the context of a study of obesity.
• *Sampling at Frito-Lay* from Program 13 of AAO or Module 17 of DTD illustrates the many uses of sampling in the context of making and selling potato chips. A student favorite.
• *The Physicians' Health Study* from Program 12 of AAO and Module 15 in DTD is a major clinical trial (aspirin and heart attacks) that introduces design of experiments.

• *Sampling Distributions* are perhaps the single most important idea for student understanding of inference. Module 19 of DTD presents the general idea, the basic facts about the sampling distribution of the sample mean x, and the application of these ideas to an x control chart. The setting is a highly automated AT&T electronics factory.

• *Battery Lifetimes* from Program 19 of AAO lead to an animated graphic that illustrates the behavior of confidence intervals in repeated sampling. Module 20 in DTD is a presentation of the reasoning of confidence intervals using the same setting that can be shown in its entirety.

• *Taste Testing of Colas* is the setting for an exposition of the reasoning of significance tests in Module 21 of DTD. This treatment is preferable to that in AAO.

• *Welfare Reform in Baltimore* from Program 22 of AAO is a comparative study of new versus existing welfare systems that leads to a two-sample comparison of means.

• *The Salem Witchcraft Trials*, revisited in Program 23 of AAO, shows social and economic differences between accused and accusers via comparison of proportions.

• *Medical Practice*: Does the treatment women receive from doctors vary with age? This story in Program 24 of AAO produces a two-way table of counts.

• *The Hubble Constant* relates velocity to distance among extra-galactic objects and is a key to assessing the age of the expanding universe. A story in Program 25 of AAO uses the attempt to estimate the Hubble constant to introduce inference about the slope of a regression line.

Here is a complete list of the documentary segments in AAO, with timings for use if your VCR measures "real time," along with ratings from one to four stars. Professor Edward R. Mansfield of the University of Alabama prepared this handy guide. We are grateful to him for permission to reproduce it here. Start your VCR timer when the first signal on the tape appears. Remember that AAO programs are packaged two to a tape; the timings for the even-numbered programs may need some adjustment because the gap between programs seems to vary a bit.

Program 1: What is Statistics?
4:48 Domino's Pizza ***
13:15 The "What is Statistics?" collage of later examples

Program 2: Picturing Distributions
31:30 When does lightning strike?
43:00 TV programming and demographics
51:45 Diagnostic-related groups

Program 3: Describing Distributions
5:55 Comparable worth in Colorado Springs *
16:07 Calories in hot dogs **
21:00 Musical analysis of urine data **

Program 4: Normal Distributions
33:50 Age distributions and Social Security *
46:07 Boston Beanstalk social club for tall people *
50:38 Why don't baseball players hit .400 any more? ***

Program 5: Normal Calculations
7:07 Auto emissions at GM Proving Ground *
14:10 Cholesterol values **
19:50 Sizes of military uniforms **

Program 6: Time Series
34:50 The body's internal clock *
43:48 Psychology: reaction time study *

Program 7: Models for Growth
3:00 Children's growth rates and hormone treatment ***
14:00 Gypsy moth infestations **

Program 8: Describing Relationships
32:25 Manatees vs. motor boats in Florida ***
37:55 Cavities vs. fluoride levels
39:31 1970 draft lottery ***
44:04 Obesity: metabolic rate vs. lean body mass *

Program 9: Correlation
5:42 Identical twins raised apart ***
16:22 Baseball players' salaries **
20:53 The Coleman Report (education in the 1960s) *

Program 10: Multidimensional Data Analysis
32:28 Chesapeake Bay pollution **
47:42 Bellcore graphics **

Program 11: The Question of Causation
5:42 Simpson's paradox ****
12:47 Smoking and cancer (historical survey) ***

Program 12: Experimental Design
32:46 Observational study of lobster behavior *
36:14 Physicians' Health Study: aspirin and heart attacks ****
43:39 Is Ribavirin too good to be true? ***
47:22 Police response to domestic violence *

Program 13: Blocking and Sampling
4:45 Strawberry field research *
13:28 Undercounting in the Census ***
20:48 Sampling potato chips at Frito Lay ****

Program 14: Samples and Surveys
41:21 National Opinion Research Center ****

Program 15: What Is Probability?
10:50 Persi Diaconis on randomness *
17:49 Traffic control in New York (simulation model) **

Program 16: Random Variables
33:36 Cheating on AP Calculus *
34:33 Space Shuttle *Challenger* disaster ****
43:02 Points in a professional basketball game
49:10 Earthquakes in California *

Program 17: Binomial Distributions
3:46 The "hot hand": free throws in basketball ***
9:45 A finance class experiment **
17:22 Sickle-cell anemia *
24:25 Quincunx: falling balls **

Program 18: The Sample Mean and Control Charts
33:45 Roulette
35:04 Interviews with gamblers **
40:44 The casino always wins ****
47:03 Control charts at Frito-Lay ***
53:41 W. Edwards Deming ****

Program 19: Confidence Intervals
11:35 Duracell batteries **
18.25 Rhesus monkeys in medical studies *
21:21 Feeding behavior of marmosets

Program 20: Significance Tests
34:18 Is this poem by Shakespeare? **
49:06 Discrimination within the FBI ***

Program 21: Inference for One Mean
5:55 National Institute of Standards and Technology **
13:30 Taste testing of cola ***
21:08 Autism *

Program 22: Comparing Two Means
33:32 Welfare programs in Baltimore **
45:05 Product development at Union Carbide ***
51:00 SAT exams: can coaching help?

Program 23: Inference for Proportions
3:03 Measuring unemployment (Bureau of Labor Statistics) *
11:58 Safety of drinking water ***
20:15 The Salem witch trials

Program 24: Inference for Two-Way Tables
34:11 Ancient humans (markings on teeth) **
43:30 Does breast cancer treatment vary by age? **
52:02 Mendel's peas **

Program 25: Inference for Relationships
3:32 How fast is the universe expanding (Edwin Hubble)? ****

Program 26: Case Study
35:49 How AZT for treatment of AIDS was tested ***

Resources on the Internet

The World Wide Web has made great amounts of information—of varying degrees of usefulness—easily available. Here are some worthwhile sites with resources for use in conjunction with *PBS*. Some of these sites have links to other interesting locations. Do remember that URLs change much more often than this Guide is reprinted. First, some general collections:

•   CAUSE Web (Consortium for the Advancement of Undergraduate Statistics Education) is a clearinghouse for materials for introductory statistics educators. There are links to many useful websites and resources including most of those listed below. Some of the many topics include applets, cartoons, lecture examples. Listings of statistics education conferences, online chats, research, and other professional development are also posted. Visit www.causeweb.org.

•   Carnegie-Mellon University maintains *StatLib*, an electronic repository of things of statistical interest, including data sets. To get started, visit http://lib.stat.cmu.edu/. Note in particular the "Data and Story Library," an online source related to the EESEE collection of case studies that is included on the *PBS* CD-ROM.

•   There is also a "Data and Story Library" from Australia and New Zealand called "OzDASL." which has different stories and data sets. Visit http://www.statsci.org/data/index.html.

•   The *Journal of Statistics Education*, an electronic journal of the American Statistical Association, contains much of interest to teachers of statistics. For more information, visit www.amstat.org/publications/jse/.

•   The Chance web site, hosted by Dartmouth College, provides timely "current events" material to supplement a statistics course. Find it at www.dartmouth.edu/~chance/.

•   If you want to find some examples of "bad statistics," visit these sites, whose names are self-explanatory: www.junkscience.com and www.mathmistakes.com.

•   The ARTIST website is run by well-known statistics education researchers at the University of Minnesota and has the goals of helping statistics educators to develop tools to assess introductory statistics students and to encourage statistical literacy. Many instructors send in exam questions to add to the pool which is sorted by topic, and it is very easy to create exams for your students using these resources. This is especially helpful if you are teaching a course for the first time on your own and want to insure that the types of questions you are asking your students are comparable to what other statistics educators use on their exams. Visit https://app.gen.umn.edu/artist/index.html.

•   MERLOT, http://www.merlot.org/merlot/index.htm, has excellent teaching resources for many disciplines, including statistics. Many of the resources have been rated by other educators.

•   You Tube, http://www.youtube.com/, also has some interesting animations and lecture demonstrations for statistical concepts. You will have to search a little bit to find the better quality examples, but new videos are posted every day.

It is very useful for students to visit "real statistics" sites to get a glimpse of the richness of the subject:

•   Ask students to locate facts about their home county at the Census Bureau, www.census.gov. The American Community Survey gives additional information from the Census Bureau, http://www.census.gov/acs/www/.

•   Or read the latest press release about employment and unemployment from the Bureau of Labor Statistics at stats.bls.gov. Look under "News Releases" and then under "Employment & Unemployment" for releases with the title "Employment Situation." Also, the unified gateway to federal statistical agencies at www.fedstats.gov is comprehensive but a bit overwhelming.

•   Find current Gallup Poll press releases and Gallup's explanations of how sample surveys work at www.gallup.com. The National Council on Public Polls (www.ncpp.org) has statements on "Principles of Disclosure" and "20 Questions for Journalists" that make interesting reading. Nielsen Media Research, provider of the usual TV program ratings, has a write-up on "What TV Ratings Really Mean" that includes an explanation of why sampling works: www.nielsenmedia.com/FAQ.

- The abstracts of current medical research in the *New England Journal of Medicine* (www.nejm.org) demonstrate that you must know some statistics to read medical literature. Choose a clinical trial and an observational study from the available abstracts, then ask students to search for them by subject and to write a description of the design, the explanatory and response variables, and the conclusions.

Applets deserve separate mention. You can find a large number of attractive interactive animated simulations that demonstrate important facts about probability and statistics. We recommend these for class demonstrations as well as for student work, particularly if you are not using software in your course. Most are at university locations, and their URLs change often. And, despite its claims, Java is quite machine- and browser-dependent. Test applets on the machines your students will use to be certain that they will run. Here are some sources that were attractive in 2007:

- David Lane of Rice University has an excellent collection of Java applets, as well as links to other similar sites: www.ruf.rice.edu/~lane/stat_sim/.
- Also look at the collection by Todd Ogden and R. Webster West at the University of South Carolina: www.stat.sc.edu/rsrch/gasp/.
- Another nice applet collection, from the University of Newcastle in Australia, is www.anu.edu.au/nceph/surfstat/surfstat-home/surfstat.html. This URL seems to change often, so you may need to search for "surfstat."
- A collection emphasizing probability by Charles Stanton of California State University at San Bernardino: www.math.csusb.edu/faculty/stanton/m262/probstat.html.
- Another that is especially strong in probability (look at the poker hand applet) is by Kyle Siegrist of the University of Alabama at Huntsville: www.math.uah.edu/stat/.
- Want to select an SRS or do experimental randomization, even for large samples, and bypass the table of random digits? Visit www.random.org or the Research Randomizer at www.randomizer.org.

Planning a Course

In preparing to teach from *PBS*, look at the **STATISTICS IN SUMMARY** sections that conclude each chapter. There you will find a detailed list of the essential skills that students should gain from study of each chapter. These learning objectives appear at the end of the chapters because they would make little sense to students in advance. You can use them for advance planning as you decide what to emphasize and how much time to devote to each topic.

Also look at the **APPLY YOUR KNOWLEDGE** exercises, short sets of exercises that cover the specific content of the preceding exposition. Their location tells students, "You should be able to do this right now." They also show the instructor what students can be expected to do at each step. The longer sets of **SECTION EXERCISES** at the end of each section ask students to integrate their knowledge, if only because their location doesn't give as clear a hint to the skills required. The **CHAPTER REVIEW EXERCISES** add another level of integration. You can help students by judicious selection of exercises from all three locations.

One of the emphases of the movement to reform teaching in the math sciences is that we should make our classrooms as interactive as possible by involving students in discussion, reaction, problem-solving, and the like. Those who try this find that course outlines cover a bit less material—but that the students master more of it. The outlines that follow reflect this; your mileage may vary. Mature students who have learned how to learn can create their own interaction with text and lecture, and so progress much faster. Reformers tend to undervalue lectures for mature students.

Course Outline, by Lori Seward

The outline that follows is intended for undergraduate business students and should be used as a guide only. Experience has shown me that the size of the class has more to do with the pace than the quantitative skills of the students. I teach a "mega" section with over 400 students. While this is clearly an undesirable way to teach a statistics course, it is a reality with which instructors at large universities are now faced. Rather than fighting the administrators I have had to develop a method that works in spite of the conditions.

After teaching my "mega" section without recitations for three semesters, I was finally given the funding to add recitations. The level of understanding of conceptual issues rose dramatically. I attribute this improvement to having time in a "safe" environment to work examples. I try to break our class time up so that I lecture for 2/3 of the time and the students work on examples together for the other third. The recitations are the times for the students to work on problems together. Someone is there in the classroom to answer questions and correct their mistakes. My TAs and I walk around the room while the students are working. I have found they ask questions when we are standing next to their desks that they simply won't ask when we are standing at the blackboard or overhead.

In the smaller classes, I try to provide the same proportion of lecture time to work time 2/3 to 1/3. In these classes, however, the work time is each class period. I typically select problems from the text or put together examples on my own for them to work in class. Again, walking around the room while they work brings out more questions than I would ever get in front of the class.

I have taught the following outline from three different perspectives:
- A 16-week semester meeting twice each week for 50 minutes with a recitation meeting for 50 minutes each week to supplement the lectures. This is a good solution for the "mega" sections. If you aren't successful in convincing the college to offer smaller classes, they might be open to recitations. I try to keep the recitations to around 40 or 50 students each. This gives the students opportunities to ask questions and spend more time working problems during class.
- A 16-week semester meeting twice each week for 75 minutes each class. This works well for classes with fewer than 100 students; 50 students is a very manageable group.
- This outline can be adapted for a five-week summer course that meets for one hour and 35 minutes each day. This also works best for classes with fewer than 50 students.

Week One:
    Introduction and Describing Data   *PBS* sections 1.1 and 1.2
    I show the film *What is Statistics?* on the first day of class.
Week Two:
    The Normal Curve   *PBS* section 1.3

I give time to master the calculators and software this week. When I have a class with fewer than 50 students, I try to take them into a computer lab for one day to give a hands-on learning experience for the software.

Week Three:
    Two variable relationships   *PBS* sections 2.1, 2.2, begin 2.3
    Regression
Week Four:
    Regression cont., Categorical Data   *PBS* sections 2.3, 2.4, and 2.5

Week Five:
      Sampling and Randomness   *PBS* Chapter 3 and section 4.1
Week Six:
      Review for **Exam I**   One day
      Exam I   One day

I find that most students can comfortably finish a 40-question multiple-choice test that is evenly distributed with calculations and concepts in less than 90 minutes.

Some of you might ask why include the start of Chapter 4 at the end of the first section of material. What I have found with business students is that the material in Chapters 1 to 3 is quite manageable, while Chapters 4, 5, and 6 are daunting. This short foray into new material gives them an idea of what is to come. The students are more likely to link the material between Chapters 1 to 3 and the rest of the textbook when I organize the course this way.

Week Seven:
      Probability, Sampling Distributions   *PBS* sections 4.2, 4.3 and 4.4

We can start to move faster at this point in the semester. Most students are now familiar with the routine of class and the vocabulary. Many of the homework problems can be done with pencil and paper and the answers to questions often take on specific numerical values, which was not always the case in chapters 1-3. Students get satisfaction out of solving for the "right" answer.

Week Eight:
      Probability, Binomial Distribution   *PBS* sections 5.1 and 5.2
Week Nine:
      Poisson Distribution, Conditional   *PBS* sections 5.3 and 5.4
      Probability
Week Ten:
      Estimation and Significance   *PBS* sections 6.1 and 6.2
Week Eleven:
      Significance, Testing Errors (define)   *PBS* section 6.3 and start 6.4
Week Twelve:
      Review for **Exam II**   One day
      Exam II   One day

I find that most students need more time to work the problems on this exam. I use approximately 30 multiple-choice questions with an even mix between calculations and conceptual questions.

Week Thirteen:
      Calculating Power   *PBS* section 6.4
Week Fourteen:
      Inference for Mean, Comparing   *PBS* sections 7.1 and 7.2
      Means
Week Fifteen:
      Inference for Proportions   *PBS* Chapter 8
Week Sixteen:
      Inference for Two-Way Tables   *PBS* Chapter 9
Comprehensive Final Exam

Chapter Comments, by Lori Seward

The comments that follow contain brief discussions of philosophy, teaching suggestions, and additional data and examples for use in teaching.

Part I: Understanding Data

One of the most noteworthy changes in statistics instruction in the past decade is the renewed focus on helping students learn to work with data. The change in instruction follows a change in research emphases. Statistics research has pulled back a bit from mathematics (though, as the wise saying goes, you can never be too rich or too thin or know too much mathematics) in favor of renewed attention to data analysis and the problems of scientific inference. It is no longer thought proper to devote a week to "descriptive statistics" (means, medians, and histograms) before plunging into probability and probability-based inference.

Contemporary introductions to statistics include a substantial dose of "data analysis." In addition to reflecting statisticians' consensus view of the nature of their subject, working with data has clear pedagogical advantages. Students who may be a bit anxious about the study of statistics can begin by learning concrete skills and exercising judgment that amounts to enlightened common sense.

Chapters 1 and 2 present the principles and some of the tools of data analysis. For teachers whose training is primarily mathematical, effective teaching of data analysis requires some reorientation. Here are four principles:

1. Emphasize the strategy, not just the skills. It is easy to treat data analysis as a longer stretch of descriptive statistics. Now we present stemplots, boxplots, the five-number summary, . . . , in addition to means, medians, and histograms. There is a larger strategy for looking at data, which these tools help implement. The STATISTICS IN SUMMARY figures at the end of Chapters 1 and 2 stress some elements of this strategy, such as:

•   Begin with a graph, move to numerical descriptions of specific aspects of the data, and (sometimes) to a compact mathematical model. *Which* graphs, numerical summaries, and mathematical models are helpful depends on the setting.
•   Look for an overall pattern and for striking deviations from that pattern. Deviations such as outliers may influence the choice of descriptive summaries, and the presence and clarity of the overall pattern suggests what mathematical models may be useful.

2. Don't import inferential ideas too soon. The point of view of data analysis is to let the data speak, to examine the peculiarities of the data in hand without at first asking if they represent some wider universe or answer some broader question. The distinction between sample and population, which is central to inference, is deliberately ignored in data analysis.
John Tukey of Bell Labs and Princeton, who shaped the subject, refers to "bunches" of data. *PBS* doesn't go that far but does delay the sample-population distinction until Chapter 3, where it is essential to the discussion of designs for producing data. One aspect of successful teaching is to resist the temptation to tell students everything at once. Let them grasp the strategy and tools of basic data analysis first. These will be under control and very helpful when we come to inference.

3. Use real data. Remember the mantra: data are not just numbers; they are numbers with a context. The context enables students to communicate conclusions in words and to judge whether their conclusions are sensible. Data come with at least a bit of background, though for beginning instruction, that background may not fully reflect the complexities of the real world. I'm willing to oversimplify for the sake of clarity, but not to ask empty operations with mere numbers. *PBS* provides small and moderate-size data sets in more than adequate number for basic instruction. You should want more.

- Two general compilations are *A Handbook of Small Data Sets* (Hand et al., 1994) and *A Casebook for a First Course in Statistics and Data Analysis* (Chatterjee et al., 1995). Both contain data with background and are accompanied by data disks. Specialized texts now often contain more data disks. For example, Thiebaux (1994) and McBean and Rovers (1998) have data on the subjects of their titles.
- Mine the electronic terrain. Many data sets and other resources are available on the internet and through other electronic means. Check the websites listed earlier in this guide for some good sources.
- Amass your own collection of data. Data about the states, with $n = 50$ or $n = 51$, are a convenient size for simple data analyses. The *Statistical Abstract of the United States* is a good place to start. The *Information Please Environmental Almanac*, which includes the provinces of Canada as well as the states, has much data of interest to students. Consider the percent of solid waste output that is recycled (Minnesota is an outlier), toxic chemical releases (Louisiana and Texas are outliers), or per capita energy use in Canada (Alberta is an outlier). The "Almanac" issue of the *Chronicle of Higher Education*, published each year around September 1, contains much data on students and education.
- The students themselves are another source of data. You should consider starting the term with a survey asking a variety of questions. Assure students that responses are anonymous. Try to get both quantitative and categorical data, and ask students' gender to allow two-sample comparisons. You can use these data for in-class illustrations throughout the course. For example, you might ask some of these items:

– Are you MALE or FEMALE?
– To the nearest inch, how tall are you?
– On a typical school day, how much time do you spend watching television?
(Answer in minutes. For example, 2 hours is 120 minutes or 1 and 1/2 hours is
90 minutes.)
– On a typical school day, how much time do you spend outside of class studying and doing homework?
(Answer in minutes.)
– How much money in coins are you carrying right now? (Don't count any paper money, just coins.)
– How old [tall, heavy] do you think Dr. X is?
– How many siblings do you have?
– How large was your high school graduating class?
– What is your favorite type of cheese?
– How many credit cards do you have? How high is your balance?

- Encourage students to look carefully at the data they encounter *outside* of class. You might ask students to collect examples of statistics used poorly or in a misleading way, and to comment on the context of the data they find. If they gain nothing else from this course, they at least should become more intelligent consumers of data. Far too many people give only slight attention to the numbers they read or hear. For example:

– A home security company, hoping to sell its services, placed an ad in a Sunday newspaper stating that: "When you go on vacation, burglars go to work. . . .According to FBI statistics, over 26% of home burglaries take place between Memorial Day and Labor Day. . . . " Is that a convincing reason to install a security system?
– Shortly before O.J. Simpson was found not guilty in his criminal trial, a poll in the Los Angeles area found that 27% of whites, and 73% of blacks, believed he was innocent. Asked their impressions of this result, quite a few students observed only that the two percentages add to 100%. This is true, but

completely coincidental (they are percentages of two separate groups!). An informed citizen should find much more interesting issues to consider here.

4. Communicating results is important. If we could offer just one piece of advice to teachers using *PBS*, it would be this: *A number or a graph, or a magic phrase such as "Reject H_0," is not an adequate answer to a statistical problem.* Insist that students state a brief conclusion in the context of the specific problem setting. We are dealing with data, not just with numbers.

Chapter 1: Examining Distributions

Students taking a first course in statistics often do not know what to expect. Some may view statistics as a field where the major task is to tabulate large collections of numbers accurately. Others have heard that statistics is more like mathematics with a lot of complicated formulas that are difficult to use. Few are expecting a course where they need to think and use their common sense.

Your presentation of the material in Chapter 1 sets the tone for the entire course. We would like students to see that they can succeed and become accustomed to making judgments and discussing findings rather than just solving problems. Try to use selected examples or exercises as a basis for class discussion. Presenting new data of special interest to your students is useful. Don't speed through the descriptive material because it seems simple—students don't always find the mechanics simple and are not accustomed to "reading" graphics. And they are certainly not used to talking about what the data show.

Section 1.1 Displaying distributions with graphs. Be flexible in assessing student graphs and interpretations: It isn't always clear whether to split stems in a stemplot or how to choose the classes for a histogram. Try by your flexibility to help students not to get hung up on minor details of graphing. Similarly, how symmetric a histogram or stemplot must be to warrant calling the distribution "symmetric" is a matter for judgment. So is singling out outliers. Be flexible, but discourage students from, for example, calling the largest observation an outlier, regardless of whether it is isolated from the remaining observations. Flexibility may also help students live with software. In making stemplots, for example, some software packages truncate long numbers and others round; some put the larger stems on top and others put the smaller stems there. These variations have little effect on our picture of the distribution.

Section 1.2 Describing distributions with numbers. The common descriptive measures summarize things we can see graphically, but they summarize only part of what we can see. The graphical presentation is primary for data analysis. Students should have a calculator that gives them $\bar{x}$ and s from keyed-in data. Do warn them that many calculators offer a choice between dividing by n and dividing by $n-1$ in finding the standard deviation s. We want $n-1$. (What is worse, many calculators label their choices as σ_n and σ_{n-1}. We haven't met σ yet, but we want to use s to denote the standard deviation of a set of data.) Use a data set in class and let students check their calculator skills. If you use software, you may find versions of a boxplot and rules for calculating quartiles that differ slightly from those in *PBS*. Encourage students to ignore this and to work with what the software reports. Do remember that no single numerical summary is appropriate for all sets of data, and that any numerical summary may miss important features such as gaps or multiple peaks.

Section 1.3 The Normal distributions. Note that Normal distributions are introduced here as models for the overall pattern of some sets of data, not in the context of probability theory. Although this ordering of material is unusual, it has several advantages. The Normal distributions appear naturally in the description of large amounts of data, so that the later assumption for inference that "the population has a Normal distribution" becomes clearer. Moreover, mastering Normal calculations at this point reduces the barrier posed by the material on probability and sampling distributions (Chapter 4). If the students already know how to compute Normal "probabilities" and have some understanding of the relative frequency interpretation from this section, the transition to ideas about probability is easier.

It is also true that meeting Normal distributions early explains the otherwise mysterious affection of statisticians for the standard deviation. The organizing idea is that we can sometimes use a mathematical model as an approximation to the overall pattern of data. Normal distributions are one example; a linear regression line (next chapter) is another. The 68–95–99.7 rule is a useful device for interpreting μ and σ for Normal distributions. It also makes it possible to think about Normal distributions without a table. Many distributions are non-Normal, so don't make this into the so-called "empirical rule" for distributions in general.

Chapter 2: Examining Relationships

Having dealt with methods for describing a single variable, we turn to relationships among several variables. At the level of *PBS*, that means mostly relationships between two variables. That a relationship between two variables can be strongly affected by other ("lurking") variables is, however, one of the chapter's themes. Note the new vocabulary (explanatory and response variables) in the chapter Introduction, as well as the reiteration of basic strategies for data analysis. Correlation and regression are traditionally messy subjects based on opaque "computing formulas" that are in turn based on sums of squares. *PBS* asks that students have a "two-variable statistics" calculator that will give them the correlation and the slope and intercept of the least-squares regression line from keyed-in data. This liberates the instructor—we can give reasonably realistic problems and concentrate on intelligent use rather than awful arithmetic. The computing formulas are anachronistic and don't appear in the text. Do remember that data input and editing can be frustrating on a calculator, so reserve large problems for computer software.

The descriptive methods in this chapter, like those in Chapter 1, correspond to formal inference procedures presented later in the text. Many texts delay the descriptive treatment of correlation and regression until inference in these settings can also be presented. There are, we think, good reasons not to do this. By carefully describing data first, we emphasize the separate status and greater generality of data analysis. There are many data sets for which inference procedures do not apply—data for the 50 states, for example. Fitting a least-squares line is a general procedure, while using such a line to give a 95% prediction interval requires additional assumptions that are not always valid. In addition, students become accustomed to examining data *before* proceeding to formal inference, an important principle of good statistical practice. Finally, correlation and regression are so important that they should certainly appear in a first course even if you choose not to discuss formal inference in these settings.

Section 2.1 Scatterplots. Using graphs should be comfortable by now. Constructing scatterplots is a relatively easy task (but tedious without software for all but small data sets.) Interpreting the plots takes some practice. In the classroom, build instruction on examples and stress that common sense and some understanding of the data are necessary to do a good job of description. Computers can make the plots, but people are needed to describe them. Again, the general rule is to look for overall patterns and deviations from them. Patterns such as clusters and positive and negative association are useful in many cases but can lead to distorted descriptions when imposed in situations where they do not apply.

Section 2.2 Correlation. Correlation is presented before regression in part because it does not require the explanatory-response distinction. This also allows us to give a meaningful formula for the regression slope, using the correlation. Students should have a calculator that gives r from keyed-in data. You can therefore use the somewhat messy formula for r as a basis for explaining how correlation behaves (fit this to your students' ability to read algebra), but avoid using it for computation.

Section 2.3 Least-squares regression. The background to regression isn't always clear to students, so don't skip over it: We'd like to draw the *best* line through the points on our scatterplot; to do this, we need an explicit statement of what we mean by "best." The least squares idea gives such a statement, one that assumes we want to use the line to predict *y* from *x*. Least squares isn't terribly natural. At this point, just say that it's the most common way to fit a line. (Least squares is easily influenced by extreme observations, but it has many nice properties that have kept it the standard method even though computers have reduced its ease-of-computation advantage.) The concepts of "outlier" and "influential observation" are important. An observation is influential if removing it would move the regression line. This is clearly a matter of degree. More advanced statistical methods include numerical measures of influence. I've defined "outlier" broadly to keep things simple for students—they only have to look for isolated extreme points in any direction. That's a matter of degree also. Outliers in *y* have large residuals; outliers in *x* are often influential.

Section 2.4 Interpreting correlation and regression. For now at least, computers can't do anything in this section. As calculations are automated, interpretive ideas become a more important part of even basic instruction.

Section 2.5 Relations in categorical data.* This is "applied arithmetic," but students don't find it trivial. There is no recipe (I do give guidelines) for deciding what percents to calculate and compare in describing a relationship between two categorical variables.

Chapter 3: Producing Data

This is a relatively short chapter with a lot of ideas and little numerical work. Students find the essentials quite easy, but they are very important. This chapter isn't mathematics, but it is core content for statistics. Weaknesses in data production account for most erroneous conclusions in statistical studies. The message is that production of good data requires careful planning. Random digits (Table B) are used to select simple random samples and to assign units to treatments in an experiment. There are numerous examples that can serve as the basis for classroom discussion.

The chapter also has a secondary purpose: the use of chance in random sampling and randomized comparative experiments motivates the study of chance behavior in Chapter 4. I have tried to motivate probability by its use in statistics, and to concentrate on the probabilistic ideas most directly associated with basic statistics. This chapter starts that process.

Section 3.1 Designing samples. The deliberate use of chance to select a sample is the central idea. Many of the inference procedures in later chapters assume that the data are a simple random sample. Others require several independent SRSs or another simple model. In this section, we learn what an SRS is and also get a glimpse of the practical difficulties that can damage a sample to the point that formal inference is of little value.

Section 3.2 Designing experiments. The randomized comparative experiment may be the single greatest contribution of statistics to the advance of knowledge. Since Fisher introduced randomization in the 1920s, these ideas have revolutionized the conduct of studies in fields from agriculture to medicine. No student should leave a first statistics course without understanding the distinction between experiments and observational studies and understanding why properly designed experiments are the gold standard for evidence of causation. When experiments can't be done, causation is a slippery subject, and statistical methods that claim to give evidence for causation are not for beginners and are often debated by experts. Good experiments allow relatively clean conclusions.

Part II: Probability and Inference

The reasoning of classical statistical inference is built on asking, "What would happen if I used this method many times?" Confidence limits, *P*-values, and error probabilities answer that question in varied settings. All of these answers utilize the *sampling distribution* of a statistic, which addresses the underlying question by displaying the distribution of the statistic in repeated samples or experiments carried out under the same circumstances. Sampling distributions are a tough idea to convey to students, but they are central to inference and can't be avoided without loss of conceptual mastery.

Distributions are the big idea of probability for understanding the reasoning of basic statistical inference. The goal of Chapter 4 is to efficiently convey the probability ideas needed to understand inference, in particular sampling distributions. Chapter 6 is (apart from the optional Chapter 5) the most difficult in the book. There is no hiding the fact that the reasoning of confidence intervals and (more so) significance tests isn't easy. But if all the calculations are done by software, as is now the case in practical applications of statistics, students must carry away this reasoning if our presentation of inference is to have much lasting value. Chapters 7 and 8 present the simplest inference procedures of interest in practice, for inference about means (Chapter 7) and proportions (Chapter 8). Chapter 7 is essential because, in it, we meet many issues relevant to applying statistical methods to real problems. Chapter 8 is not essential, but it is short and easy. You can shorten your path through this part of *PBS* by omitting Chapter 8 if you wish. Chapters 10 and 11, but not Chapter 9, are accessible by this route.

Chapter 4: Probability and Sampling Distributions

Section 4.1 Randomness. Much evidence shows that even students who can do formal probability exercises have little conceptual understanding of random behavior. We therefore start very informally. Do take the time to do some of the simulation exercises in this section. If you have the capability to automate simulations, use it here. Most statistical software packages and many graphing calculators will, for example, simulate the Bernoulli and binomial distributions. That allows you to have students actually do simulations. Perhaps they will see that coin tossing, Shaq's free throws, and the results of a "Yes/No" opinion poll question are instances of the same setting. We think that's a more profound "mathematical" insight than learning the binomial formula.

Section 4.2 Probability models. This section introduces the simplest facts about probability—all we need to use the language of probability to discuss statistical inference. A probability model is a set of possible outcomes plus a way of assigning probabilities that satisfies some basic rules. There are two common ways to assign probabilities: assign a number to each of a finite set of outcomes, or assign a number as the area under a density curve. That's it. If you find it necessary to do more, you can jump to Section 5.1, but don't do that out of mere habit. Probability is a high barrier to students, and this is a statistics course.

Yes, we know discrete distributions can take infinitely many values. That's not very helpful to students without a math background that includes infinite series. Recall the saying of the physicist Richard Feynman that "The real problem in speech is not precise language. The problem is clear language." He was talking about mathematics textbooks when he said that. We need not tell students everything we know.

Section 4.4 Sampling distributions. Section 4.2 gave us a language to use. Now we continue the main track, following up on the discussion of sampling in Chapter 3. Sampling distributions are of course one of the big ideas of statistics. We also get in context some important probability facts, the law of large numbers and the central limit theorem. Do simulations here.

An easy one to do in class is to pass around dice to the students. Have them roll the dice any number of times (but at least five times) and record their individual rolls and then calculate their average. If you have a computer in class you can easily create a picture of the two distributions: one of the individual rolls and one of their means. I also use this opportunity to calculate the mean and standard deviation from the probability distribution and then look at the sample means and standard deviations. This is a great hands-on illustration of the idea of sampling variability and the Central Limit Theorem.

Chapter 6: Introduction to Inference

This chapter contains many fundamental ideas. We introduce confidence intervals and tests along with some cautions concerning the use and abuse of tests. Throughout, the setting is inference about the mean μ of a Normal population with known standard deviation σ. As a consequence, the z procedures presented are not applicable to most real sets of data. They introduce ideas in a setting where students can do familiar Normal calculations, and they pave the way for the more useful t procedures presented in the next chapter. Experience shows that many students will not master this material upon seeing it for the first time. Fortunately, they will meet the key ideas again in the next chapter. By the time they have completed both chapters and worked many exercises, they should grasp the fundamentals. Be patient, and remember that understanding the reasoning of inference is more important than the number of procedures learned.

Section 6.1 Estimating with confidence. Figures 6.3 and 6.4 display the big idea: the recipe for a 95% confidence interval produces intervals that hit the true parameter in 95% of all possible samples. (In formal language, the recipe has probability 0.95 of producing an interval that catches the true parameter.) Simulation can help students understand this central idea.

Section 6.2 Tests of significance. The reasoning of significance tests is conceptually the hardest point in a first course in statistics. *LS:* I try to appeal to the students' common sense when working with these types of problems. It helps to bring published results of real studies to show what the language is and how the results are used. I give many examples of conclusion statements along with business actions to get their minds thinking in this way.

Section 6.3 Making sense of statistical significance. In discussing z confidence intervals, *PBS* offers a "warning label" reminding users of conditions for proper use. That label applies to the z tests also. Tests are, however, more difficult to interpret than are confidence intervals. Many statisticians feel that tests are overused, or at least over-interpreted. Hence this short section. The discussions of "choosing a level of significance" and "statistical significance and practical significance" offer some cautions about the interpretation of statistical significance. "Statistical inference is not valid for all sets of data" and "beware of multiple analyses" apply to confidence intervals as well, but abuses seem more common in the setting of tests.

Section 6.4 Error probabilities and power.* Some instructors stress P-values in teaching beginners; others stress the two types of error and their associated error probabilities. We are in the former camp. Why begin with P-values? First, "assessing the strength of evidence" is a better description of practical inference than is "making decisions." Second, P-values are prominent in the output from statistical software, so users of statistics must understand them. The fact that there is an elegant mathematical theory (Neyman-Pearson) based on the fixed-α approach should not be allowed to sway practical instruction for beginners. That said, P-values are not sufficient for a full account of statistical tests. The idea of *power,* how likely is this test to detect an alternative you really want to detect if it is true, is certainly important in practice.

For business students that will go on to study business process design and improvement, understanding that decisions involve risk and being able to quantify those risks are important concepts. Power is a way to quantify the risks involved in making business decisions. I don't believe it should be left out of a business statistics course. Be warned, however, that the material is difficult. I try to stick with one or two examples and spend extra time asking the students to consider the consequences of their business decisions.

Chapter 7: Inference for Distributions

The one- and two-sample t procedures are among the most-used methods of inference. One sample t confidence intervals and significance tests are a short step from the z procedures of Chapter 6. The two-sample procedures present a complication: the "textbook standard" method assumes equal variances in the population, an assumption that is hard to verify and often not justified. *PBS* ignores that method in favor of two alternatives that work even if the population variances differ: a reasonably good conservative approximation for hand use and a very accurate approximation that is implemented in almost all statistical software packages. Another deviation from the "textbook standard" occurs in the optional Section 7.3, where the basic recommendation concerning inference about population spread is, "Don't do it without expert advice." This choice is also well justified by literature citations. The exposition in this chapter pays at least some attention to the problems of applying statistical inference to real data.

Section 7.1 Inference for the mean of a population. If you want to do inference about μ but don't know σ, just replace the unknown σ by its sample estimate s in the z procedures. That's the driving idea. It leads to the t distributions and to the use of all of Table C. Because the mechanics are so similar to those of Chapter 6, you can replay the reasoning of inference and pay more attention to interpreting the results. The section calls attention to the use of one-sample methods for matched pairs data and to the conditions needed to use the methods in practice.

Section 7.2 Comparing two means. Students now need to distinguish one-sample, matched pairs, and two-sample settings. That's how this section opens. For inference about the difference $\mu 1 - \mu 2$ of two population means, we start with the natural sample estimator $x1 - x2$ and its sampling distribution. The distribution is (at least approximately) Normal, so standardize the estimator and replace the unknown σi by the sample standard deviations si. You may not wish to emphasize this intuitive "derivation," depending on your students' capacities for generalization, but it repeats the logic of earlier settings. We then come to the actual two-sample t procedures: just use the smaller of $n1 - 1$ and $n2 - 1$ as the degrees of freedom. Everything else is optional, but if you are using software, you will want students to read the section headed "more accurate levels."

Section 7.3 Inference for population spread. The contrast in the practical usefulness of the t procedures for means and the chi-square and F procedures for standard deviations is a good argument for not allowing theoretical statistics to set the agenda for a first course in statistical methods. These tests are all (at least approximately) likelihood ratio tests for Normal distributions. They therefore share a widely accepted general principle and some large-sample optimality properties. But they are vastly different in their actual usefulness. The t tests (and their extension to ANOVA for comparing many means) are relatively little affected by deviations from Normality. Tests for standard deviations, on the other hand, are so sensitive to deviations from Normality that I do not believe they should be used in practice.

What then should we do about the standard tests for standard deviations in the context of a first statistics course? *PBS* allows three choices: 1. you can ignore the issue altogether—this section is optional; 2. you can discuss the issue and also present the most common of the questionable procedures, the F test for comparing two standard deviations; 3. or you can discuss the first subsection in Section 7.3, bluntly titled "Avoid inference about standard deviations," and omit the actual F test on the grounds that we have explained why it is not of much value. I usually take the third approach.

Chapter 8: Inference for Proportions

This chapter presents the z procedures for one-sample and two-sample inference about population proportions. The procedures are approximate, based on the large-sample normal approximation. Note that we avoid a common source of confusion by giving only the normal approximation for $\hat{p}$, rather than starting with the normal approximation for binomial counts. By now the students should be comfortable with the general framework for confidence intervals and significance tests. Those who have not yet mastered these concepts get an additional opportunity to learn these important ideas.

Section 8.1 Inference for a population proportion. Here are confidence intervals and significance tests for a single proportion. Students will just follow the recipes given, but you may want to point out why the basic ideas are reasonable. *LS:* Evidence in the literature is overwhelmingly in favor of the "add two successes and two failures" approach to estimating proportions. This is the approach taken in *PBS*.

Section 8.2 Comparing two proportions. This section presents confidence intervals and significance tests for comparing two population proportions. Students should be able to distinguish two-sample from one-sample settings from their work in Chapter 7. As in the previous section, we use different standard errors for confidence intervals and tests. Pooling the two samples in the test statistic, while making the test inconsistent with the confidence interval, keeps the two-sample test consistent with the 2×2 case of the chi-square test for two-way tables in Chapter 9.

Part III: Topics in Inference

The concluding six chapters of *PBS* present independent accounts of inference in more advanced settings: two-way tables of count data (Chapter 9), simple linear regression (Chapter 10), multiple regression (Chapter 11), statistics for quality and control (Chapter 12), time series forecasting (chapter 13), and one-way analysis of variance (Chapter 14).

Chapter 9: Inference for Two-Way Tables

The Pearson chi-square test is one of the most common inference procedures and, because it tests the existence of a relationship between two categorical variables under several sampling models, one of the most versatile. Do note the stress that the overall test ("Yes, these variables are related") is not a full analysis of the data. The descriptive analysis of the nature of the relationship is essential.

The chi-square test, like the tests in Chapter 8, is an approximate test whose accuracy improves as the cell counts increase. There is an "exact" test for two-way tables, called the Fisher exact test. For example, this test reports $P = 0.0071$ rather than the chi-square test's $P = 0.0052$ for the data of Example 9.1 of *PBS*. This test treats *both sets of marginal totals* as fixed in advance. In Example 9.1, only one set was fixed by the design of the study. Some statisticians prefer to always do inference "conditional" on the observed marginal totals, as Fisher's test does. This is a debate that you don't want to reveal to your students! You can find a description of the Fisher test in Agresti (1990) and a more advanced survey in Agresti (1992).

Chapter 10: Inference for Regression

There are many interesting problems in which the relationship between two variables can be summarized graphically and numerically with a least-squares line. Not all of these can be analyzed using the methods presented in this chapter. Inference for linear regression is based on a statistical model that expresses the assumptions underlying the inference procedures. The section headed "The regression model" is therefore essential to understanding regression inference. This section also introduces s, the "standard error about the line," as the key measure of sample variability in the regression setting. You will sometimes find s called "residual standard error" or "root MSE" in computer output or other texts.

The calculations required for regression inference, even after the least-squares line is in hand, are quite unpleasant without software. Most exercises in this chapter therefore give the output from a regression program. If your students are using software, you can ask them to produce the equivalent output from the data. If your students lack software access, you can give them the results of key calculations (see the exercise solutions).

Chapter 11: Multiple Regression

The model for multiple regression and a brief overview of the inference procedures are presented. This chapter can be omitted without loss of continuity.

Chapter 12: Statistics for Quality: Control and Capability

This chapter is especially useful to business students. It applies statistical ideas to a number of common situations in manufacturing and management. The first two sections could be assigned for instructors who want a less-taxing introduction to the subject.

Chapter 13: Time Series Forecasting

This chapter is very useful for business students to understand. Time series models are presented.

Chapter 14: One-Way Analysis of Variance

The idea of using a statistical test to compare population means is familiar from Chapter 7. New issues arise because we may have more than two means to compare.

References
1. Agresti, Alan (1990), *Categorical Data Analysis*, Wiley, New York.
2. Agresti, Alan (1992), A survey of exact inference for contingency tables, *Statistical Science*, 7, pp. 131–177.
3. Chatterjee, Samprit, Handcock, Mark S., and Simonoff, Jeffrey S. (1995), *A Casebook for a First Course in Statistics and Data Analysis*, Wiley, New York.
4. Hand, D. J., Daly, F., Lunn, A.D., McConway, K. J., and Ostrowski, E. (1994), *A Handbook of Small Data Sets*, Chapman and Hall, London.
5. McBean, Edward A. and Rovers, Frank A. (1998), *Statistical Procedures for Analysis of Environmental Monitoring Data & Risk Assessment*, Prentice Hall, Upper Saddle River, New Jersey.
6. Moore, David S. (1993), The place of video in new styles of teaching and learning statistics, *The American Statistician*, 47, pp. 172–176.
7. Moore, David S. and discussants (1997), New pedagogy and new content: the case of statistics, *International Statistical Review*, 65, pp. 123–165.
8. Thiebaux, H. Jean (1994), *Statistical Data Analysis for Ocean and Atmospheric Sciences*, Academic Press, San Diego, California.

Chapter 1: Examining Distributions

1.1 Answers will vary.

1.2 a) Type of wood is categorical. **b)** Water repellent is categorical. **c)** Paint thickness is quantitative. **d)** Paint color is categorical. **e)** Weathering time is quantitative.

1.3 a) The columns in the chart to the left display nominal data and therefore can be shown in any order desired. **b)** No, a pie chart would not be appropriate since the categories do not make up a whole (or 100%).

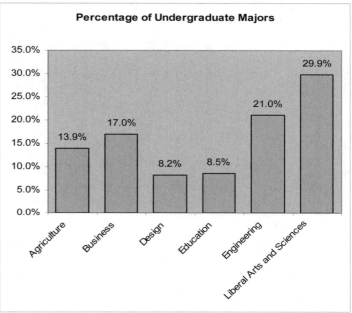

1.4 a)

Occupational deaths	Count	Percent of total
Agricultural	659	12%
Mining	152	3%
Construction	1224	21%
Manufacturing	459	8%
Trans and utilities	880	15%
Wholesale	203	4%
Retail	372	7%
Finance	115	2%
Service	1054	18%
Government	526	9%
Other occupations	59	1%

The "other" category represents occupational deaths not found in the 10 specified categories. This percentage is 1%.

b)

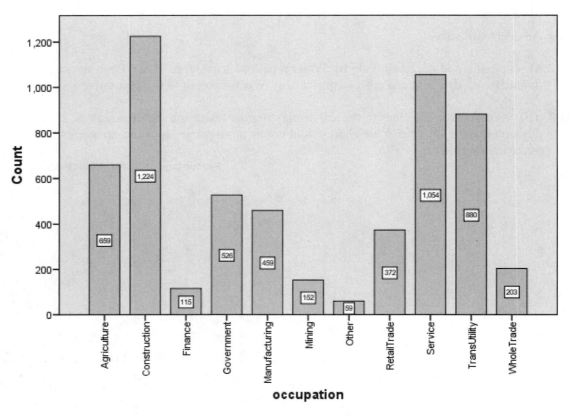

Cases weighted by Number of deaths

c) We can see that the first three categories, Construction, Transportation and Public Utilities, and Agricultural deaths, make up 50% of the total occupational deaths in 1999.

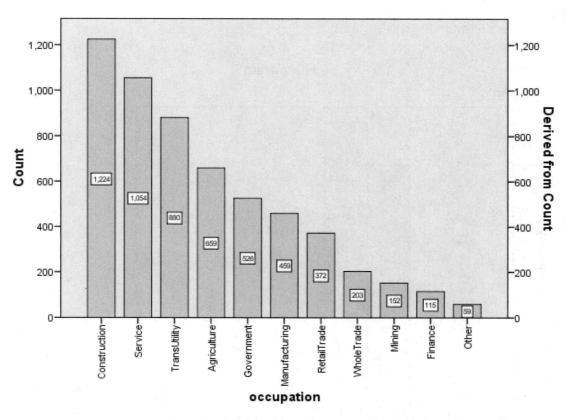

Cases weighted by Number of deaths

d) Yes, we could use a pie chart to display the data because we know the total number of occupational deaths.

1.5

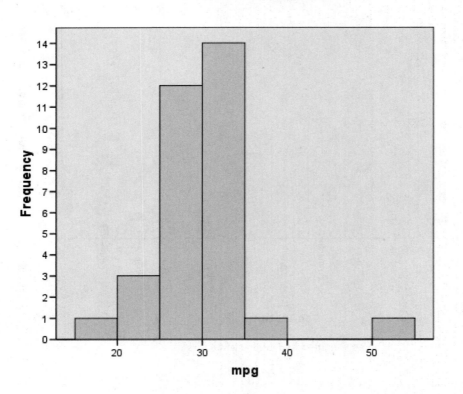

Histogram

Mean =29.28
Std. Dev. =5.589
N =32

1.6

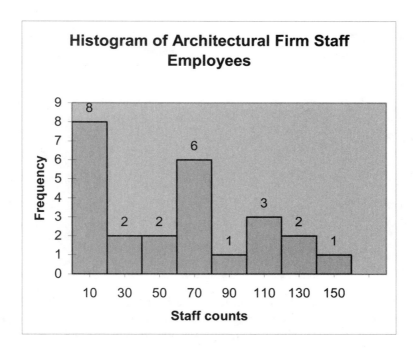

1.7 a) The distribution of mileage is roughly symmetric except for a high outlier (Toyota Prius at 51). The range of the data without the outlier is 19 to 37. (Refer to the histogram shown in problem 1.5.) **b)** The Rolls-Royce Phantom (19 mpg) and Mecedes-Benz E55 AMG (21 mpg) are the two lowest mileages and should be subject to the "gas guzzler" tax. However, there are no low outliers.

1.8 The average salaries in Figure 1.3 appear to have a somewhat symmetric distribution with a center at 2.25 or 2.5 million. The spread of average salaries is 0.5 million to 3.5 million with a range of 3 million. Figure 1.4 shows the average salaries of the Cincinnati Reds. The distribution is not symmetric, is skewed to the right, with a wide range of 10 million. The center is hard to describe. One could say the distribution is centered at 1 million since this class has approximately half of the observations. One could also say that the average may be close to 4 million since the distribution is skewed right.

1.9 a) The distribution of monthly returns appears unimodal and fairly symmetric. **b)** The center of the distribution is close to zero. **c)** The range of returns is –18% to 18%. **d)** Roughly 35 to 40% of the monthly returns were less than zero.

1.10 The stemplot of staff counts is shown below. The distribution is strongly skewed to the right, which we also observed in the histogram shown in Problem 1.6,

```
 0| 7
 1| 3 4 5 5 5 7 7
 2| 2 4
 3|
 4|
 5| 2 7
 6| 1 2 8
 7| 0 0 2
 8|
 9| 6
10|
11| 0 1 5
12| 6
13| 1
14|
15| 5
```

1.11 The stemplot is shown below. The center of the distribution is near 28. There do not appear to be any clear outliers, although the distribution appears skewed to the right. The range of values is 3 to 93. The split stemplot is also shown on the following page.

```
0| 3 9 9
1| 1 3 4 5 6 7 7 8 8 9
2| 0 0 0 1 2 3 4 5 5 6 6 8 8 8 8
3| 2 5 6 9 9
4| 1 3 4 5 5 7 9
5| 0 3 5 9
6| 1
7| 0
8| 3 6 6
9| 3
```

Split stemplot

```
0 | 3
0 | 9  9
1 | 1  3  4
1 | 5  6  7  7  8  8  9
2 | 0  0  0  1  2  3  4
2 | 5  5  6  6  8  8  8
3 | 2
3 | 5  6  9  9
4 | 1  3  4
4 | 5  5  7  9
5 | 0  3
5 | 5  9
6 | 1
6 |
7 | 0
7 |
8 | 3
8 | 6  6
9 | 3
9 |
```

1.12 a)

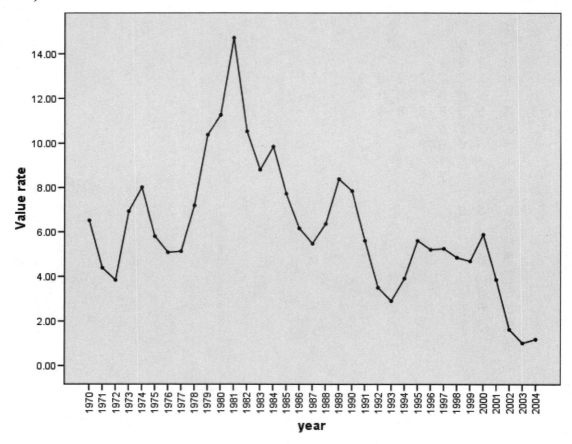

b) The temporary peaks in rates can be seen in years 1974, 1981, 1984, 1989, 1995, and 2000. (*Note*: 1984 is not an obvious peak.) **c)** The highest rate occurred in 1981, and since that time there has been a noticeable downward trend in rates.

1.13

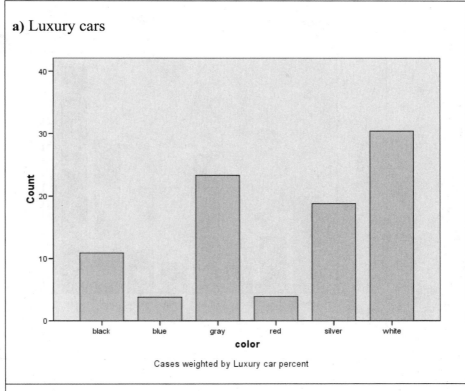

a) Luxury cars

Cases weighted by Luxury car percent

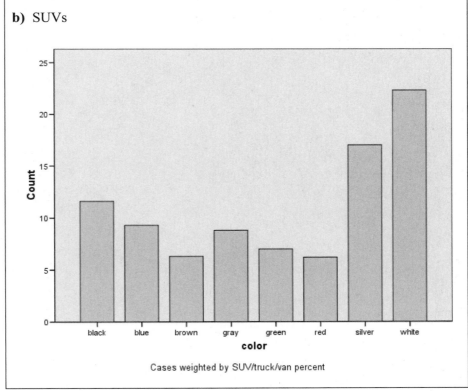

b) SUVs

Cases weighted by SUV/truck/van percent

c) Combined bar graph (answers will vary)

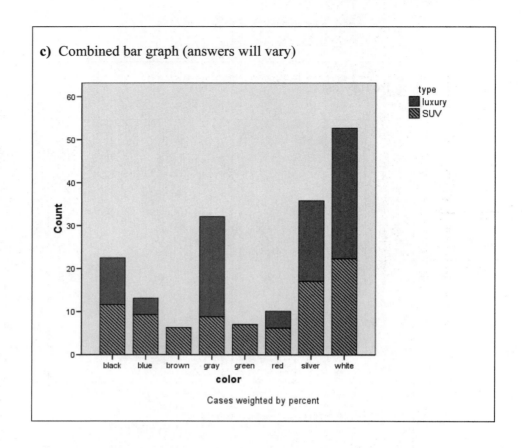

1.14 Graphs for (a) and (b) are below. **c)** The bar graph in part (b) is called a Pareto bar graph.

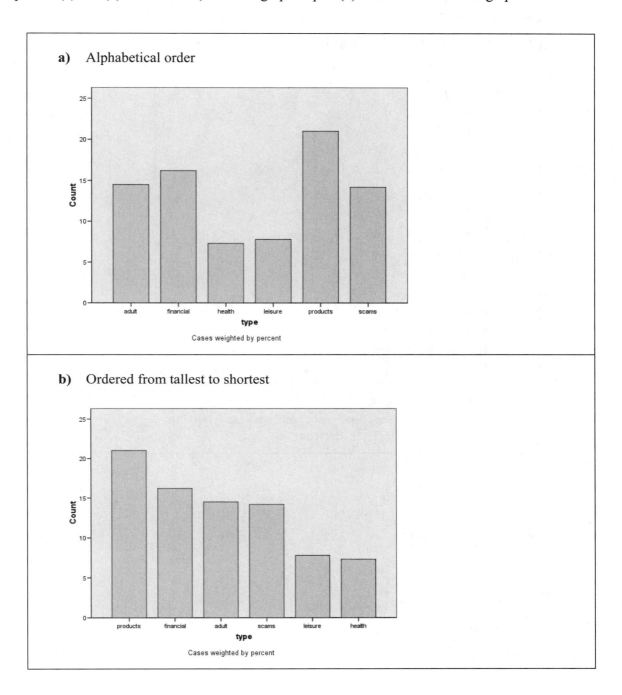

1.15 a) The top five states for tornado damage are Texas, Minnesota, Oklahoma, Missouri, and Illinois. The bottom five are Alaska, Puerto Rico, Rhode Island, Nevada, and Vermont. **b)** See the histogram below. The distribution is unimodal and has strong right-skewness. The range is 0 to 90. There is a large peak in the $0 \leq$ damage ≤ 10 group. The three states with the most damage (Texas, Minnesota, and Oklahoma) may be outliers.   **c)** See the histogram below, but answers will vary depending on software used.

b) Histogram with groups of size 10

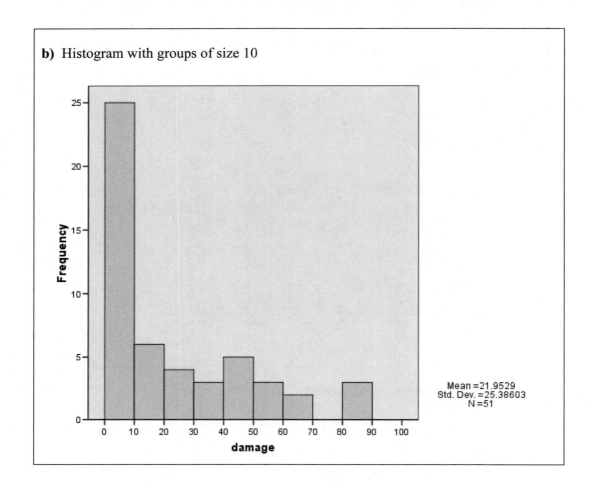

c) Default histogram from SPSS (more bars than previous histogram)

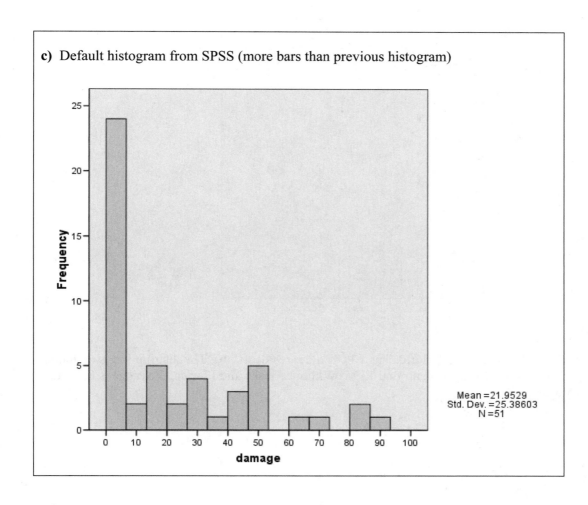

Mean =21.9529
Std. Dev. =25.38603
N =51

1.16 a) Smaller countries will automatically have lower total emissions than larger countries, so it would not be a fair comparison if population is not taken into account. **b)** Either a histogram or a stemplot would be appropriate. The distribution is strongly right-skewed with a large peak in the smallest group. The range is 0 to 20. The top three countries (U.S., Canada, and Australia) may be outliers.

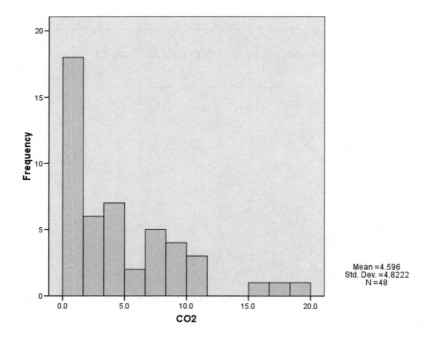

1.17 a) Alaska has 5.7% and Florida has 17.6% older residents. **b)** The distribution is unimodal and symmetric with a peak around 13%. Without Alaska and Florida, the range is 8.5% to 15.6%.

1.18 The regular stemplot is less spread out and shows the pattern better.

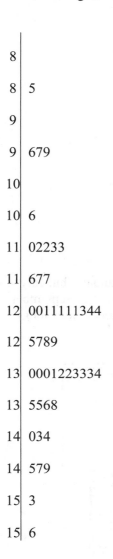

```
 8 |
 8 | 5
 9 |
 9 | 679
10 |
10 | 6
11 | 02233
11 | 677
12 | 0011111344
12 | 5789
13 | 0001223334
13 | 5568
14 | 034
14 | 579
15 | 3
15 | 6
```

1.19 GM had more complaints than Toyota each year, but both companies seem to have fewer complaints in general over time. On the time plot below, GM is the top line and Toyota is the bottom line.

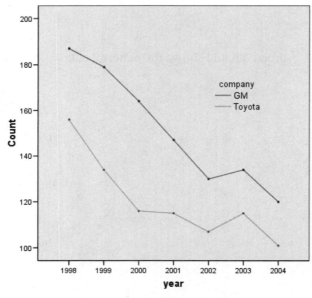

Cases weighted by complaints

1.20 a) See the time plot that follows. **b)** Mass layoffs are most common in January, but July also has a smaller regular increase in layoffs. Mass layoffs are least common in September, but March also has a smaller regular decrease in layoffs. **c)** There is not an obvious long-term trend. There is perhaps a slight increase over time, but it is very small.

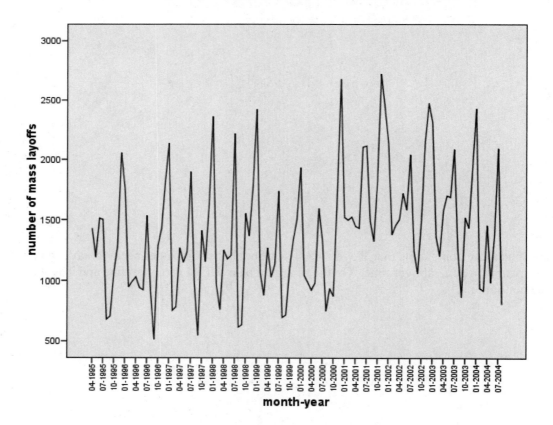

1.21 a) Vehicles **b)** Variables: vehicle type (categorical), transmission type (categorical, number of cylinders (quantitative), city MPG (quantitative), and highway MPG (quantitative).

1.22 a) Gender is categorical. **b)** Age is quantitative. **c)** Race is categorical. **d)** Smoker is categorical. **e)** Blood pressure is quantitative. **f)** Calcium level is quantitative.

1.23 a) The individuals described by this data set are Mutual Funds. **b)** In addition to the name of the fund, there are four other variables. The "category" and "largest holding" variables are categorical, and the "net assets" and "year-to-date return" variables are quantitative. **c)** The unit of measurement for "net assets" is millions of dollars and for "year-to-date return" it is percentage.

1.24 a)

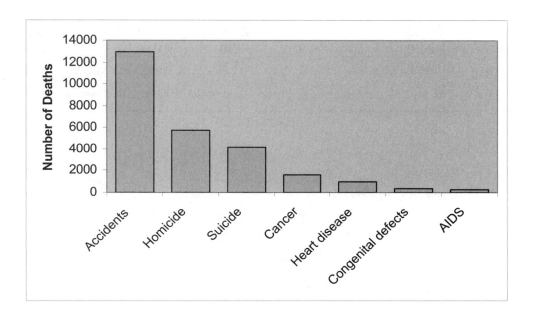

   b) To make a pie chart we need to know the total number of deaths in this age group in 1997.

1.25 Obviously reasons will vary. Reasonable suggestions include market potential for their business, availability of employees, tax benefits from municipality, accessibility to an airport, public education system (for employees relocating), housing costs, construction costs, and predicted growth in the area.

1.26 The distribution appears slightly skewed to the right with the majority of years seeing no more than 4 hurricanes. It appears that the center of the distribution is between 3 and 4 per year.

1.27 Sketches should vary. The distribution will be skewed left because there are more new coins in students' pockets than old coins.

1.28 a) *Note:* The 1950 total listed as 151.1 on the chart in the book, but if you add up the 1950 percentages, the total is really 150.9. The difference is probably caused by rounding. The percentages in the table below for 1950 were found by dividing each count by 151.1.

Age group	1950	2075	% of total 1950	% of total 2075
Under 10 yrs	29.3	53.3	19.39%	13.20%
10-19	21.8	53.2	14.43%	13.18%
20-29	24	51.2	15.88%	12.68%
30-39	22.8	50.5	15.09%	12.51%
40-49	19.3	47.5	12.77%	11.77%
50-59	15.5	44.8	10.26%	11.10%
60-69	11	40.7	7.28%	10.08%
70-79	5.5	30.9	3.64%	7.65%
80-89	1.6	21.7	1.06%	5.38%
90-99	0.1	8.8	0.07%	2.18%
100-109		1.1		0.27%

b) The highest percentage age group is the under-10 age group with almost 20%.

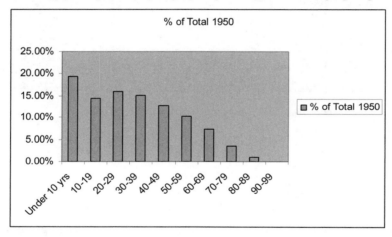

c) The most obvious change between 1950 and 2075 is the more uniform distribution observed in 2075. There are also observations in a new category, the 100-109 age group.

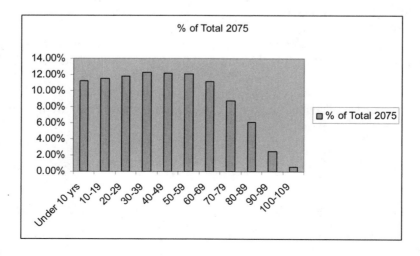

1.29 The count of service calls is not an appropriate measure to report when comparing reliability between Brand A and Brand B dishwashers. The total number of owners of Brand A and Brand B included in the study are very different (13,376 vs. 2942). **b)** A better measure of reliability might be the percentage of owners of each brand that requested a service call. Comparing these percentages shows that 22% (2942/13,376) of Brand A owners requested a service call, while 40% of Brand B owners requested a service call. It appears that Brand B has a much lower reliability than Brand A.

1.30 a)

```
1 │ 0  4  4  4  5  9
2 │ 0  2  2  6  6  7
3 │ 4  6
4 │ 2  7  8
```

Split stemplot

```
1 │ 0  4  4  4
1 │ 5  9
2 │ 0  2  2
2 │ 6  6  7
3 │ 4
3 │ 6
4 │ 2
4 │ 7  8
```

The split stemplot shows the skewness of the distribution much more clearly.

b) The distribution of percentage decline is skewed to the right. **c)** The center appears to be at 22. The range of values is 10 to 48. It makes sense to explain that, during a bear market, stocks fall around 22% but can fall close to 50% during some markets. It would be interesting to look at the duration of the decline for those years with a very high percentage decline in stock prices.

1.31 Other variables that might indicate "size" of a company include market share in their particular market, number of employees, number of facilities, and profit (not simply revenue).

1.32

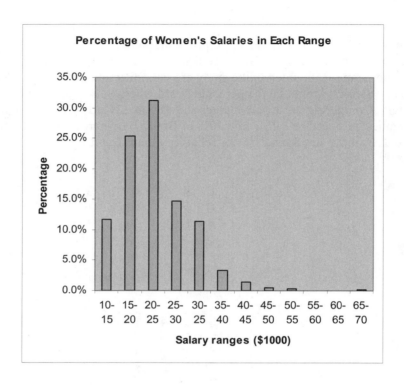

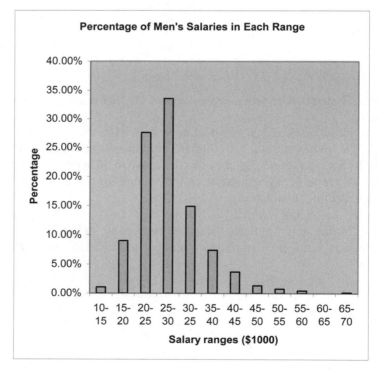

The overall shape for both distributions is similar: both are heavily skewed to the right. The distributions also have the same spread. The difference between the two is the center of the distribution. The center for women's salaries appears to be in the $20,000-$25,000 range whereas the men's salaries appear to center in the $25,000-$30,000 range. An interesting observation is that almost 70% of the women in this factory earn less than $25,000 while only 40% of the men earn less than $25,000.

1.33

```
0|
0| 8 9
1| 0 0 2 3 4
1| 5 5 5 5 8 8 9 9
2| 0 0 0 0 0 0 0 0 0 0 0 0 0 0 1 1 1 1 1 2 2 2 2 2 2 2 2 2 3
2| 5 9
3| 0
3| 5
4| 0 0
4|
5| 0
5|
```

The distribution does not appear heavily skewed, although the majority of monthly fees are less than $23. The $50 monthly charge may be an outlier. Most ISPs were charging around $20 a month in August 2000. The charges in the high end of the distribution may have been early subscribers. ISPs offered their services at a fairly high premium in the beginning and subscription rates tended to drop as more subscribers signed up. (Although it may be possible that early subscribers were offered low rates to initially sign on.)

1.34

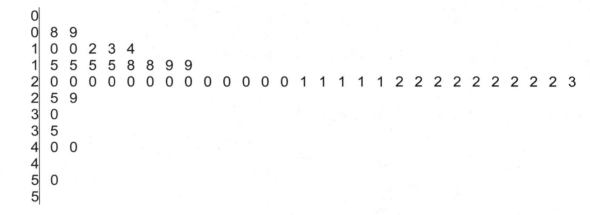

																Engineers				Architects						
4	4	3	2	1	1	1	0	0	0	0	0	0	0	0	0	0	0	2 2 3 3 3 4 4
															7	0	5 5 5 5 5 5 6 8 9
											4	3	2	2	1	0 2 2
														1	9 9
										3	3	1	2	1 4
													2	9
													3	1
									5	3	

The distribution of engineers is much more heavily skewed to the right than the distribution of architects. There appears to be an outlier of 53 engineers for one firm.

1.35

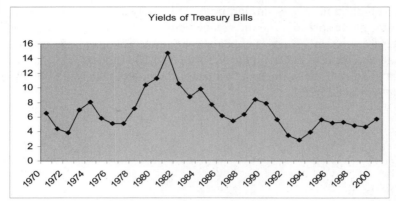

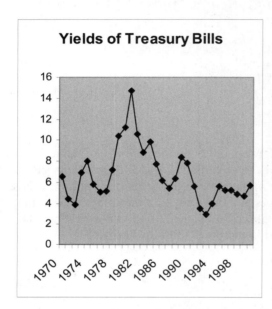

1.36

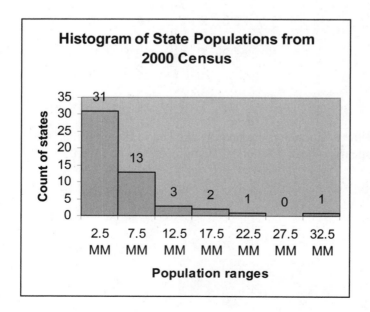

Population Stem-and-Leaf Plot

```
0 .  00000000111111111
0 .  22222333
0 .  444444555555
0 .  667
0 .  8889
1 .  1
1 .  22

4 Extremes      (>=15982378)
```

The distribution of state populations is skewed to the right. This makes sense because we expect there to be a small number of states with very large populations, such as California and Texas. More than half of the states fall into the smallest range. The center appears to be around 5 million, and the spread is approximately 20-25 million. I would consider California to be an outlier. (The stemplot was produced by SPSS.)

1.37   **a)** Household income includes all people living under one roof. You would expect a household to have a greater income than an individual.

b)

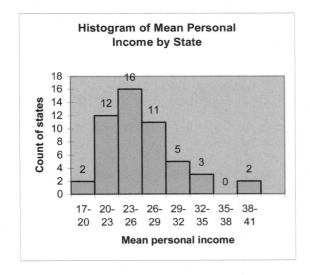

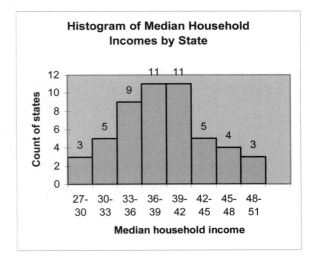

Personal Income Stem-and-Leaf Plot

```
1 .  99
2 .  00011112222233344444
2 .  55555555566667788888999
3 .  00234

2 Extremes      (>=38)
```

Household Income Stem-and-Leaf Plot

```
2 .  679
3 .  0111233344
3 .  5555666667778899999
4 .  000011123344
4 .  66779
5 .  00
```

c) The mean personal income distribution is skewed to the right with two states possibly being outliers. This makes sense because we would expect more variability in personal income than household income. If we looked at the distribution of personal income within each state, we would probably see that they are heavily skewed to the right also. The median household income is greater for most states, which is what we explained in part (a). The shape is more symmetrical because we are looking at the distribution of medians, rather than means. (Medians are resistant to outliers, whereas means are not.)

1.38   **a)** Two states with the same number of doctors may not offer the same level of health care if their populations are very different.
b) This histogram does not give a clear look at the distribution because of the outlier. The outlier is for Washington, D.C., and can be taken out of the data set since D.C. is not technically a state. The resulting histogram, without the outlier, shows a skewed distribution. States average close to 200 doctors per 100,000 people with the range being from 100-450.

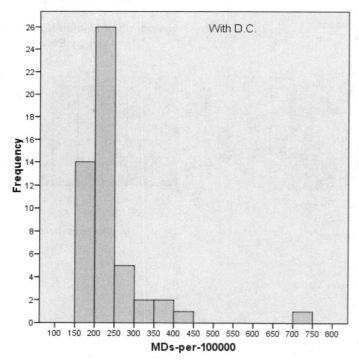

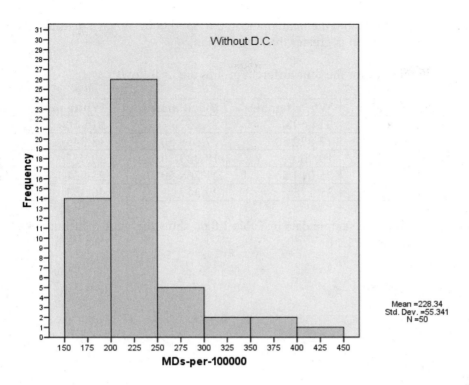

1.39   The mean earnings for Black males is $19,804.17, for White females is $21,484.80, and for White males is $21,283.93. The mean values suggest that there may be a difference in earnings between Black and White employees and between Black male and female employees. The more striking difference appears between Black and White employees.

1.40   **a)** The mean amount spent by a grocery shopper is $34.70. **b)** The trimmed mean of the lowest 46 observations is $30.15. The outliers inflate the mean.

1.41   The median earnings for Black males is $18,383.50, for White females is $19,960, and for White males is $19,977. The median values do show the same difference as the mean values. In each case, however, the median is less than the mean indicating the distribution on salaries may be skewed to the right.

1.42   **a)**

```
2 | 9
3 | 2   9
4 | 1   4   6   7
5 | 2   4
6 | 2
7 | 2
8 |
9 | 4
```

b) The mean and median with the outlier are: 5.1 and 4.65. **c)** The mean and median without the outlier are 4.709 and 4.6. The median did not change much (only by 0.05) when the outlier is removed. The mean shifted by 0.391, which is a lot.

1.43   The mean income is $675,000 and the median income is $330,000. When a distribution is skewed to the right, the mean is greater than the median.

1.44   The five-number summaries for the four different groups are as follows:

	Black females	White females	Black males	White males
Low	$12,641	$14,698	$16,576	$15,100
Q_1	16,555	17,879.50	17,018.50	18,245
Median	17,516	19,960	18,383.50	19,977
Q_3	19,090	25,014.50	21,268.50	23,531
High	20,788	31,176	29,347	30,383

The boxplots created from the sample data in Table 1.8 do show the same distributions of salary data as shown in Figure 1.11.

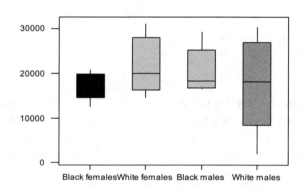

1.45   **a)** The five-number summary is shown in the table below:

	Asian countries	Eastern European countries
Low	2.9	-12.1
Q_1	4.0	-1.6
Median	4.65	1.4
Q_3	5.8	4.3
High	9.4	7

b) The boxplot on the following page shows the distribution of growth of consumption for the two groups of countries. We can see that the growth for the Asian countries was much stronger over this time period than for the Eastern European countries.

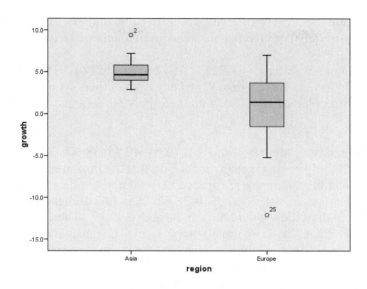

1.46 **a)**

3	4	5	6	7	8	9	10	11	12	13	14
				9							
				8	9						
		5		7	3						
	6	5		6	3	8					
	5	3	9	6	1	7	4				
	2	1	8	5	0	4	0				
2	1	0	7	3	0	4	0				1

b) It is hard to say whether the mean or the median will be higher. The distribution is a little skewed-left, but then there is a high outlier. The left-skewness would make the median higher than the mean, but the high outlier would make the mean higher than the median. **c)** The mean is 74.47 and the five-number summary is 32, 55, 76.5, 89, and 141. The median is greater than the mean ($76.5 > 74.47$), but not by much. **d)** The range of the middle half of managerial and administrative average annual wages is $89 - 55 = 34$.

1.47 **a)** 983.5 **b)** 347.23

1.48 **a)** Refer to Problem 1.38 (b). The second graph shows the distribution of MDs without D.C. **b)** The five-number summary is 402, 242, 220, 196, and 150. The mean and standard deviation are as follows: $\overline{x} = 228.34$, $s = 55.34$. Based on the histogram, the five-number summary shows that the distribution is skewed to the right. (Note the small distance between the median and the minimum compared to the median and the maximum.) **c)** The graph shows that 40 of the states have less than 250 MDs per 100,000 people. This is 80% of all states.

1.49 A rare, catastrophic loss would be considered an outlier, and averages are not resistant to outliers. The five-number summary is more appropriate for describing the distribution of data with outliers.

1.50   The distribution is probably right-skewed with some outliers. The majority of young adults will earn a smaller income, but a few individuals will have very large salaries.

1.51   **a)** The five-number summary is 5.7, 11.7, 12.75, 13.5, 17.6. The IQR is 1.8. Any low outliers would have to be less than 9, and any high outliers would have to be greater than 16.2. Therefore, Florida and Alaska are definitely outliers, but so is the state with 8.5% older residents.

1.52   **a)** The five-number summary is 0, 2.14, 10.64, 40.96, 88.60. The minimum, Q_1, and median are all fairly close together, indicating that the peak would be in this range. The median, Q_3, and the maximum are spaced very far apart, indicating the tail would be on this side of the median. **b)** The IQR is 38.82. Any low outliers would have to be below -56.09. Any high outliers would have to be above 99.19. There are no data points in either of these ranges, so there are no outliers. **c)** The mean is 21.9529. The distribution is strongly skewed-right, which explains why the mean is so much above the median.

1.53   **a)** The five-number summary is 0, 0.75, 3.2, 7.8, 19.9. **b)** The IQR is 7.05. Any low outliers would have to be less than -9.825, and any high outliers would have to be greater than 18.375. The histogram shows that the U.S., Australia, and Canada all have CO_2 emissions much higher than the rest of the countries, but only the U.S. is officially considered an outlier using the 1.5*IQR rule.

1.54   **a)** The median's position is 7,480. The median is around 40 thousand dollars. **b)** The position of the first quartile is 3,740. The position of the third quartile is 11,220. The first quartile is approximately 30 thousand dollars. The third quartile is approximately 70 thousand dollars.

1.55   **a)** The 5th percentile is approximately at the 748th position. The 95th percentile is approximately at the 14,211th position. **b)** The 5th percentile value is approximately $10,000. The 95th percentile value is approximately $140,000.

1.56   As the level of education increases, the median income increases. The 5th percentile income stays approximately the same for all the groups except "advanced." The 95th percentile has a fairly steady increase as education increases until a big jump for "advanced." There is more spread in the distributions as education level increases. All education levels are right-skewed, but the skewness increases as education level increases.

1.57   **a)** The distribution is skewed left with a possible low outlier. **b)** Use stems from the tens place as –3, 2, -1, -0, 0, 1, 2, 3.

Histogram

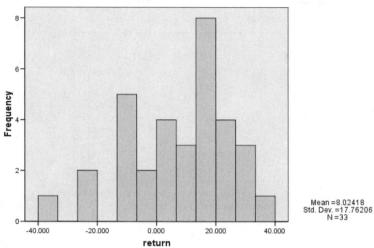

Mean =8.02418
Std. Dev. =17.76206
N =33

return

-3	5								
-2	1	3							
-1	2	2	2	3					
-0	1	2	8						
0	0	2	4	4	7				
1	0	1	5	7	7	7	7	8	8	9
2	5	6	6	6	6	8			
3	1	4							

1.58 **a)** The mean is 8.024, and the median is 11.677. Because the distribution is skewed left, it makes sense that the mean is below the median. **b)** Q_1 is -5.4715, and Q_3 is 22.4145. The IQR is 27.886. Any low outliers would have to be below -47.3005, and any high outliers would have to be above 64.2435. There are no suspected outliers.

1.59 The median is 27.86. The median is less than the mean, which was 34.70. This is because the distribution is skewed to the right.

1.60 The distribution appears skewed to the right; therefore, a five-number summary would be a better numerical description of the distribution. The five-number summary for this distribution is: 3, 4.1, 4.6, 5.6, 11.2. ($\bar{x} = 4.93, s = 1.39$)

1.61 **a)** $\bar{x} = 28.77$, $s = 17.77$ **b)** $\bar{x} = 31.71$, $s = 14.15$. The outlier inflates the values of the mean and standard deviation. **c)** The advertiser means that the vehicles are similar in make, model, year. The objective is to remove any variation due to different vehicle sizes, ages, or any other performance related issues.

1.62 – 1.64 Applet

1.65   a)

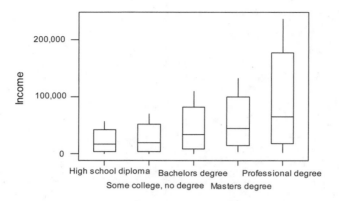

b) From the boxplots, it appears that income increases as education level increases. The average income level does not increase as much as the range of income within each educational category. For example, the range of income in the first category, high school diploma, is $56,294, whereas the range of income in the last category, professional degree, is $233,667.

1.66   For the category "high school diploma," the 5th percentile is at position 1598, the first quartile is at position 7993, the median is between positions 15,985 and 15,986, the third quartile is at position 23,978, and the 95th percentile is at 30,371. For the category "professional degree," the 5th percentile is at position 61, the first quartile is between positions 307 and 308, the median is at position 615, the third quartile is between positions 922 and 923, and the 95th percentile is at position 1167.

1.67   The mean number of violent crime incidents per 100,000 people is 523, and the standard deviation is 320. The histogram below shows that the distribution is skewed to the right. There is also a clear outlier. This happens to be D.C. again.

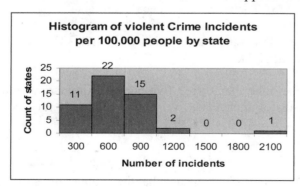

1.68   Northern states $\overline{x} = 371.89$, $s = 220.63$

```
 0  |
 1  | 13 20 21
 2  |
 3  | 34 91
 4  | 42 93
 5  |
 6  | 44 89
 7  |
 8  |
 9  |
10  |
```

Southern states $\overline{x} = 621.5$, $s = 259.07$

```
 0  |
 1  |
 2  | 19
 3  | 17 45
 4  | 69
 5  | 65
 6  |  7  7 78
 7  | 90
 8  | 47
 9  | 90
10  | 24
```

Midwestern states $\overline{x} = 419$, $s = 204.35$

```
 0  | 87
 1  | 97
 2  | 71
 3  | 10 38
 4  |  9 35 38
 5  | 15 77 90
 6  |
 7  |
 8  | 61
 9  |
10  |
```

Based on the stemplots and numerical summaries, one can see that the Southern states have a higher incidence of violent crime than the Northeastern or Midwestern states. When comparing small data sets, both pictures and numerical summaries help us see the differences. Note the higher mean and standard deviation for the Southern states.

1.69 $\bar{x} = 7.5$, $s = 2.03$ for both data sets. The stemplot below shows that data set A is skewed left and data set B is skewed right. Both data sets have outliers as well.

Data A		Data B
10	3	
74	4	
	5	25 56 76
13	6	58 89
26	7	4 71 91
77 74 14 10	8	47 84
26 14 13	9	
	10	
	11	
	12	50

1.70   The mean wealth is $2.2 million, and the median wealth is $800,000. One would expect the distribution on average wealth to be skewed heavily to the right.

1.71   **a)** The five-number summary is 9%, 30%, 49.5%, 66%, and 14.7%. **b)** The distribution appears to be skewed to the right; therefore the median is less than the mean.

1.72   **a)** The mean salary is $62,500. All the employees earn less than the mean. The median salary is $25,000. **b)** The mean increases to $87,500. This increase in the owner's salary does not affect the median.

1.73   **a)** I chose a histogram because the data set was very large.

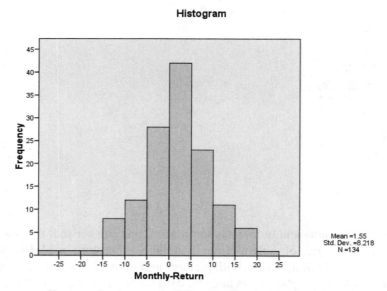

b) The two outliers on the low end of the distribution have values −26.6 and −22.9. The distribution appears symmetric about a center of 2.5 with a spread of approximately 40

(25 - (-15)). **c)** If the two outliers are included, the mean is 1.55 and the standard deviation is 8.22. If one invested $100 and realized the mean return, they would have 101.55 at the end of the month. **d)** If one invested $100 and realized a return of –26.6%, they would have $73.40 left at the end of the month. The mean and standard deviation without the two low outliers are 1.95 and 7.60. The mean increased and the standard deviation decreased after removing the outliers. Leaving out these outliers should not substantially affect the median and quartiles because they are resistant to outliers.

1.74   It makes sense that the mean change in price was a positive 111%, while the median change in price was a negative 31%. One would expect the distribution on stock price change of IPOs to be skewed to the right.

1.75   The *mean* of all salaries in the NBA is $2.36 million. If this were the *median,* then half of all players would be making less than this amount.

1.76   **a)** You should use the mean in this case. Even though income would be heavily skewed to the right, the mean will give the government a better estimate of the tax base because it will be greater than the median. **b)** The median should be used in this case. Again, the distribution is likely to be skewed to the right and the median will more accurately reflect the center of the distribution.

1.77   **a)** Choose all four numbers the same. **b)** The numbers 0, 0, 10, and 10 give a standard deviation of 5. **c)** There is more than one choice in part (a) but only one choice in part (b). The standard deviation measures the variation about the mean. Choosing numbers all the same gives a standard deviation of zero. Choosing an equal set of numbers as far from the mean as possible will give the largest standard deviation.

1.78   **a)** The IQR for Black females is 2535 (see Problem 1.39). Q_1 minus the low observation is 3914. 3914 > 1.5(2535); therefore, the low observation can be considered an outlier. **b)** Yes. The IQR for Black males is 4250. 29,347 is above Q_3 (21,268.5) plus 1.5*IQR (cut-off of 27,643.5).

1.79   Sketches will vary but check to see that students understand the difference between *symmetric* and *skewed left.*

1.80   **a)** This is a 1×1 square, and the area inside this square is equal to 1. **b)** The area under the square between 0.8 and 1.0 is 0.2 or 20%. **c)** 60%. **d)** 50%. **e)** $\mu = 0.5$.

1.81   **a)** The mean is at point C and the median is at point B. The mean is greater than the median because the distribution is skewed right. **b)** The mean and median are equal at point A because the distribution is symmetric. **c)** The mean is at point A and the median is at point B. The mean is less than the median because the distribution is skewed left.

1.82

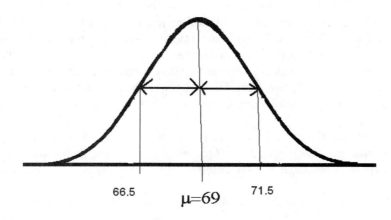

66.5 $\mu=69$ 71.5

1.83   **a)** 2.5%. **b)** 64 – 74 inches. **c)** 16%.

1.84   **a)** 50%. **b)** 2.5%. **c)** 60 to 160.

1.85   The Z-score for Eleanor is 1.8 and the Z-score for Gerald is 1.5. Eleanor scored higher based on her standardized score.

1.86   **a)** .9978. **b)** .0022. **c)** .9515. **d)** .9978 - .0485 = .9493.

1.87   **a)** Z = 1.64. The area above 1.64 is 0.0505; therefore, 5.05% of vehicles have an MPG rating of 30 or greater. **b)** The area between 30 and 35 equals the area above 1.64 minus the area above 2.57. 4.54% of vehicles have an MPG rating between 30 and 35. **c)** Z = -1.64. The area below -1.64 is 0.0505; therefore, 5.05% of vehicles have an MPG rating less than 12.45.

1.88   **a)**

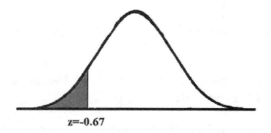

z=-0.67

b)

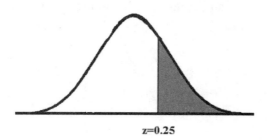

z=0.25

1.89   **a)** 59.48%. **b)** 452. **c)** 711.

1.90   The measurements are taken to the nearest hundredth of an inch and as we can see on the vertical axis there are many observations with the same values. (In essence, the data have been *made discrete,* which means that the distances are forced to take on values in the set (.01, .02, .03, .04, .05, .06, .07, .08). This results in the odd runs at each point.)

1.91   It appears that less than 5% of the observations are beyond two standard deviations from the mean. One might conclude that the density curve has a very steep middle with most points clustered around the mean.

1.92   **a)** The mean is 8.024, and the standard deviation is 17.762. **b)** Between -45.262 and 61.310. **c)** The lowest actual return -34.540, and the highest actual return +34.167. The actual returns don't match up to the theoretical limits, but this was a skewed distribution.

1.93   Answers will vary. Examples below.

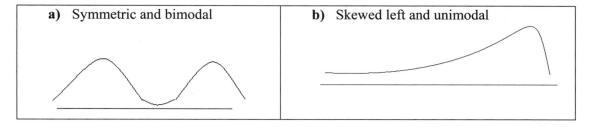

1.94   **a)** See the histograms and Normal quantile plots that follow. **b)** No, neither variable appears to be Normally distributed. The histograms do not look symmetric, and the dots do not follow the diagonal on the Normal quantile plots. **c)** Apartment building #14 appears to be an outlier with respect to both selling price ($7,900,000) and building area (114,412 square feet).

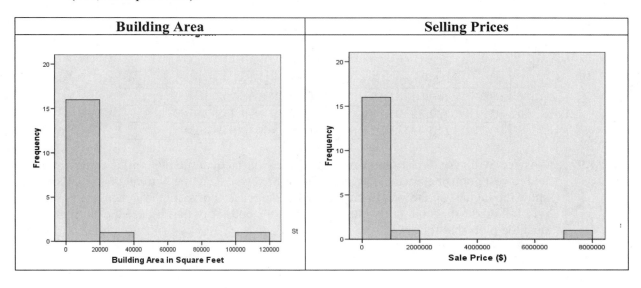

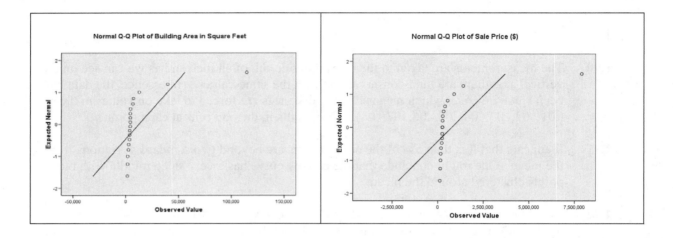

1.95   **a)** No, this apartment building is no longer an outlier. It's not even one of the top two data points now. It fits in perfectly with the rest of the data. **b)** See the histogram and Normal quantile plot below. **c)** The distribution looks fairly Normal except for 2 new high outliers (#11 and #13). It looks much better than the distributions in 1.94.

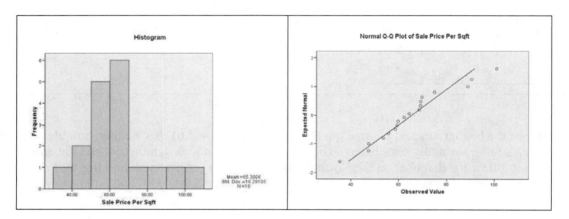

1.96   **a)** The mean is 65.3006, and the standard deviation is 16.291. **b)** and **c)** See table below. **d)** Yes, the table does provide a clear indication of Normality for the data values.

	Theoretical intervals	Actual % of data in that range
68%	(49.01, 81.59)	12/18 = 66.7%
95%	(32.72, 97.88)	17/18 = 94.4%
99.7%	(16.43, 114.17)	18/18 = 100%

1.97   Answers will vary. For right-skewed data, the Normal quantile plot will show the highest and lowest points below the diagonal. For left-skewed data, the Normal quantile plot will show the highest and lowest points above the diagonal. For symmetric data, the points will follow the diagonal fairly closely, even at the ends. For part **b),** see the Normal quantile plots that follow.

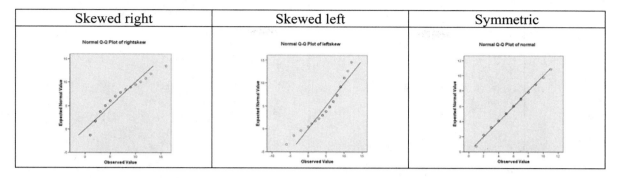

Skewed right	Skewed left	Symmetric

1.98   **a)** The mean is 579,338.41, and the standard deviation is 1,496,814. **b)** (-3911103.6, 5069780.4). **c)** There were no negative volumes in our data, and 21 out of the 22 data points are between 0 and 2,410,204. The data clearly does not follow the 68-95-99.7% rule.

1.99   **a)** Mean = -0.0224, standard deviation = 0.2180. **b)** $\bar{x} \pm s = (-0.2404, 0.1956)$; $\bar{x} \pm 2s = (-0.4584, 0.4136)$; $\bar{x} \pm 3s = (-0.6764, 0.6316)$. **c)** 72.7%, 90.9%, and 100%. The distribution is not exactly Normal.

1.100   See the histogram and Normal quantile plot below.

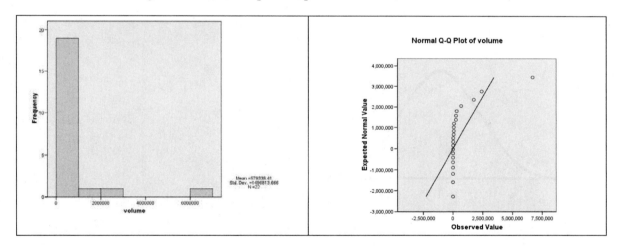

1.101   The stemplot shows a fairly symmetric distribution with a high and low outlier. The Normal quantile plot shows a fairly good fit to the diagonal line in the middle, but the two outliers stick out again. See the stemplot and Normal quantile plot that follow.

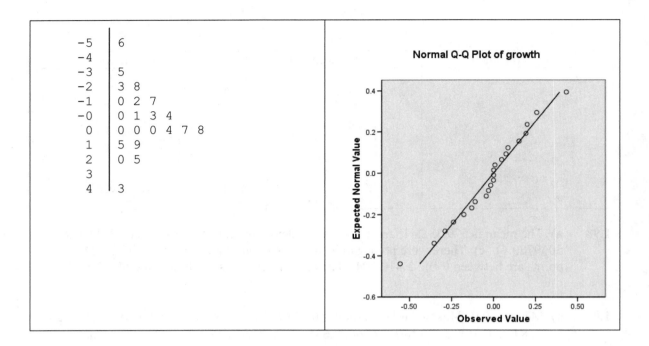

```
-5 | 6
-4 |
-3 | 5
-2 | 3 8
-1 | 0 2 7
-0 | 0 1 3 4
 0 | 0 0 0 4 7 8
 1 | 5 9
 2 | 0 5
 3 |
 4 | 3
```

1.102   The taller curve has an approximate standard deviation of 0.2, and the shorter curve has an approximate standard deviation of 0.5. Answers will vary.

1.103

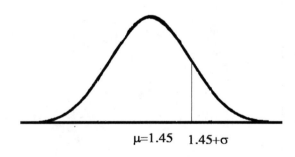

(0.65, 2.25)

1.104   **a)** Between 234 and 298 days. **b)** 234 days or less. **c)** It is unlikely. 218 is three standard deviations below the mean, which tells us only 0.15% of all women give birth in 218 days or less.

1.105   a)

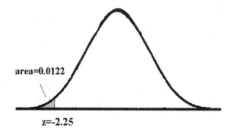

b)

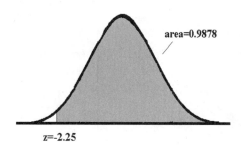

c)

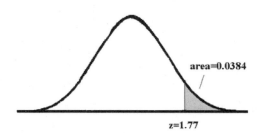

d)

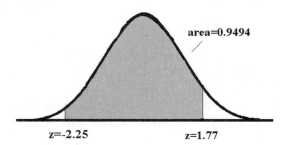

1.106   a) Z = 0.84. **b)** Z = 0.39.

1.107   17.11%

1.108   7.64%

1.109   **a)** –21% - 47%. **b)** 22.36%. **c)** 23.89%.

1.110   **a)** 5.16%. **b)** 54.71%. **c)** 279.44 days.

1.111   **a)** 0.25, $Q_1 = -0.67$, $Q_3 = 0.67$. **b)** $Q_1 = 255.28$, $Q_3 = 276.72$.

1.112   **a)** –1.28 and 1.28. **b)** 8.93 oz. and 9.31 oz.

1.113

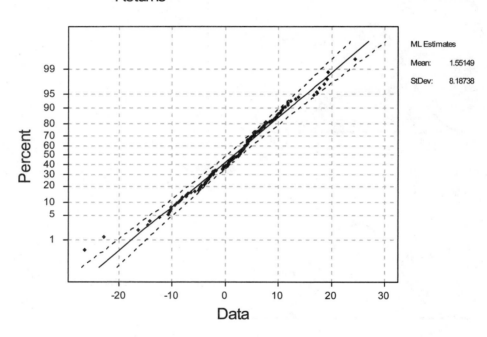

The distribution on the previous page appears fairly Normal. One can see the two low outliers that fall above the line.

1.114   The histograms and quantile plots will differ for each student. Check to see that the student can use the software package correctly.

1.115   As in Problem 1.114, the histograms will all look different since random data is being generated. The uniform density curve should look different than the bell curve. There may be some slight deviations but overall the curve should take on the shape of a rectangle. The Normal plot will have an s-shaped curve rather than a straight line. The low values will fall below the Normal line, and the high values will lie above the Normal line.

1.116   **a)** Iowa **b)** Iowa would take up almost all the space, so it would be very difficult to compare any other states. **c)** See the pie chart below. "Other" has a count of 42 and takes up 3.84% of the area. Iowa has a count of 1053 and takes up 96.16% of the area on the pie chart.

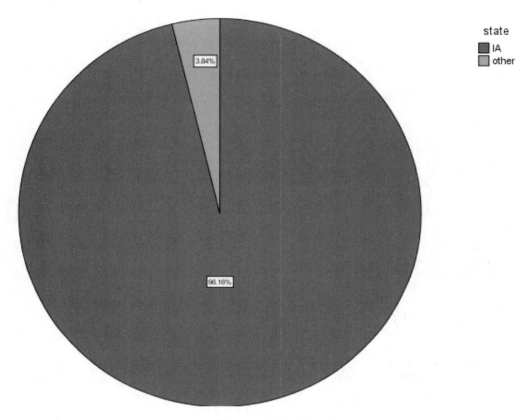

Cases weighted by stores

1.117   **a)** The mean is 64.49. See the time plot that follows. **b)** The beginning years are all below average until January 1966. **c)** The values are high (in the 80s) between 1/00 and 7/00, but then the last month to be above average is 4/01.   Then there is a severe drop with no recovery. **d)** The "dot-com" economy was still booming in January 2000. As 2001 progressed, the "dot-com" economy started to crash, and September 11, 2001 did bad things to the economy as well.

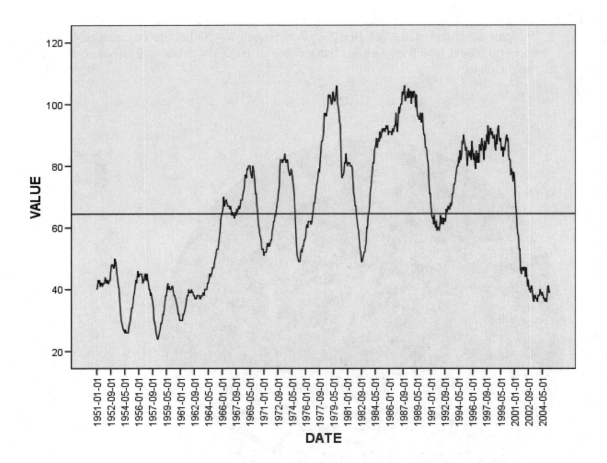

1.118 **a)** The five-number summary is: -78, -10, -6, -5, -2. **b)** 75.7% of all refunds in 2005 were $10 or less. **c)** See the boxplot that follows. **d)** The data is very left-skewed with lots of low outliers.

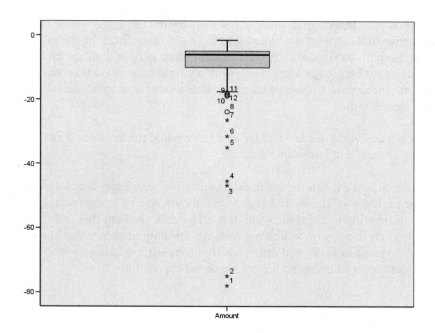

1.119 **a)** Min = 1, Q_1 = 1, M = 1, Q_3 = 1. **b)** See the boxplot below. The box has a length of 0. This makes sense because Q_1, M, and Q_3 are all the same. **c)** The boxplot indicates very, very right-skewed data. Almost all the data were = 1.

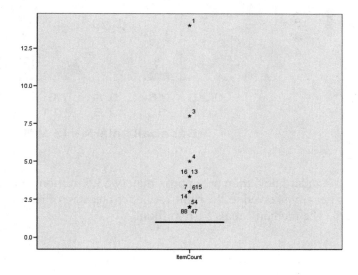

1.120 **a)** 0.6316. **b)** 0.15%. **c)** 0%. This percentage is not really different from the 0.15% because 0.15% of 22 cases is 0.033 cases, which rounds to 0. Therefore, the assumption of a Normal distribution for the model of Telecom revenue growth is appropriate.

1.121 **a)** 11 / 22 = 50%. **b)** Negative revenue growth means the previous year's revenue was higher than this year's revenue. **c)** 0.82%. **d)** The top 25% of all Telecom companies had revenue growth greater than 0.12475.

1.122   **a)** For each pair, the smaller value is the median and the larger value is the mean. It makes sense that incomes are skewed to the right; therefore, the mean would be greater than the median. **b)** Households may contain more people than are included in a family. There may also be greater variation within a single household than within a single family if there are more than two wage earners. This would lead to households having a smaller income than families.

1.123   The categorical variables are gender and automobile preference. The quantitative variables are age and household income.

1.124   **a)** I would expect the number of patients admitted with heart attacks to be roughly the same for each day of the week because the occurrence of a heart attack would not be dependent on which day of the week it is. The data confirm this expectation. **b)** The distribution on the day on which patients are discharged shows that the number of discharges rises to Friday and dramatically drops off for Saturday and Sunday. It may be that patients want to be home for the weekend if possible.

1.125

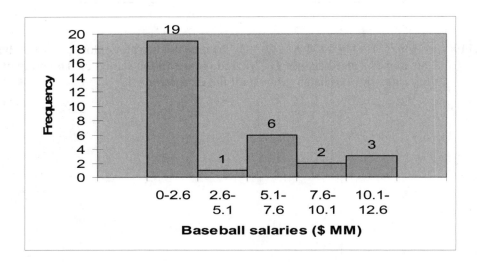

The mean and standard deviation are approximately $3.5 million and $4 million. The distribution is heavily skewed to the right. A better measure of central tendency would be the median. The median equals $1.6 million.

1.126

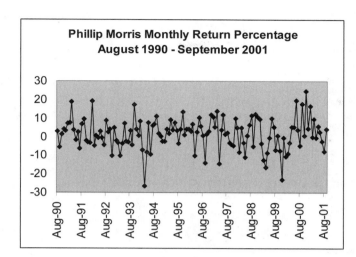

The time plot shows that the returns did not display any obvious trends up or down over this 10-year period. The two outliers discovered in problem 1.53 are shown as the low points on the plot. The two effects of action against smoking and sharp rises in stock prices may have produced this random-looking time plot.

1.127 **a)** The five-number summary for normal corn is 462, 400.5, 358, 337, and 272. The five-number summary for new corn is 477, 428.5, 406.5, 383.5, and 318. The boxplots are shown below. We can see that the new corn has a more symmetrical distribution than the normal corn with a smaller spread and higher median. There is a higher weight gain overall for the new corn.

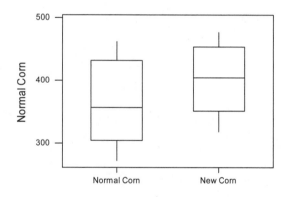

b) The mean and standard deviation of weight gain for the normal corn is 366.3 grams and 50.81 grams. The mean and standard deviation for the new corn is 402.95 grams and 42.73 grams. The mean weight gain of chicks fed the new corn is 36.65 grams higher than for chicks fed the normal corn.

1.128 **a)** This histogram shows a distribution skewed to the right. The mean is 20.11, and the standard deviation is 2.94. The five-number summary is 15, 18, 19, 22, 27. The Toyota RAV4 is a high outlier at 27 MPG.

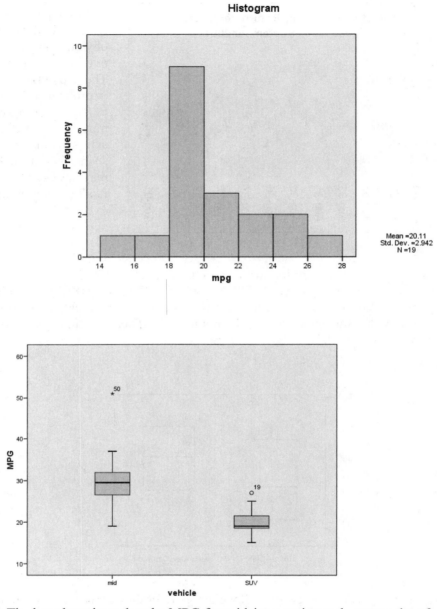

b) The boxplots show that the MPG for midsize cars is much greater than for SUVs. It also appears that the distribution of MPG for midsize cars is more symmetrical than for SUVs.

1.129 a)

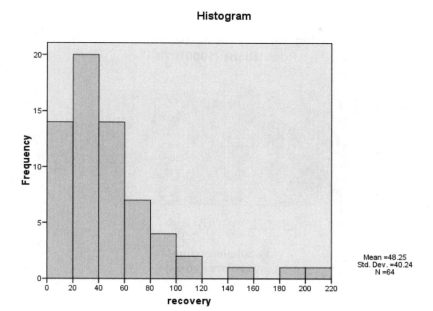

Histogram

Mean =48.25
Std. Dev. =40.24
N =64

The distribution is heavily skewed to the right. **b)** The mean is 48.25, and the median is 37.9. Because the distribution is skewed to the right, the mean is greater than the median. **c)** The five-number summary is 204.9, 59.45, 37.9, 21.6, and 2. Note the large range between the third quartile and the maximum value. This reflects the skewed nature of the data. (*Note:* Quartiles were calculated using the Excel percentile command. The values may differ slightly than finding the quartiles by hand.)

1.130 The IQR is 37.85. The value 204.9 lies more than 1.5*IQR above the third quartile and is considered an outlier. There are four other values that would be considered high outliers using this criteria.

1.131 $\mu = 250$, $\sigma = 175.78$. Z-scores of 1.28 and −1.28 are associated with an upper and lower tail area of 0.10, respectively. Setting each of these equal to the formula for the Z-score results in two equations with two unknowns. One can solve for σ and then find the value of μ, or vice versa.

1.132 These graphs will vary from student to student. Check to see that graphs are properly labeled and that the student's written comments are consistent with the graphs shown.

1.133 The median value of California county populations is 156,000. The mean value is 583,993.93 with Los Angeles (high outlier) included and 427,230 without Los Angeles. The median is a better numerical summary measure since the distribution is so heavily skewed to the right. This histogram does not include Los Angeles since it was such a high outlier.

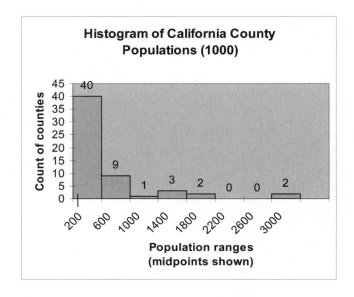

One possible division would be to set Los Angeles aside as one county. The population of Los Angeles makes up 28% of the population of California. The next group of counties might be Orange, San Diego, San Bernardino, Santa Clara, Riverside, Alameda, and Sacramento. These seven counties make up 39% of the state. The third division would be the remaining 50 counties. The populations of these counties are all under 1 MM people and they make up the remaining 33% of the state.

1.134

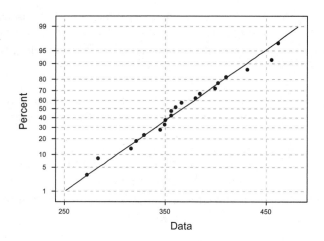

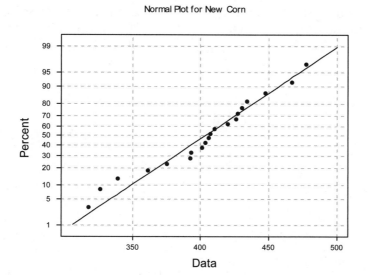

The Normal plot for normal corn shows a fairly normal distribution. The use of the mean and standard deviation is justified. The Normal plot for new corn can be considered roughly Normal, although a few low points fall above the line.

1.135 Because the values and graphs will vary from student to student, the points to look for are an understanding of how to use a random number generator and recognizing that the values generated should follow a Normal curve with a mean of 20 and standard deviation of 5. The distribution of the mean should look fairly symmetrical, have a bell shape curve, and the center should be close to 20. The distribution of s will not look like a bell curve. The Normal plots will verify these observations.

Case Study 1.1

   A. All workers

The first histogram below shows all the incomes. The second histogram below shows the distribution of salaries after the top 1% was removed. The average of all 55,899 individuals was $37,864 and the average of those earning up to $210,000 was $35,660. Note the heavily right-skewed distribution. This is not surprising for a variable of this type.

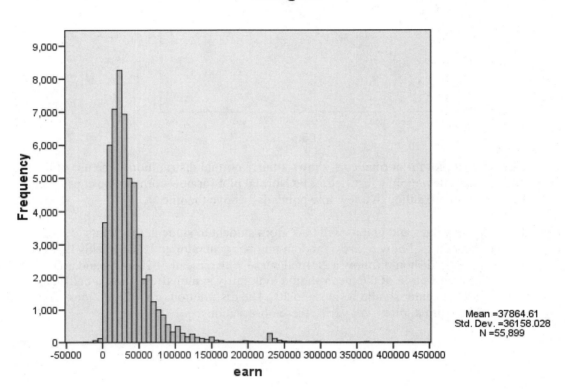

Histogram

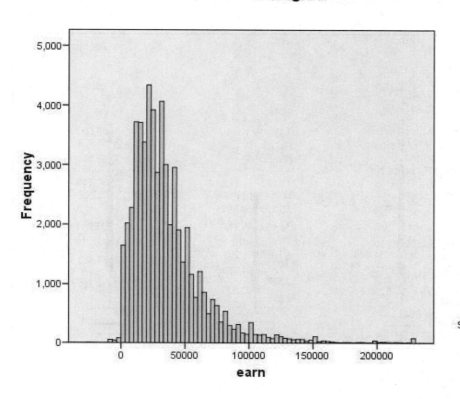

Mean =35659.73
Std. Dev. =28624.921
N =55,340

B. Comparing sectors of the economy

Below are side-by-side boxplots comparing private sector (labeled 5), government (labeled 6), and self-employed (labeled 7). There are many high outliers for all groups with more variability for the self-employed people and less variability for government employees.

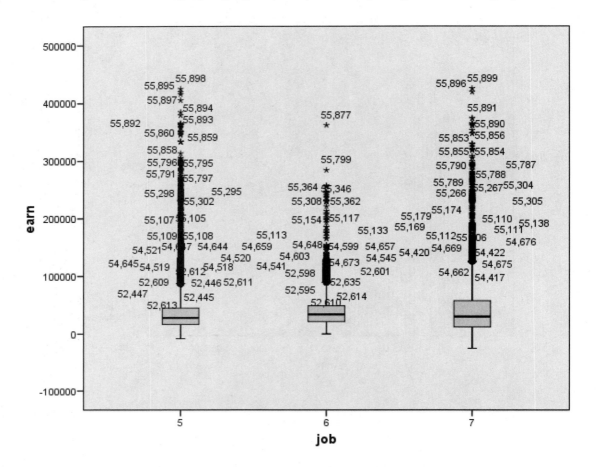

Job	Mean	St. dev.	M	Min	Max
Private	36681	34552	28035	-7999	424770
Government	37783	25314	34000	30	362302
Self-employed	46689	56396	30000	-24998	425510

Case Study 1.2

The average salary for full-time employees is $21,292 and for part-time employees is $19,034. It appears from these numbers and the histograms below that there is a significant difference between the salaries of full-time employees and part-time employees.

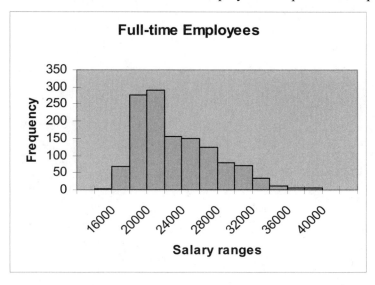

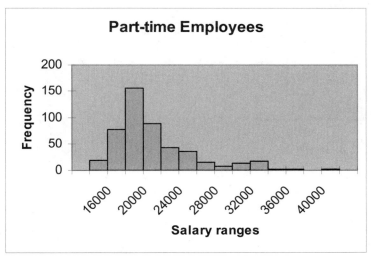

Average Full-time Salary for Blacks	$19,179
Average Part-time Salary for Blacks	$17,362
Average Full-time Salary for Whites	$22,315
Average Part-time Salary for Whites	$19,664

The differences between average full-time salaries and average part-time salaries for both Blacks and Whites show the same gap that was seen in the comparison without separating by race. Furthermore, the percentage of Whites employed part-time is higher than the percentage of Blacks employed part-time (28% compared to 23%). Histograms below show the salary distributions of the races by their job classification.

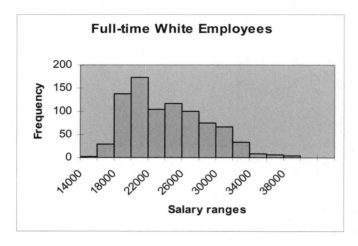

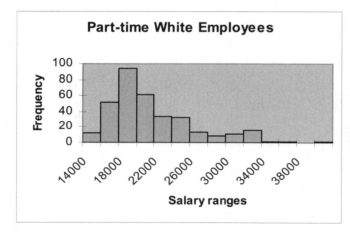

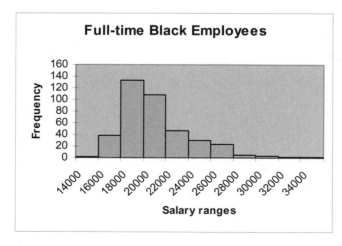

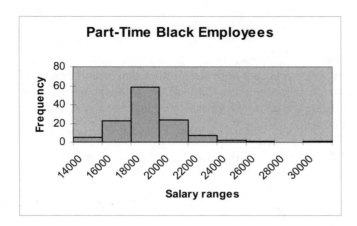

Chapter 2: Examining Relationships

2.1 **a)** *Time studying* would be the explanatory variable, and *grade* would be the response variable. **b)** Neither *weight* nor *height* is an obvious choice for an explanatory variable. **c)** *Amount of yearly rainfall* would be the explanatory variable, and *yield* would be the response variable. **d)** It is not obvious which variable is the explanatory variable. One is probably more interested in identifying a relationship between *salary* and *sick days used* rather than predicting one from the other. **e)** Most people would choose *the economic class of a father* to be the explanatory variable and *the economic class of the son* to be the response variable because the father's class precedes the son's. This may not always be true.

2.2 *Price at beginning of year* would be the explanatory variable, and *price at end of year* would be the response. These are quantitative variables.

2.3 The explanatory variable would be *type of hand wipe*. The response variable would be *level of skin irritation*. These are categorical variables.

2.4 **a)** Because the firm makes a decision on how many staff members to hire, I would choose *staff* as the explanatory variable and *billings* as the response variable.
b) The scatterplot below shows a linear relationship between *staff* and *billings*.

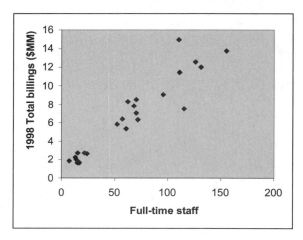

2.5 **a)** The Honda Insight gets approximately 62 MPG in the city and approximately 70 MPG on the highway. **b)** The relationship appears to be linear with highway MPG greater than city MPG. This is logical because city driving requires more stops and starts, thus reducing your gas mileage. **c)** Yes, the Insight fits the pattern fairly well, but its highway and city MPG are so much higher than those of the other two-seater cars.

2.6 **a)** The variables are positively related. **b)** The relationship is linear. **c)** Yes, billings can be predicted from staff levels, although there appears to be more variation in billings as staff levels increase. With a staff level of 75 members, I would predict the billings to be approximately $7 MM.

2.7 **a)** The explanatory variable is *speed*.

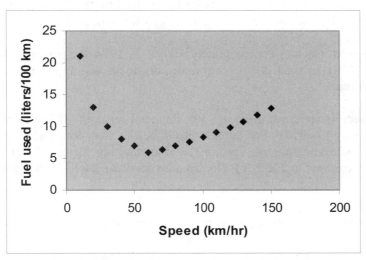

b) The relationship is curved, not linear. This makes sense because we've already observed that fuel consumption is higher for city driving (lower speeds) than highway driving (higher speeds). As speeds increase beyond normal highway driving, one would expect the fuel consumption to go up as well. **c)** It does not make sense to describe a nonlinear relationship as positive or negative because the relationship shows a negative trend up to 50 km/hr and an increasing trend above 50 km/hr. **d)** The relationship appears to be quite strong. The pattern is clearly shown on the scatterplot.

2.8 **a)** The explanatory variable is *lean body mass*.

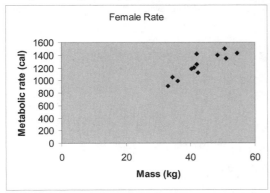

b) The association is a linear positive association and it appears strong.

c)

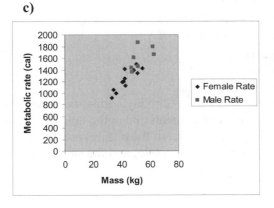

The pattern for the men is similar to that for the women in that we can see an increasing trend. The difference is that the linear pattern is not as strong and there appears to be more variation among the seven men observed.

2.9   Explanatory variable: parent income. Response variable: money student borrows. Both variables are quantitative and probably have a negative association because the more money the parents have, the less a student will probably need to borrow to pay for college tuition.

2.10   **a)** In 1954, the percent return on stocks was approximately +50%. In 1974, the percent return on stocks was approximately -30%. **b)** In 1981, the percent return on stocks was approximately +15%. **c)** There is no clear pattern.

2.11   **a)** The means for the market sectors are consumer (30.960), financial services (32.760), natural resources (23.317), and technology (54.314). See the scatterplot below, with consumer = group 1, financial services = group 2, natural resources = group 3, and technology = group 4. **b)** Technology was the best place to invest in 2003. **c)** No, because market sector is a categorical variable.

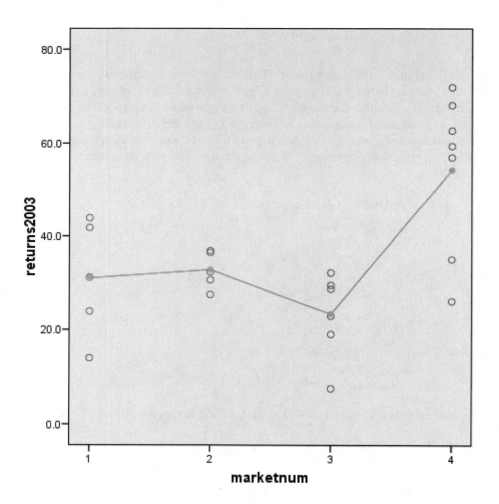

2.12   See the side-by-side boxplot and scatterplot below. There is a relatively strong, negative, linear relationship between the 2002 and 2003 returns, if you assume each line in the table represents the same stock measured in each year. All the 2002 returns (except the outlier) are negative. All the 2003 returns are positive. For 2002 returns, the average is -16.026, and the standard deviation is 23.5142. For 2003 returns, the average is 36.465, and the standard deviation is 16.9913. The 2002 returns are skewed left with a high outlier. The 2003 returns are a little right-skewed with two high outliers.

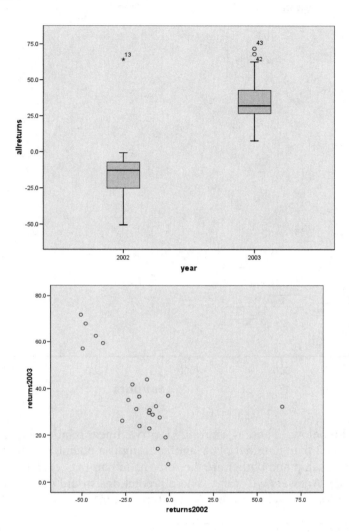

2.13   **a)** Explanatory variable = accounts, response variable = assets. **b)** See the scatterplot that follows. **c)** Strong, positive, and linear, but two points stand out at the top right corner of the plot. **d)** Charles Schwab and Fidelity.

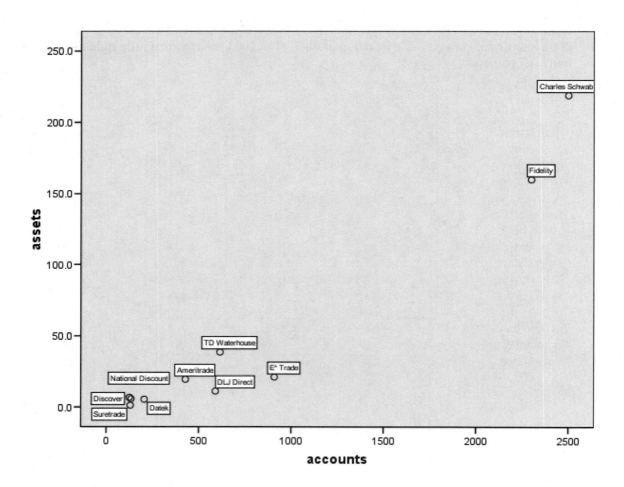

2.14   **a)** See scatterplot below. There is a strong, positive, linear relationship between 1997 paid employees and 2002 paid employees. Manufacturing is a potential outlier. **b)** See the scatterplot below. The relationship and outlier are the same as in part (a). **c)** The comments are the same for (a) and (b). **d)** Answers will vary. These predictions would be needed if there is 1997 data but no 2002 data (or vice versa) for a business type not mentioned in this table.

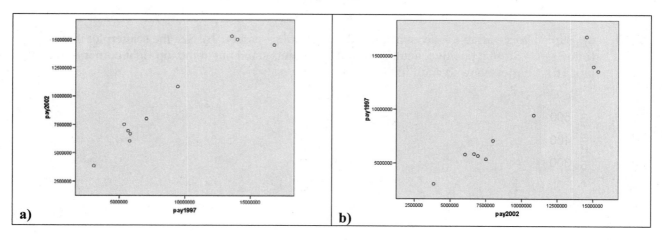

2.15 **a)** A positive association means that the greater the duration, the longer the decline in earnings. Shorter durations resulted in shorter declines in earnings. **b)** The form of the relationship is roughly linear, but not very strong. The scatterplot shows some variation at the lower durations, less than 10 months. As the durations increase to beyond 10 months the linear pattern appears stronger. **c)** The greatest decline is approximately 48% and lasted about 20 months.

2.16 The form of the relationship between GDP and life expectancy is nonlinear and displays an increasing trend, which is what we expected. The points on the scatterplot do show a strong pattern, even though the pattern in not linear.

2.17 **a)** One would expect that, if the household income increases, then the personal income would increase. Because household income includes more than one person, it makes sense that this would be greater than personal income. **b)** In some states (or in D.C.), it is possible that there are a few extremely wealthy people that will skew the distribution of income. Because the mean is not resistant to outliers, these few wealthy individuals will make the mean quite large. **c)** The overall pattern is positive linear. **d)** Both Connecticut and D.C. show up as outliers on the scatterplot. Connecticut is next to New York, and many people who live in Connecticut work in New York; therefore, it makes sense that the mean personal income relative to median household income has a similar relationship to New York. Also, both D.C. and New York are political and financial capitals of the United States and would have a larger group of wealthy individuals than other states.

2.18

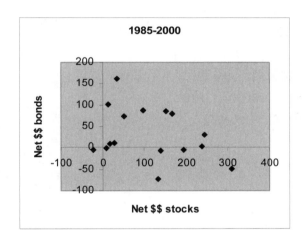

This scatterplot shows a negative trend with a weak linear relationship.

2.19

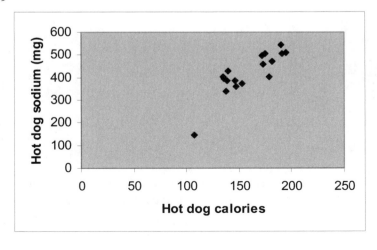

a) This scatterplot shows a strong linear relationship with a positive trend. Hot dogs that are high in calories tend to be high in sodium. **b)** The "Eat Slim Veal Hot Dog" is probably brand 13.

2.20   **a)** *Planting rate* is the explanatory variable.

b)

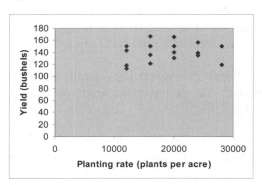

c) This scatterplot shows a slight nonlinear pattern. The yield increases from 12,000 plants per acres to 20,000 plants per acre and then starts to decrease beyond that level. **d)** I would recommend a rate of 20,000 plants per acre. This resulted in the highest average yield.

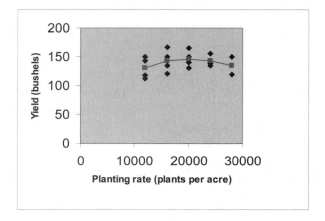

2.21   **a)**

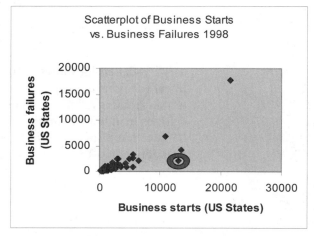

b) The association is said to be positive because, as the variable *starts* increases, the variable *failures* also increases. **c)** See the scatterplot to find Florida. **d)** The outlier in the upper-right-hand corner is California with 21,582 starts and 17,679 failures. **e)** The four states outside the cluster in the lower-left-hand corner are California, Florida, New York, and Texas.

2.22   **a)** Crude oil production does not have a linear relationship with years. It does show an increasing trend as years go by, but the shape of the relationship is nonlinear.

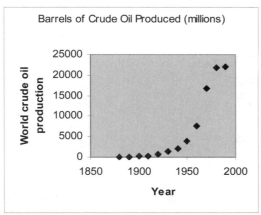

b) The overall pattern in this scatterplot is linear with a positive trend.

2.23   **a)**

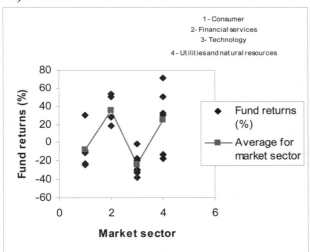

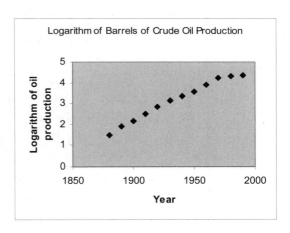

b) Financial Services and Utilities and Natural Resources were good sectors in which to invest.
c) Because we cannot rank the sectors in increasing order, we could not describe any relationship between the sector and a quantitative variable as positive or negative.

2.24   **a)**

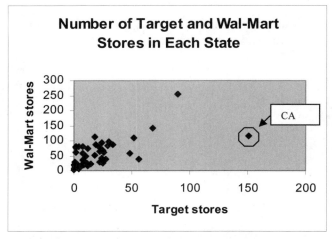

b) California stands out on the scatterplot because it has an unusually large number of Target stores compared to Wal-Mart stores. It appears that in most states the number of Wal-Mart stores is greater than Target stores. California does not follow this trend. **c)** This relationship is a weak positive relationship. It has a slight linear appearance.

2.25   **a)**

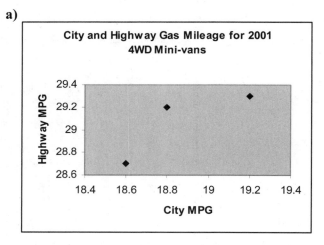

b) r = 0.849 **c)** The relationship is positive and appears to be a fairly strong linear relationship.

2.26   **a)** The relationship appears to be linear, positive, and fairly strong. **b)** r = 0.979.

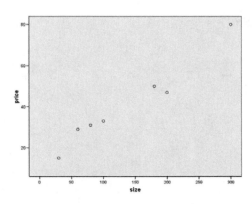

2.27   **a)** The correlation between duration of decline and magnitude of decline is positive but shows some scatter in the points. It would be safe to say that *r* is positive, but not near 1, perhaps .75 or .80. **b)** The scatterplot in Figure 2.2 also shows a positive linear relationship, but the points seem to fall closer to a straight line. The correlation coefficient is probably closer to 1 than in part (a).

2.28   **a)** The correlation coefficient should be exactly 1.0. Every point will fall on the same line.
b) The correlation coefficient should be exactly 1.0. Every point will fall on the same line.
These two examples should start the student thinking about having an equation for a line describe a set of paired data points.

2.29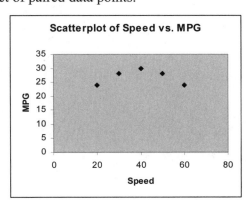

The correlation coefficient is 0. The relationship between speed and gas mileage is clearly not linear. Correlation measures the strength of *linear* relationships only.

2.30   **a)** See scatterplot that follows. **b)** The correlation for all 23 funds is -0.623. The correlation for the 22 funds other than Gold is -0.872. Because Gold is so far to the right, it makes the correlation weaker if it is included. Without Gold, the relationship between 2002 and 2003 is fairly strong.

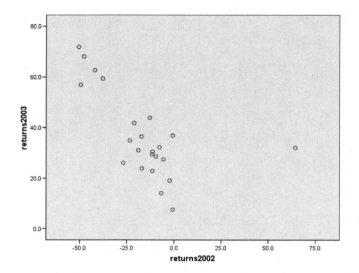

2.31   **a)** Explanatory variable = price. The pattern is strong, positive, and linear. See scatterplot below. **b)** For price, the mean is 50.000 and the standard deviation is 16.325. For deforestation, the mean is 1.738 and the standard deviation is 0.928. The correlation is 0.955.

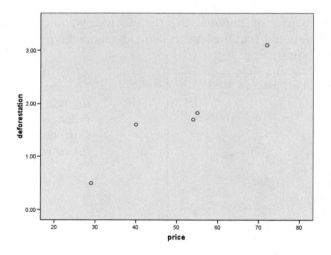

2.32   No, unit of measurement changes do not affect the correlation.

2.33   **a)** In Problem 2.31, we found that the scatterplot shows a strong, positive, linear relationship and the correlation is 0.955. **b)** Answers will vary, but results should look fairly random and without pattern. **c)** The correlation should be close to 0.

2.34   **a)** The correlation is 0.968. **b)** The correlation would still be the same. **c)** There is no change. The relationship between accounts and assets is the same. The units of measurement used has no affect on correlation.

2.35   **a)** 0.968. **b)** 0.707. **c)** These points are apparently not outliers because the correlation dropped quite a bit when they were removed.

2.36   Applet

2.37

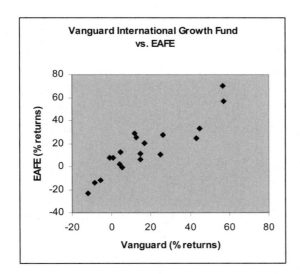

This scatterplot shows a clear positive linear relationship. The correlation coefficient is 0.898, which indicates a strong linear relationship. There do not appear to be any extreme outliers from the linear pattern.

2.38   a)

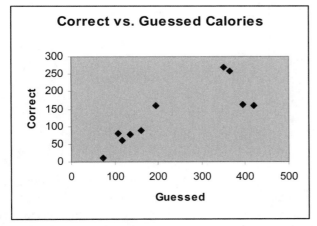

b) r = 0.825. This value of *r* makes sense based on the above scatterplot. The points show a fairly strong relationship, but the two foods, spaghetti and snack cake do not lie close to the other points. **c)** The fact that every guess was higher than the correct number of calories does not influence the correlation. If every guess were exactly 100 calories higher than the correct one, then the correlation would be 1.0.

d) The correlation coefficient is now 0.984. The correlation increased because, after removing the spaghetti and snack cake, the remaining eight points fall very close to a straight line.

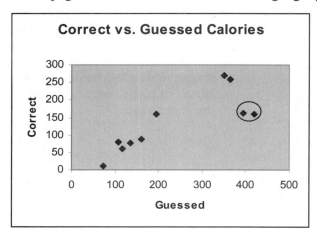

2.39   **a)** and **b)**

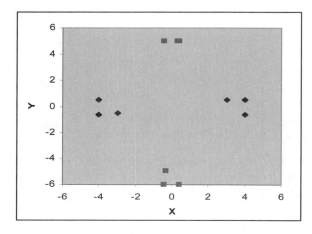

c) The correlation between x and y is 0.253. This is the same value for the correlation between x^* and y^*. Even though the values of x and y have changed, the *linear relationship* between the two variables has not changed. Correlation measures the strength of a linear relationship between two variables. As can be seen in the scatterplot, the points have shifted but how they appear in relation to each other has not.

2.40   **a)** r = 0.659. **b)** The correlation should increase. California is an outlier and does not fall on the linear pattern that the rest of the data do. $r = 0.746$. The correlation increased for the reason stated. **c)** The correlation for all 50 states will most likely decrease if Texas is removed. Texas helps define the linear pattern observed on the scatterplot. Without this data point, the linear relationship does not appear as strong. $r = 0.584$.

2.41   The study's conclusion means that there is no linear relationship between CEO compensation and company's stock performance. We cannot make a prediction about company performance from CEO compensation. The magazine must have misinterpreted the meaning of correlation. If high CEO compensation resulted in poor company stock performance, then the correlation would have been close to -1, not 0.

2.42 **a)** Rachel should choose small-cap stocks because that has a much smaller correlation with municipal bonds than large-cap stocks. **b)** Rachel should look for a negative correlation.

2.43 The outlier in Figure 2.2 helped define the linear pattern observed on the scatterplot. Removing that point left a group of points that did not have an obvious line to fall on. The outlier in Figure 2.8 did not fall in the pattern of the rest of the data points. By removing the outlier before calculating the correlation, we saw an increase in correlation.

2.44 See exercise 2.7 for the scatterplot. The correlation is –0.172. Because the relationship is not linear, the correlation is near zero.

2.45 **a)** Gender is a categorical variable. It does not make sense to calculate a correlation coefficient. **b)** Correlation cannot be greater than 1.0. **c)** Correlation has no units.

2.46 **a)** Standard deviations help explain variability in something. The fact that one fund has a standard deviation of only 9.94% and another fund 23.77% means that the first fund has much less spread or variability. **b)** Having a correlation of 0.85 with the S&P 500 means the Fidelity Magellan Fund more closely follows the stock market. A correlation of 0.55 means the Fidelity Small Cap Stock does not follow the stock market as closely. If an investor wants a fund whose performance he can predict based on the stock market, then the Fidelity Magellan Fund is his better choice.

2.47 **a)** The equation of the least-squares regression line is: $\hat{y} = 1.089 + 0.189x$. **b)** Using $r = 0.995$, $\overline{x} = 22.313$, $s_x = 17.738$, $\overline{y} = 5.306$, and $s_y = 3.368$, the slope is 0.189 and the y-intercept is 1.089.

2.48 **a)** See the scatterplot below. **b)** The observed total billings for 111 staff member is y = 11.5. The predicted total billings from the regression line is $\hat{y} = 10.46$. This is a difference of 1.04.

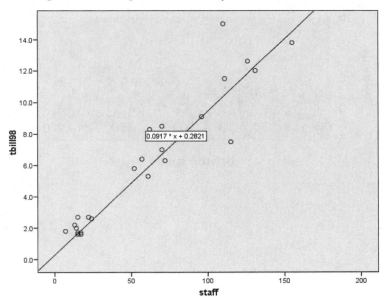

2.49   **a)** 35.5% of the variation in yearly changes is explained by the January change.   **b)** The equation of the regression line is $\hat{y} = 6.083 + 1.707x$.   **c)** The prediction for the change in the year when the January change is 1.75% is 9.07%. We could have answered this without using the regression equation because we know that the point ($\overline{x}, \overline{y}$) will always fall on the regression line.

2.50   Applet

2.51   **a)**

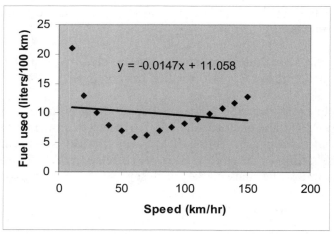

b) The scatterplot shows a definite curved pattern. I would not use the regression line to predict fuel used from speed. **c)** The sum of the residuals is –0.01. This is very close to zero.
d)

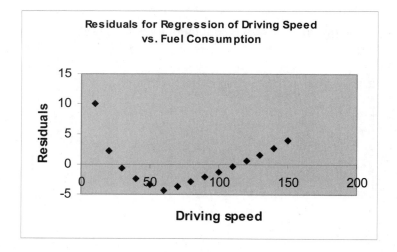

2.52 **a)** See scatterplot below. **b)** This outlier is in the upper right-hand corner far away from the pattern of the other data points. It is pulling the regression line up towards it.

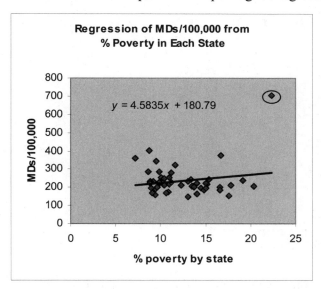

c) Now the regression line has a negative slope, which means the number of MDs will decrease as poverty increases. The D.C. point was an influential point.

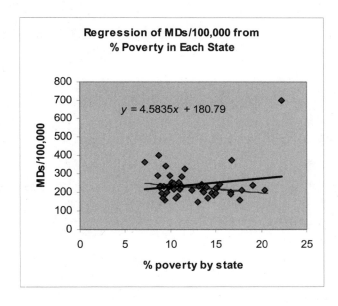

2.53   **a)**

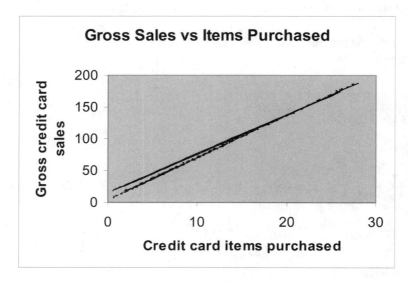

Yes, observation 1 does appear to influence the slope of the regression line. Gross sales estimates are much lower after observation 1 is removed from the analysis. **b)** After removing observation 1, the value of r^2 increases from .59 to .73. Because r^2 is not resistant to outliers, removing an outlier will increase its value.

2.54   **a)**

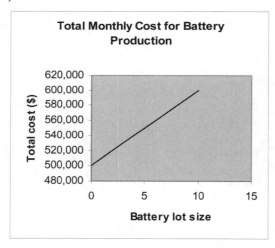

b) $700,000. **c)** $y = 500,000 + 20,000x$

2.55   **a)** $y = 96 - 4x$. **b)**

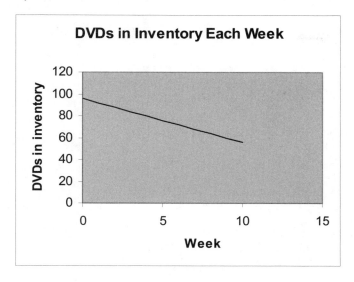

c) No, the initial inventory has only 96 DVDs. This inventory will last for 24 weeks.

2.56   **a)**

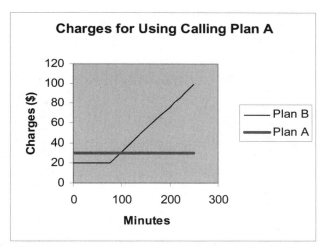

b) A user would need to talk almost 100 minutes a month to benefit from Plan B.

2.57   No, you could not make an accurate prediction of stock returns because the R^2 is so low and the scatterplot shows a very weak association between Treasury bills and stock returns.

2.58   **a)** With all 23 points, the regression line is $\hat{y} = 29.251 - 0.450x$. With only 22 points, the regression line is $\hat{y} = 18.111 - 0.943x$. The scatterplot with both lines follows. The one with the shallower slope is the one using all 23 points. **b)** The Fidelity Gold Fund makes the slope shallower than it otherwise would be.

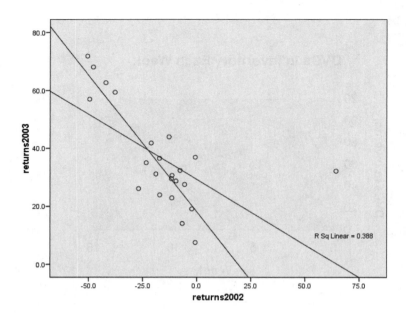

2.59 **a)** Slightly parabolic, opening downward, very weak. See the scatterplot below. **b)** $R^2 = 2.3\%$, which is very low. The regression line with year does not do a good job of explaining the variation in returns.

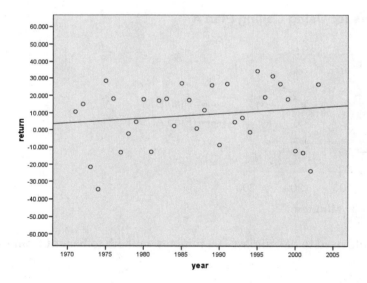

2.60 **a)** For every cent the coffee price increases, deforestation increases by 0.0543%. **b)** If coffee is free, then the forest would regrow!

2.61 **a)** There is a fairly strong, positive, linear relationship between appraised value and selling price. See the scatterplot below. **b)** $\hat{y} = 127.270 + 1.047\,x$. The predicted selling price is 967.6 thousand dollars for a unit appraised for $802,600.

Estimates   127
127.2705
1.0466

(Intercept)
Appraised Value

Question 3 of Quiz
Page 4

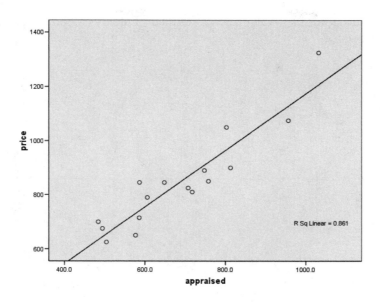

2.62 **a)** See the residual plot below. There is no obvious pattern, which is good for a residual plot. The residuals are the difference in the actual y-value from the data and the line's predicted y-value. **b)** See the residual plot below. There is a rising trend as time passes, which fits that fact that selling prices were increasing rapidly as time passes, and time was not used as part of the regression in this problem.

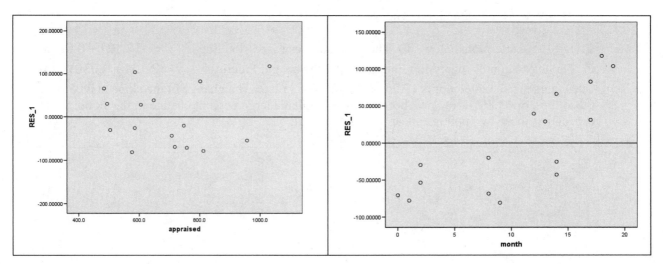

2.63 **a)** Slope = b = 0.0832, and intercept = a = -17.1275. **b)** $\hat{y} = -17.1275 + 0.0832x$. If 793.6 is substituted for x, then y will be 48.9. Therefore Fact 3 is true for this least-squares line. **(c)** $R^2 = 93.76\%$. R^2 is the percent of the variation in the values of total assets that is explained by the least-squares regression line of total assets on number of accounts.

2.64 **a)** $\hat{y} = -17.21 + 0.083x$. **b)** The ten residuals are: 1.00975, 28.10897, -20.76946, 5.56447, 11.87202, -37.41186, -14.25002, 13.52087, 7.60484, 4.75041. See the residual plot below. **c)** The residuals show a negative linear pattern with Schwab and Fidelity not part of that pattern. (Another answer could be: The points show a curved or quadratic pattern.) **d)** Schwab (#2 on the graph) is unusual for its x-value and its residual. Fidelity (#7 on the graph) is unusual only because of its x-value.

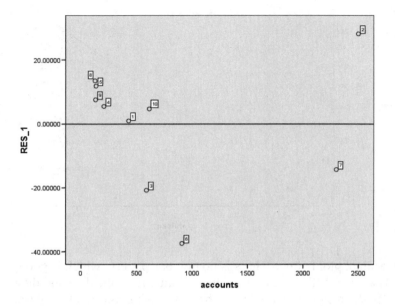

2.65   **a)** The predicted assets for DLJ Direct with 590 accounts will be 31.849. **b)** The actual assets are 11.2, so the prediction is an overestimate. The actual assets – the predicted assets = -20.76946 = the residual. **c)** The residual is -20.76946. Yes.

2.66   **a)** See the scatterplots below. **b)** The least-squares regression line is: $\hat{y} = -17.121 + 0.083x$.
c) The least-squares regression line without Schwab and Fidelity is: $\hat{y} = 2.131 + 0.030x$. **d)**
The change in the intercept is 19.252 (absolute) or 112%. The change in the slope is 0.053 (absolute), or 63.86%. **e)** Yes, because there is such a large percent change in the slope, especially, these two points appear to be influential.

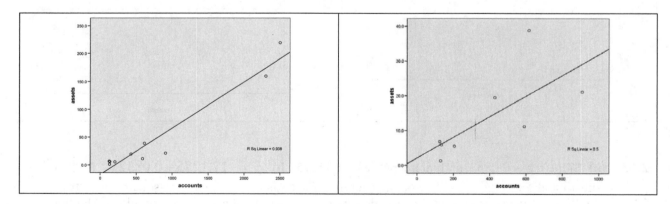

2.67   **a)** $R^2 = 93.4\%$, a = 1,859,988, and b = 0.879. **b)** $R^2 = 93.4\%$, a = 1.860, and b = 0.879. **c)** Only the intercept is affected by the change in units.

2.68   **a)** The residuals (in millions) are: 0.665, -0.072, 0.102, -0.328, 1.561, -0.711, -2.095, 0.934, 0.866, and -0.923. **b)** See the residual plot below. There is a slight uphill trend with perhaps a low outlier at #7 (residual = -2.09497). **c)** The regression line doesn't exactly capture the overall pattern in the data. There is probably at least one lurking variable, another economic factor, which plays a role.

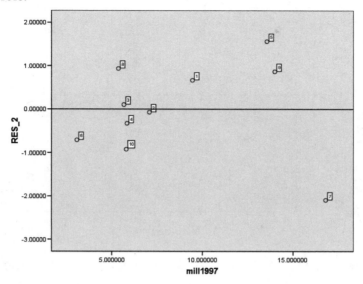

2.69 **a)** Yes, there is a fairly strong, positive, linear relationship. **b)** R = 0.928, R^2 = 86.1%. R^2 is the percent of the variation in the selling price that is explained by the least-squares regression line of selling price on appraisal values. **c)** $\hat{y} = 127.270 + 1.047x$. **d)** The predicted selling price will be $848,391. **e)** The mean selling price is $848,130, and the mean appraisal is $688,750.

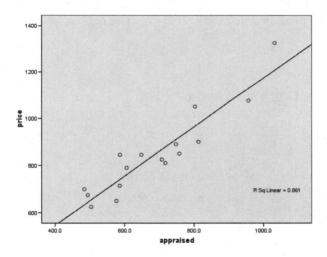

2.70 See the residual plot that follows. Yes, the residuals look random with no obvious patterns. This indicates that the regression line fits the data well.

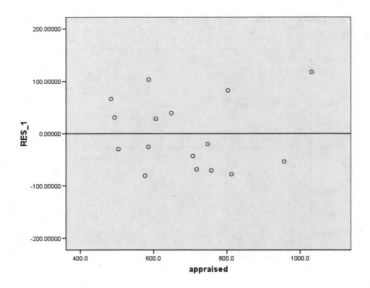

2.71   Because the correlation between American and European share prices is fairly high and positive, this means that, when American share prices rise, European share prices will rise as well. Unfortunately, when American share prices fall, European share prices will also fall.

2.72   No, this is not true. R^2 is the measure the reporter needed. Only 64% of the change in Wall Street will explain the change in European share prices.

2.73   **a)** $y = 15.46 + .8584x$. **b)** Approximately 40% of the variation in declines can be explained by this relationship. **c)** The predicted decline is 28.34%. The residual for this market is –14.34%.

2.74   **a)**

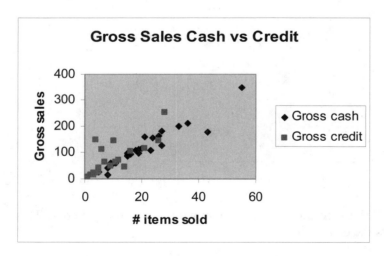

b)

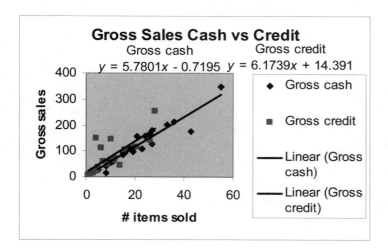

The slope for the gross cash sales regression line is 5.7801. The slope for the gross credit sales regression line is 6.1739. The larger slope for gross credit sales means that, on average, when people purchase with credit cards, they tend to purchase more expensive items.

2.75

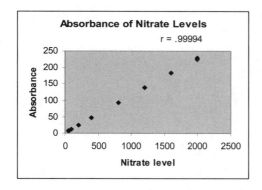

a) No, the calibration does not need to be redone.
b) The least-squares line is $y = 1.6571 + .1133x$. For a specimen with 500 mg of nitrates, the expected absorbance would be 58.31. Yes, the prediction should be quite accurate.

2.76   **a)**

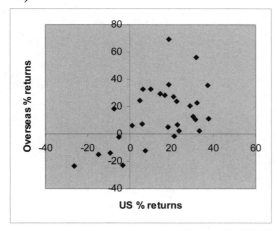

b) The correlation between U.S. percent returns and overseas percent returns is .5043. This does not indicate a strong linear relationship. This can be seen in the scatterplot as well. Only 25.43% of the variation in overseas returns can be explained by U.S. returns. **c)** Predictions will not be accurate with this regression line because the relationship between U.S. and overseas returns is not strong.

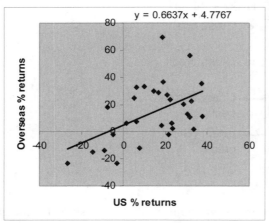

d) The circled point is year 1986. There do not seem to be any influential points.

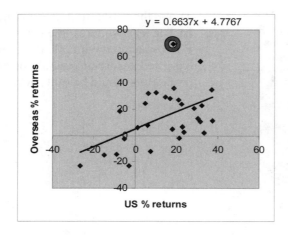

2.77   Applet

2.78   Applet

2.79   **a)**

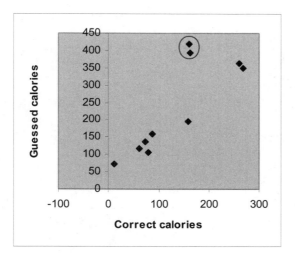

b) The regression line with all 10 data points is $\hat{y} = 58.59 + 1.3x$. The regression line with spaghetti and snack cake removed is $\hat{y} = 43.88 + 1.15x$. **c)** Yes, it appears that the two points circled are influential observations because they influence the slope of the line. We can also see this in how the correlation coefficient increases in value after removing the two data points.

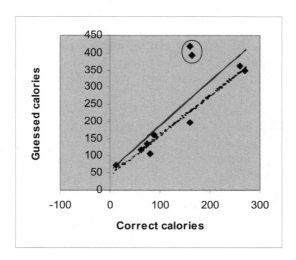

2.80   **a)** For data set A: $y = 3.0001 + 0.5x$ and $r = .816421$. For data set B: $y = 3.0009 + 0.5x$ and $r = 0.816237$. For data set C: $y = 3.0025 + 0.4997x$ and $r = .816287$. For data set D: $y = 3.0017 + 0.4999x$ and $r = .816521$. Notice that all values of r are very close and all the equations are close. With $x = 10$, the prediction for y is 8 for each regression line.

b)

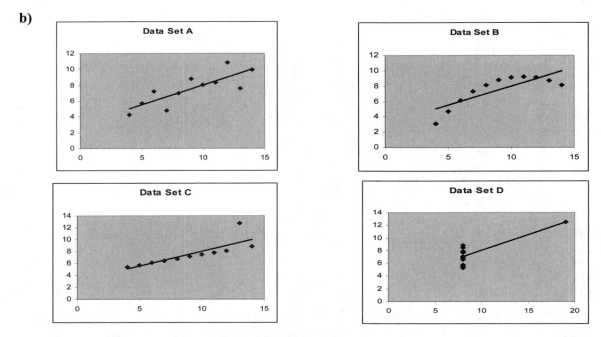

c) I would use the regression line for prediction with data sets A and C. While sets B and D have the same correlation coefficient, it is obvious from the scatterplots that they do not have a linear pattern. Data set C has one outlier but it does not appear to be influential.

2.81   **a)** The slope is 0.16 and the intercept is 30.2. **b)** 78.2. **c)** $r^2 = 0.36$, which means that only 36% of the variation in final exam scores can be explained by the total score before the exam. It is entirely possible that Julie scored higher on the final exam than Professor Friedman's prediction.

2.82   **a)** The five-number summary for U.S. returns is: 37.6, 28.6, 18.4, 5.1, –26.4. The five-number summary for overseas returns is: 69.4, 28.5, 12, 2.1, –23.2. **b)** Returns were about the same in the U.S. and overseas, as is shown by the IQR on the boxplots below. **c)** There was more variability in the overseas, as can be seen by the length of the "whiskers" on the boxplots. The overseas returns had a greater range than the U.S. returns.

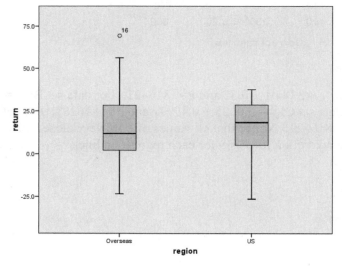

2.83 $r = -0.80$.

2.84 **a)** $y = -6.12 + 0.967x$. **b)** 96.8% of the variation in city MPG can be explained by highway MPG. **c)** City gas mileage for the Mercedes-Benz SL600 is predicted to be 12.25 MPG. Estimating city MPG to be 13 from Figure 2.2, the residual for this car is approximately 0.75.

2.85 Since $\bar{y} = 46.6 + 0.41\bar{x}$, then $\bar{y} + \text{points} = 46.6 + 0.41(\bar{x} + 10)$. This results in points $= 0.41(10) = 4.1$. Octavio is predicted to score 4.1 points above average on the final exam.

2.86 **a)** The line would change to have a negative slope. The new equation would be: $y = 31.76 - 0.436x$. This is an influential observation because it changes the direction of the linear relationship from positive to negative. **b)** By adding the new data point, the original regression line stays almost the same, same slope and same intercept. The new data point is an outlier but is not influential. It is "anchored" by the three data points below.

2.87 **a)** $y = -0.525 + 0.38x$. **b)** 96 Target stores, residual $= -6$. **c)** $y = 30.31 + 1.13x$. **d)** 132 Wal-Mart stores, residual $= 122$.

2.88 **a)**

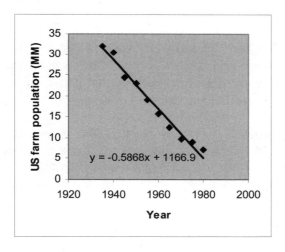

b) The regression line shows that population declined by approximately 580,000 people each year. 97.7% of the observed variation in population can be explained by time. **c)** Using this regression line one would predict that the farm population in 1990 would be –832,000. This is not a sensible result. The population cannot be negative.

2.89 The correlation would be lower because there would be much more variation in the individual stock prices than in their average. More scatter means more variation, which leads to lower correlation.

2.90 The sketch should look similar to Figure 2.21 with the cluster closest to the *x*-axis representing academia and the cluster closest to the *y*-axis representing businesses.

2.91 Large fires require many more firefighters than small fires. Large fires also cause more damage than small fires. The lurking variable is the size of the fire, not the number of firefighters at the fire.

2.92 It is possible the cause-and-effect relationship goes the other way: performing well at something causes individuals to feel good about themselves. Excellent teachers could be the lurking variable. An excellent teacher is usually excellent at instruction, which leads to high performance by an individual. An excellent teacher is also a wonderful encourager, which can help raise self-esteem for individuals.

2.93 No, larger hospitals most likely treat more seriously ill patients than smaller hospitals. Seriously ill patients tend to have longer hospital stays.

2.94 If the groups for the higher incomes are very large compared to the other income groups, the overall mean income can increase even if the individual groups' mean incomes decrease.

2.95 Answers will vary but may include age, years of education, years of experience in job, and location.

2.96 **a)** 2.264%. **b)** 5.504%. **c)** You should trust the answer in part (a) more than part (b) because (b) is an extrapolation. $1.20 is far away from the prices in our data, so we do not know if the linear trend continues at that price.

2.97 a) The story states that these are the "ten kinds of business that employ the *most* people" so it would not be possible to have *greater* x-values than the ones listed in this data. (b) Yes, this is an extrapolation because it is very unlikely that a kind of business that has 0 employees in 1997 is unlikely to have 1.86 million employees only 5 years later.

2.98 **a)** The regression line with the outlier is $y = -91.2 + 3.212x$. The regression line without the outlier is $y = 46.9 + 2.4x$. The scatterplot below shows the two lines. The outlier was not extremely influential. In fact, the correlation coefficient was slightly higher with the outlier than without the outlier because the outlier point was part of the overall linear pattern.

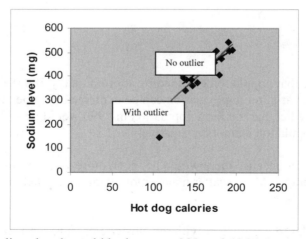

b) The sodium level would be between 390 and 406 mg.

2.99   The high school students that choose to take several math courses have most likely already made a decision to go to college. Once a decision is made to pursue an education beyond high school, it is likely an individual will be successful. Those students who choose not to take additional math classes in high school may not intend to attend college. If they decide later to attend college, they may not be successful because they were not as prepared as if they had made the decision during high school. Another point to consider is that the better students tend to take harder classes such as math. The better students are also the ones that are likely to be successful in college.

2.100   A more plausible explanation is that heavier people tend to be on diets and try to reduce calories from sugar. Therefore, they use artificial sweeteners.

2.101   **a)** Consumption has actually risen over this time period. This contradicts the economists' expectation.

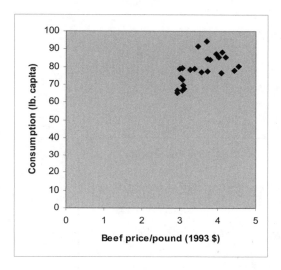

b) 35.8% of the variation in consumption can be explained by the price of beef.

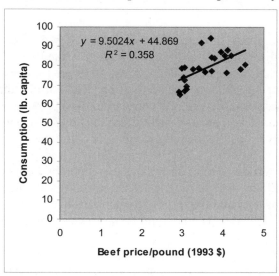

c) There do seem to be cycles. Consider the series from 1980 to 1988. As the residual values go from negative to positive, this shows that the regression line is first underestimating beef consumption and then overestimating beef consumption. Prices during that time period were dropping steadily and yet consumption was declining also. There may be a time delay in the response to the price of beef.

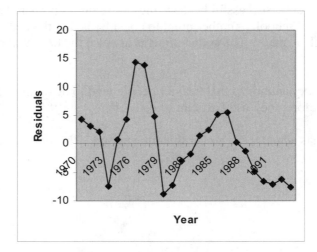

2.102 a)

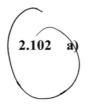

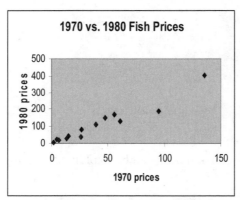

b) The overall pattern appears linear in the positive direction. It is difficult to say if the two points to the far right are outliers or not. They appear to follow the linear trend. **c)** $r = 0.967$, 93.5% of the variation in 1980 prices is explained by the 1970 prices. **d)** $r = 0.9538$. No, these observations do not have a strong effect on the correlation. The correlation decreased from 0.967 to 0.9538, not a significant decrease. **e)** Yes, the correlation does provide a good measure for the relationship between these variables because the scatterplot shows a strong linear pattern and there are no influential observations that heavily weight the correlation.

2.103 a) $r^2 = 0.910$ tells us the proportion of total daily sales explained by item count. In other words, the number of items sold explains 91% of the total daily sales. **b)** I would expect the correlation between the numbers of items sold and the transaction amount in an individual transaction to be less than the summary daily measure. There would be more variation in the individual transactions than in the daily totals.

2.104 The explanatory variable is herbal tea and the response variable is the residents' mood. The lurking variable that might explain a more cheerful mood could be simply the students' visits, not the tea itself.

2.105   A possible lurking variable could be that higher paying jobs carry with them an expectation that the employee will continue his education while employed. Also, social status may play a role. Affluent families can afford to pay for higher education. The men from these families also have access to higher paying jobs through their contacts.

2.106   It would be important to know family history of the children that have leukemia. It is also important to track the rate of leukemia in children who do not live near power lines so we can compare the rates.

2.107   **a)** The pattern seen on the residual plot is a funnel shape. As the salaries increase, the residual values also increase. The regression model will predict lower salaries more accurately. **b)** The second residual plot does not show an increasing trend in error terms. Instead, it appears that the new model will overestimate salaries during the first 3 years, underestimate from 5–10 years, and then even out up to around 15 years. From 15 years and beyond, the model will overestimate again.

2.108   4% are single, 94% are married, 1.5% are divorced, and 0.5% are widowed.

2.109   **a)** 5375 students. **b)** 18.7% of these students smoke. **c)** Neither parent smokes: 1356, 25.2%. One parent smokes: 2239, 41.7%. Both parents smoke: 1780, 33.1%.

2.110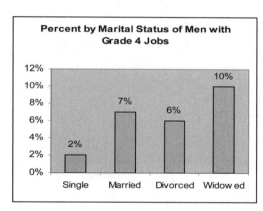
The graph shows that the group of widowed men has the largest percentage of men in the grade 4 job classification.

2.111   The percentages are as follows: 14% of students with neither parent smoking smoke, 19% of students who have one smoking parent smoke, and 22% of students with both parents smoking smoke. It appears there may be some validity to the claim that a parent who smokes might encourage their student to smoke.

2.112   The conditional distribution of marital status among men with grade 4 jobs is: 1.3% single, 96.7% married, 1.3% divorced, and 0.7% widowed.

2.113   **a)**

	Female	Male	Total
Accounting	68 (30.2%)	56 (34.8%)	124 (32%)
Administration	91 (40.4%)	40 (24.8%)	131 (34%)
Economics	5 (2.2%)	6 (3.7%)	11 (3%)
Finance	61 (27.1%)	59 (36.6%)	120 (31%)
Total	225 (58%)	161 (42%)	386

The conditional distribution for each major by gender is given in the preceding table. A column chart comparing the genders is given below.

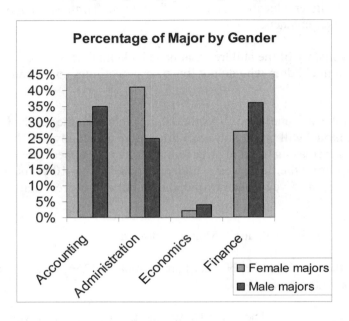

The percentages of men and women majoring in accounting, economics, and finance are close. Administration has a much higher percentage of women than men. **b)** The nonresponse rate is 46.5%.

2.114   First Count: 30 20   Second Count: 10   40
                           30 20   50   0

2.115   **a)** 3%, 2% **b)** 3.8%, 4%. Poor patients fare better in hospital A. **c)** 1%, 1.33%. **d)** Based solely on these data, choose hospital A. **e)** There is a lurking variable: patient condition.

2.116   **a)** The marginal distribution of how long before a trip divers do their planning is: 21.4%, 38.6%, 30.0%, 10.0%. **b)** The conditional distribution of advance planning for men is: 25.6%, 41.9%, 23.3%, and 9.3%. The conditional distribution of advance planning for women is: 14.8%, 33.3%, 40.7%, and 11.1%. Men are most likely to do their planning 1 to 3 months in advance, and women are most likely to do their planning 4 to 6 months in advance. Both men and women are least likely to do their planning 7 or more months in advance.

2.117   The marginal distribution for payment method is: cash (0.351), check (0.155), and credit card (0.495). The conditional distribution of payment method for impulse purchases is: cash (0.452), check (0.129), and credit card (0.419). The conditional distribution of payment method for planned purchases is: cash (0.303), check (0.167), and credit card (0.530). For impulse purchases, cash is most likely. For planned purchases, credit card is most likely. For both types of purchases, check is least likely. Answers will vary for explaining the choice of payment method for impulse purchases.

2.118   **a)** 14,340,000. **b)** 55.8%.
　　　　　c)

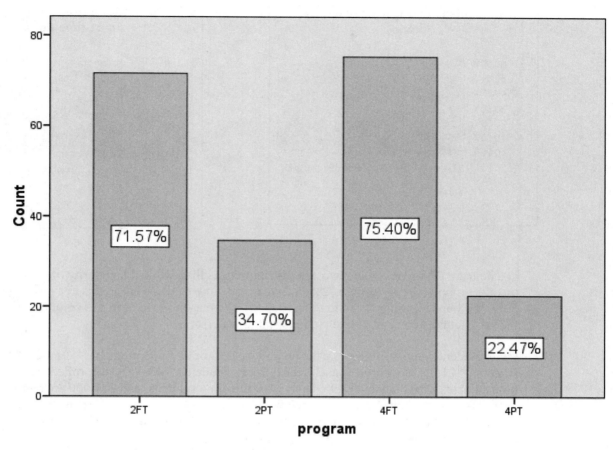

Cases weighted by Percent who are 18-24 years old

d) In full-time programs, the 18- to 24-year-olds make up approximately ¾ of the students. In part-time programs, the 18- to 24-year-olds make up much less than half the students.

2.119   **a)** 38.8%. **b)** 31.5%.

2.120   **a)** By age, the counts of undergraduates are: Under 18 = 353,000, 18 to 24 = 8,001,000, 25 to 39 = 4,272,000, 40 and up = 1,716,000.

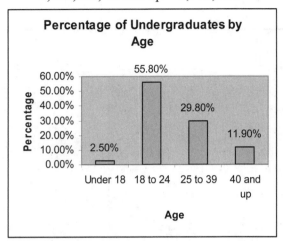

b)

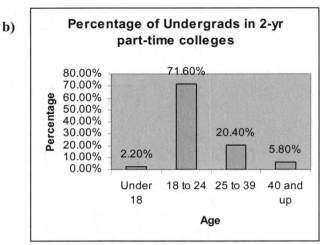

c) The main difference in the two age distributions is that, while the majority of students are in the age group 18 to 24, almost 72% of 2-year part-time students are in this age group, while only 56% of all undergraduates are in this group. **d)** The reason the total in this column is different than the actual sum is most likely due to round-off error.

2.121   Older students (age 40 and up) make up almost 12% of all undergraduates. Of these older students, 121,000 are enrolled as 2-year full-time students, 748,000 are enrolled as 2-year part-time students, 236,000 are enrolled as 4-year full-time students, and 611,000 are enrolled as 4-year part-time students. The graph below shows the distribution of this group of students in each of the four college types. What we see is that older students tend to enroll as part-time students more than full-time, whether it is in a 2-year college or a 4-year college.

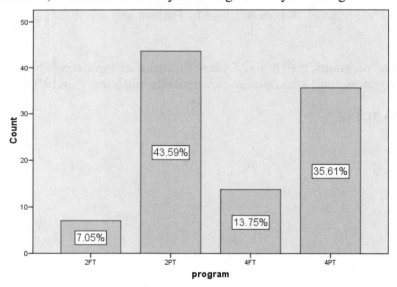

Cases weighted by Where the "older" students enroll

2.122   **a)** 55.8%. **b)** 48.5%. **c)** 29.6%.

2.123   **a)** P(Hired | age < 40) = .0644, P(Hired | age ≥ 40) = .0061
b)

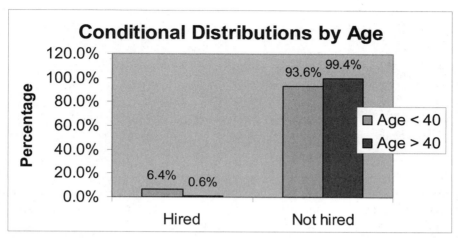

c) Based on these conditional distributions, it does appear that the company is hiring young candidates more than older candidates. **d)** A lurking variable could be whether the candidates are equally qualified or not.

2.124   **a)** 59%. **b)** The nonresponse rate for each size company (small, medium, and large) is 37.5%, 59.5%, and 80%, respectively. As the company size increases, it appears that the response rate decreases.
c)

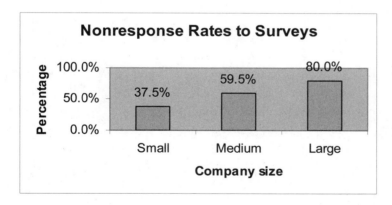

2.125 a)

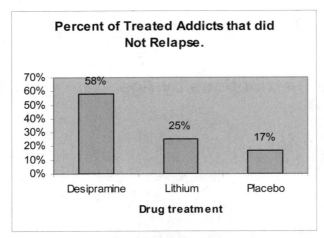

b) Yes, it appears that there is such a large reduction in relapses with the use of desipramine that this constitutes evidence of a cause and effect relationship. A placebo was used to discount the influence of simply being in the study. The placebo rate of relapse was much higher than either of the two anti-depressant drug treatments.

2.126 a) 7.4%. **b)**

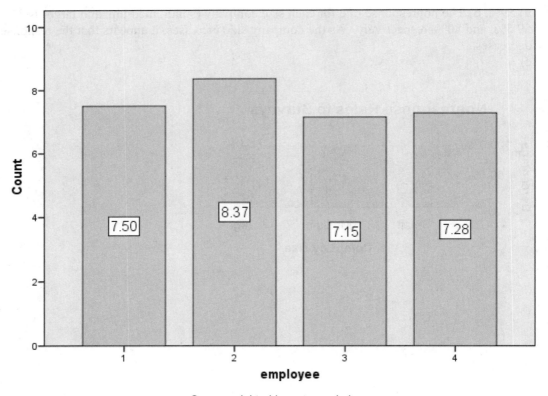

c) From the evidence, it appears that each employee is missing roughly the same percentage as the overall percentage. There appears no reason to single out a certain employee.

2.127 **a)** The difference may be due to round-off error.

b)

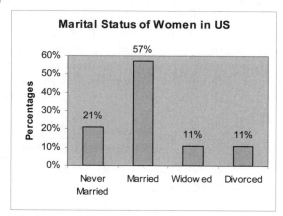

2.128

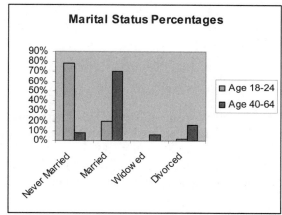

a) In the age group 18 to 24, almost 80% of women have never been married. This changes dramatically for the 40 to 64 age group. Over 70% of these women are married. **b)** The magazine should aim for 18 to 39.

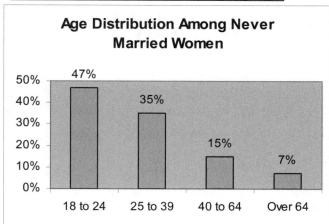

2.129 a)

	Admit	**Deny**
Male	490	210
Female	280	220

b) 70% of male applicants are admitted, and 56% of female applicants are admitted. **c)** For the Business School: Male = 80%, Female = 90%. For the Law School: Male = 10%, Female = 33%. **d)** Without considering the variable of which professional school the applicant has applied to the percentages do not reflect a clear picture. More men apply to Wabash's professional schools overall; therefore, based solely on applications to professional school, more men are being admitted than women. Once we separate the data by type of school, we see that Wabash is actually accepting a higher percentage of their women applicants. An important question for follow up study would be why there are so many more men than women applying to Wabash.

2.130

Smokers

	Overweight	Not
Early death	10	50
No	8	50

Nonsmokers

	Overweight	Not
Early death	20	10
No	30	20

Grouped Together

	Overweight	Not
Early death	30	60
No	38	70

2.131 **a)** See scatterplot that follows. (b) There is a fairly strong, positive, linear association with an outlier from point Professor #9 (102300, 144200). (c) Professors #3 and #5 have 2002 salary similar to this one. Professor #16 has a 2005 salary similar to this one. Professor #9 does not follow the overall pattern and would be considered an outlier. (d) Professor #15 has the highest 2002 and 2005 values, but the data point follows the general trend of the other data. It would not be considered an outlier.

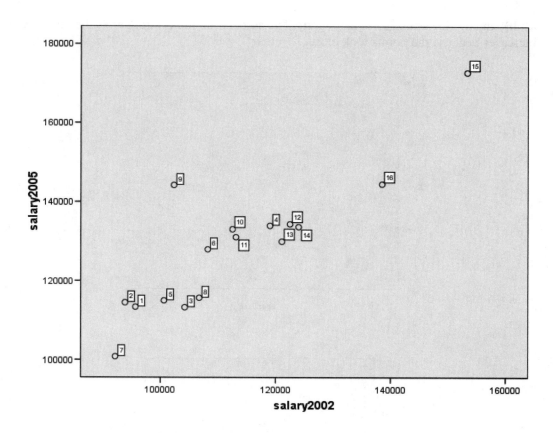

2.132 **a)** See scatterplot above. **b)** r_B should be the highest because it removes the outlier. r_A and r_B both will be smaller than r_A, but it's hard to say which will be the smaller of these two. **c)** $r_A = 0.870$, $r_B = 0.954$, and $r_C = 0.765$.

2.133   **a)**, **b)**, and **c)** See scatterplots below. **d)** The association looks stronger as the range of axes increases because the points look closer together.

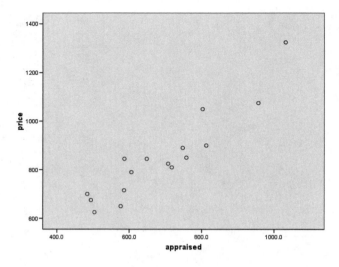

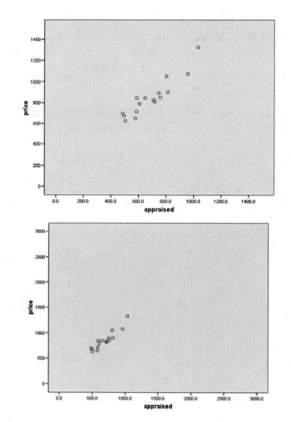

2.134 **a)** See the first scatterplot in the preceding exercise. **b) and c)** See the scatterplots below.
d) Part (b) makes the slope look much shallower. Part (c) makes the slope look much steeper.

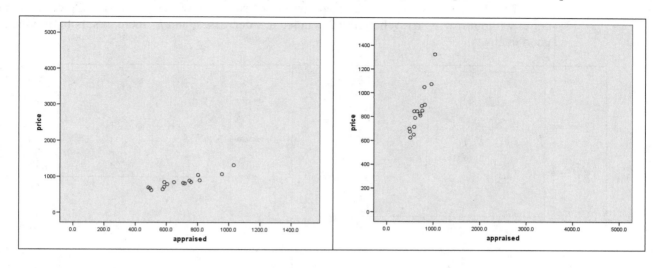

2.135 **a)** 0.966. **b)** 0.966. **c)** 0.966. **d)** The calculations are the same, which is a general fact. Units of measure don't change the correlation between two variables. **e)** The rounding didn't have an effect for this data because the part of each data point that was rounded off was a small percentage of the actual data value.

2.136 **a)** $\hat{y} = 27459.441 + 0.896x$, $s = 8710.554$, $R^2 = 75.6\%$. **b)** For every increased dollar of salary in 2002, the 2007 salary will be increased by $0.896. **c)** R^2 is the percent of variation in 2005 salary which is explained by the least squares regression of 2005 salary on 2002 salary.

2.137 **a)** If a professor had a 2002 salary of $0, his or her 2005 salary would be $27,459.44. This is not a "practical" interpretation because no professor would have had a 2002 salary of $0. **b)** See the scatterplot below. **c)** The "zero intercept" line completely misses all the data because it is too low. The estimated intercept raises the least-squares regression line to the right height to pass through the data.

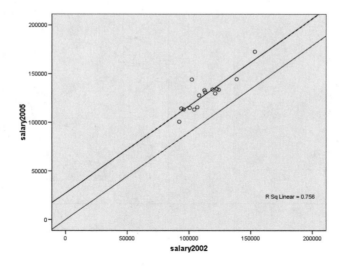

2.138 **a)** See the residual plot on the left below. $s = 8710.554$, $R^2 = 75.6\%$. **b)** Without the outlier, $s = 5332.727$, $R^2 = 91.0\%$. See the residual plot on the right below. **c)** The residual plot looks much better without row 9. **d)** When row 9 is deleted, s decreases, and R^2 increases, both of which are good changes.

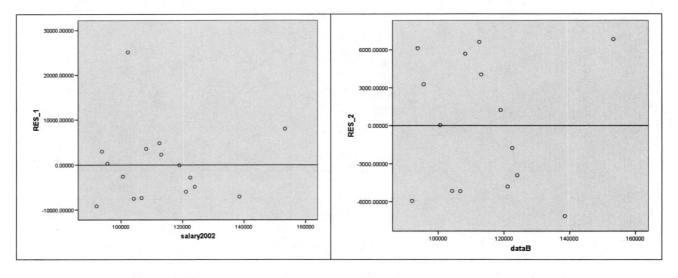

2.139 **a)** With all data points: $\hat{y} = 27459.441 + 0.896x$, $R^2 = 75.6\%$, $s = 8710.554$. With #15 removed: $\hat{y} = 42976.52 + 0.75x$, $R^2 = 58.6\%$, $s = 8519.287$. **b)** Yes, #15 is an influential observation because R^2, s, and the slope all changed when it was removed.

2.140 **a)** See the scatterplot below. There is a moderately weak, positive, linear relationship between weight and amp values. **b)** $\hat{y} = 5.8 + 0.4x$, $s = 0.782$, $R^2 = 45.7\%$. **c)** For every 1-amp increase, there is a 0.4-pound increase in weight, on average. **d)** A 1-amp increase would correspond to a 0.4-pound increase in weight, on average. **e)** See the residual plot below. There seems to be a general uphill trend, but it is hard to determine if there is curvature.

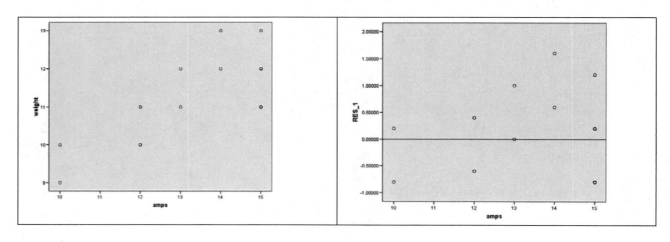

2.141 a) 0.676. **b)**

Amps	10	12	13	14	15
Average weight	9.5	10.5	11.5	12.5	11.56

c) 0.877. The correlation of amps with average weight is greater than the correlation of amps with the individual weights.

2.142 a) Correlation = 0.928, $R^2 = 86.1\%$, $\hat{y} = 127.270 + 1.047x$. See the residual plot below left. **b)** Correlation = 0.811, $R^2 = 65.8\%$, $\hat{y} = 150.800 + 1.047x$. See the residual plot below right. **c)** The additional condo appears to be a residual in the y-direction. **d)** The additional condo decreased the correlation and R^2, but the estimated intercept increased. The estimated slope stayed the same. **e)** The correlation, R^2, and slope would be about the same as with the other additional condo in part (b) because the selling price is about the same distance away from where we would expect the selling price to be for a condo appraised at this level. The estimated intercept would be decreased.

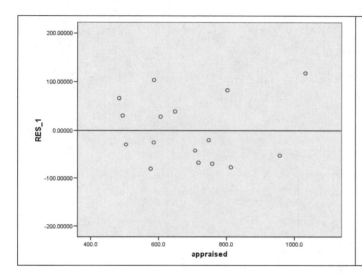
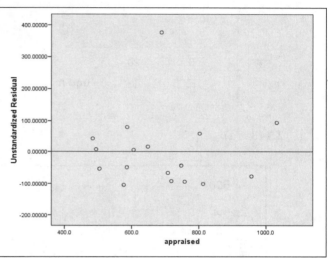

2.143 The scatterplot does not show a strong pattern between Treasury bill return and stock return. It is reasonable to conclude that high interest rates do not greatly decrease returns on stocks.

2.144 a) $\hat{y} = 16.24 - 0.57x$. For x = 5%, y = 13.39%. **b)** The slope tells us that as interest rates increase, stock returns decrease. This supports the belief that, in general, high interest rates are bad for stocks. **c)** Knowing the return on Treasury bills for next year would not help predict the return on stocks. The scatterplot shows little relationship between the two variables, and this is supported by the low value of R^2.

2.145 Removing this point would increase the correlation because the point lies outside the bulk of the data. This data point pulls the regression line down to the right. I don't believe it will strongly influence the regression line because the entire data set is heavily scattered and does not show a strong correlation to begin with.

2.146 a) $\hat{y} = .352 + 1.17x$ and $r^2 = 0.276$, so approximately 28% of the change in Phillip Morris stock is explained by the S&P index. **b)** For every one unit change in the S&P index, Phillip Morris returns increase by 1.17. Their returns increase faster than the index. **c)** We want our individual stocks to rise faster than the market rises, but we want our stocks to drop more slowly than the market drops.

2.147 For two funds to be perfectly correlated, their returns simply have to be proportional to each other. For every $1 fund A returns, fund B might return $0.50. Using fund A as the explanatory variable and fund B as the response variable means the slope of the line is less than 1. The graph below illustrates this point.

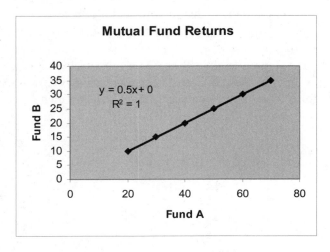

2.148   a)

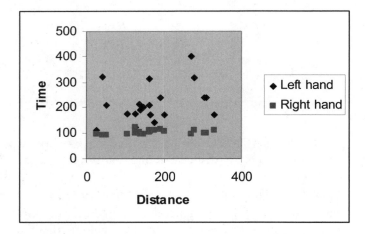

b) The data for the right hand show a horizontal pattern. The data for the left hand is much more scattered.

c)

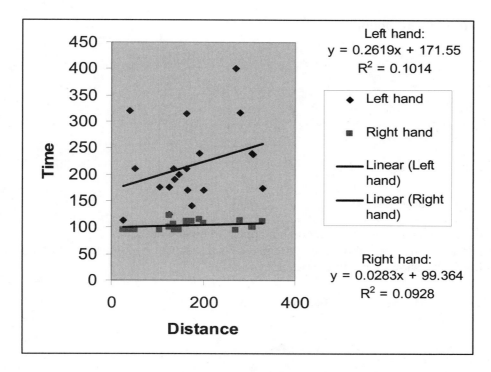

The regression line for the left hand does a better job of predicting time because it describes a little over 10% of the variation in time. The regression line for the right hand is not as predictive. Distance contributes less than 10% (9.3%) to the variation in time on the right hand.

d)

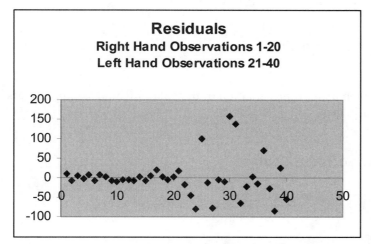

No, there does not appear to be a systematic effect of time.

2.149 **a)**

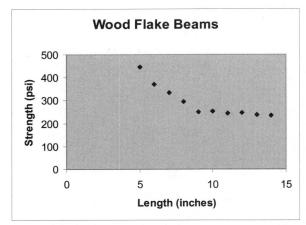

b) The overall pattern is nonlinear. There do not appear to be any outliers.

c) No, a straight line is not a good fit, even though the r-squared value might suggest otherwise.
The scatterplot clearly shows a nonlinear pattern.

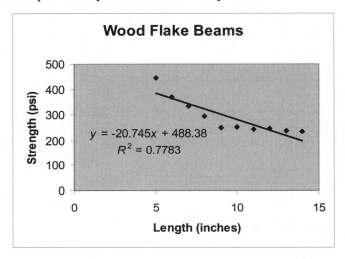

d) These two lines show a much better representation of the data. I would ask the experts why
the strength levels out after 9 inches.

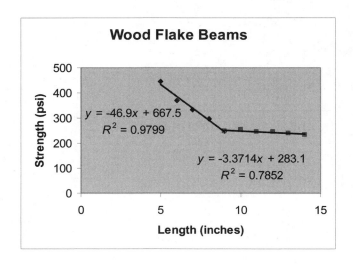

2.150   a)

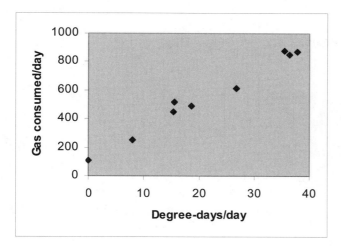

b)

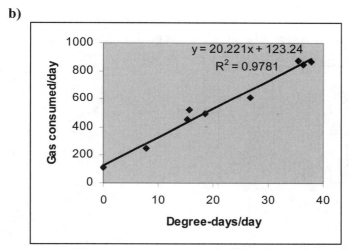

For every unit of degree-day increase, gas consumption goes up approximately 20 cubic feet.
c) Last winter, Joan would have used 932 ft^3 of natural gas during the month of February, rather than the 870 ft^3 she actually used. Yes, the insulation reduced gas consumption.

2.151 $r = 0.988966$, $\overline{x} = 21.54$, $\overline{y} = 558.9$, $s_x = 13.42$, $s_y = 274.4$. Slope has units cubic feet per degree-day.

2.152 **a)** The mean and median for the selling price data are $138,595 and $127,125, respectively. This distribution is skewed right, as shown below, and therefore the mean is greater than the median. The standard deviation is $54,517.

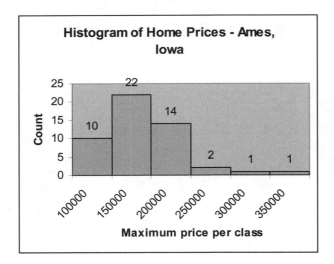

b) The relationship between square footage and selling price is positive linear.

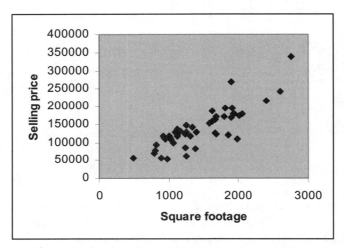

c) $\hat{y} = 92.82x + 4786.46$. On average, each square foot adds $93 to the selling price of the home.   **d)** I would expect the selling price of a 1600-square-foot home to sell for $153,300. **e)** 69.6% of the variability in the selling price of homes can be attributed to differences in square footage.

2.153 **a)**. $\hat{y} = -1334.5x + 189,226$. **b)** $189,226, $187,892, $186,557, $185,223. Each year that the house ages drops the average selling price by approximately $1300. **c)** This regression line should not be used to predict the selling price of a home built before 1900. The regression line explains only 50% of the variability in selling prices, so the model itself is not the best. In addition, extrapolation outside the range of x produces results that are unreliable.

2.154 **a)** Using a correlation on 0.3481, we find that only about 12% of the variation in Apple stock can be explained by the S&P index. The overall market is not a good predictor of Apple stock movement. **b)** The most likely explanation is that each calculation used a slightly different data set. Perhaps the NASDAQ data set was smaller than the one used at the Yahoo website, which was also different than the 60 months of data used by the author.

2.155 These data show that 2.3% of the physicians taking aspirin suffered a heart attack or stroke and 3.1% of the physicians that took a placebo suffered a heart attack or stroke. Because the sample size is so large, it seems logical that this difference in percentages is large enough to conclude that aspirin reduces heart attacks.

2.156 a)

	Smoker	Not
Dead	139	230
Alive	443	502

The percentage of smokers that were alive after 20 years is 76%, and the percentage of nonsmokers that were still alive after 20 years is 69%. **b)** Within the age group 18 to 44, 93% of the smokers were alive after 20 years and 96% of the nonsmokers were still alive. Within the age group 45 to 64, the percentages were 68% and 74%, respectively. Within the age group 65 and older, the percentages were 14% and 15%, respectively. **c)** This explanation makes sense. The percentage of smokers in the three age groups, starting youngest to oldest, are 46%, 55%, and 20%.

2.157 a) The marginal distribution of opinion about quality is: higher (0.368), same (0.241), lower (0.391). The proportions for "higher" and "lower" are very close, with the proportion for "lower" slightly bigger. These are the proportions of opinion in general, not separated out for buyers and nonbuyers. **b)** The conditional distribution of opinion for buyers is: higher (0.556), same (0.194), and lower (0.250). The conditional distribution of opinion for nonbuyers is: higher (0.299), same (0.258), and lower (0.443). For buyers, the majority voted for "higher." For nonbuyers, the largest proportion was for "lower." For both groups, the smallest proportion was for "same." Yes, we can conclude that using recycled filters causes more favorable opinions.

Case Study 2.1

A. A state's population explains approximately 50% of the variation in the number of Wal-Mart stores in each state. This is a good starting point for predicting Wal-Mart stores, but there are likely other variables that contribute such as: tax benefits for locating in a particular state and existing buildings or suitable land for putting in a large store. The scatterplot below shows the relationship. If a state increased by 1 million people, this regression line predicts another 5.27 stores will be added.

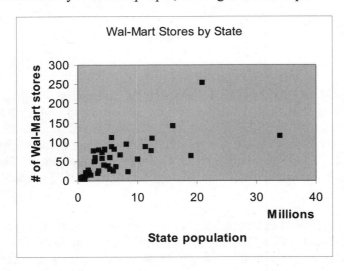

B. By removing California from the data set, the value of r^2 increases to 0.60, an improvement from the previous value of 0.50. California could be considered an influential data point.

Case Study 2.2

A.

	Correlation with GPA
HSM	0.436499
HSS	0.329425
HSE	0.289001
SATM	0.251714
SATV	0.11449

The correlation values for the explanatory variables tell us the strength of the linear relationship between each variable and GPA. HSM and HSS are the two best predictor variables. This makes sense for computer science majors.

B.

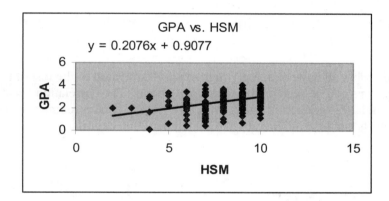

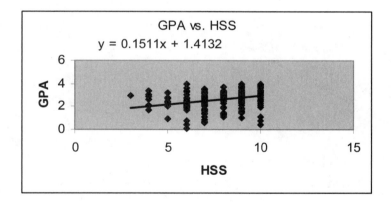

The scatterplots show that, while there is a relationship between HSS and GPA and HSM and GPA, there are other variables that would probably help the prediction. There is one unusual observation seen on the plot of GPA vs. HSS. This point shows a fairly high GPA but the student had a low HSS score.

Case Study 2.3
   A.

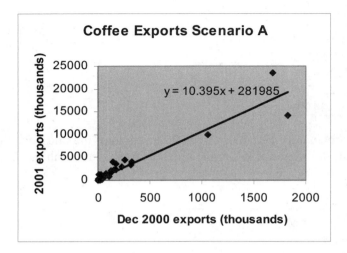

Brazil, Vietnam, and Columbia all have extremely high exports compared to the rest of the countries in the data set. This can be seen on the scatterplot above. The correlation between December 2000 exports and 2001 exports is strong with an *r* = 0.9516. Approximately 91% of the variation in 2001 exports can be explained by the December 2000 exports.

B.

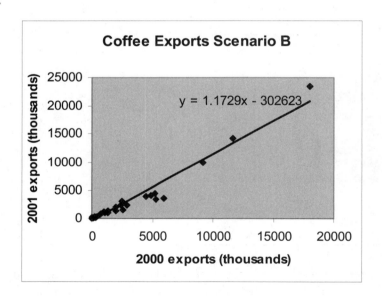

The correlation between 2000 exports and 2001 exports is 0.9788. Approximately 96% of the variation in 2001 exports can be explained by 2000 exports. The three countries mentioned in part A still have very high export values but they fit in to the linear pattern better in this prediction scenario. (Brazil, Vietnam, and Columbia are the three values to the right on the scatterplot above.) This regression is a better predictive tool than the one from part A.

C.

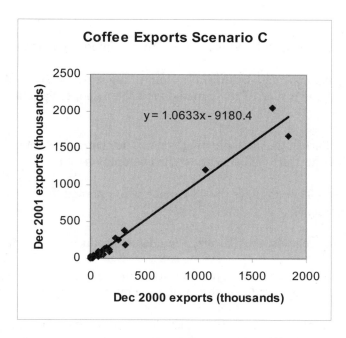

The correlation between December 2000 and December 2001 exports is 0.9864. Approximately 97% of the variation in December 2001 exports can be explained by December 2000 exports. One would expect this r^2 to be higher than the others because there will be less variation in a month than in a year.

Chapter 3: Producing Data

3.1   This is not an experiment. The researcher is merely asking a question, not imposing a treatment.

3.2   This is an experiment. The company is imposing a treatment by controlling which study method a group is given. The explanatory variable is type of study method and the response variable is increase in test scores.

3.3   Certainly the state of the economy will affect the unemployment rate. The change in population over time with respect to demographics and size will also affect the unemployment rate.

3.4   The population is all employed women. The sample is the 48 women who returned the questionnaire. The nonresponse rate is 52%.

3.5   **a)** U.S. population of adults. **b)** U.S. households. **c)** All voltage regulators produced at this plant.

3.6   I would not be convinced that the movie is bad based on the Internet rating. My friends would be a biased sample. The Internet raters are also biased. Neither group is a random sample.

3.7   Starting at line 139 will result in the sample 04, 10, 17, 19, 12, and 13. The sample of minority managers will vary depending on how the student numbers the names. One possible result is: Bowman, Fleming, Liao, Naber, Gates, and Goel.

3.8   Starting at line 145 will result in the sample 19, 26, 06, and 09. The individuals will vary depending on how the student numbers the names. One possible result is Liu, Sanchez, Collins, and Gonzalez.

3.9   The retail outlets could be labeled 001–440. Starting at line 105, the sample would be 400, 077, 172, 417, 350, 131, 211, 273, 208, and 074.

3.10   Starting at line 121, the sample of four would include 07, 22, 10, and 25. The sample of two is 05 and 09. The names will vary depending on how the student numbers the lists. One possible result is: Fisher, Hein, O'Brien, Reinmann, Kim, and West.

3.11   The first strata, midsize accounts, could be numbered 001–500. The second strata, small accounts, could be numbered 0001–4400. The first five numbers for the first strata are 417, 494, 322, 247, and 097. The first five from the second strata are: 3698, 1452, 2605, 2480, and 3716.

3.12   **a)** Households not listed in the phone directory will be left out of the sample. These people either don't own telephones or have unlisted numbers. **b)** Those people with unlisted numbers will be included in this sampling frame.

3.13   The period from July 1 to August 31 most likely gave the highest nonresponse rate. Many people vacation during those months and may be away from home. High nonresponse rates can bias results because the group that chooses to respond may have different views from the group that chooses not to respond.

3.14   Question A most likely drew 80% favoring banning contributions. Question A used the phrases "special interest" and "huge sums of money." Question B appealed to our sense of fairness by using the phrases "right to contribute" and "candidates they support."

3.15   **a)** To make this an experiment, randomly assign 25 members to a control group that just has them visiting a health club and 25 members to a treatment group that has them visiting a health club and working with a trainer. The unseen bias involved in using the study as written in the exercise is that currently individuals have decided on their own to work with the trainer. These individuals may be more health conscious, more actively training for some athletic event, or more seriously trying to lose weight. **b)** To make this an experiment, start with a sample of tellers, all of the same experience and ability, and randomly select half to participate in the advanced training, while the other half get no additional training. An alternate way of doing this is to treat it as a matched pairs experiment, where pairs of tellers with similar backgrounds and experience are paired up, with one from each pair completing the training and the other not. The unseen bias in the study as written in the exercise is that, since the tellers were allowed to select themselves for advanced training, these are probably the tellers who are more experienced or more interested in advancing their careers.

3.16   **a)** You could post signs in doctor's offices, pharmacies, or in newspapers. The bias from using doctors' offices and pharmacies is that you might get people with other health issues or people with more severe headaches already seeking help. The bias from using newspapers is you might get older, more educated people. **b)** You could stand in the pain reliever aisle at a pharmacy or grocery store and question people shopping there. Depending on the time of day you interviewed shoppers, your sample may contain mostly people of a particular age group (retired people during the day, younger working people in the early evening hours, etc.).

3.17   **a)** The site is a true random number generator that uses little variations in amplitude in atmospheric noise picked up by a radio. **b)** There are testimonials on the website. **c)** Answers will vary. **d)** Answers will vary.

3.18   **a)** Randomizer.org uses the "Math Random" method within the Java Script random number generator. This is only a pseudo-random number generator. The numbers are generated by use of a complex algorithm seeded by the computer's clock that gives the appearance of randomness. **b)** No, Randomizer.org does not offer any evidence or testimonials about how well it generates random numbers (at least not as of September 2007). **c)** Answers will vary. **d)** Answers will vary.

3.19   **a)** The committee intends for the population to be all local businesses, but in actuality, the population they are using is all local businesses listed in the telephone book. **b)** The sample is 150 randomly selected businesses. **c)** 51.33%. **d)** Answers will vary. Some businesses list only in the yellow pages and some only in the white pages. Some businesses are listed by a person's name. Some businesses may only use cell phones or websites and choose not to be listed in the phone book at all. How did the committee know which names in the phone book were businesses?

3.20   **a)** Companies 36, 51, 55, 14, and 43 are in the random sample. **b)** Answers will vary.

3.21 **a)** Population = all small businesses, Sample = 150 eating and drinking establishments. **b)** Population = all constituents, Sample = 228 letters received. **c)** Population = all loss claims from automobile policy holders, Sample = the SRS from that month

3.22 **a)** The sample size is 29777. **b)** This is a voluntary response sample, not an SRS. It is likely the results are biased. **c)** Since women may be underrepresented, the percentage of "yes" responses may be too low.

3.23 These results may not reflect the views of the entire population of constituents. The letters were not part of an SRS and may be biased toward those with strong negative opinions.

3.24 **a)** One might put a question in the campus newspaper and ask students to respond via email. **b)** One might choose a sample from only those students who purchased a parking permit. This could result in biased results.

3.25 Starting at line 111, the sample numbers are: 12, 04, and 11. The bottle numbers will vary depending on how the student numbers the bottles. A possible result is: A1117, B1102, and A1098.

3.26 Starting at line 117, the sample numbers are: 16, 32, and 18. The apartment complexes will vary depending on how the student numbers the complexes. A possible result is: Fairington, Waterford Court, and Fowler.

3.27 Start by numbering the blocks from 01 to 44, where 01 corresponds to block 1000 and 44 corresponds to block 3025. Starting at line 125 in Table B, the sample numbers are 21 (block 3002), 37 (block 3018), 18 (block 2011), 23 (block 3004), and 19 (block 3000).

3.28 **a)** False. Over many, many rows of 40 digits, the proportion of zeroes in each row should be 0.10 (4 out of 40), but this will not be true for every single row. **b)** True. There are 100 pairs of digits and each is equally likely. **c)** False. This is a random pattern. Even though a string of four zeroes is not as likely as a string of different digits, it can still occur.

3.29 **a)** Because we need to choose five clusters out of 200, we can think of the list as five lists of 40 clusters. Using Table B, starting at line 120, the first cluster is 35. The other four would be 75, 115, 155, and 195. **b)** Before the first item is selected, all individuals have an equal chance of being selected. Once the first item is selected, the sample is determined. With an SRS, the sample is not determined based on the first item selected.

3.30 This is not an SRS because there are some samples that have no chance of being chosen. A sample with all men cannot be selected.

3.31 Use a systematic random sampling technique. With the male engineers, once the first engineer is chosen, the next engineers will be every 10th person in the alphabetized list of 2000. The labels might go from 0001 to 2000. The female engineers could be labeled from 001–500. Once the first female is selected, you can choose every third engineer in the list. Using the random number table starting with line 122, the first five females are 138, 159, 052, 087, and 359. Continuing in the table, the first five males are 1369, 0815, 0727, and 1868.

3.32 **a)** This is a poorly worded question because it suggests a link between cell phones and brain cancer. **b)** This question is worded in order to elicit a response in favor of economic incentives for recycling by using the phrases "escalating environmental degradation" and "incipient resource depletion."

3.33   Answers will vary.

3.34   The first question most likely drew 60% favoring a tax cut. The question gave "fund new government programs" as an alternative to a tax cut. This phrase was vague and drew on most people's desire to reduce new government spending. The second question gave popular areas of concern as alternative recipients of excess funds, which are less controversial.

3.35   The subjects are the 300 sickle-cell sufferers. This experiment has one factor: type of medication given to the subjects. This factor had two levels: hydroxyurea and a placebo. With one factor and two levels, this experiment has two treatments. The response variable is the number of episodes of pain each subject reported.

3.36   **a)** The individuals are the 20 pairs of package liners. **b)** The factor is jaw temperature. It has four levels: 250°F, 275°F, 300°F, and 325°F. **c)** The response variable is the force needed to peel each seal.

3.37   **a)** The individuals are the production batches. The response variable is the yield. **b)** There are two factors and six treatments.

Factor A
Stirring Rate

		60 rpm	90 rpm	120 rpm
Factor B Temperature	50°C	1	2	3
	60°C	4	5	6

c) She will need 12 batches.

3.38   **a)**

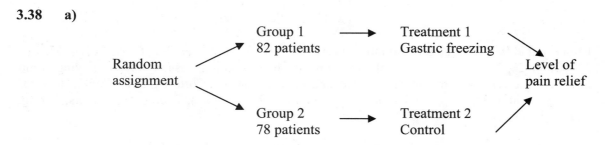

b) The subjects can be labeled 01 to 82. Starting at line 131, the first five members of the gastric freezing group would be: 05, 71, 66, 32, and 81.

3.39

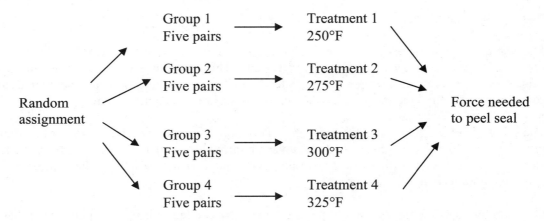

Using Table B at line 120, the 20 pairs could be assigned as follows:

16, 04, 19, 07, 10   Group 1
13, 15, 05, 09, 08   Group 2
18, 03, 01, 06, 11   Group 3
02, 20, 12, 14, 17   Group 4

3.40   a)

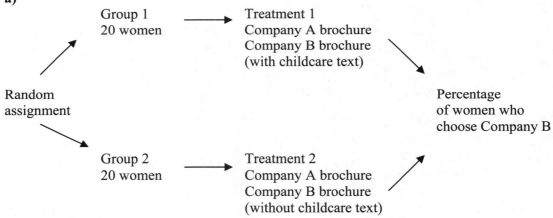

b) Starting at line 131, the random numbers are: 05, 32, 19, 04, 25, 29, 20, 16, 39, 31, 18, 07, 13, 33, 02, 36, 23, 27, 37, and 35. Numbering down the name columns results in the following group that reads the version with childcare: Adamson, Brown, Cansico, Cortez, Garcia, Gupta, Howard, Hwang, Iselin, Kim, Lippman, McNeill, Ng, Rivera, Roberts, Rosen, Thompson, Travers, Turing, and Williams.

3.41   In order to ensure that factors influencing electricity use are equal for comparison groups, a control group is needed. Comparing electricity use last year to this year (with the indicator) does not control the factors that may be different between the two years.

3.42 The second design includes the element of randomization to reduce the chance variation. Also, in the second design, the treatment is imposed (exercise regimen) rather than using an observational study as in the first design.

3.43 "Significant difference" means the salary differences were so large they could not have been due to chance alone. "No significant difference" means the differences could be due to change only.

3.44 The experimenter rated their anxiety level both before and after treatment and the experimenter knew which subjects had received meditation instruction and which had not. Bias could have been introduced if the experimenter had an expectation that meditation would reduce anxiety. It is likely the experimenter unknowingly communicated this expectation to the subjects also.

3.45 This experiment is not conducted in a real-world setting. There are other reward factors that contribute to a team member's frustration level (or lack of frustration) in a real-world setting that cannot be replicated over the course of a single evening of game playing. (One evening is a much shorter time than three months.)

3.46 Design 1: Randomized Design

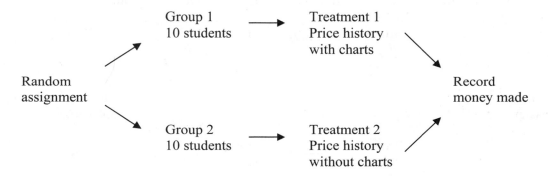

Design 2: Matched Pairs Design
Each student is randomly assigned treatment 1 first or treatment 2 first. The money each student makes using each set of information is compared. The random groups and assignments will vary.

3.47 **a)** Block 1: Williams, Deng, Hernandez, and Moses. Block 2: Santiago, Kendall, Mann, and Smith. Block 3: Brunk, Orbach, Rodriguez, and Loren. Block 4: Jackson, Stall, Brown, and Cruz. Block 5: Birnbaum, Tran, Nevesky, and Wilansky. **b)** One way to randomly assign the 20 individuals after separating into five blocks is as follows: Starting with block 1, give each individual a two-digit number. (Williams will be 01, Deng 02, Hernandez 03 and Moses 04.) Continue with the remaining four blocks in this fashion. As an example, starting at line 113 on Table B, the first acceptable two-digit random number is 02. Deng is assigned to weight-loss treatment A. We could then assign numbers 06, 10, 14, and 18 to weight-loss treatment A. Continue using Table B to find suitable random numbers for assignments to the next three weight-loss treatments. The assignments are given below.

     Treatment A: 02, 06, 10, 14, and 18.
     Treatment B: 08, 12, 16, 20, and 04.
     Treatment C: 11, 15, 19, 03, and 07.
     Treatment D: 01, 05, 09, 13, and 17.

3.48   **a)**

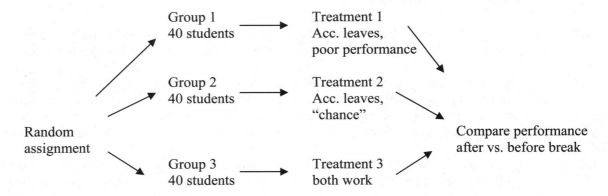

b) Answers will vary using software. Using line 123, the first four subjects for Treatment 1 are: 102, 063, 035, 090.

3.49   **a)** This is a completely randomized design with two treatment groups.

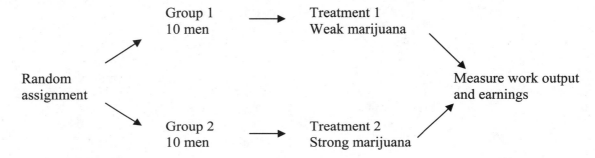

b) Answers will vary using software, but using line 131 on Table B, Group 1 will contain: Dubois (05), Travers (19), Chen (04), Ullman (20), Quinones (16), Thompson (18), Fluharty (07), Lucero (13), Afifi (02), Gerson (08). Group 2 will then contain the remaining subjects: Abate, Brown, Engel, Gutierrez, Hwang, Iselin, Kaplan, McNiell, Morse, and Rosen.

3.50   **a)**

	Treatments	Factor B Fraction of shoes on sale	
		50%	100%
Factor A discounts	20%	1	2
	40%	3	4
	60%	5	6

b) Outline of completely randomized design. Answers will vary for treatment assignment if software is used. Using Table B at line 111, the 10 subjects assigned to the first treatment would be 48, 60, 51, 30, 41, 27, 12, 38, 50, 59.

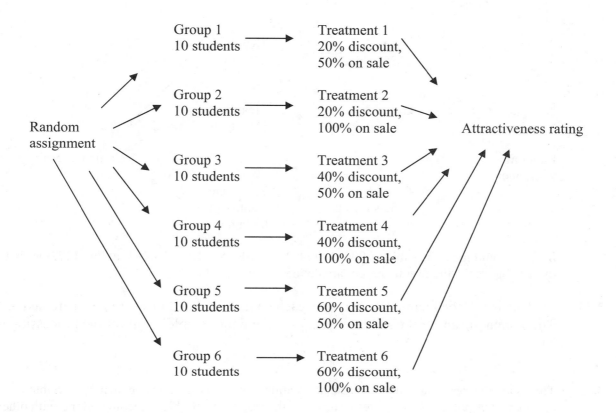

3.51 **a)** Randomly assign your subjects to either Group 1 or Group 2. Each group will taste and rate both the regular and the light mocha drink. However Group 1 will drink them in the regular/light order, and Group 2 will drink them in the light/regular order. For each group, the taste ratings of the regular and light drinks will be compared, and then the results of the two groups will be compared to see if the order of tasting made a difference to the ratings. To properly blind the subjects, both mocha drinks should be in identical opaque (we are only measuring taste, not appearance) cups with no labels on them.
b) Using line 141 on Table B, the regular/light group will use subjects with labels: 12, 16, 02, 08, 17, 10, 05, 09, 19, 06. The light/regular group will use the remaining 10 subjects.

3.52 **a)** This is a completely randomized design. The outline of the experiment follows. Some variables of interest might include how many days until the subject is employed, how long the subject stayed employed, and the salary of the new job. Answers will vary.

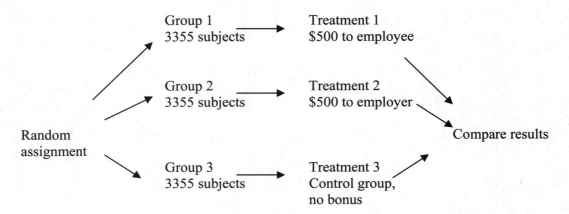

b) You could label the subjects 00001, 00002, ..., 10065. Using Table B at line 127, the first three subjects for the first treatment are 06565, 00795, and 08727.

3.53 a) This is matched pairs data because, each day, two related measurements are taken. b) The sample mean for the kill room is 2138.5, and the sample mean for the processing is 314.

3.54 This is an observational study because no treatment is imposed. The explanatory variable is acceptance of public housing (yes or no), and the response variable is income (along with other variables that were not specified.) There are certainly lurking variables that affect income levels that will confound the results of this study.

3.55 This is an experiment because the students see a treatment (steady price versus price cuts). The explanatory variable is which price history is shown, and the response variable is what price the student expects to pay.

3.56 If, in addition to the usage variables of the new system, the experimenter would like to compare how many phone calls are made with the current phone system and how many are made with the computer system, then a control group should be used. There would then be three treatments: low flat rate for group 1, two-rate structure for group 2, and no new service for group 3.

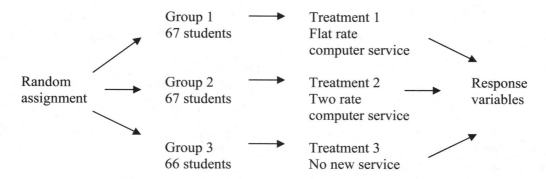

If no control group is wanted, then randomly assign 100 students to group 1 and 100 students to group 2.

3.57 **a)** The subjects are the 210 children. **b)** The factor is the beverage set and there are three levels. The response variable is which type of drink is selected.
c)

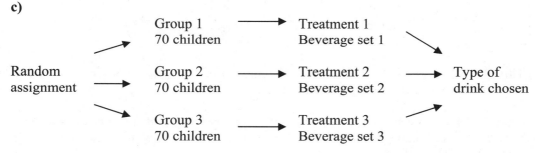

d) Assign the numbers 001 to 210 to the list of children. Starting at line 125 in Table B, the first five subjects for treatment 1 would be: 119, 033, 199, 192, and 148.

3.58 **a)** It is important to have a control group that receives a placebo but is handled the same way as the group that receives the new medication. The placebo effect needs to be considered in any testing of new medications.

b)

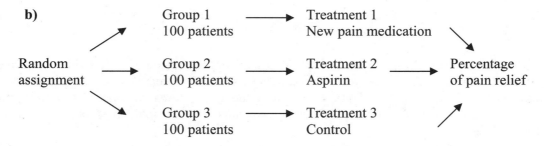

c) No, patients should not be told which drug they are receiving. This information might affect how they perceive their pain relief. **d)** Yes, the experiment should be double-blind as well. Double-blind will ensure that the medical personnel handle the three groups the same way.

3.59   **a)** Two possible lurking variables could be age of the patient and severity of the cancer.

b)

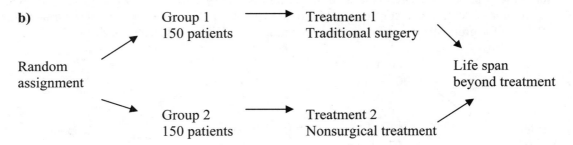

3.60   **a)** The subjects were the 22,000 physicians. The factor was the pill the subject took every other day. There were two levels: aspirin and placebo. The response variable was number of heart attacks each group experiences.

b)

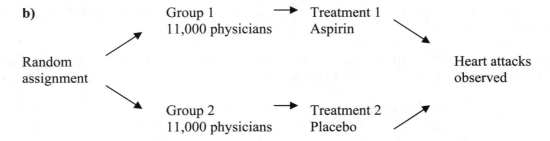

c) This phrase means that the difference in the number of heart attacks observed in each group was so large that it was not due to chance alone.

3.61   A controlled study is a study that has been conducted by looking at recovery rates while accounting for differences in individuals. Some differences to be considered would be age, gender, type of ailment, and severity of ailment.

3.62   **a)**

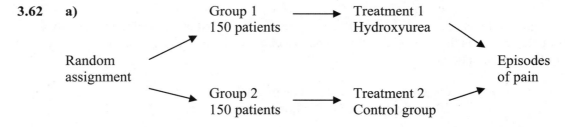

b) The placebo effect is the phrase used to describe the phenomenon of an individual showing a positive response (in this case a reduction in pain episodes) to a treatment, even when the treatment is a placebo (inert). Without comparing the hydroxyurea treatment to a control group the experimenters would not know if the positive results were due to the medication or due to the placebo effect.

3.63 **a)**

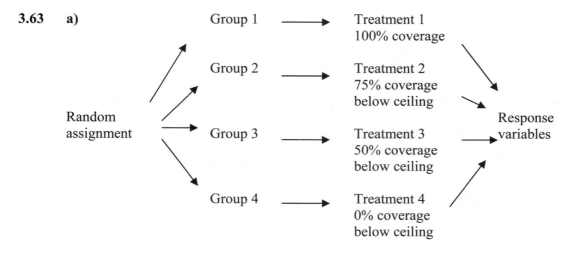

b) Randomly assigning individuals to this type of insurance plan is not an easy task. An individual may not be willing to take part in this experiment if they are assigned to treatments 2, 3, or 4 if these treatments are less than their current coverage. From an ethical perspective, it would be difficult for a company to justify providing less coverage to some individuals than to others.

3.64 Random assignment will assign six students to each of the six treatments. The treatments are as shown in Figure 3.3. The students' responses toward recall of the commercial, their attitude toward the camera, and their intention to purchase the camera will be compared between the six treatment groups. The random assignments are shown here. Group 1: James, Chao, Vaughn, Liang, Bikalis, and Padilla. Group 2: Trujillo, Maldonado, Imrani, Kaplan, Denman, and Wei. Group 3: Asihiro, Zhang, O'Brian, Han, Rosen, and Willis. Group 4: Marsden, Valasco, Plochman, Durr, Farouk, and Fleming. Group 5: Hruska, George, Howard, Solomon, Montoya, and Clemente. Group 6: Alomar, Bennett, Edwards, Ogle, Tullock, and Wilder.

3.65 **a)**

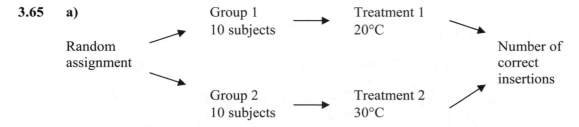

b) A matched pairs experiment would have each subject perform the dexterity test at both temperatures. The order of the treatments would be randomly selected for each subject so that order does not play a role. After each subject performs the dexterity test twice, the difference in the number of correct insertions for each subject would be used to determine if the temperature of the work place has an effect.

3.66 **a)** A matched pairs design involves administering the two tests (BI and ARSMA) to each individual in the experiment. The randomization in the design will come into play when choosing which test the individual will receive first. **b)** Whether the student uses Table B or a software package will determine the random sample. Answers will vary.

3.67

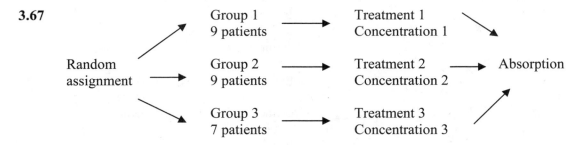

3.68   There are two factors with three levels each, so there will be nine treatments for this comparative experiment. The students' diagram should show that they have a different combination of concentration and method for each treatment level.

3.69   Using Table B, starting at line 145, to randomly select the 10 plots that will be planted with method A, the randomized experiment looks like the following:

Plot 01	Plot 02	Plot 03	Plot 04
Method A	Method A	Method B	Method B
Plot 05	Plot 06	Plot 07	Plot 08
Method B	Method A	Method A	Method A
Plot 09	Plot 10	Plot 11	Plot 12
Method A	Method A	Method B	Method B
Plot 13	Plot 14	Plot 15	Plot 16
Method B	Method B	Method B	Method A
Plot 17	Plot 18	Plot 19	Plot 20
Method B	Method B	Method A	Method A

3.70   52% is a parameter, and 43% is a statistic.

3.71   68% is a parameter, and 73% is a statistic.

3.72   **a)** 60% of the digits in the random number table will be a 0, 1, 2, 3, 4, or 5. 40% of the digits will be a 6, 7, 8, or 9. This simulates a population where 60% of the people find shopping frustrating and 40% do not. **b)** If drawing one digit simulates drawing one person at random then drawing 100 digits will simulate drawing 100 people at random. A table of random digits is generated with each digit independently selected from a distribution where each digit has a 10% chance of being selected. **c)** Starting at line 104, 56 of the digits are between 0 and 5, so $\hat{p} = 56/100 = 0.56$.

3.73   **a)** $\bar{x} = 25.324$ million dollars. This value is less than the mean from the first two samples. **b)** $s = 30.788$ million dollars. This value is also less than the standard deviation from the first two samples. **c)** The median is 13.3 million dollars, which is also less than the median from the first two samples. Note, however, that the medians are much closer in value than either the means or standard deviations.

3.74   **a)** This histogram shows a slightly skewed shape to the right with a center at approximately 25 million dollars and a spread of 60 million dollars. **b)** It is reasonable to say that the sample mean from a sample of 25 could be as much as 30 million dollars greater or 20 million dollars less than the true mean.

3.75   **a)** The approximate range is 60 (70 – 10) million dollars. **b)** The approximate range is 75 (80 – 5) million dollars. The spread is greater with the smaller sample size. **c)** The approximate range is 26 (42 – 16) million dollars. This range is smaller than the range in parts (a) and (b). **d)** These three sampling distributions illustrate that, as the sample size increases, the spread of the distribution (or variability) decreases.

3.76   The firm increases its sample size to decreases sampling variability (decrease margin of error).

3.77   **a)** The population for this survey is all the people in Ontario. The sample is the 61,239 residents interviewed. **b)** Yes, these sample statistics are likely to be very close to the true population parameters because the sample size is very large and the sample was a probability sample.

3.78   **a)** The worst-case scenario would be if $p = 1$ and $\hat{p} = 0$. This is very unlikely, though. There will be sampling variability every time you take a sample, but $\hat{p}$ is much more likely to be close to p.

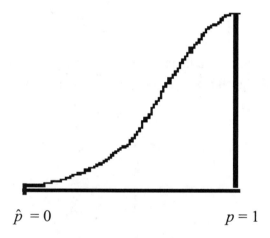

$\hat{p} = 0$ $p = 1$

b) If $\hat{p}$ is 0.5, the worst-case scenario is if p is 0 or 1 because then $\hat{p}$ would be 0.5 off of p. The drawing below represents a $p = 1$, but a $p = 0$ drawing would just be the mirror image.

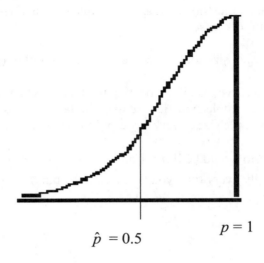

$$\hat{p} = 0.5 \qquad p = 1$$

3.79 **a)** The worst-case scenario would be that we have a $\hat{p}$ of 1, which would be 0.8 away from the true proportion. On the sketch below, $p = 0.2$ is in the center of the distribution, and $\hat{p} = 1$ would be very, very far to the right.

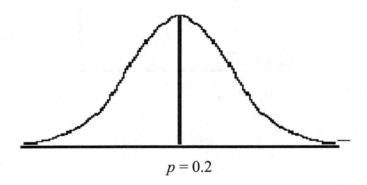

$$p = 0.2$$

b) If we use a p of 0.5, then $\hat{p}$ would only be 0.5 away from the true proportion at most.

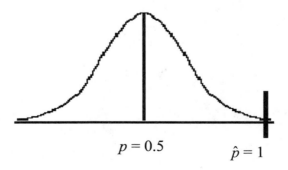

$$p = 0.5 \qquad \hat{p} = 1$$

3.80 **a)** The worst-case scenario here is that $\hat{p} = 0$, which would mean $\hat{p}$ is 0.7 away from p, which would be very far to the left on the sketch below.

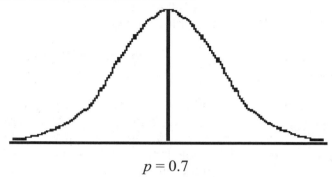

$$p = 0.7$$

b) If p is actually 0.5, then $\hat{p}$ would only be 0.5 away from the true proportion at most. (See sketch from part (b) above.)

3.81 **a)** $\hat{p} = 0.8133$. **b)** The worst-case scenario is the true proportion is 0. Then the estimate would be 0.8133 away. **c)** It is impossible to know how far off this sample proportion is from the true population proportion because we do not know what the true population proportion is.

3.82 **a)** It worked very well. We had $\hat{p} = 0.8133$ vs. $p = 0.863$. **b)** $\hat{p} = 0.887$, so the method worked even better than in part (a). **c)** Only two samples is not enough proof that the method works well. You would need to apply this method to many other samples. Because of sampling variability, two samples would not be enough evidence.

3.83 **a)**

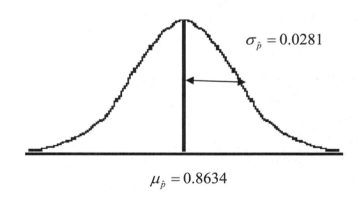

$$\sigma_{\hat{p}} = 0.0281$$

$$\mu_{\hat{p}} = 0.8634$$

b) Approximately 95% of the $\hat{p}$ values are inside the interval (0.8072, 0.9196).
c) Approximately 95% of the $\hat{p}$ values from 1200 samples are between 0.8072 and 0.9196, so this is a good indication of where the true proportion is.

3.84   6.2% is a statistic because it is a number that describes the sample.

3.85   The value 2.503 is a parameter because it is the true mean of the carload. 2.515 is a statistic because it describes the sample from the carload.

3.86   **a)** High variability, high bias. **b)** Low variability, low bias. **c)** High variability, low bias. **d)** Low variability, high bias.

3.87   The larger sample size will reduce sampling variability and the sample statistics will likely be closer to the population parameters than with a sample of only 25 students.

3.88   **a)** The sampling variability will be the same for each state as long as the sample size is the same for each state. Sampling variability depends on sample size, not population size. **b)** Sampling variability *will* be different for each state if the sample size is a percentage of the population rather than a fixed amount. Because each state has a different population, the sample sizes will also be different.

3.89   The margin of error for men is larger because the sample of men was smaller than the sample of all adults.

3.90   **a)** Answers will vary. **b)** Be sure the student properly constructs the stemplot or histogram. The center should be close to 0.50.

3.91   **a)** Using Table B starting at line 119, the first random sample would be invoice numbers 9, 5, 8, and 7. The days late for this sample are 6, 3, 7, and 9, which gives an $\bar{x} = 6.25$. **b)** Be sure the student properly constructs the stemplot or histogram. The center should be near 8.2.

3.92   Applet

3.93   **a)** The sample is 19, 22, 39, 50, and 34. Of these, only 39, 50, and 34 are White. The proportion in this sample that thinks shopping is frustrating is 0.60. **b)** The next nine samples are:

73, 67, 64, 71, and 50 $\hat{p} = 0.4$
45, 46, 71, 17, and 09 $\hat{p} = 0.6$
52, 71, 13, 88, and 89 $\hat{p} = 0.4$
95, 59, 29, 40, and 07 $\hat{p} = 0$
68, 41, 73, 50, and 13 $\hat{p} = 0.6$
82, 73, 95, 78, and 90 $\hat{p} = 0.2$
60, 94, 07, 20, and 24 $\hat{p} = 0.8$
36, 00, 91, 93, and 65 $\hat{p} = 0.8$
38, 44, 84, 87, and 89 $\hat{p} = 0.6$

c)

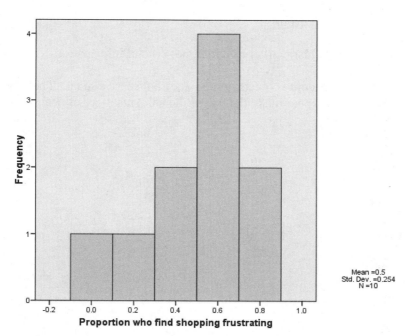

Proportion who find shopping frustrating

Mean =0.5
Std. Dev. =0.254
N =10

d) There were four samples that had a proportion equal to 0.6. This is the highest column, although the distribution is slightly skewed to the left. If we took many samples of a larger size, we should see 0.6 in the center of the distribution because that is the true population proportion. The sample proportion will approximate the true proportion as the sample sizes get larger.

3.94 **a)** Minimal. **b)** Probably minimal. **c)** Not minimal.

3.95 **a)** Many of the subjects will be non-scientists, and their viewpoint is important to consider. Scientists may be so concerned with the experiment itself that they do not fully consider the experience of participating in the experiment from the subject's point of view. **b)** Answers will vary. Choosing a member of the clergy might be tricky—which religion would be picked? A medical doctor might be considered just another scientist. An activist for patients' rights might be acceptable; however, the activist would have a bias before even reviewing the experiment.

3.96 Answers will vary.

3.97 **a)** This is acceptable. **b)** This is acceptable as long as no names will be reported and the social psychologist doesn't interfere in any way. **c)** This is not acceptable.

3.98 **a)** Yes. **b)** Probably. **c)** Answers will vary.

3.99 This is not anonymous because it takes place in the person's home. However, it is confidential if the name/address is then separated from the response before the results are publicized.

3.100 The practice offers anonymity because the name is never given.

3.101 **a)** The pollsters must tell the potential respondents what type of questions will be asked and how long it will take to complete the survey. **b)** This is required so the respondents can make sure the polling group is legitimate or so the respondent can issue a complaint if necessary. **c)** Yes, so that readers know whether to question the motivation of the poll, the wording of the question, and the legitimacy of the polling group.

3.102   Answers will vary. This is just market research, not crucial information.

3.103   Psychology 001 uses dependent subjects, which does not seem ethical. The other two courses have acceptable alternatives that make the use of the students more ethical.

3.104   Answers will vary.

3.105   Answers will vary.

3.106   Answers will vary.

3.107   Answers will vary.

3.108   Answers will vary.

3.109   Answers will vary.

3.110   Answers will vary.

3.111   Answers will vary.

3.112   **a)** This is an experiment because the students are reacting to the ads they were shown. The ads are the treatment which is applied to the subjects. **b)** The explanatory variable is the type of ad which is shown to the student, and the response variable is the expected price for the cola which the student states.

3.113   **a)** Stratified random sample. **b)** Using Table B, starting at line 111 and labeling the area codes as "01, 02, …, 25", the SRS of 10 area codes would be: 559, 209, 805, 562, 707, 425, 650, 619, 626, and 661. Answers will vary if software or a different labeling method is used.

3.114   **a)** All adults. **b)** 37.17%. **c)** Most people probably will not be able to accurately remember how many movies they have watched in a movie theater over the past 12 months. That is a very long time period, and they were not warned ahead of time to keep track of their ticket stubs. **d)** The results would be more accurate if the question concerned just the past month.

3.115   This is a completely randomized design. It also would be helpful if a standard diet was prescribed to both groups so dietary intake of calcium other than the supplement would be regulated.

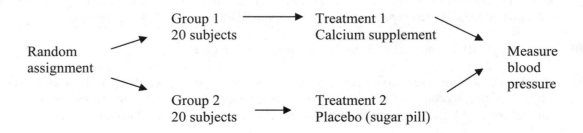

b) Here are the names for the treatment group which will receive the drug, using Table B, starting at line 141 and labeling the subjects in alphabetical order starting with 01.

Krushchev (23)	Curtis (08)
O'Brian (29)	Lawless (24)
Farouk (12)	Moore (28)
Guillen (16)	Han (17)
Liang (25)	James (21)
Rosen (33)	Marsden (27)
Asihiro (02)	Townsend (36)
Rodriguez (32)	Durr (10)
Madonado (26)	Chen (05)
Solomon (34)	Denman (09)

3.116 a) This is a completely randomized design with two treatment groups (20 women in each group). One group would receive the brochures for Company A and for Company B with child-care. The other group would receive the brochures for Company A and for Company B without child-care. At the end of the experiment, record each woman's choice of company.

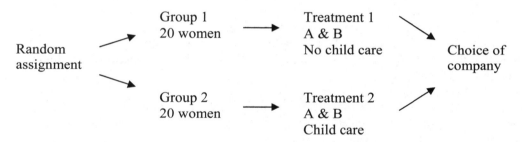

b) Using Table B, starting at line 161, Group 1 will consist of: Wong (40), Adamson (02), Rivera (31), Chen (06), Morse (28), Roberts (32), Janle (21), Ullmann (38), Gupta (16), Brown (04), Chen (06), Sugiwara (34), Gerson (14), Travers (36), Kim (23), Edwards (11), McNeill (27), Danielson (09), and Afifi (03). The other 20 subjects would be in Group 2.

3.117 a) Perhaps the job became less stressful coincidentally. Also, maybe the benefit doesn't come just from meditation. Maybe it is from having a routine of doing something positive for mental health on a daily basis. Did the meditation happen during working hours? If so, maybe just having the time away from the work routine was beneficial. **b)** He or she would be looking for improvement in job satisfaction in everyone and might not be objective. Job satisfaction is a very subjective result to measure. **c)** Answers will vary. A proper experimental design might be a completely randomized design. Treatment groups might include the meditation group, a reading group, a walking group, and a group that doesn't do anything special. Another experiment might be a matched pairs design, where pairs of closely matched employees would have one subject do the meditation while the other subject does nothing different for many pairs of employees. The "blind diagnosis" could be if all employees take a standardized questionnaire on paper (without the researcher involved or even in the room) to describe their job satisfaction with only code numbers at the top. The results could then be compiled before matching the code numbers to which the treatment groups.

3.118   This is an observational study because no treatment is applied. The researcher is just measuring the men as they already are.

3.119   This is an experiment because there is a treatment imposed: the subjects are asked to taste two muffins and compare the tastes.

3.120   There are many variables that will affect a fund's performance. The fund manager does not have total control over the performance of a mutual fund.

3.121   Opinion polls can often produce conflicting results when the wording of the statements or questions is subjective. As an example, the phrase "Employees with higher performance must get higher pay" received a 72% agreement in a recent survey on the attitudes Spaniards have toward private business and state intervention. This conflicts with a 71% agreement with the phrase "Everything a society produces should be distributed among its members as equally as possible and there should be no major differences." The first phrase focused on the individual, which appeals to our desire to be rewarded for individual efforts. The second phrase focused on a group (society) and appealed to our desire to have a fair and equitable treatment of society as a whole.

3.122   **a)** An experiment to help answer this question would need to compare the number of accidents in an area where most cars have daytime running lights and the number of accidents in an area where most cars do not have daytime running lights. The response variable would be the number of accidents over a specified period of time. **b)** One should be cautious when conducting this type of experiment because, over time, daytime running lights will become less noticeable. It is possible that the number of accidents will drop initially but then increase as the lights become less noticeable.

3.123   **a)** There may be variability due to the lecture time, which might hide any true difference in performance using the online game. Letting only those students attending the 8:30 lecture use the online game does not address this potential variability. **b)** Ten recitations should be randomly assigned to Treatment 1 (using the online game), and ten recitations should be randomly assigned to Treatment 2 (discussion only). At the end of the section on markets, the professor can compare performance between the two groups. Random assignments will vary.

3.124   The students can be labeled 0001 to 3478. Starting at line 105, the first five students would be: 2940, 0769, 1481, 2975, and 1315.

3.125   It can be difficult to gather data from a population that changes over short periods of time. As an example, consider the population of new businesses. A survey of new business owners showed only a 37% response rate. Follow up surveys had better results with a response rate of 42% from those businesses still in existence after two years. This population is likely to change over time as companies cease to exist either due to being sold or simply going out of business.

3.126   The three groups discussed in the problem would provide criteria for stratifying the population of interest. An SRS of current standard cable subscribers, an SRS of current satellite owners, and an SRS of households that do not subscribe to a pay TV service could be used. The response variable would be whether or not the subject would actually subscribe to the new service.

3.127   The four groups provide stratification of the population of faculty in this state. An SRS from each of the four groups could be used to study attitudes towards collective bargaining. Each stratum could provide 50 faculty members for the sample.

3.128 **a)** The population for this study could be all students enrolled at your school, including part-time students. It makes sense to include part-time students because they purchase college-brand apparel. **b)** A stratified sample makes sense here because there are distinct groups of students enrolled. Gender may be a way to stratify. Full-time or part-time status may be another way to stratify. It might make sense to stratify by whether or not a student is involved in a Greek organization or a member of an athletic team with the reasoning that those students are likely to identify with the school more than others and therefore purchase more college apparel. **c)** Mailing surveys to college students does not ensure a high response rate. Many students move frequently while in college and tend to use their parents' address for mailings. Asking for feedback on this question using the campus newspaper is not a way to collect a random sample. Perhaps a good way to contact a random sample is through the use of email. This may result in a higher response rate.

3.129 It is possible that some people who did not vote said they did when asked on the survey. Adults are told over and over to vote, that their vote does count. Many people are embarrassed to admit they did not vote.

3.130 Answers will vary.

3.131 **a)** The explanatory variable is risk of colon cancer. The response variable is incidence of colon cancer after four years. **b)** The experiment has one factor with four levels. The levels are: daily beta-carotene, daily vitamins C and E, all three vitamins every day, and daily placebo. Each group will have 216 subjects. **c)** The first five subjects for treatment 1 are 731, 253, 304, 470, and 296. **d)** A double-blind experiment means that neither the subjects nor the medical technicians know which subjects are receiving which treatments. **e)** The phrase "no significant difference" means that any difference between the four groups is most likely due to chance alone. **f)** People who eat lots of fruits and vegetables also tend to exercise frequently, do not smoke, and in general, lead a healthy lifestyle.

3.132 "Not significantly different from zero" means that the average returns do not appear to decrease over the first three Mondays in a month. If we compare the average return for the first three Mondays to the average return for the last two Mondays, a "significantly higher average return" means that the last two Mondays combined show a decrease that is not due to chance alone.

3.133 **a)** There are two factors: (1) time between harvest and processing and (2) whether the potatoes are allowed to sit an hour at room temperature or not. The first factor has three levels and the second factor has two levels. This results in an experiment with six treatments. The response variables are taste and appearance after preparation. **b)** This experiment starts with a group of potatoes of the same variety. An equal number of potatoes should be subjected to each treatment. The tasters will need to taste the French fries once the potatoes are prepared and assign their ratings. This should be a single-blind experiment, meaning the tasters should not know which treatment the potatoes received before being turned into French fries. **c)** Randomization can be used to randomly order each treatment group for each taster.

3.134 The two factors in this experiment would be time of day and zip code (yes or no). One main post office should be selected, not a drop box. (Drop boxes tend to have only one pick up time each day.) The time of day factor could have several levels such as 9:00 am, 12:00 pm, and 3:00 pm. There would then be six treatments (3 × 2). The first treatment would be mailed at 9:00 am with a zip code. There may be variability based on the day of the week the letter is mailed. To ensure equal exposure to this variability, an equal number of letters for each treatment could be mailed on each day of the week.

3.135   The consumer should not be told which two fast food restaurants are being compared and randomization should be used in determining which cheeseburger the subject is given first.

3.136   Answers will vary.

3.137   Using Table B at line 125, the first group of fifteen would be 21, 18, 23, 19, 10, 03, 25, 06, 08, 25, 11, 15, 27, 06, and 13.   Out of this group, five are from the group with the genetic defects. 5/15 = 1/3.   This is the same proportion of rats with genetic defects in the original group of rats. 10/30 = 1/3.

3.138   The simulations will obviously give various results.   Look for the students' understanding of how to use the software to simulate and their understanding of the difference between the numbers of *yes* results (a discrete value) and the $\hat{p}$ values.   Shown below are three histograms for samples generated with $p = 0.1$, $p = 0.3$, and $p = 0.5$.   Note that, for $p = 0.1$, the average should be close to 0.1 and the standard deviation should be close to 0.0424.   For $p = 0.3$, the average should be close to 0.3 and the standard deviation should be close to 0.0648.   For $p = 0.5$, the average should be close to 0.5 and the standard deviation should be close to 0.0707.

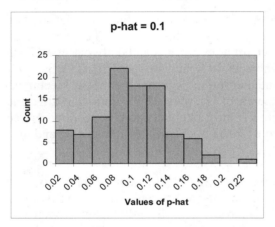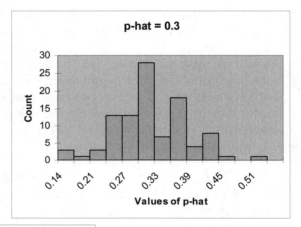

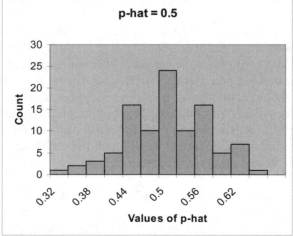

3.139   The sampling distributions will vary by standard deviation.   As the sample size increases, the standard deviation will decrease.   The mean for each set of simulations should be close to 0.6.

For the sample size of 50, the standard deviation should be close to 0.0693; for $n = 200$, $\sigma = 0.0346$, and for $n = 800$, $\sigma = 0.0173$.

Case Study 3.2

    A.

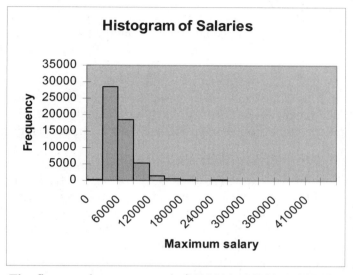

The five-number summary is \$425510, 46503.5, 29718.5, 17000, -24998. The distribution is heavily skewed to the right. Removing the top 1% of the earnings data still shows a right-skew.

B. To take a random sample of earnings data from such a large data set you may use the sampling function in Excel under the Tools>Data Analysis toolpak option. Note that Minitab cannot handle a data set this large. The histogram and numerical summaries will be similar to the ones found in part (a), although some may include negative salaries.

Chapter 4: Probability and Sampling Distributions

4.1   Previous experiments estimate the probability of a head is closer to 0.40 than 0.50. What constitutes a true spin? Do you count spins if the nickel falls off the table? These decisions will affect how you determine this probability.

4.2   Students will be challenged in balancing the nickel to begin with. Then the way the nickel falls will be affected by how level the surface is. In one experiment, the nickel fell with heads up 48 out of 50 times.

4.3   Answers will vary. For part (a), six rolls is not exactly a long run, so it is not a large enough number of trials to give evidence that the die is not fair if you do not get exactly one 6 out of six rolls. The probability of an event is the proportion of times the event occurs in *many* repeated trials of a random phenomenon.

4.4   **a)** Answers will vary. **b)** The probability of getting HH flips is 2/8 (or ¼), but this is not a guarantee of the outcome. The probability of an event is the proportion of times the event occurs in *many* repeated trials of a random phenomenon. Eight coin flips is not a large number of trials. **c)** Answers will vary, but one possibility would be to use a deck of playing cards with four suits (hearts, diamonds, clubs, and spades). Since there are 13 cards of each suit, there is a ¼ probability of each suit coming up if the deck is shuffled thoroughly and all 52 cards are in the deck each time before picking a new card.

4.5   0.105.

4.6   **a)** 0.5. **b)** 0.67.

4.7   The probability should be close to 0.5.

4.8   You would see three-of-a-kind every 50 hands over the long run.

4.9   **a)** 0. **b)** 1. **c)** 0.01. **d)** 0.6.

4.10   Applet

4.11   Applet

4.12   Applet

4.13 **a)** Answers will vary, but most should be between 0.31 and 0.61. The $P(X \geq 14) = 0.4166$.

b)

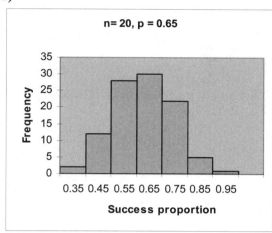

The shape is fairly symmetric with a center at 0.65 and a spread of 0.60.

c)

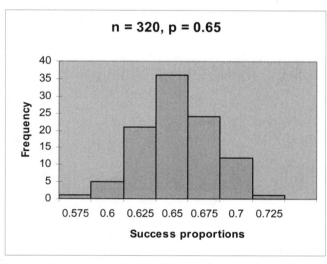

The shape is fairly symmetric with a center at 0.65 and a spread of 0.15. **d)** The histograms look very much alike except for the spread. The shape and center are the same but the variation in the sample size of 320 is much smaller, as was expected.

4.14 **a)** Answers will vary but should be close to 50 successes out of 300 trials (or 1/6), which is equivalent to 16.67%. **b)** Answers will vary but should be close to 5000 successes out of 30,000 trials (or 1/6), which is equivalent to 16.67%. **c)** Answers will vary. **d)** Answers will vary, but since the probability of an event is the proportion of times the event occurs in *many* repeated trials of a random phenomenon, the 30,000 trials should show the probability of success much closer to either 1/6 or 0.17, depending on which probability was used. There will be more variability with using only 300 trials.

4.15   **a)** Answers will vary but should be close to 6%. **b)** This simulation represents 100 randomly selected items which have been purchased. A success is an item which is returned. Over the long run, there is a 0.06 probability that an item which is purchased will be returned.

4.16   **a)** S = {open, closed}. **b)** S = $(0, \infty)$. **c)** S = {A, B, C, D, F}. **d)** S = {AAAA, AAAU, AAUA, AUAA, UAAA, AAUU, AUUA, UUAA, UAUA, AUAU, UAAU, UUUA, UUAU, UAUU, AUUU, UUUU}. **e)** S = {0, 1, 2, 3, 4}.

4.17   **a)** There is some variation here depending on the unit of measure. If we measure in hours S = {0, 1, . . . ,24}. **b)** S = {0, 1, 2, . . ., 11,000}. **c)** S = {0, 1, 2, . . ., 12}. **d)** S = $(0, \infty)$. **e)** S = $(-\infty, \infty)$.

4.18   0.54.

4.19   0.253, 0.747.

4.20   **a)** 0.45 because the probabilities must add up to 1. **b)** 0.42.

4.21   Model 1 is illegitimate because the probabilities do not add up to 1. Model 2 is legitimate. Model 3 is illegitimate because the probabilities add up to more than 1. Model 4 is illegitimate because the probabilities are all greater than or equal to 1.

4.22   **a)** The values add up to 1. **b)** 0.87. **c)** 0.191.

4.23   **a)** 0.39 because the probabilities must add up to 1. **b)** 0.14.

4.24   **a)** 0.4. **b)** 0.6. **c)** 0.2. **d)** 0.2.

4.25   **a)** Area = $\dfrac{1}{2}bh = \dfrac{1}{2}(2)(1) = 1$. **b)** $P(Y < 1) = 0.5$

   c) $P(Y < 0.5) = 0.125$

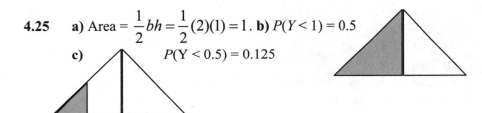

4.26   **a)** $P(X \geq 32)$. **b)** 0.025.

4.27   **a)** $P(Y > 300) = 0.50$. **b)** $P(Y > 370) = 0.025$.

4.28   **a)** 0.11. **b)** 0.41.

4.29   **a)** 0.19. **b)** 0.287. **c)** 0.790.

4.30   **a)** $P(X \geq 1) = 0.9$. **b)** "At most two nonword errors," $P(X \leq 2) = 0.6$, $P(X < 2) = 0.3$.

4.31   **a)** $P(Y > 1) = 0.69$. **b)** 0.28. **c)** 0.65.

4.32   **a)** 0.065. **b)** 0.642. **c)** 0.788.

4.33   **a)** Yes, the percentages add up to 100%. **b)** 0.02. **c)** 0.919.

4.34   **a)** S = {UUUU, UUUD, UUDU, UDUU, DUUU, UUDD, DDUU, UDUD, DUDU, UDDU, DUUD, DDDU, DDUD, DUDD, UDDD, DDDD}. **b)** S = {0,1,2,3,4}.

4.35   **a)** 0.08. **b)** 0.93. **c)** 0.07.

4.36   0.295, 0.348.

4.37   **a)** 0.10. **b)** 0.20. **c)** 0.50, 0.50.

4.38   1/6.

4.39   **a)** Legitimate. **b)** Not legitimate, sum > 1. **c)** Not legitimate, sum < 1.

4.40   **a)** S = {Abby Deborah, Abby Sam, Abby Tonya, Abby Roberto, Deborah Sam, Deborah Tonya, Deborah Roberto, Sam Tonya, Sam Roberto, Tonya Roberto}. **b)** 1/10.   **c)** 4/10. **d)** 3/10.

4.41   **a)** $P(A)$ = 0.29, $P(B)$ = 0.18. **b)** "The farm is at least 50 acres," $P(A^c)$ = 1 – $P(A)$ = 0.71.   **c)** "The farm is less than 50 acres or at least 500 acres," $P(A \text{ or } B)$ = 0.47.

4.42   **a)** 1/38 = 0.026. **b)** 18/38 = 0.474. **c)** 12/38 = 0.316.

4.43   **a)** NNN, NNO, NON, ONN, NOO, ONO, OON, OOO. **b)** 3/8. **c)** X = {0,1,2,3}, $P(0)$ = 1/8, $P(1)$ = 3/8, $P(2)$ = 3/8, $P(3)$ = 1/8.

4.44   **b)** 0.94. **c)** 0.86. **d)** $P(X \geq 4)$ = 0.06.

4.45   **b)** 0.11. **c)** 0.04. **d)** 0.32. **e)** 0.75. **f)** $P(X > 2)$ = 0.43.

4.46   **a)** Height = ½. **b)** ½. **c)** 0.4. **d)** 0.6.

4.47   **a)** Continuous. **b)** Discrete. **c)** Continuous. **d)** Discrete.

4.48   **a)** This could be either. If you count number of hours, it is discrete. If you measure time, it would be continuous. **b)** Discrete. **c)** Continuous.

4.49   **a)**

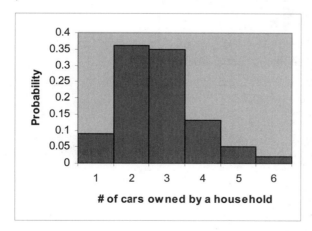

b) $P(X \geq 1)$ means "what is the probability that a household owns at least one car?" This equals 0.91. **c)** 0.20.

4.50   **a)** 0.40. **b)** 0.6. **c)** 0.2. **d)** 0.2. **e)** 0.487.

4.51   **a)** 0.50. **b)** 0.0344. **c)** 0.0344.

4.52

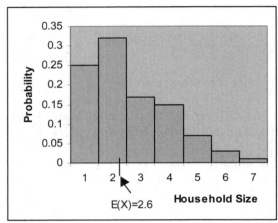

The expected value, the mean, equals 2.6. The census value is greater perhaps because they are including the few households that have more than seven people.

4.53   The mean, μ, of hard-drive size for laptop computers is 57 GB. This is the expected size of hard drives for purchases over a long period of time. This is not useful because hard drives don't actually come in this size.

4.54   **a) and b)**

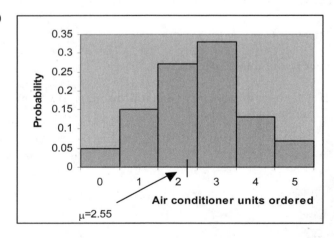

c) $P(X > 2.55) = 0.53$.

4.55   **a)** $\mu_X = 280$, $\mu_Y = 195$. **b)** $\mu_{\$25X} = \$7000$, $\mu_{\$35Y} = \$6825$. **c)** $\mu_{\$25X + \$35Y} = \$13,825$.

4.56 $\mu_r = 0.936\%$.

4.57 $\sigma^2_Y = 19225$, $\sigma_Y = 138.65$.

4.58 $\sigma = 20.27$.

4.59   **a)** $\sigma_X^2 = 5600$, $\sigma_X = 74.83$. **b)** $\sigma_Y^2 = 6475$, $\sigma_Y = 80.47$.

4.60 $\mu_{X-Y} = \$100$, $\sigma_{X-Y} = \$128.06$. The fact that Tamara has a higher mean sales value does not necessarily mean she sells more each day. She has a higher standard deviation and therefore may not be as consistent as Derek.

4.61 $\sigma_{X-Y} = \$100$. When two variables have a positive correlation, if one variable increases, the other will also. If one variable decreases, then the other will also decrease. This will result in their average differences being smaller than if they were independent. With independence, if one variable increases, the other could increase or decrease.

4.62   **a)** $\sigma_{\$25X} = \$1871$, $\sigma_{\$35Y} = \$2816$. **b)** $\sigma_{\$25X + \$35Y} = \$3381$. **c)** $\sigma_{\$25X + \$35Y} = \$4457$. **d)** Same as (b). **e)** $\$1732$.

4.63   **a)** 720. **b)**

# of transactions	0	1	2	3	4	5
% of clients	0.08	0.17	0.25	0.19	0.18	0.13

c) Yes, if for 5 transactions the 0.125 is rounded to 0.13, then the probabilities add up to 1. If the 0.125 is rounded down to 0.12, the probabilities add up to 0.99.

4.64   **a)** See the probability histogram below. **b)** 2.61. **c)** The variance is 2.198, and the standard deviation is 1.48. The units for variance will be transactions squared. The units for standard deviation will be transactions.

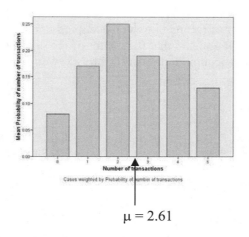

$\mu = 2.61$

4.65   **a)** 0.0010. **b)** 0.1131. **c)** 394.24 bets per second.

4.66   **a)** 0.0094. **b)** 0.6216.

4.67   **a)** -1280. **b)**

X	218,720	-1280
probability	0.003	0.997

c) On a probability histogram of the probability distribution of X, the only bar that shows up is the bar for X = 0 (not destroyed). The histogram will have only one very large bar because there is such a big difference in probabilities between X = 0 and X = 1.

4.68   **a)** The mean is -$620. **b)** To the policy holder, the mean value of the policy represents the expected amount of money the policy is worth to him. He is expected to lose $620 to the company. This would be meaningful to the policy holder if he is comparison shopping and wants to find the best deal among several different policies. **c)** To the insurance company, the mean value of the policy represents the expected amount of money the policy is worth to it. It is expected to have a profit of $620 on this policy. This number would be meaningful to the company if it is making a budget or considering whether it is worthwhile to accept this homeowner as a good client for them to recruit. The insurance company can control the mean value of the policy by adjusting the cost of the policy.

4.69   **a)**

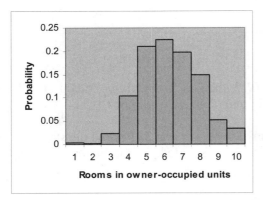   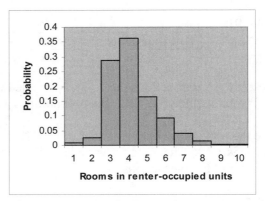

The distribution on number of rooms in owner-occupied units has more mass toward the higher end, 6 through 10 rooms. It appears that the center of the distribution is at 6. The distribution on number of rooms in renter-occupied units is slightly skewed right with a central tendency of 4.
b) $\mu_o = 6.3$, $\mu_r = 4.2$.

4.70

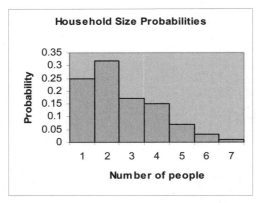   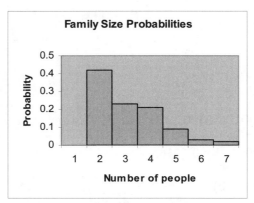

The average size of a household is 2.6 people, and the standard deviation is 1.42. The average size of a family is 3.14 people, and the standard deviation is 1.25. Both distributions are skewed to the right. The most obvious difference is that there are households that consist of only one person and there are no families of only one person.

4.71 The distribution on number of rooms in owner-occupied units appears to be more spread out than number of rooms in renter-occupied units. $\sigma_o = 1.64$, $\sigma_r = 1.31$.

4.72 $\mu_X = 2$. Let Y = the number of heads on a single coin toss. $\mu_Y = 0.5$. X = Y + Y + Y + Y. $\mu_X = 4\mu_Y = 4(0.5) = 2$.

4.73 Let X = expected payoff for a $1 bet on the box. X = $83.33 or $0. $P(\$83.33) = 0.0014$, $P(\$0) = 0.9986$. $\mu_X = \$0.12$.

4.74 $\sigma^2_X = 1$. $\sigma^2_Y = 0.25$. $\sigma^2_{Y+Y+Y+Y} = 4\sigma^2_Y = 4(0.25) = 1$.

4.75 **a)** Independent. **b)** Dependent. **c)** Dependent.

4.76 **a)** Dependent. **b)** Independent.

4.77 **a)** Let X = time to bring part from bin to chassis and Y = time to attach part to chassis. $\mu_{X+Y} = 31$ seconds. **b)** No. **c)** There would be no change.

4.78 $\mu = 70$ minutes.

4.79 $\sigma_{X+Y} = 4.47$ seconds. If dependent, $\sigma_{X+Y} = 4.98$ seconds. Positive correlation means that, when one variable increases, the other also increases. The variation then builds to result in increased variation on their sum.

4.80 $\sigma = 2.24$ minutes.

4.81

X	$p(X)$
$\mu - \sigma$	0.5
$\mu + \sigma$	0.5

$$\mu_X = 0.5(\mu-\sigma) + 0.5(\mu + \sigma) = \mu,\ \sigma^2_X = 0.5(\mu-\sigma)^2 + 0.5(\mu + \sigma)^2 - \mu^2 = \sigma^2$$

4.82 **a)** $\mu_{Y-X} = 0.001$, $\sigma_{Y-X} = 0.0022$. **b)** $\mu_Z = 2.0005$, $\sigma_Z = 0.00112$. The average Z is more variable than the reading Y. Y gives a biased reading.

4.83 **a)** $\sigma_{X+Y} = \$2796$. **b)** $\sigma_Z = \$5,606,738$.

4.84 For $\rho = 0.01$, $\sigma_{X+Y} = \$2798$. For $\rho = 0.99$, $\sigma_{X+Y} = \$2930$.

4.85 **a)** The students' scores should not be influenced by each other. **b)** $\mu_{F-M} = 15$, $\sigma_{F-M} = 44.82$. **c)** No, you cannot calculate a precise probability because even though we know the mean and standard deviation, we do not know the shape of the probability distribution.

4.86 $\mu_{WY} = 1.23\%$, $\sigma_{WY} = 4.58\%$.

4.87 With $\rho = 0$, $\sigma_{WY} = 3.95\%$. There would be no change in the mean.

4.88 $\mu_R = 1.034\%$, $\sigma_R = 1.95\%$.

4.89   For $\rho = 1.0$, $\sigma^2_{X+Y} = \sigma^2_X + \sigma^2_Y + 2\sigma_X\sigma_Y = (\sigma_X + \sigma_Y)^2$, and therefore $\sigma_{X+Y} = \sigma_X + \sigma_Y$.

4.90   **a)**

X	$p(X)$
$1,690	0.25
562.50	0.25
975	0.25
975	0.25

$P(X > \$1000) = 0.25$.
b) $\mu_X = \$1,050.63$.

4.91   **a)** $\mu_X = 550°$, $\sigma_X = 5.7°$. **b)** $\mu_{X-550} = 0°$, $\sigma_{X-550} = 5.7°$. **c)** $\mu_Y = 1022°F$, $\sigma_Y = 10.26°F$.

4.92   **a)** $\mu = 300$ people. **b)** There is no difference in the two choices. **c)** No, people do not appear to be using the means. Words like "definitely save" and "definitely lose" can play with people's emotions.

4.93   Parameters describe fixed populations. If we treat the set of tasks completed for this study as a sample of all tasks that could be performed on a computer, then these numbers represent statistics.

4.94

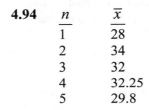

n	$\bar{x}$
1	28
2	34
3	32
4	32.25
5	29.8

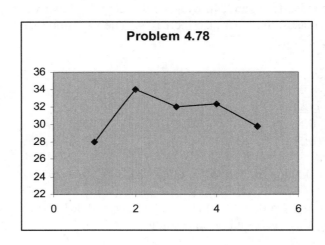

4.95   Each time Joe plays, his return is either 0 or 600. If he averages his winnings over many years, he'll find an average very close to $0.60.

4.96   **a)** The spins of the wheel are independent of each other. This means that, each time the wheel is spun, the chance of getting a red (or black) is the same as every other time the wheel is spun. **b)** No, each time a card is dealt, the probability on the remaining cards changes.

4.97   The "law of averages" assumes independent trials. This means that each time Tony is at bat, his chance of getting a hit is the same. Therefore, Tony is not "due" a hit.

4.98   Applet

4.99   **a)** $\mu = 69.4$. **b)** Answers will vary. One sample is 7, 3, 6, 4 with an $\bar{x} = 65.25$.

c) The histogram below is one example.

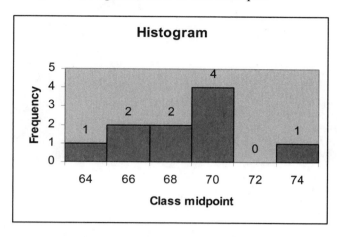

4.100 **a)** 5.77. **b)** n = 4.

4.101 **a)** $\overline{x}$ is an unbiased estimator of μ because, if we were to take many, many samples and calculate many, many values of $\overline{x}$, the average of all the $\overline{x}$'s would be equal to μ, the mean of the population. **b)** The Law of Large Numbers tells us that, when we take larger and larger samples, the value of $\overline{x}$, the sample mean, gets closer and closer to μ, the population mean.

4.102 **a)** 0.3409. **b)** $\mu_{\overline{x}} = 18.6$, $\sigma_{\overline{x}} = 0.834$. **c)** 0.002.

4.103 Approximately 0.0.

4.104 $P(\overline{x} > 15\%) = 0.2148$, $P(\overline{x} < 7) = 0.0089$.

4.105 500,000,000 is a parameter, and 5.6 is a statistic.

4.106 34 and 88,163 are both parameters.

4.107 The number 19 is a parameter and 14 is a statistic.

4.108 Both numbers are statistics.

4.109 Over a large number of plays, a player will win 94.7 cents for each dollar he bets.

4.110 a)

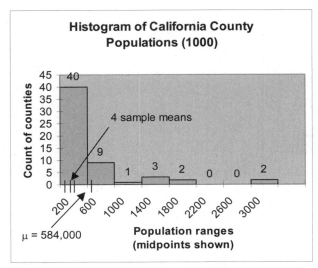

b) $\mu = 583{,}994$. **c)** $\overline{x} = 47010.5$. **d)** 97065.25, 85281, 56809, 42831.25. We would not expect all the sample means to be greater than μ. The distribution is heavily skewed to the right, so most of the observations will be less than μ. **e)** Even though the distribution is skewed to the right, the center of the sampling distribution should still be close to *μ*.

4.111 a) $\overline{x}$ has an approximate Normal distribution with a mean of 123 mg and a standard deviation of 0.0462. **b)** $P(\overline{x} > 124) \approx 0$.

4.112 $\mu_{\overline{x}} = 40.125mm,\ \sigma_{\overline{x}} = 0.001$

4.113 $P(\overline{x} > 210.53) = 0.0052$.

4.114 a) Approximately 1. **b)** 0.9920.

4.115 0.0125.

4.116 a) Even though there is a very small probability that a house will be destroyed, if only 12 policies are sold, it would be a financial disaster to the company if even one of the houses was actually destroyed. If thousands of policies are sold, there is more of a buffer to the company. The law of large numbers says the average claim on many policies will be close to the mean, so the premiums the company collects will most likely cover any losses it incurs. **b)** 0.0062.

4.117 a) 0.1587. **b)** 0.0071.

4.118 a) 0.0668. **b)** 0.0013. **c)** In order to avoid unnecessary medical procedures, the testing method in part (b) would be more reliable because the method has a much smaller probability of incorrectly diagnosing Sheila as having gestational diabetes if she does not.

4.119 Between 0.1108 and 0.1892 average defects.

4.120 a) $\mu_{\overline{x}} = 2.2$ accidents, $\sigma_{\overline{x}} = 0.1941$. **b)** 0.1515. **c)** 0.0764.

4.121 **a)** $P(\overline{x} > 400) \approx 0$. **b)** We need the shape of the population distribution. The Central Limit Theorem allowed us to approximate the probability in part a.

4.122 **a)** $\mu_{\overline{x}} = 0.9$, $\sigma_{\overline{x}} = 0.0134$. **b)** L = 0.9313 NOX.

4.123 L = 133.23 mg/dl.

4.124 **a)** -$1280. **b)**

X (value of policy)	218,720	-1280
$P(X)$	0.003	0.997

c)

Y (value of house)	0	220,000
$P(Y)$	0.003	0.997

4.125 **a)** $E(X) = -620$ and $\sigma = 12031.808$. **b)** $E(Y) = 219,340$ and $\sigma = 12031.808$. **c)** The standard deviation is the same for both.

4.126 **a)**

X (value of policy)	218,720 (house destroyed)	218,720 (house destroyed)	-1280 (house not destroyed)	-1280 (house not destroyed)
Y (value of house)	0 (house destroyed)	220,000 (house not destroyed)	0 (house destroyed)	220,000 (house not destroyed)
$W = (X + Y)$	218,720	438,720	-1280	218,720
Probability	0.003	Not possible	Not possible	0.997
House destroyed?	Yes			No

The only possible value for W is 218,720. This means that the owner of the house, no matter what happens, will have the same outcome. **b)** The mean value of W is $218,720. **c)** The standard deviation is 0. There is no risk involved. **d)** The correlation is -1. As X increases, Y decreases.

4.127 **a)** 0.0866. **b)** 9. **c)** There is always sampling variability, but this variability is reduced when an average is used instead of an individual measurement. The larger the sample size, the smaller the variability.

4.128 **a)** 0.0078. **b)** 0.0003.

4.129 **a)** 0.3544. **b)** 0.8558. **c)** 0.9990. **d)** The probabilities using the central limit theorem are more accurate as the sample size increases. The 150-bag probability calculation is probably fairly accurate, but the 3-bag probability calculation is probably not.

4.130 **a)** The probabilities are all between 0 and 1 and their sum is 1. **b)** 35%.

4.131 0.55.

4.132　No, Zeke has not given a legitimate assignment. Based on his statements, he has assigned the following probabilities to the teams' chances of winning: NC – 0.6, Duke – 0.3, NC State – 0.1, and UVA – 0.1. These add up to more than 1.

4.133　**b)** 0.43. **c)** 0.96. **d)** 0.28. **e)** 0.72.

4.134　**a)**

X	P(X)
2	1/36
3	2/36
4	3/36
5	4/36
6	5/36
7	6/36
8	5/36
9	4/36
10	3/36
11	2/36
12	1/36

b) 8/36. **c)** 30/36.

4.135

Y	P(Y)
1	3/36
2	3/36
3	3/36
4	3/36
5	3/36
6	3/36
7	3/36
8	3/36
9	3/36
10	3/36
11	3/36
12	3/36

4.136　**a)** 0.3694. **b)** $\mu_{\bar{x}} = 100, \sigma_{\bar{x}} = \dfrac{15}{\sqrt{60}}$. **c)** 0.0049. **d)** The answer to (a) would be affected.

4.137　The weight of the carton, Y, has the N(780, 17.32) distribution. $P(750 < Y < 825) = 0.9535$.

4.138　**a)** No, the distribution is not Normal because the variable takes on integer values. **b)** The distribution of $\bar{x}$ is approximately Normal with $\mu_{\bar{x}} = 1.5$, $\sigma_{\bar{x}} = \dfrac{0.75}{\sqrt{700}}$. **c)** The total number of passengers in the 700 cars, Y, will have the $N(1050, 19.84)$ distribution. $P(Y > 1075) = 0.1038$.

4.139　**b)** $\mu = 2.45$.

4.140 In a simulation of 100 plays of this game, there were 18 outcomes that did not have a run of three heads or three tails. Using this proportion as an estimate of the probability of no runs of three, the expected amount of winnings over the long run would be $(0.18)(\$2) - (0.82)(\$1) = -\$0.46$.

4.141 If you sold only 10 policies, you would probably lose a lot of money. Even though the average loss per person is only $400, that average comes from a distribution that has some losses equal to zero and a very few losses that are greater, perhaps $200,000 or more. One loss would be much more than the profit from nine policies. If, instead, you sold thousands of policies, the gain from the many, many policies that paid out $0 would be much more than the few losses incurred.

4.142 $P(\overline{x} > 410) = 0.0004$.

4.143 $P(\$1250) = 0.99058$, $\mu_x = \$303.35$.

4.144 For each loss of $100,000, the company would gain $1,250 many times over.

4.145 $\sigma_x = \$9707.6$.

4.146 **a)** $\mu_z = \$303.35$, $\sigma^2_z = 0.5^2\sigma^2_x + 0.5^2\sigma^2_y$, $\sigma_z = \$6864.3$. **b)** $\mu_z = \$303.35$, $\sigma_z = \$4853.8$.

4.147 **a)** $S = \{1,2,3, \ldots, 50\}$. **b)** Discrete because the variable takes on integer values. **c)** There are 50 possible values.

4.148 **a)** $S = \{0,1,2,3, \ldots\}$. **b)** Discrete because the variable takes on integer values. **c)** Infinite.

4.149 **a)** $(0, 35]$. **b)** Continuous because the variable is described on intervals. **c)** Infinite.

Chapter 5: Probability Theory

5.1 **a)** It is reasonable to assume high school ranks are independent because a student's performance is not influenced by another student's high school performance. **b)** $(0.41)(0.41) = 0.1681$. **c)** $(0.41)(0.01) = 0.0041$.

5.2 No, these events are probably not independent of each other. A college education has an influence on the type of job you take.

5.3 **a)** $P(5 \text{ calls fail to reach an individual}) = (0.80)^5 = 0.3277$. **b)** $(0.92)^5 = 0.6591$.

5.4 $P(A) = 0.9$, $P(A^c) = 0.1$, $P(B) = 0.8$, $P(B^c) = 0.2$, $P(A^c \text{ and } B^c) = (0.1)(0.2) = 0.02$.

5.5 $P(\text{lights work for 3 years}) = P(\text{no lights fail in 3 years}) = (1-0.02)^{20} = 0.6676$.

5.6 **a)**

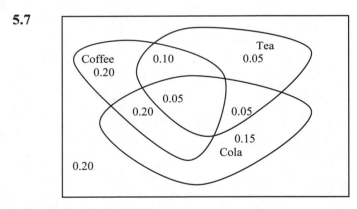

$P(A \text{ or } B) = 0.308$

b) $P(A^c \text{ or } B) = 0.174$.

5.7

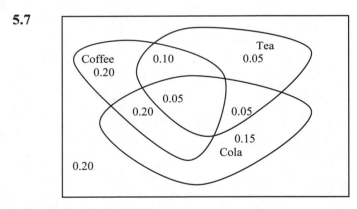

a) 15%. **b)** 20%.

5.8 **a)** 0.377 **b)** The sites are independent and are each equally likely to be lost within two years after publication.

5.9   **a)** $W = \{0, 1, 2, 3\}$.

W	Arrangements	Part (b) Probability of each arrangement	Part (c) Probability for W
$W = 0$	DDD	$(0.73)^3 = 0.389$	0.389
$W = 1$	DDF	$(0.27)(0.73)^2 = 0.144$	0.432
	DFD	$(0.27)(0.73)^2 = 0.144$	
	FDD	$(0.27)(0.73)^2 = 0.144$	
$W = 2$	DFF	$(0.27)^2(0.73) = 0.0532$	0.160
	FDF	$(0.27)^2(0.73) = 0.0532$	
	FFD	$(0.27)^2(0.73) = 0.0532$	
$W = 3$	FFF	$(0.27)^3 = 0.0197$	0.197

5.10   **a)** See Venn diagram below. A is the whole oval, and B is inside the A oval. **b)** $P(A \text{ or } B) = P(A) = 0.71$. **c)** $P(A \text{ and } B) = P(B)$, so $P(A)P(B)$ will not be the same as $P(A \text{ and } B)$. A and B are not independent.

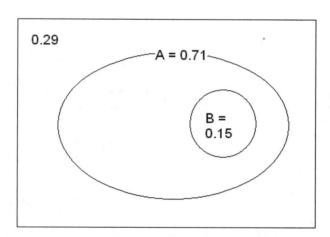

5.11   **a)** $(0.09)^6 = 0.0000005$. **b)** $(0.91)^6 = 0.568$. **c)** $6(0.91)^5(0.09) = 0.337$.

5.12 $P(\text{hiring vice president}) = 0.6$, $P(\text{hiring all three managers}) = (0.8)^3 = 0.512$. Offer the job to the vice president candidate.

5.13 $P(\text{win at least once}) = 1 - P(\text{lose all five times}) = 1 - (0.98)^5 = 0.0961$.

5.14 $P(\text{all 12 chips work properly}) = (1 - 0.05)^{12} = 0.5404$.

5.15   **a)** $(0.65)^3 = 0.2746$. **b)** Since we assume the years are independent, the third year has probability of 0.65 of going up. **c)** $P(\text{up two years in a row or down two years in a row}) = (0.65)(0.65) + (0.35)(0.35) = 0.545$.

5.16   **a)**

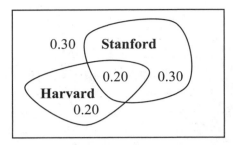

b) *P*(neither university admits Ramon) = 0.30. **c)** 0.30.

5.17   *P*(A or B) = 0.6 + 0.5 - 0.3 = 0.8.

5.18   **a)**

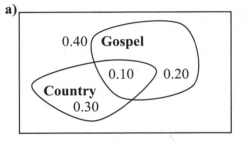

b) *P*(C and G^c) = 0.30. **c)** *P*(C^c and G^c) = 0.4.

5.19   If *P*(A)*P*(B) = *P*(A and B) then A and B are independent. We were given *P*(A), *P*(B), and *P*(A and B). *P*(A)*P*(B) = (0.6)(0.5) = 0.3. This is equal to *P*(A and B); therefore, A and B are independent of each other.

5.20   *P*(husband is a suitable donor for a wife with type B) = *P*(Type B or Type O) = 0.45 + 0.11 = 0.56.

5.21   *P*(husband and wife are same type) = $(0.45)^2 + (0.40)^2 + (0.11)^2 + (0.04)^2$ = 0.3762.

5.22   *P*(wife has A and husband has B) = (0.40)(0.11) = 0.044. *P*(one has A and one has B) = *P*(wife has A and husband has B) + *P*(wife has B and husband has A) = 2(0.044) = 0.088.

5.23

Blood Type/RH Factor	O Rh+	O Rh-	A Rh+	A Rh-	B Rh+	B Rh-	AB Rh+	AB Rh-
U.S. Probability	0.378	0.072	0.336	0.064	0.0924	0.0176	0.0336	0.0064

5.24   **a)** *P*(under 65) = 0.321 + 0.124 = 0.445, *P*(65 or older) = 0.365 + 0.190 = 0.555.
b) *P*(tests were done) = 0.321 + 0.365 = 0.686, *P*(tests not done) = 0.124 + 0.190 = 0.314.
c) No, the events A and B are not independent. *P*(A and B) = 0.190 *(from table)* *P*(A)*P*(B) = (0.445)(0.314) = 0.1397. Since *P*(A and B) does not equal *P*(A)*P*(B), then they are not independent. The tests were omitted more frequently on older patients.

5.25   **a)** *P*(throwing an 11) = 2/36 = 0.05556, *P*(throwing three 11s in a row) = $(0.05556)^3$ = 0.000172.

b) Using the probability values from part (a) and the formula given, the odds against throwing an 11 are 17 to 1. The odds against throwing three 11s in a row are 5812 to 1. The writer is correct about his first statement, but not about his second statement. (He should have multiplied $18 \times 18 \times 18$. Note that if we use 1/18 as the probability of rolling an 11, then the odds of throwing three 11s are calculated exactly to be $18^3 - 1$, or 5831 to 1. In only one out of 5832 tries will we throw three 11s in a row.)

5.26 Yes, X has a Binomial distribution. There is a fixed number of trials (20), there are only two possible outcomes for each trial (girl or boy), the trials are independent, and we assume the probability of each child being a girl is the same.

5.27 X does not have a Binomial distribution. There is not a fixed number of trials.

5.28 X does not have a Binomial distribution. The probability of answering the question right changes since the student receives help in between the exercises.

5.29 **a)** 0, 1, 2, 3, 4, or 5. **b)**

X	p(X)
0	0.2373
1	0.3955
2	0.2637
3	0.0879
4	0.0146
5	0.0010

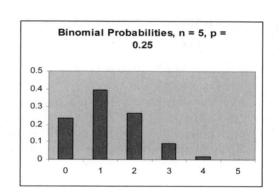

5.30 **a)** 0.1700. **b)** 0.2969.

5.31 0.0074.

5.32 **a)** The number of trials is fixed. It is reasonable to assume that the responses from the 20 different households will be independent of each other. The question asked during the survey has a yes or no answer, so there are only two possible outcomes for each trial. By making the assumption that the national result is true in this local area, the probability of success should be constant from trial to trial. **b)** $P(X \geq 10) = 1 - P(X \leq 9) = 0.2466$. This probability is not so small that we would believe the true proportion of people who say they are concerned about nutrition is higher than the national proportion. I would conclude that this local area is similar to the national result.

5.33 $\mu = 8$, $\sigma = 2.19$.

5.34 **a)** $\mu = 4.5$. **b)** $\sigma = 1.775$. **c)** $\sigma = 1.162$, $\sigma = 0.385$. As p gets closer to zero, the standard deviation gets smaller.

5.35 **a)** $\mu = 16$. **b)** $\sigma = 1.79$. **c)** $\sigma = 1.34$, $\sigma = 0.445$. As p gets closer to one, the standard deviation gets smaller.

5.36 **a)** $\mu = 80$, $\sigma = 6.93$. **b)** $P(75 \leq X \leq 85) = P(-0.72 \leq Z \leq 0.72) = 0.7642 - 0.2358 = 0.5284$.

5.37   **a)** Using the Normal approximation to the Binomial, $P(X \geq 100) = P(Z \geq 2.89) = .0019$. **b)** Sample size can greatly influence the probabilities, which in turn can influence your conclusions. The larger the sample size, the more noticeable the differences between two populations.

5.38   **a)** See table below for the distribution. **b)** $P(X = 8) = 0.1208$, $P(X \geq 8) = 0.1938$.

X	0	1	2	3	4	5	6	7	8	9	10	11	12
$P(X)$	.0002	.0029	.0161	.0537	.1208	.1933	.2255	.1933	.1208	.0537	.0161	.0029	.0002

5.39   **a)** $\mu_x = np = 6$, $\mu_{\hat{p}} = p = 0.5$. **b)** $\mu_x = 60$ if n = 120, and $\mu_x = 600$ if n = 1200. $\mu_{\hat{p}}$ stays the same regardless of sample size.

5.40   **a)** Using the Binomial distribution, $P(X \geq 6) = 0.8497$. **b)** Using the Normal approximation to the Binomial for proportions, $\mu_{\hat{p}} = 0.7$, $\sigma_{\hat{p}} = 0.0458$, and $P(\hat{p} \geq 0.5) = P(Z \geq -4.37) \approx 1$.

5.41   **a)** X is Binomial with $n = 1555$ and $p = 0.20$. **b)** Using the normal approximation to the Binomial for proportions, $\mu_{\hat{p}} = 0.20$, $\sigma_{\hat{p}} = 0.0101$, and the $P(\hat{p} \leq 0.193) = 0.2451$. Using software for the binomial distribution, $P(X \leq 300) = 0.254$.

5.42   **a)** X does not have a Binomial distribution because there is not a fixed number of trials. **b)** X does have a Binomial distribution. There is a fixed number of trials: 52. The trials are independent of each other. There are two possible outcomes for each trial: wins a prize or does not win a prize. The probability of winning a prize should be the same as long as he plays the same game each time.

5.43   **a)** X does not have a Binomial distribution. The probability of performing satisfactorily on the exam will be different for each machinist. **b)** X does have a Binomial distribution. There is a fixed number of trials: 100. Each trial is independent of the others. There are only two possible outcomes for each trial: yes or no. If we assume there is a fixed proportion of people in the population who choose to take part in studies, then the probability the individual will say yes is the same for each person.

5.44   **a)** 0.4095. **b)** $\mu = 4$.

5.45   **a)** $n = 10$, $p = 0.25$ **b)** $P(X = 2) = 0.2816$. **c)** $P(X \leq 2) = 0.5256$. **d)** $\mu = 2.5$, $\sigma = 1.37$.

5.46   **a)** $n = 20$, $p = 0.25$. **b)** $\mu = 5$. **c)** $P(X = 5) = 0.2023$.

X	p(X)
0	0.0053
1	0.0488
2	0.1811
3	0.3364
4	0.3124
5	0.1160

5.47 **a)** *n*=5, p = 0.65 **b)** 0, 1, 2, 3, 4, or 5. **c)**

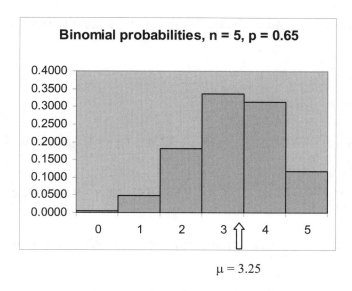

μ = 3.25

d) μ = 3.25, σ = 1.07.

5.48 **a)** $P(X = 12) = (0.8)^{12} = 0.0687$, $P(X \geq 1) = 1 - 0.0687 = 0.9313$. **b)** μ = 2.4, σ = 1.39. **c)** $P(X < 2.4) = P(X \leq 2) = 0.5583$.

5.49 **a)** μ = 75, σ = 4.33, $P(X \leq 70) = 0.1251$. **b)** A score of 70% on a 250 question test is 175 correct answers. μ = 187.5, σ = 6.85, $P(X \leq 175) = .0344$.

5.50 **a)** μ = 59. **b)** Using the Normal approximation to the Binomial, $P(X \geq 70) = .0643$.

5.51 **a)** It is reasonable to use the Binomial distribution to the number who respond because you have a fixed number of trials, they can be assumed to be independent, there are only two possible outcomes (either they respond or they do not) and the probability of a response stays the same for each trial. **b)** μ = 75. **c)** $P(X \leq 70) = 0.2061$. **d)** n = 200.

5.52 **a)** Using a software program to calculate the probability, $P(X \leq 86) = 0.1239$. (Note that if you use the Normal approximation with μ = 90 and σ = 3, $P(X \leq 86) = 0.0918$. Some authors recommend using a continuity correction factor when approximating Binomial probabilities with the Normal distribution. In that case, $P(X \leq 86) \approx P(X \leq 86.5) = P(Z \leq -1.17) = 0.1210$. This value is a better approximation. You will find that, as the values of np and n(1-p) become much greater than 10, the approximations get closer to actual probabilities.) **b)** From our calculations, we see that in more than 12 out of 100 samples, we will have a sample on-time percentage that is 86% or less *even* when the overall on-time percentage is actually 90%. This sample result is not unreasonable based on the population assumptions.

5.53 **a)** μ = 180, σ = 12.6. **b)** $P(X \leq 170) = 0.2148$.

5.54 **a)** $P(X = 7) = 0.149$. **b)** $P(X \leq 7) = 0.5987$.

5.55 **a)** Poisson with μ = 84. **b)** $P(X \leq 66) = 0.0248$.

5.56   **a)** 0.00467. **b)** 0.004618. **c)** 0.4599.

5.57   **a)** The employees are independent and each equally likely to be hospitalized. **b)** 0.0620.
c) 0.938. **d)** 0.256.

5.58   **a)** 0.0498. **b)** 0.9502. **c)** 0.0119.

5.59   **a)** 0.0821. **b)** 0.2424.

5.60   **a)** $P(X = 110) = 0.038$. **b)** $P(X \le 100) = 0.1832$. **c)** $P(X > 125) = 1 - P(X \le 125) = 0.0721$. **d)**
$P(X \ge 125) = 1 - P(X \le 124) = 0.0855$.

5.61   **a)** $P(X \ge 50) = 1 - P(X \le 49) = 0.445$. **b)** $\sigma = 6.98$, $\sigma = 9.87$. **c)** Using $\mu = 97.4$, $P(X \ge 100) =$
$1 - P(X \le 99) = 0.4095$.

5.62   **a)** Poisson with $\mu = 220$. **b)** Using the Normal approximation with $\mu = 220$ and $\sigma = 14.83$,
$P(X \le 200) = 0.0885$.

5.63   **a)** $\sigma = 4.12$. **b)** $P(X \le 10) = 0.0491$. **c)** $P(X > 30) = 1 - P(X \le 30) = 0.0014$.

5.64   **a)** $\mu = 160$. **b)** $P(100\overline{x} > 110) = 1 - P(100\overline{x} \le 110) = 0.9999$. **c)** Using $\mu_{\overline{x}} = 1.6$ and $\sigma_{\overline{x}} = 0.126$,
$P(\overline{x} > 1.1) = 1.0$. **d)** The results are very close. The question of accuracy depends on if the
random variable of interest is the total number of flaws in the 100 square yards, or the average
number of flaws in a square yard from a sample of 100.

5.65   **a)** $P(X \ge 5) = 0.9982$. **b)** $P(X \ge 5) = 0.827$. **c)** 0.2746.

5.66   **a)** Excel responds with $1 - 0.107 = 0.893$. **b)** Using a distribution of $\overline{x} \sim N(108.33, 1.34)$,
$P(\overline{x} \ge 106.7) = P(Z \ge -1.19) = 1 - 0.1190 = 0.8810$.

5.67   **a)** $\sigma = 1.52$. **b)** $P(X > 5) = 1 - P(X \le 5) = 0.03$. **c)** $P(X > 3) = 0.20$ and $P(X > 4) = 0.0838$, so k =
3.

5.68   **a)** $P(X < 3) = P(X \le 2) = 3.95 \times 10^{-5}$. **b)** $P(X < 15) = P(X \le 14) = 0.4656$. **c)** 0.4757. **d)** 0.4900.

5.69 $P(A \text{ and } B) = 0.1472$.

5.70 $P(\text{dollar falls and contract renegotiation}) = 0.32$.

5.71   **a)** 0.4335. **b)** 0.4766. **c)** 0.4617. **d)** 0.0489.

5.72   **a)** 0.5574. **b)** 0.4444. **c)** No, $P(\text{female}) \ne P(\text{female} \mid \text{professional degree recipient})$.

5.73   **a)** $P(B \mid A) = 0.597$. **b)** $P(A \mid B) = 0.315$. **c)** No, $P(A)P(B) \ne P(A \text{ and } B)$.

5.74

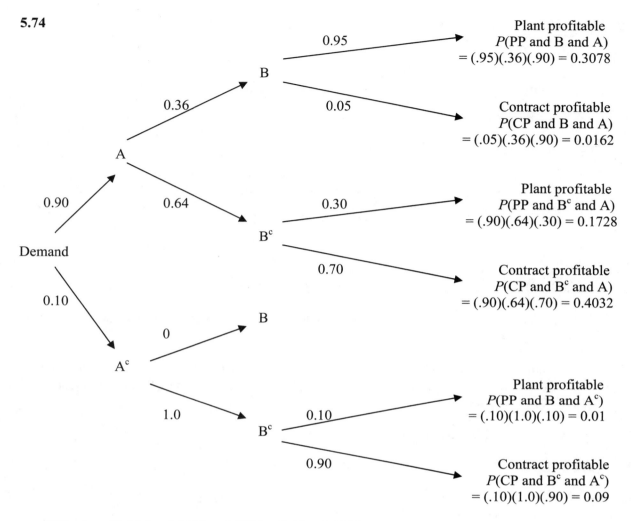

The branches of the tree diagram:

Demand → A (0.90), A → B (0.36), A → B^c (0.64)
Demand → A^c (0.10), A^c → B (0), A^c → B^c (1.0)

B → Plant profitable (0.95): P(PP and B and A) = (.95)(.36)(.90) = 0.3078
B → Contract profitable (0.05): P(CP and B and A) = (.05)(.36)(.90) = 0.0162
B^c → Plant profitable (0.30): P(PP and B^c and A) = (.90)(.64)(.30) = 0.1728
B^c → Contract profitable (0.70): P(CP and B^c and A) = (.90)(.64)(.70) = 0.4032
B^c → Plant profitable (0.10): P(PP and B and A^c) = (.10)(1.0)(.10) = 0.01
B^c → Contract profitable (0.90): P(CP and B^c and A^c) = (.10)(1.0)(.90) = 0.09

P(Plant profitable) = 0.3078 + 0.1728 + 0.01 = 0.4906.
P(Contract profitable) = 0.0162 + 0.4032 + 0.09 = 0.5094.
Because the probability of the new plant being profitable is less than the probability of the contracting decision being profitable, Zipdrive should contract with Hong Kong for the production.

5.75 P(B and A) = (0.04)(0.45) = 0.018. P(B and A^c) = (0.01)(0.55) = 0.0055. P(B) = 0.018+0.0055.
P(A | B) = 0.766.

5.76   See the tree diagram below. *P*(Next customer pays at least $20) = 0.445.

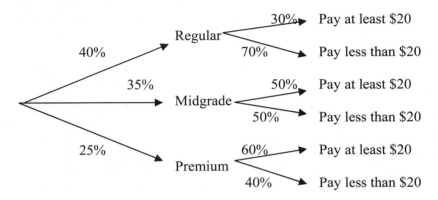

5.77   0.3371.

5.78   **a)** $P(D \mid O) = 0.08$, $P(D \mid O^c) = 0.006$, $P(O) = 0.4$. **b)** 0.0356.

5.79   0.8989. Given that the customer defaults on the loan, there is an 89.89% chance that the customer overdraws the account.

5.80   **a)** *P*(Income at least $100,000) = 0.0841, *P*(Income at least $1 million) = 0.00186. **b)** *P*(income ≥ $100,000 and income ≥ $1 million) = *P*(income ≥ $1 million), *P*(income ≥ $1million | income ≥ $100,000) = 0.0221.

5.81   **a)** $P(G \mid C) = 0.25$. **b)** $P(G \mid C^c) = 0.3333$.

5.82   **a)** $P(M) = 0.4426$. **b)** $P(B \mid M) = 0.6899$. **c)** $P(B$ and $M) = 0.3053$.

5.83   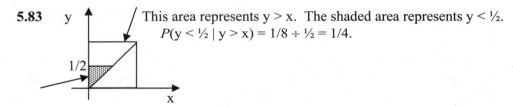 This area represents y > x. The shaded area represents y < ½.
                     $P(y < ½ \mid y > x) = 1/8 \div ½ = 1/4$.

5.84   **a)** P(F | A) = 0.39. **b)** P(F | D or E) = 0.1786. **c)** P(F) = 0.43, P(F) ≠ P(F | A) therefore gender is not independent of job type.

5.85

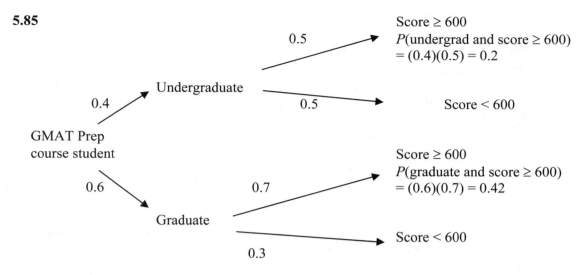

Undergraduate

0.5 → Score ≥ 600
P(undergrad and score ≥ 600)
= (0.4)(0.5) = 0.2

0.4

0.5 → Score < 600

GMAT Prep
course student

0.6

Graduate

0.7 → Score ≥ 600
P(graduate and score ≥ 600)
= (0.6)(0.7) = 0.42

0.3 → Score < 600

a) *P*(undergrad and score ≥ 600) = 0.2, *P*(graduate and score ≥ 600) = 0.42. **b)** *P*(score ≥ 600) = 0.62.

5.86

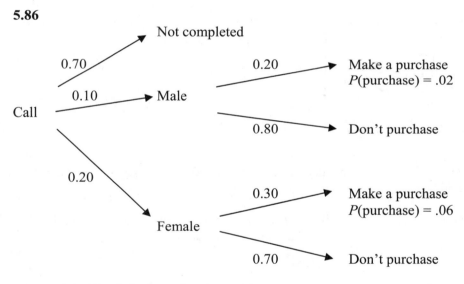

Not completed

0.70

0.10 → Male

Call

0.20 → Make a purchase
P(purchase) = .02

0.80 → Don't purchase

0.20

Female

0.30 → Make a purchase
P(purchase) = .06

0.70 → Don't purchase

P(call ends in a purchase) = 0.08.

5.87 *P*(undergraduate | score ≥ 600) = 0.3226.

5.88 *P*(female | purchase was made) = 0.75.

5.89 Let D = event that a credit card customer defaults and L = event that a credit card customer is late for two or more monthly payments. **a)** $P(\text{D} \mid \text{L}) = 0.0637$. **b)** Between 93% and 94% of customers who have their credit denied will *not* default on their payments. **c)** No. Only 3% of the customers default. Of those who are late, only 6.37% default. Knowing that a customer is late on payments does not dramatically increase the chance that they will default on their payments.

5.90 $P(\text{A or B}) = 0.6 + 0.5 - 0.3 = 0.8$.

5.91   Yes, $P(A)P(B) = P(A \text{ and } B)$.

5.92   **a)** $P(A \text{ and } B) = 0.3$. **b)** $P(A \text{ and } B^c) = 0.3$. **c)** $P(A^c \text{ and } B) = 0.2$. **d)** $P(A^c \text{ and } B^c) = 0.2$.

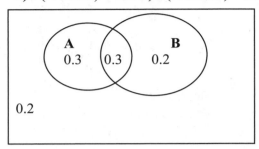

5.93   Let NC = event that an item is nonconforming and C = event that an item is conforming. Let I = event that an item was completely inspected. $P(NC) = 0.08$, $P(C) = 0.92$, $P(I \mid NC) = 0.55$, $P(I \mid C) = 0.20$. $P(NC \mid I) = 0.1930$.

5.94   **a)** See Venn diagram below. **b)** 0.31. **c)** 0.08.

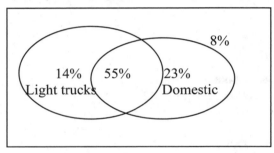

5.95   **a)** 0.1416. **b)** 0.1029. **c)** The people are independent from each other, and each person has a 70% chance of being male.

5.96   **a)** 0.3636. **b)** $P(C) P(I) = (0.31)(0.22) = 0.0682$. $P(C \text{ and } I) = 0.08$. Since these are not the same, "vehicle is a car" and "vehicle is imported" are not independent.

5.97   0.75.

5.98   **a)** 0.001125. **b)** 0.044125.

5.99   **a)** $\mu = 3.75$. **b)** 0.000795. **c)** 0.034.

5.100   0.0123.

5.101 $\mu = 1250$. **b)** 0.5596.

5.102   0.0934.

5.103   **a)** It is reasonable to use the Binomial distribution because there are a fixed number of trials (n), the trials can be considered independent, there are only two possible outcomes, and the probability stays the same for each trial (since we are observing at the same location on the same day). **b)** It is more likely that the male will be driving after a dance on campus than after church on Sunday. **c)** 0.4557. **d)** 0.1065.

5.104 **a)** P(A and C). **b)** P(C|A) or P(A|C).

5.105 Use the relationships P(I) = P(I and F) + P(I and S) and P(S) = P(I and S) + P(I^c and S).
P(I^c and S) = 0.84.

5.106 For those who did not finish high school the unemployment rate is 0.0774, for those who finished high school but did not attend college the unemployment rate is 0.0466. For those who have less than a bachelor's degree the unemployment rate is 0.0407 and for those with a college degree the unemployment rate is 0.0274. The unemployment rate is not independent of education because the rate goes down with increasing education levels.

5.107 **a)** P(L) = 0.6739. **b)** P(L|C) = 0.7870. **c)** No, P(L) $\neq$ P(L|C).

5.108 P(C|E) = 0.3166, P(E|C) = 0.7654.

5.109 **a)**

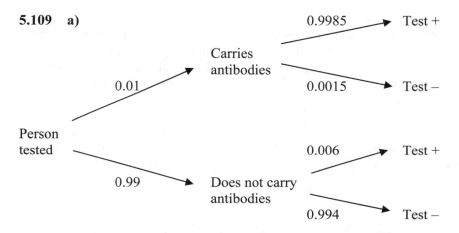

   b) P(test +) = 0.01(0.9985) + 0.99(0.006) = 0.0159. **c)** P(carry antibodies | test +) = 0.628.

5.110 **a)** 0.1428. **b)** 0.949. **c)** The lesson illustrated is that as the percentage of the population that has the AIDS virus increases, the chance of observing a false positive increases dramatically.

5.111 **a)** 0.1389. **b)** 0.1157. **c)** 0.0965, 0.0804. P(first 1 occurs on kth toss) = p(1 − p)$^{k-1}$

5.112 **a)** P(A) = 0.10, P(C) = 0.20, P(A|C) = 0.05. **b)** P(A and C) = (0.05)(0.20) = 0.01.

5.113 **a)** 0.751. **b)** 0.48.

5.114 P(C|A) = P(A and C) / P(A) = 0.1.

5.115 **a)** 0.125. **b)** P(H|B) = 0.0242.

5.116

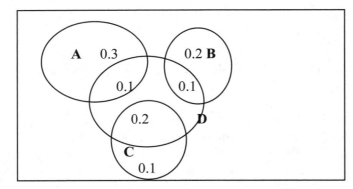

$P(D) = 0.1 + 0.1 + 0.2$

5.117 $P(\text{iMac}) = .05$, $P(\text{did not buy an iMac}) = .95$, $P(\text{First Time} \mid \text{iMac}) = .32$, $P(\text{First Time} \mid \text{did not buy iMac}) = .40$, $P(\text{iMac} \mid \text{First Time}) = 0.04$. Approximately 4% of first time computer buyers bought an iMac.

5.118 Let SI be the event that an employee has illegally installed software at home and knows it. Let S be the event that the individual has illegally installed software at home but does not know it is illegal. Let D be the event that a person with illegally installed software at home denies knowing it was illegal when confronted. $P(\text{SI}) = 0.05$, $P(\text{S}) = 0.02$, $P(\text{D} \mid \text{SI}) = 0.80$, $P(\text{D}|\text{S}) = 1.0$. $P(\text{SI} \mid \text{D}) = 0.67$.

Case Study 5.1

Verify the calculations. **a)** $P(\text{one or more errors in 365 days}) = 1 - (1 - (1/9000000000))^{(365 \times 1000)} = 0.000041$. **b)** $P(\text{one or more errors in 365 days}) = 1 - (1 - (1/100000000))^{(365 \times 4200000)} = 0.9999998$.

Case Study 5.2

a) $P(\text{one or more errors in 24 days}) = 1 - (1 - (1/100000000))^{(24 \times 4200000)} = 0.6351$. Based on this probability it is likely that an individual will see an error in 24 days. There is a better than 50% chance of seeing an error. **b)** $P(\text{one or more errors in one day}) = 0.04113$. For 100,000 users the expectation is over 4000 mistakes.

Chapter 6: Introduction to Inference

6.1 $\sigma_{\bar{x}} = \$22$.

6.2 $44.

6.3 $44.

6.4 Applet.

6.5 (189.91, 250.09).

6.6 The margin of error would be larger. $m = 39.54$.

6.7 $n = 1244.68$, so use a sample size of 1245.

6.8 The sample size would be smaller. $n = 311.17$, so use a sample size of 312.

6.9 **a)** 11.3%. **b)** No, the response rate is too small to believe the results.

6.10 **a)** (64, 88). **b)** The margin of error would be greater than 12. The $z*$ for a 99% confidence level is larger than the $z*$ for a 95% confidence level. Since $m = \dfrac{z*\sigma}{\sqrt{n}}$, as $z*$ increases, the margin of error increases.

6.11 As the sample size increases, the width of the confidence interval decreases. The center of the confidence interval remains unchanged.

n	10	20	40	100
$\bar{x} \pm m$	50 ± 3.10	50 ± 2.19	50 ± 1.55	50 ± 0.98
CI	(46.90, 53.10)	(47.81, 52.19)	(48.45, 51.55)	(49.02, 50.98)

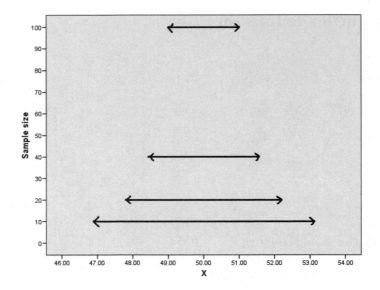

6.12   As the confidence level increases, the width of the confidence interval increases. The center of the confidence interval remains unchanged.

Confidence level	80%	90%	95%	99%
$\bar{x} \pm m$	70 ± 3.85	70 ± 4.94	70 ± 5.88	70 ± 7.73
CI	(66.15, 73.85)	(65.06, 74.94)	(64.12, 75.88)	(62.27, 77.73)

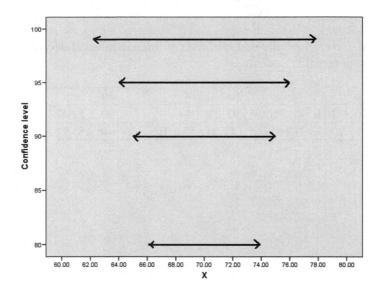

6.13   The students in your major will have a smaller standard deviation because many of them will be taking the same classes which require the same textbooks. The smaller standard deviation leads to a smaller margin of error.

6.14   **a)** 0.648. **b)** 18.48 ± 1.27 or (17.21, 19.75).

6.15 30.8 ± 4.51 or (26.29, 35.31).

6.16 49.28 ± 7.22 or $(42.06, 56.50)$.

6.17 5.96 ± 0.41.

6.18 $(584.22, 695.78)$.

6.19 **a)** $(101.75, 128.25)$. **b)** No, this is an interval that describes the average, not a single value.

6.20 **a)** 0.919. **b)** $(60.062, 63.664)$. **c)** No, this interval describes the average weights, not the weights of individual runners.

6.21 **a)** 136.099 pounds. **b)** 2.02 pounds. **c)** $(132.137, 140.061)$.

6.22 $(59.496, 64.230)$. This interval is wider than the 95% confidence interval. If we want to be more confident that our interval captures the true mean, the interval must be wider (provided the sample size and standard deviation are the same.)

6.23 $(11.03, 12.57)$.

6.24 $(28.85, 41.05)$.

6.25 $(16567, 18491)$.

6.26 $n = 67.95$, so use a sample size of 68.

6.27 $n = 74.37$, so use a sample size of 75.

6.28 $n = 86.68$, so use a sample size of 87.

6.29 **a)** No. We are 95% confident that the interval contains the true population percent. **b)** This particular interval was produced by a method that will give an interval that contains the true percent of the population that like their job 95% of the time. When we apply the method once, we do not know if our interval correctly includes the population percent or not. Because the method yields a correct result 95% of the time, we say we are 95% confident that this is one of the correct intervals. **c)** 1.531. **d)** No, the margin of error only covers random variation.

6.30 **a)** 91%. **b)** $(88, 94)$.

6.31 Answers will vary. Some possibilities include blue collar vs. white collar jobs, management vs. entry- and mid-level employees.

6.32 **a)** 0.8574. **b)** $P(X \geq 2) = 0.9928$.

6.33 **a)** 95 out of 100 of the samples will produce an interval this wide that contains the true percentage. **b)** If the margin of error is 3%, we are 95% confident that the true percentage is between 49% and 55%. Because 50% lies in this interval, we conclude that the election is too close to call.

6.34 If a sample of earnings for the trainee positions were used to compute this range, then it is appropriate to call this a confidence interval. The confidence level should also be reported.

However, it is likely that this represents a range of salaries for all trainees. If this is the case, then this is not a confidence interval.

6.35   No, this result is not trustworthy because the results are biased. A voluntary response sample was used.

6.36   **a)** (61.28, 64.88). **b)** Because the mean is not resistant and can be influenced by outliers, the confidence interval calculated in 6.20 would be a better choice.

6.37 $H_0: \mu = 0$ $H_a: \mu < 0$.

6.38 $H_0: \mu = 1.4$ $H_a: \mu \neq 1.4$.

6.39   **a)** $z = -1.58$.

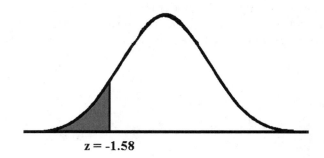

z = -1.58

b) *P*-value = $2 \times 0.0571 = 0.1142$. No, this is not strong evidence that Cleveland is different than the national average.

6.40 $H_0: \mu = 31$ $H_a: \mu < 31$. The *P*-value is 0.0571. This *P*-value indicates there is strong evidence that Cleveland is less than the national average. The two results differ because the evidence is used for different alternative hypotheses. Remember that the sample evidence is used against the null hypothesis and in favor of an alternative hypothesis. The same sample may provide different evidence for different hypotheses.

6.41   You must state what you want the evidence to support *before* you take the sample, not after sampling.

6.42   "Significantly different at the 0.01 level" means that there is only a 1% chance that these sample results were observed, if in fact there is no difference in burial artifacts. The conclusion, therefore, is that the assumption of no difference is not true.

6.43 $|z| \geq 2.81$.

6.44 $z \geq 2.575$.

6.45 $\alpha = 0.0456$ (using Table A) or $\alpha = 0.05$ using the 68-95-99.7 rule, $\alpha = .0026$ (using Table A) or $\alpha = .003$ using the 68-95-99.7 rule.

6.46   No, *P*-value = 0.4840.

6.47   **a)** 0.0287. **b)** 0.9713. **c)** 0.0574.

6.48   No, we didn't set out to prove they were of the same purity. We assumed they were the same and looked for evidence to show they were different. The results of this hypothesis test tell us that we don't have strong evidence to say the purities are different but the results do not prove that they are the same.

6.49   **a)** Yes, a 95% confidence interval is the same as conducting a two-sided test using an $\alpha = 0.05$. Since the P-value is greater than 0.05, the results of the test are not significant and we can conclude that 10 would be in the confidence interval. **b)** No, using the same reasoning as above. A 90% confidence interval is the same as conducting a two-sided test using an $\alpha = 0.10$. Since the P-value is less than 0.10, the results of this test are significant and we can conclude that 10 would not be in the confidence interval.

6.50   **a)** Reject the null hypothesis because the interval does not contain 34. **b)** Do not reject the null hypothesis because 17 is inside the interval.

6.51   **a)** Yes. **b)** No. **c)** The P-value is greater than 0.01 but less than 0.05. If the P-value is $\leq$ the significance level, then the null hypothesis can be rejected.

6.52   **a)** No. **b)** No. **c)** The P-value is 0.051, which is greater than both significance levels of 0.01 and 0.05. The lowest level of significance would be 0.051.

6.53   **a)** The null hypothesis should be $\mu = 0$. The alternative hypothesis could be $\mu > 0$. The null hypothesis always has the equal sign and represents "no effect." **b)** The standard deviation of the sample mean should be $18/\sqrt{30}$. The square root was left out. **c)** The hypothesis test uses the population parameter μ, not the sample statistic $\bar{x}$. Hypothesis tests and confidence intervals always give us information about the population parameters, not the sample statistics.

6.54   **a)** The null hypothesis should be $\mu = 0$. The alternative hypothesis could be $\mu > 0$. The null hypothesis always has the equal sign and represents "no effect." **b)** The hypothesis are always written to refer to the population parameter, not the sample statistic. The null hypothesis should be $\mu = 35$. **c)** This is a very large P-value, and there is no reasonable significance level which would allow us to reject the null hypothesis with a P-value this high. The results are not statistically significant.

6.55 $H_0 : \mu = 100$, $H_a : \mu \neq 100$, $Z = -0.108$, P-value $= 2\,(0.4562) = 0.9124$. Do not reject the null hypothesis. There is not enough evidence to say that the average north-south location is significantly different from 100.

6.56 $H_0 : \mu = 100$, $H_a : \mu \neq 100$, $Z = 5.75$, P-value ≈ 0. Reject the null hypothesis. There is strong evidence that the average east-west location is significantly different from 100.

6.57   If a significance level of 0.05 is used, do not reject the null hypothesis. There is not enough evidence to say that private four-year students have significantly higher debt than public four-year borrowers.

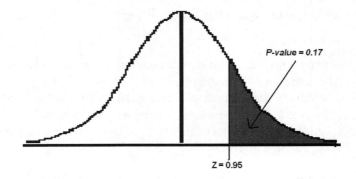

6.58   If any reasonable significance level is used, the null hypothesis should be rejected. There is very strong evidence of a significant increase in the true mean debt between 1997 and 2002.

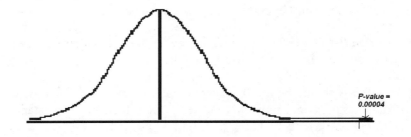

6.59   **a)** $H_0: \mu = 31$ $H_a: \mu > 31$. **b)** $H_0: \mu = 4$ $H_a: \mu \neq 4$. **c)** $H_0: \mu = 1400$ $H_a: \mu < 1400$.

6.60   **a)** $H_0: \mu = 26$ $H_a: \mu \neq 26$. **b)** $H_0: \mu = 22$ $H_a: \mu < 22$. **c)** $H_0: \mu = 75$ $H_a: \mu > 75$.

6.61   **a)** $H_0 : p_M = p_F$, $H_a : p_M > p_F$, where the parameters of interest are the percent of males, p_M, and the percent of females, p_F, in the population who name economics as their favorite subject. **b)** $H_0 : \mu_A = \mu_B$, $H_a : \mu_A > \mu_B$, where μ_A is the mean score on the test of basketball skills for the population of all sixth-grade students if all were treated as those in group A and μ_B is the mean score on the test of basketball skills for the population of all sixth-grade students if all were treated as those in group B. **c)** $H_0 : \rho = 0$, $H_a : \rho > 0$, where the parameter of interest is the correlation ρ between income and the percent of disposable income that is saved by employed young adults.

6.62   **a)** $H_0: \mu = 62500$ $H_a: \mu > 62500$. **b)** $H_0: \mu = 2.6$ $H_a: \mu \neq 2.6$.

6.63   If there were no difference in blood pressure between those who take a calcium supplement and those who do not, then the chance of seeing this large a difference in the sample results is very small (less than 1 in 100 times). Therefore, the appropriate conclusion is that there actually is a difference in blood pressure between the two groups.

6.64 r^2 tells how much variation in fires can be explained by the decade variable. 61% of the change in the number of fires over the past nine decades can be explained by the decade. A low level of significance means that the chance of observing an r^2 greater than zero from a sample if in fact there is no relationship between the two variables is so low we can conclude there is a relationship.

6.65 **a)** H_0: $\mu_A = \mu_B$ and H_a: $\mu_A \neq \mu_B$, where group A are students who exercise regularly and group B are students who do not exercise regularly. **b)** No, the *P*-value is large; therefore, this sample result does not give evidence in favor of the alternative hypothesis. **c)** It would be good to know how the sample was collected and if this was an observational study or a designed experiment.

6.66 The differences seen between average earnings of men and women are large enough to be caused by true population effects rather than sampling variation. However, the differences in average earnings between Black and White students are most likely due to sampling variation rather than true effects due to race.

6.67 $z = 3.56$. *P*-value ≈ 0. The sensible conclusion is that the poems were written by a different author.

6.68 **a)** $z = 3.03$. The *P*-value $= 0.0012$. See the sketch below. Yes, there is evidence that older students have significantly better study attitudes on average. **b)** The assumptions were that the data come from a SRS and that the population has a Normal distribution. The assumption of a SRS is most important.

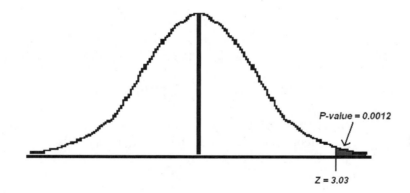

P-value = 0.0012

$Z = 3.03$

6.69 $z = 2.40$. *P*-value $= 0.0164$. Yes, since the *P*-value is so small, this sample provides very strong evidence against H_0. There is evidence that the population mean corn yield is not 135 bushels per acre. Since $n = 40$, this sample size is large enough to overcome a slightly non-Normal population.

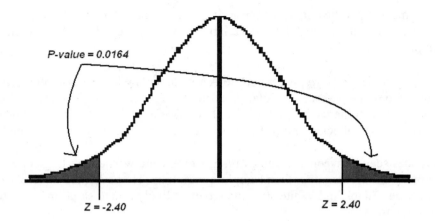

6.70   **a)** H_0: $\mu = 1.4$ mg H_a: $\mu > 1.4$ mg. **b)** Yes, the *P*-value is 0.0091 which is less than 0.05. **c)** Yes.

6.71   **a)** No, *P*-value = 0.2040, which is greater than 0.05. **b)** No.

6.72   If a sample result is significant at 1%, then the *P*-value must be less than 0.01. This means the *P*-value must also be less than 0.05.

6.73   *P*-value < 0.001.

6.74   *P*-value > 0.25.

6.75   **a)** $z \geq 1.645$. **b)** $|z| \geq 1.96$. **c)** Part (a) is a one-sided test and part (b) is a two-sided test.

6.76 $-1.282 < (Z = -1.27) < -1.036$, $0.20 < (P\text{-value} = 0.2040) < 0.30$.

6.77   **a)** (99.038, 109.222). **b)** H_0: $\mu = 105$ H_a: $\mu \neq 105$. Since we are 95% confident that μ is between 99.038 and 109.222 we cannot conclude that the null hypothesis is false.

6.78   **a)** (60.04, 63.56). **b)** No, 61.3 is in the interval. **c)** No, 63 is in the interval.

6.79   **a)** H_0: $\mu = 7$ H_a: $\mu \neq 7$. Yes, the interval does not contain 7 therefore it is reasonable to conclude that the null hypothesis is false. **b)** No, 5 is in the interval.

6.80   *P*-value = 0.1292. "Not statistically significant" means the sample results could be due to sampling variability alone. Even though the sample showed that patents and trade secrets contributed 2% to market share, this increase could be due to variation in the sample only and not a true advantage.

6.81   **a)** No, the z statistic is 1.64, which is less than the critical value of 1.645. **b)** Yes, the z statistic is 1.65, which is greater than the critical value of 1.645.

6.82   **a)** The sample data did not differ greatly from our assumption about the population. **b)** If the effects are small, then we know that our results make sense and are not due to a small sample being unable to detect a large effect.

6.83 Answers will vary. Suppose we are testing a new soft drink in a supermarket. People will be influenced by comments from other shoppers tasting the soda. Results from this type of sample are probably biased.

6.84 Looking for significant differences among many variables is likely to produce results, even though the results are not indicative of true effects. Also, consider that these variables may not be independent of each other if we have many variables on the same trainees. A better study would be to design a test for each variable of interest and collect a random sample of independent trainees.

6.85 Statistical significance and practical significance are not necessarily the same thing. With a significance level this high, we would be willing to reject the null hypothesis even when no practical effect exists. A P-value of 0.5 corresponds to a z value of 0, which means that our sample statistic would be 0 standard deviations away from the null hypothesis mean, but we would still reject the null hypothesis.

6.86 Yes, the P-value of 0.049 just barely rejected the null hypothesis at the 5% significance level. The P-value of 0.00002 gives very strong evidence for rejecting the null hypothesis. The sample results for the second hypothesis test must have been very different from the population mean proposed in the null hypothesis.

6.87 Answers will vary.

6.88 **a)** Disagree. Hypothesis tests never *prove* anything. If the P-value is not less than 0.05, then there is not enough evidence to reject the null hypothesis. This is not the same thing as stating that the null hypothesis is proven or correct. **b)** Agree. Very small effects can be statistically significant when a test is based on a large sample. **c)** Disagree. Significance tests are not always valid. Faulty data collection, outliers in the data, running the hypothesis test on the same data that suggested the hypothesis, and running many tests at once can all invalidate the results. Just because you have the computing power to run a test doesn't mean you can trust the results you get. **d)** Disagree. You need to set up your hypotheses first, then design a study and collect data, and finally perform the hypothesis tests. You don't collect the data first and then set up the hypotheses.

6.89 **a)** No. **b)** Yes. **c)** No.

6.90 Yes, this was a designed experiment that used a control group to compare effects. The results show that the probability of observing this large of a difference is very small if in fact there is no difference in the populations. Therefore, the conclusion is that vitamin C can help prevent colds.

6.91 **a)** P-value = 0.3821. **b)** P-value = 0.1711. **c)** P-value = 0.0013.

6.92 **a)** (492.224, 543.76). **b)** (509.85, 526.15). **c)** (515.424, 520.576).

6.93 No, the sample was a voluntary response sample, which can lead to biased results.

6.94 **a)** No, with a significance level of 0.01, we expect five to do better than guessing just by being "lucky" (random variation). **b)** Retest the four individuals to see if they are consistently better.

6.95 The P-values 0.008 and 0.001 are statistically significant.

6.96   The *P*-values 0.001, 0.004, and 0.002 are statistically significant.

6.97   **a)** The distribution on X is binomial. **b)** $P(X \geq 2) = 0.9027$

6.98   The power is the probability that the significance test will reject the null hypothesis when the alternative hypothesis is true at a fixed significance level. This is the probability that the test correctly will show the effect is significant. A power of 20% is not very high. We would like to see the power much closer to 100%. Many government agencies that provide research funds require a sample size to be sufficient for 80% power with a significance level of 0.05. This study should not be run as is. Increasing the sample size would increase the power.

6.99   As the sample size increases, the power increases, assuming everything else about the studies is the same.

6.100   The power would be exactly the same for the alternative of $\mu = -10$ as it is for the alternative of $\mu = 10$ since these alternatives are equal distance from the null hypothesis mean of $\mu = 0$ and this is a two-sided test. The power calculations will be $P(\overline{x} \leq z^* \sigma_{\overline{x}}) + P(\overline{x} \geq -z^* \sigma_{\overline{x}})$, with z* determined by the significance level. The power pictures will be mirror images of each other.

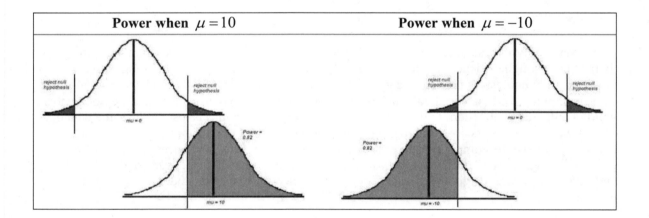

6.101   Since 80 is farther away from 50 than 70 is, the power will be higher than 0.5.

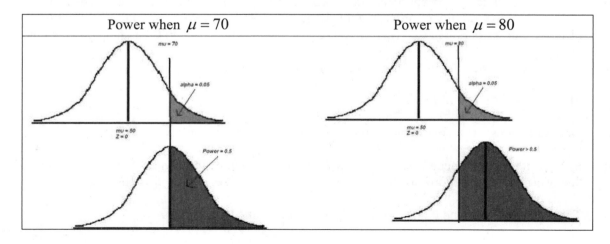

6.102   Power = 0.2776.

6.103   **a)** Power = 0.496. **b)** The power will be higher with a lower value of μ because, as the alternative value of the mean moves away from the null hypothesis, it is easier to distinguish between the two populations.

6.104   **a)** P(Type I error) = 0.2743. **b)** P(Type II error) = 0.1151. **c)** P(Type II error) = 0.0082. **d)** When n is large we can overlook slight deviations from normality in the population.

6.105   Power = 0.9099.

6.106 P(Type I error) = 0.01, P(Type II error) = 0.7224.

6.107 P(Type I error) = 0.05, P(Type II error) = 0.504.

6.108   **a)** P(Type I error) = 0.50. **b)** P(Type II error) = 0.30.

6.109   **a)** H_0: The patient is ill (or "the patient should see a doctor"); H_a: The patient is healthy (or "the patient should not see a doctor"). A Type I error means a false negative: clearing a patient who should be referred to a doctor. A Type II error is a false positive: sending a healthy patient to the doctor. Note that some students may switch the null and alternative hypotheses. They may assume the patient is healthy and let the results of the test provide evidence that the patient should see a doctor. **b)** One might wish to lower the probability of a false negative so that most ill patients are treated. On the other hand, if money is an issue, or there is concern about sending too many patients to see the doctor, lowering the probability of false positives might be desirable.

6.110   **a) and b)**

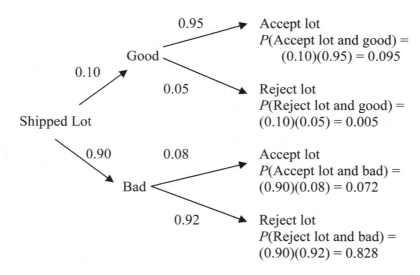

P(Accept lot) = 0.167. **c)** P(Lot is bad | Accept lot) = 0.431.

6.111   **a)** See the table below. **b)** See the graph that follows. **c)** The graph shows that as age increases, the months employed also increases. The width of the confidence intervals is the same for each of the ages.

Age	18	19	20	21	22	23	24	25	26
Months employed, $\bar{x}$	2.9	4.2	5.0	5.3	6.4	7.4	8.5	8.9	9.3
95% CI, $\bar{x} \pm 0.32$	(2.58, 3.22)	(3.88, 4.52)	(4.68, 5.32)	(4.98, 5.62)	(6.08, 6.72)	(7.08, 7.72)	(8.18, 8.82)	(8.58, 9.22)	(8.98, 9.62)

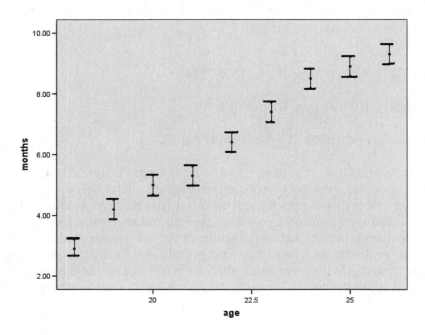

6.112   a) See the table below. **b)** See the graph below.

Workplace size	Fewer than 50 (small)	50 to 200 (mid)	More than 200 (big)
Mean SCI, $\bar{x}$	67.23	70.37	74.83
Part a) 95% CI, $\bar{x} \pm 2.78$	(64.45, 70.01)	(67.59, 73.15)	(72.05, 77.61)
Part c) 95% CI, $\bar{x} \pm 3.40$	(63.83, 70.63)	(66.97, 73.77)	(71.43, 78.23)

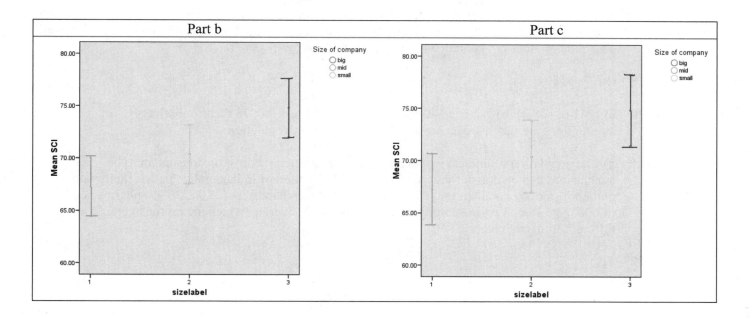

c) See the table and graph above. The means are the same for the two methods, and the mean SCI score increases as the workplace size increases. The width of the confidence intervals increased with the method in part (c). There is much more overlap of the intervals with the method in part (c). In part (b), there is close to no overlap between small and big companies' confidence intervals, but in part c there is overlap of all the confidence intervals.

6.113 Applet.

6.114 Applet.

6.115 There is less than a 5% chance that this result would be observed if in fact there were no difference in companies with high SHRUSED values and companies with low SHRUSED values.

6.116 **a)** The sample results do not show a relationship between the level of exchange rate and foreign investment relative to domestic investment. This is consistent with our assumption that this relationship does not exist in the population as a whole. **b)** Because we have a large sample size we trust the results of this study.

6.117 **a)**

```
2 │0  3  4
2 │
3 │0  1  1  2  4
3 │6
4 │3
```

b) (26.06, 34.74). **c)** Yes, because 25 is not in the interval, we can conclude that the average odor threshold of beginning students is higher.

6.118   **a)** The 95% confidence interval would be wider. Greater confidence results in a wider interval. **b)** Yes, a two-sided hypothesis test with an $\alpha = 0.10$ can be decided using a 90% confidence interval. This interval does not contain $40,000; therefore, we can reject H_o.

6.119   ($777, $789).

6.120   **a)** (141.6, 148.4). **b)** H_0: $\mu = 140$ H_a: $\mu > 140$. *P*-value = 0.0078 therefore reject H_o. **c)** The assumptions are that the data are a SRS from a Normal population.

6.121   **a)** The population of interest would be all nonprescription medication consumers. The conclusions can be drawn for certain about the population of Indianapolis that has their phone number listed. **b)** Food stores: (15.22, 22.12) mass merchandisers (27.77, 36.99) pharmacies (43.68, 53.52). **c)** Yes, the confidence intervals do not overlap, which means the averages are different from each other.

6.122   **a)**

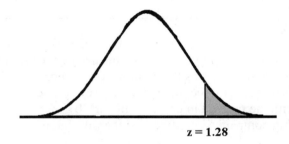

z = 1.28

b) *P*-value = 0.10. **c)** No, the results are not significant at the 0.05 level. This study does not give strong evidence that CEO pay went up.

6.123   **a)** With an increased sample size, the margin of error will decrease and the width of the interval decreases. **b)** As n increases, the sampling variability gets smaller and therefore the *P*-value decreases. **c)** As in part (b), as n increases, the sampling variability gets smaller and the power increases.

6.124 H_0: $p = 18/38$ H_a: $p \neq 18/38$.

6.125   No, 0.05 is a probability about the sample mean, not about μ.

6.126   Yes, significant results have low *P*-values, which tell us the probability of making an observation due to chance alone.

6.127   **a)** The probability of seeing this large a difference in the samples, if in fact the populations were not different, is very small. Therefore, the results of this study are considered to be significant. **b)** 95% confidence means that 95 out of 100 samples will provide an interval that is greater than zero. **c)** No, since the mothers voluntarily chose to participate, we cannot attribute a woman's being off welfare simply to training. There may be lurking variables involved.

6.128   A 95% confidence means that approximately 95 out of 100 samples will produce an interval that contains μ. In this simulation one would expect to see 95 that contain μ. It is possible that students will see 93, 94, 95, 96, or 97.

6.129 As in the previous problem, one would expect to reject H$_o$ approximately 5 times out of 100.

6.130 The power of this test to reject when $\mu = 22.5$ is 0.2005. One would expect to reject H$_0$ approximately 20 times out of 100.

6.131 **b)** With n = 100, this is a reasonable assumption. **c)** $m = 10.11$. **e)** One would expect approximately half of the intervals to contain 240. Repeated simulations will not give the exact same results (unless the same seed was used for the random number generator). In a very large number of simulations, one would expect 50% to contain μ.

6.132 Students may find that none of their tests reject H$_0$ or perhaps one or two tests. 5% of 25 is 1.25. In a very large number of samples, 5% would falsely reject H$_0$.

Case Study 6.1

For the 50 to 64-year age group: When looking at the category "ambience," the response "Tables are too close together" has the highest mean. This is followed by the restaurants being too noisy and the background music being too loud. The category "menu design" showed that the complaint with the highest mean was that the menu print was not large enough. "Service" showed that most people in this age group would rather be served than serve themselves.

The rank of the responses for the 65 to 79-year age group was the same as described for the 50 to 64-year age group.

The table below contains the averages for each response. The responses with an * indicate those that showed significant differences in means between the two age groups.

Question	50 to 64	65 to 79	z	P-value
Ambience				
Tables too close	3.79	3.81	−0.25	0.8026
Restaurants too loud*	3.27	3.55	−3.50	0.0005
Background music too noisy	3.33	3.43	−1.25	0.2113
Tables too small*	3.00	3.19	−2.38	0.0176
Too smoky	3.17	3.12	0.63	0.5320
Most restaurants are too dark*	2.75	2.93	−2.25	0.0244
Menu design				
Print size not large	3.68	3.77	−1.13	0.2606
Glare*	2.81	3.01	−2.50	0.0124
Colors*	2.53	2.72	−2.38	0.0175
Service				
Want service rather than self-serve*	4.23	4.14	1.13	0.2606
Rather pay server than cashier*	3.88	3.48	5.00	5.74E-07
Service too slow	3.13	3.10	0.38	0.7077
Hard to hear*	2.65	3.00	−4.38	1.22E-05

Case Study 6.2

The responses with an asterisk (*) are those that had a significant difference in means between the two age groups.

	50 to 64	65 to 79	z	P-value
Accessibility and comfort inside				
Salad bars/buffets difficult to reach	3.04	3.09	−0.63	0.5320
Aisles too narrow*	3.04	3.20	−2.00	0.0455
Bench seats are too narrow*	3.03	3.25	−2.75	0.0060
Floors around bars/buffets often slippery*	2.84	3.01	−2.13	0.0336
Bathroom stalls too narrow*	2.82	3.10	−3.50	0.0005
Serving myself is difficult*	2.58	2.75	−2.13	0.0336
Most chairs are too small	2.49	2.56	−0.88	0.3816
Outside accessibility				
Parking lots too dark at night*	2.84	3.26	−5.25	1.52E-07
Parking spaces too narrow*	2.83	3.16	−4.13	3.71E-05
Curbs near entrance difficult*	2.54	3.07	−6.63	3.49E-11
Doors too heavy*	2.51	3.01	−6.25	4.12E-10
Distance from parking lot too far*	2.33	2.64	−3.88	0.0001

Chapter 7: Inference for Distributions

7.1   **a)** 24.54. **b)** 11.

7.2   2.060, 2.639.

7.3   (481.19, 604.81).

7.4   The margin of error would be larger. In order to have larger confidence you need a wider interval. The new interval is: 543 ± 88.81.

7.5 H_0: μ = \$500 H_a: μ > \$500, t = 1.574, *P*-value = 0.075 (using software). Based on this *P*-value, there is not strong evidence to believe that average apartment rents are greater than \$500.

7.6   **a)** 0.01 < *P*-value < 0.02. The result is significant at the 0.05 level. **b)** 0.05 < P-value < 0.10. The result is not significant at the 0.05 level. **c)** The *n* = 5 curve has more area in the tails than the *n* = 25 curve, even though the cut-offs are the same.

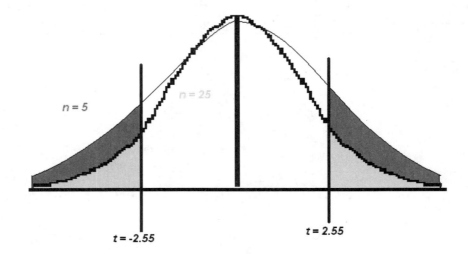

7.7   **a)** H_0: μ = 0 H_a: $\mu \neq$ 0. **b)** Using df = 40 to be conservative, t = 2.47, 0.01 < *P*-value < 0.02. Reject the null hypothesis. **c)** No, this result tells us about the average, not the sales in every store.

7.8   (16.5, 28.5).

7.9   **a)** The t statistic must be at least 2.581. **b)** df = 1000. This shows that as the sample size increases, the t statistic gets closer to the z statistic.

7.10 H_0: μ = 0 H_a: μ > 0, t = −31.214, *P*-value < 0.0005. Based on the *P*-value, there is strong evidence that cooking WSB reduces the level of vitamin C.

7.11   −55 ± 4.89.

7.12 A t confidence interval for estimating the average fuel savings does not make sense with this data set. The number of observations is small, and it is slightly skewed right but has a high outlier.

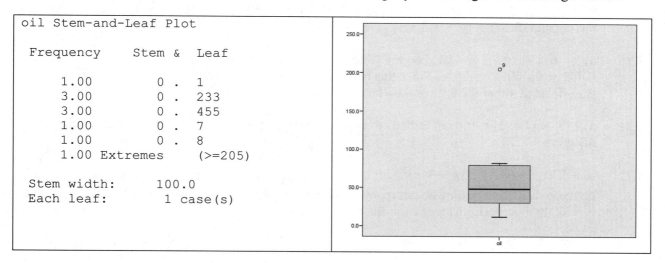

7.13 a)
```
1 01233344
1 5566667778999999
2 00124444
2 5555566667
3 244
3 5
4 1
4 8
5
5
6 3
6
7
7 9
```
b) 23.56 ± 3.58.

7.14 You would expect the power to be higher. As you move further away from $\mu = 0$, the test becomes better at distinguishing between different populations.

7.15 Power = 0.9394.

7.16 H_0: $p = 0.5$ H_a: $p > 0.5$ (if using before – after to measure change), P-value = $P(X \geq 5) = 0.0313$. Since the P-value is so low, the conclusion is that the median amount of vitamin C in WSB after cooking is less than before cooking.

7.17 a) 2.262. **b)** 2.064. **c)** 2.797. **d)** As the sample size increases, t* decreases for the same confidence level. As the confidence level increases, the t* also increases for the same sample size.

7.18 a) 1.771. **b)** 1.703. **c)** 2.052. **d)** As the sample size increases, t* decreases for the same confidence level. As the confidence level increases, the t* also increases for the same sample size.

7.19 **a)** 19. **b)** 2.093 and 2.205. **c)** 0.025 and 0.02. **d)** $0.02 \leq P$-value ≤ 0.025. **e)** Yes, significant at 0.05 but not significant at 0.01. **f)** Excel gives 0.02145.

7.20 **a)** 24. **b)** t = 0.07 is not listed on the table. The best we can say is that t < 0.685, so the right-tailed probability > 0.25. **c)** Since this is a two-tailed test, the P-value > 0.50. **d)** It is not significant at either the 0.01 or 0.05 levels. **e)** Excel gives 0.94477.

7.21 **a)** 119, but use df = 100 on Table D to be conservative. **b)** P-value < 0.0005. **c)** Excel (using 119 df) gives 9.7287 x 10^{-6}.

7.22 $\bar{x} = 570, s = 68.127, se = 34.064$. It is not appropriate to calculate a confidence interval based on these data because they do not represent a random sample. They are roommates at school, and it is likely their performances are influenced by each other.

7.23 (17.022, 19.938).

7.24 (25.556, 36.044) or 30.8 ± 5.244.

7.25 **a)** The standard deviation for the individual weights is 4.86, but the standard deviation (standard error) of $\bar{x}$ is 0.9916. **b)** (59.811, 63.914). **c)** No, this is the confidence interval for the population average weight, not for individuals.

7.26 **a)** 28.1193. **b)** The standard deviation for the individual weights is 2.2081, but the standard deviation (standard error) of $\bar{x}$ is 0.4507. **c)** (27.1869, 29.0517).

7.27 **a)** See the stemplot and Normal quantile plot below. The distribution is fairly symmetric with no outliers, and the Normal quantile plot looks good. **b)** (22719.87, 27350.63).

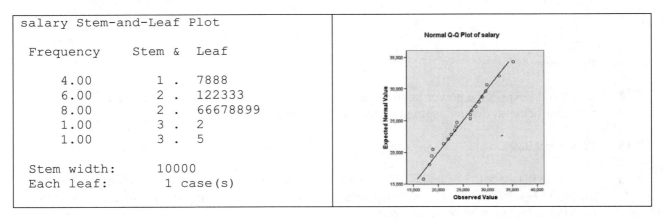

```
salary Stem-and-Leaf Plot

 Frequency     Stem &  Leaf

     4.00       1 .  7888
     6.00       2 .  122333
     8.00       2 .  66678899
     1.00       3 .  2
     1.00       3 .  5

 Stem width:      10000
 Each leaf:        1 case(s)
```

7.28 **a)** See the stemplot and normal quantile plot that follows. The distribution is strongly skewed left (no outliers), but with a large sample size of 49, it is still appropriate to use the *t* procedures. **b)** (60.69, 71.19).

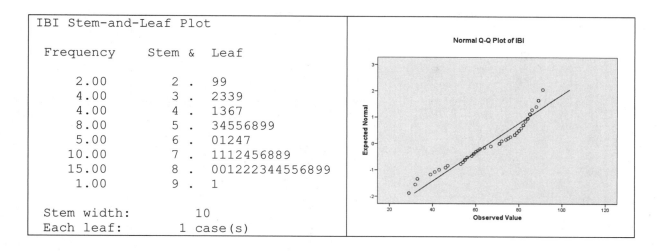

```
IBI Stem-and-Leaf Plot

  Frequency      Stem &   Leaf

      2.00         2 .    99
      4.00         3 .    2339
      4.00         4 .    1367
      8.00         5 .    34556899
      5.00         6 .    01247
     10.00         7 .    1112456889
     15.00         8 .    001222344556899
      1.00         9 .    1

 Stem width:          10
 Each leaf:       1 case(s)
```

7.29   Yes, the sample does give good evidence that the average earnings of white female hourly workers is greater than $20,000. t = 4.552, and the *P*-value is 0.0000.

7.30   We are not at all surprised that the mean IBI is not 0. The smallest IBI in this sample was 29. It might be more interesting to measure the IBI from the same streams a year later to see if there is a significant change from the previous year (matched pairs).

7.31   **a)** See the stemplot and Normal quantile plot below. The data show a distribution heavily skewed to the right with three high outliers. **b)** $\bar{x} = 34.156, s = 21.369, se = 3.379$. **c)** (27.3218, 40.9902).

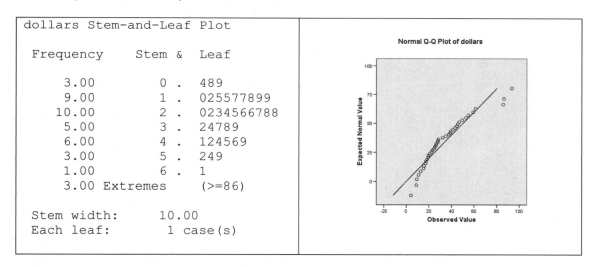

```
dollars Stem-and-Leaf Plot

  Frequency      Stem &   Leaf

      3.00         0 .    489
      9.00         1 .    025577899
     10.00         2 .    0234566788
      5.00         3 .    24789
      6.00         4 .    124569
      3.00         5 .    249
      1.00         6 .    1
      3.00 Extremes      (>=86)

 Stem width:       10.00
 Each leaf:       1 case(s)
```

7.32   **a)** See the stemplot and Normal quantile plot that follow. Now the distribution is only a little right skewed with no outliers. **b)** $\bar{x} = 29.750, s = 15.089, se = 2.481$. **c)** (24.719, 34.781). Yes, these three high values do influence the analysis. The distribution now appears more Normal, and the standard deviation is smaller. The sample mean is lower. The confidence interval is quite different also.

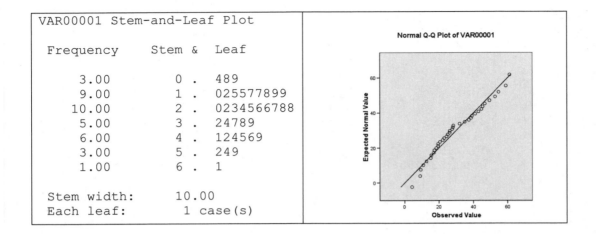

```
VAR00001 Stem-and-Leaf Plot

  Frequency      Stem &  Leaf

       3.00        0 .  489
       9.00        1 .  025577899
      10.00        2 .  0234566788
       5.00        3 .  24789
       6.00        4 .  124569
       3.00        5 .  249
       1.00        6 .  1

  Stem width:       10.00
  Each leaf:       1 case(s)
```

7.33   **a)** Six streams are classified very poor or poor out of 49 total, so the sample proportion is 0.122. **b)** No, sample proportions use Z*, not t*. Sample proportions are for categorical data, sample means are for quantitative data. We have converted quantitative data into categorical data by sorting the streams into very poor, poor, and other.

7.34   (16.76, 35.88).

7.35   (1.755, 2.445).

7.36   The problem does not specify a sample size, only says that the sample is large. Using 1000 df, t* = 1.646. The resulting confidence interval is (88.44, 105.56).

7.37   (3.734, 3.866).

7.38   **a)**
```
      -3 0
      -2 00
      -1 0
       0 00
       1 0
       2 000
       3 00000
       4 0000000
       5 00
       6 000
       7 00000
       8
       9 00
```
   b) $\bar{x} = 3.618, s = 3.055, se = 0.524$.   **c)** 3.618 ± 1.07.

7.39 $H_0: \mu = 0$ $H_a: \mu > 0$, t = 6.905, P-value < 0.0005. Conclude that piano lessons do improve the spatial–temporal reasoning of pre-school children. This is in agreement with the confidence interval found in 7.34.

7.40   **a)** $H_0: \mu = 0$ $H_a: \mu > 0$, t = 52.097, P-value < 0.0005. Yes, there is significant evidence that the mean amount charged increases under a no-fee offer. **b)** ($370.34, $399.66) using df = 100 on Table D to be conservative. **c)** The large sample size makes the result trustworthy. **d)** Use a control group that does not get the offer and compare the two groups.

7.41   (18.69, 70.19).

7.42   **a)**
```
 9 1
 9 5679
10 134
10 5
11 1
11 9
12 2
```
b) H_0: $\mu = 105$ H_a: $\mu \neq 105$, t = −0.32, *P*-value > 0.50. This evidence is not convincing that the true value is different from 105 pCi/l.

7.43   **a)** H_0: $\mu = 0$ H_a: $\mu < 0$, where μ is the mean difference in Vitamin C level from factory to Haiti. **b)** t = −4.94, *P*-value < 0.0005. There is strong evidence to conclude that the Vitamin C level decreases over time. **c)** 95% confidence intervals for the factory level of Vitamin C, for the level in Haiti and for the difference are given in the following Minitab output:

T Confidence Intervals

Variable	N	Mean	StDev	SE Mean	95.0 % CI	
Factory	27	42.852	4.793	0.923	(40.956,	44.748)
Haiti	27	37.519	2.440	0.469	(36.553,	38.484)
difference	27	−5.330	5.590	1.080	(−7.540,	−3.120)

7.44   **a)** Each person involved in the experiment should be randomly assigned either the right-hand thread first or the left-hand thread first. **b)** H_0: $\mu = 0$ H_a: $\mu > 0$ where μ is the mean difference of left-hand thread time minus right-hand thread time. **c)** t = 2.90, *P*-value = .0039 (from Minitab). Conclude that right-handed people can turn the right-hand thread knob faster.

7.45   The 90% confidence interval for the mean difference between left-hand and right-hand thread times is (5.47 seconds, 21.17 seconds). The mean time for right-hand threads is 89% of the mean time for left-hand threads. This could be a significant difference in an assembly line. A 10% reduction in time will accumulate if the task is performed repeatedly throughout a day.

7.46   **a)** H_0: $\mu = 0$ H_a: $\mu > 0$, where μ is the mean of the post-test scores minus the pretest scores.
b)   Pretest   The pretest and post-test scores are slightly skewed to the left,
```
1 5
2 000
2 56688999
3 00011144
```
but the sample size is greater than 15, so the t procedures should be trustworthy.
```
Posttest
1 68
2
2 5578899
3 00122222234
```

c) t = 2.02, *P*-value = 0.029. The results of this test are significant at the 0.05 level but not at the 0.01 level. **d)** The 90% confidence interval for the mean increase in listening score is (0.211, 2.689).

7.47   Taking the differences (Variety A – Variety B) to determine if there is evidence that Variety A has the higher yield corresponds to the hypotheses $H_0 : \mu = 0$ and $H_a : \mu > 0$ for the mean of the differences. t = 1.29, 0.10 < P-value < 0.15. No, the sample data do not give overwhelming evidence in support of Variety A having a higher mean yield than Variety B.

7.48   **a)** Two sample design. **b)** Matched pairs design if every student is asked to rate both products; two sample design if two separate groups of students are used with each group rating only one of the products.

7.49   **a)** One sample design. **b)** The best answer is 2 independent samples. Even though we are looking at changes of opinion over time from the same basic group, problems with missing values for one survey due to nonresponse or customers leaving the pool would make the paired sample difficult. However if the exact same sample was used both years with a stable population of customers, matched pairs would also be an acceptable answer.

7.50   It does not make sense to estimate because this data does not represent a sample. A simple random sample is necessary for creating a confidence interval.

7.51   **a)** t* = 2.403 from Table D using df = 50 to be conservative. **b)** Reject H_0 when t > 2.403 or Reject H_0 when $\bar{x} > 34.745$. **c)** $P(\bar{x} > 34.745 \,|\, \mu = 100) = P(z > -4.513) \approx 1$. There is no need to include more customers in the study.

7.52   **a)** Power $= P(\bar{x} > 0.498 | \mu = 0.6) = P(Z > -0.375) = 0.6462$. **b)** $P(\bar{x} > 0.294 | \mu = 0.6) = P(Z > -1.78) = 0.9625$.

7.53   **a)** H_0: median = 0 H_a: median > 0 or H_0: $p = 0.5$ H_a: $p > 0.5$. **b)** Taking the left-hand time minus the right-hand time we count up the number of positives values (these correspond to right-hand times being faster than left-hand times.) Using the Normal approximation to the binomial, $P(X \geq 19) = P(Z \geq 2.86) = 0.0021$. From software we can find that $P(X \geq 19) = 0.0033$. This data shows evidence against the null hypothesis in favor of the median difference being greater than 0.

7.54   Taking the post test scores minus the pretest scores results in 14 positive values. The $P(X \geq 14)$ when $p = 0.5$ is 0.0577. The results of this experiment are significant at the 0.10 level but not at 0.05 level.

7.55   **a)** A two-sided test makes more sense. We don't have information to tell us if one design should be better than another. **b)** 29. **c)** 0.002 < P-value < 0.005.

7.56   t > 2.045.

7.57   The individual observations are no longer independent of each other, by design. You must compare individual sales for each day of the week.

7.58   **a)** Assignments will vary. **b)** 1.2 ± 1.184. **c)** Yes, based on the confidence interval, we are 95% confident that the mean satisfaction index is different from zero. There is no need to do a formal hypothesis test because a 95% confidence interval can be used in place of a two-sided test with level of significance of 0.05.

7.59 By assigning the next ten employees to a new monitor and the following ten to a standard monitor, there may be influences due to time differences. At the end of the test period, the new monitor users will all have greater usage times. There may also be influences simply from employees talking to each other about their impressions.

7.60 Confirm calculation.

7.61

Software	Means	Variability	Test statistic	DF	*P*-value	Confidence interval?
Excel	Variable 1 = 2.9325 Variable 2 = 3.591	Variance = 0.000415625 and 0.000251875	t = −56.99216386	8	1 tail = 4.98679E-12 2 tail = 9.97357E-12	No
SPSS	JULY = 2.9325 SEPT = 3.591	Std. deviation = 2.03869E-02 and 1.58706E-02	t = −56.99	8	2 tail = 0.000	Yes
Minitab	JULY = 2.9325 SEPT = 3.591	StDev = 0.0204 and 0.0159	T = −56.99	7	P = 0.0000	Yes
SAS	July = 2.9072 Sept = 3.5713	Std Err = 0.0091 and 0.0071	t value = −56.99	8	Pr > |t| < 0.0001	Yes

7.62 Answers will vary.

7.63 t = 17.133, df = 133, *P*-value < 0.001. The test shows significant results for the difference in wheat prices between September and July.

7.64 SPSS and SAS give pooled results. The pooled results give a t score = −56.99 with a P-value ≈0.

7.65 Assume $n_1 = n_2 = n$.

Show that $s_p^2 \left(\dfrac{1}{n} + \dfrac{1}{n} \right) = \dfrac{s_1^2}{n} + \dfrac{s_2^2}{n}$.

$$s_p^2 = \frac{(n-1)s_1^2 + (n-1)s_2^2}{n+n-2} = \frac{(n-1)(s_1^2 + s_2^2)}{2(n-1)} = \frac{1}{2}(s_1^2 + s_2^2)$$

$$\frac{1}{2}(s_1^2 + s_2^2)\left(\frac{1}{n} + \frac{1}{n} \right) = \frac{1}{n}(s_1^2 + s_2^2) = \frac{s_1^2}{n} + \frac{s_2^2}{n}.$$

7.66 **a)** No, the results are probably not Normally distributed. There are only seven discrete answer choices. They may have a general symmetric shape, but it probably won't fit the Normal distribution very well. **b)** The sample sizes for each group are so large (well above 40) that, even if the data are not exactly Normal, the t procedures will still be appropriate. It is very unlikely that any outlier will be present with only seven answer choices available. **c)** H_0: $\mu_I = \mu_C$ H_a: $\mu_I > \mu_C$. The one-sided hypothesis test was selected because the program was designed to "improve" dietary behavior and thus should increase the average test scores. A two-sided test may have been used instead if the researchers are interested in determining whether there is a difference in the average test results of the two groups. **d)** t = 6.26, df = 164 but use df = 100 for

Table D. The one-sided *P*-value < 0.0005, and the two-sided *P*-value < 0.001. With either choice, the null hypothesis can be rejected. There is strong evidence that the multimedia program significantly improves average test scores. **e)** (0.512, 0.988). This confidence interval clearly shows that 0 is not included in this range, so the average test results for the intervention group are significantly different from the control group. **f)** Economic, age, education, cultural, environmental, media, and other factors should be considered when trying to apply these results to other populations.

7.67 **a)** The data are probably not exactly Normally distributed because there are only five discrete answer choices. **b)** Yes, the large sample sizes would compensate for uneven distributions. The two-sample comparison of means t test is fairly robust. **c)** $H_0 : \mu_I = \mu_C$ and $H_a : \mu_I > \mu_C$. (A "$\neq$" would also be appropriate in the alternative hypothesis, but be sure to double the *P*-value when checking your answer with this one.) **d)** t = 3.57, *P*-value < 0.0005. Reject the null hypothesis. There is strong evidence the average self-efficacy score for the intervention group is significantly higher than the average self-efficacy score for the control group. **e)** (0.191, 0.669).

7.68 **a)** Answers will vary. Since these workers received routine health checkups, were they healthier in general than other workers? Perhaps their company was more concerned with worker safety than other employers are. Some dust may be more dangerous than others. Where was this company located? Maybe climate makes a difference to how much dust workers are exposed to. **b)** (9.987, 13.013) using df = 100 on Table D. **c)** $H_0 : \mu_{D/B} = \mu_C$ and $H_a : \mu_{D/B} \neq \mu_C$ A two-sided alternative is used here because it was not specified ahead of time whether the researchers thought the drill and blast workers had a higher mean. However, a one-sided hypothesis test would also be reasonable because the drill and blast workers might be suspected to be exposed to more dust simply due to the nature of their work. t = 15.072, and for a two-sided test, *P*-value 0.001 using df = 100 on Table D. There is strong evidence that there is a difference in the average exposure for drill/blast workers and concrete workers. **d)** No, the analysis is not invalid. The sample sizes of both groups are large, so skewness will no affect the results.

7.69 **a)** See Exercise 7.68. **b)** (4.374, 5.426). **c)** $H_0 : \mu_{D/B} = \mu_C$ and $H_a : \mu_{D/B} > \mu_C$. See the explanation in Exercise 7.68. t = 18.49, *P*-value is close to 0. Reject the null hypothesis. There is very strong evidence the average exposure to respirable dust is significantly higher for the drill and blast workers than it is for the concrete workers. **d)** The sample sizes are so large that a little skewness will not affect the results of the two-sample comparison of means test.

7.70 We would need to know the standard deviation and sample size for each group. The 13.1 ounces and 19.9 ounces reported are just sample means, so a confidence interval would allow us to estimate the difference in the population means. The hypothesis test only tells us whether the difference in the population means is significant, but it doesn't estimate what that difference in the population means is.

7.71 **a)** No. If we use the 68-95-99.7% rule, then 68% of the younger kids would consume between -2.5 and 18.9 ounces of sweetened drinks every day. The same problem with negative consumption for the older kids (starting with 95%) as well.
b) $H_0 : \mu_{older} = \mu_{younger}$ and $H_a : \mu_{older} \neq \mu_{younger}$. t = 1.44, 0.2 < *P*-value < 0.3. Do not reject the null hypothesis. There is not enough evidence to say that there is a significant difference between the average consumption of sugary drinks between the older and younger groups of children. **c)** Using df = 4, t* = 2.776, (-5.85, 18.45). **d)** The sample sizes are very uneven and fairly small. The sample data are not Normally distributed either. The t procedures are not

particularly appropriate here. **e)** How were these children selected to participate? Were they chosen because they consume such large quantities of sweetened drinks?

7.72 **a)** The population means should be used when writing hypotheses, not the sample means. **b)** Two-sample comparison of means tests require two independent groups. The scores of the 10 boys could be compared to the scores of the 10 girls, but the scores of the 10 boys cannot be compared to the scores of the entire group of 20 children. **c)** A P-value of 0.96 is very large and indicates that the null hypothesis cannot be rejected.

7.73 **a)** Reject the null hypothesis because 0 is not inside the confidence interval. $H_0 : \mu_A = \mu_B$ can also be written as $H_0 : \mu_A - \mu_B = 0$. **b)** As sample size increases, the margin of error decreases.

7.74 **a)** $0.002 < P$-value < 0.005. Yes, the null hypothesis can be rejected at the 5% significance level. **b)** $(1 - 0.001) > P$-value $> (1 - 0.0025)$, which is $0.9975 < P$-value < 0.999. The negative test statistic indicates that the difference in means is not positive, and the P-value strongly confirms this. The null hypothesis cannot be rejected at the 5% significance level.

7.75 95% CI = (15.54, 24.46) using 40 degrees of freedom as the conservative estimate from the t-table. A 99% CI will be wider than a 95% CI because the t* value increases as the confidence level increases.

7.76 Yes, the data give good evidence that healthy firms have a higher ratio of assets to liabilities on the average. (t = 7.17, P-value < 0.0005.) The 99% confidence interval is 0.902 ± 0.346.

7.77 The 95% confidence interval for the difference in rent for one and two bedroom apartments is (-$0.66, $160.66) using software.

7.78 **a)** H_0: $\mu_2 - \mu_1 = 0$ H_a: $\mu_2 - \mu_1 > 0$. **b)** t = 2.084. Using Table D with 9 degrees of freedom, $0.025 < P$-value < 0.05. Using software with 17.941 degrees of freedom, P-value $= 0.026$. There is evidence that two-bedroom apartments rent for significantly more, on average, than one-bedroom apartments. The results are significant at the 0.05 level. **c)** No, this is a test of means, not single observations. **d)** The confidence interval is more useful because it shows the range of averages, which could be very helpful when comparison shopping or planning a budget. The 95% confidence interval actually shows that the difference of the averages could be negative.

7.79 **a)** H_0: $\mu_1 - \mu_2 = 0$ H_a: $\mu_1 - \mu_2 > 0$, t = 22.18, degrees of freedom are 1, $0.01 < P$-value < 0.02. Based on this small P-value, the conclusion is that the bread loses vitamin C after several days after baking. **b)** 26.93 ± 7.665 mg.

7.80 **a)** The individual observations are no longer independent. The observations are dependent on the loaf of bread. **b)** t = 49.81, $0.005 < P$-value < 0.01.

7.81 **a)** H_0: $\mu_1 - \mu_2 = 0$ H_a: $\mu_1 - \mu_2 > 0$, t = -0.32, degrees of freedom are 1, P-value > 0.25. There is no evidence that bread loses vitamin E several days after baking. **b)** -0.55 ± 10.73.

7.82 The confidence intervals show that the test results make sense.

7.83 **a)** The P-value for this test is really $1 - 0.07 / 2 = 0.965$. The test statistic indicates that the first mean is actually smaller than the second mean, which is the opposite of what we were testing.

The conclusion would be to not reject the null hypothesis. **b)** The *P*-value for this test is 0.035, and the conclusion would be to reject the null hypothesis. This *P*-value just represents the upper tail of the two-tailed test.

7.84   **a)**

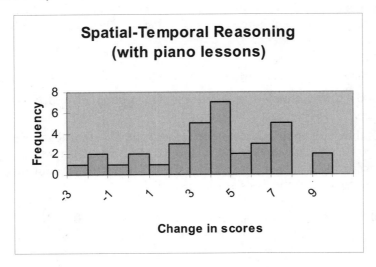

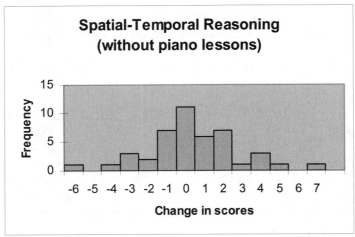

There is a wider range in score changes for the children who did not take piano lessons. It appears that the average change is close to 3 or 4 for those children with piano lessons and close to 0 for those children without piano lessons.

b)

	Piano lessons	No Piano Lessons
n	34	44
$\bar{x}$	3.617647	0.386364
s	3.055196	2.422913
se	0.523962	0.365268

c) H_0: $\mu_1 - \mu_2 = 0$, H_a: $\mu_1 - \mu_2 > 0$, t = 5.059, *P*-value < 0.0005. The sample data provides evidence that the children with piano lessons show an improvement in their scores of spatial-temporal reasoning.

7.85 3.232 ± 1.277.

7.86 Exercises 7.84 and 7.85 actually design an experiment with a control group to take out lurking variables due to time lapse between testing. This approach is preferable to the approach taken in Exercises 7.38 and 7.39.

7.87 **a)** H_0: $\mu_1 - \mu_2 = 0$ H_a: $\mu_1 - \mu_2 \neq 0$, $t = -8.238$, P-value < 0.0005. The conclusion is that there is a significant difference in mean ego strength between the low fitness and high fitness groups. **b)** This is an observational study, not a designed experiment. There may be several lurking variables. **c)** Again, the lurking variables may be the cause of ego strength. Middle-aged men who think highly of themselves may be more disciplined and have a strong physical regimen than men who do not think highly of themselves.

7.88 **a)** H_0: $\mu_1 - \mu_2 = 0$ H_a: $\mu_1 - \mu_2 > 0$, $t = 5.987$, P-value < 0.0005. Yes, this result is significant at the 1% level. **b)** The data is integer valued. The t procedure is robust because we assume that sample averages are close to a normal distribution with samples close to 15.

7.89 In this case, the observations would no longer be independent of each other. A matched pairs procedure would be used to compare individual differences in ego strength scores.

7.90 **a)** H_0: $\mu_1 - \mu_2 = 0$ H_a: $\mu_1 - \mu_2 < 0$, $t = -7.34$, P-value < 0.0005. There is significant evidence to indicate that the birth weights of babies whose mothers tested positive for cocaine use were lower than the group called "other." **b)** -385 grams ± 102.95 grams. **c)** The group "other" may have included babies whose mothers were also cocaine users. The confidence interval does not tell us much about the actual mean difference in birth weights.

7.91 **a)** $(-0.91, 6.91)$ using 50 df on Table D. **b)** It is possible that there was actually a drop in average sales between the last year and this year. The data describe a sample of stores, not all stores in the chain.

7.92 H_0: $\mu_A = \mu_B$ H_a: $\mu_A \neq \mu_B$, $t = 3.175$, $0.001 < P$-value < 0.002. The results show a significant difference in the plans. **b)** Large samples make the t procedure trustworthy.

7.93 **a)** See the stemplots below. The data are fairly Normally distributed for each group with no major skewness or outliers. The sample sizes are similar, too. The t procedures are appropriate. **b)** H_0: $\mu_W = \mu_M$ H_a: $\mu_W > \mu_M$, $t = 2.223$, P-value $= 0.0165$ using software. The data support the belief that men have a lower mean SSHA score than women. **c)** $(-35.981, -4.907)$ for $\mu_M - \mu_W$.

Women			Men		
Frequency	Stem &	Leaf	Frequency	Stem &	Leaf
10.00	1 .	0112222334	5.00	0 .	77899
7.00	1 .	5555667	11.00	1 .	11111122334
1.00	2 .	0	4.00	1 .	5688
Stem width:	100		Stem width:	100	

7.94   **a)** 917.23 ± 200.50. **b)** The sample sizes are large enough to make the procedure trustworthy. **c)** Yes, there is no reason to think there is bias based on an alphabetized list of names. **d)** It would be nice to know the response rate for this survey.

7.95   Verify.

7.96   The confidence interval is 1.2 ± 1.287. With this method, you cannot reject the null hypothesis that the mean satisfaction for the two types of monitors is the same versus the two-sided alternative because 0 is inside this confidence interval. (We could reject the null hypothesis in Exercise 7.58). The conclusions may be different depending on your choice of method.

7.97   **a)** $t = 12.71$. **b)** $t = 4.303$. **c)** With the pooled procedure, it is easier to see a significant result in sample data.

7.98   For part (a) the width is 30.86 and for part (b) the width is 10.448. The unpooled interval has a larger width than the pooled interval.

7.99   **a)** $F* = 2.20$. **b)** For a two-sided test, this value is significant at the 10% level but not at the 5% level.

7.100   **a)** $F* = 3.05$. Yes, this is significant at the 5% level. **b)** $0.02 < P\text{-value} < 0.05$.

7.101 $H_0: \sigma_1 = \sigma_2$ $H_a: \sigma_1 \neq \sigma_2$, $F = 1.59$. Using (30, 40) for the degrees of freedom, $1.54 < F*_{(33,43)} < 1.74$, $0.1 < P\text{-value} < 0.20$. The results indicate that the standard deviations are not equal.

7.102 $F = 1.65$, $P\text{-value} > 0.20$. If the populations are Normally distributed, the results of this sample give no indication that the standard deviations are not equal.

7.103   **a)** $F* = 647.79$. The power is extremely low for unequal variances. **b)** $F = 3.96$. Fail to reject the null hypothesis.

7.104   **a)** $F* = 647.79$. The power is extremely low for unequal variances. **b)** $F = 4.90$. Fail to reject the null hypothesis.

7.105   **a)** $H_0: \sigma_1 = \sigma_2$ $H_a: \sigma_1 > \sigma_2$. **b)** $F = 1.74$. **c)** $P\text{-value} > 0.10$ using $F (19, 15)$ on Table E. The results of this sample are not significant.

7.106   Using the Normal approximation to the noncentral t distribution gives the power of this test for a sample size of 100 to be 0.9452.

7.107 For n = 25, power = 0.4801. For n = 50, power = 0.7422. For n = 75, power = 0.879.

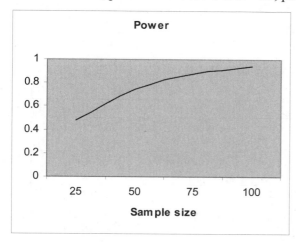

7.108 For n = 25, m = 369.4. For n = 50, m = 257.9. For n = 75, m = 210.6. For n = 100, m = 182.38.

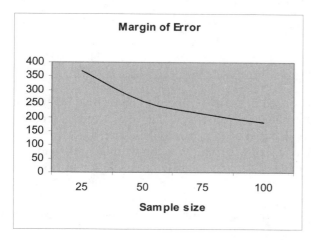

7.109 **a)** Power = 0.5948. **b)** Power = 0.7794.

7.110 $H_0 : \mu_B = \mu_S$ and $H_a : \mu_B > \mu_S$ for both competence and intelligence tests. For competence, t = 4.076, and 0.0005 < P-value < 0.001. For intelligence, t = 2.372, and 0.01 < P-value < 0.02. For both competence and intelligence, if a significance level of 0.05 is used, there evidence that the average ratings are significantly higher for the women who dressed business-like than for the women who dressed sexy. The evidence for this difference is stronger for competence than for intelligence. In order for these tests to have meaning, we have to assume fairly Normal distributions without skewness or outliers and that the ratings of the two groups are independent.

7.111 There is a significant difference between the high- and low-performing restaurants with regard to food serving in promised time, staff being well-dressed, serving ordered food accurately, and employees knowing the menu. There is not a significant difference in the other qualities. We need to assume fairly Normally distributed data without outliers and that a simple random sample was taken from each group.

Perceived quality	$\overline{x}_H - \overline{x}_L$	$\sqrt{\dfrac{s_H{}^2}{170} + \dfrac{s_L{}^2}{224}}$	t	*P*-value	Conclusion
Food served in promised time	0.45	0.139	3.24	Between 0.001 and 0.002	Reject H_0
Quickly corrects mistakes	0.16	0.125	1.28	Between 0.2 and 0.3	Do not reject H_0
Well-dressed staff	0.39	0.136	2.87	≈ 0.005	Reject H_0
Attractive menu	0.21	0.143	1.47	Between 0.1 and 0.2	Do not reject H_0
Serving accurately	0.37	0.123	3.01	Between 0.002 and 0.005	Reject H_0
Well-trained personnel	0.06	0.125	0.48	> 0.5	Do not reject H_0
Clean dining area	0.08	0.127	0.630	> 0.5	Do not reject H_0
Employees adjust to needs	0.14	0.123	1.14	Between 0.2 and 0.3	Do not reject H_0
Employees know menu	0.29	0.119	2.44	Between 0.01 and 0.02	Reject H_0
Convenient hours	0.24	0.129	1.86	Between 0.05 and 0.1	Do not reject H_0

7.112 Answers will vary. **a)** Only one woman was used in the experiment. There could be qualities of this particular woman which would affect the subjects' responses. The age of the subjects (18 to 24) might play a role—if the woman in the video had been closer to their own age or much older, the results might have been different. Race could play a role. Was the woman in the video the same race as the students? Did the woman in the video have a different background from these students? You could write the conclusion in terms which mention the limitations of the study (e.g., the limited background of the subjects, only one woman was used in the video). The results would not necessarily apply in other situations. **b)** You could have more men and women in the videos. You could pick a broader group of subjects to do the rating.

7.113 **a)** Study was done in South Korea; results may not apply to other countries. Only selected QSRs were studied; results may not apply to other QSRs. Response rate is low (394/950); we would trust the results more if the rate were higher. The fact that no differences were found when the demographics of this study were compared with the demographics of similar studies suggests that we do not have a serious problem with bias based on these characteristics. **b)** Answers will vary.

7.114 **a)** The difference between the kill room and processing room CFUs is compared over four different days. Since two related measurements are compared repeatedly for each unit (the days), this is considered matched pairs. **b)** Kill room sample mean = 2138.50, and processing room sample mean = 314.00. The 90% confidence interval (from software) is (843.047, 2805.953).

7.115 $H_0 : \mu = 4.88$ and $H_a : \mu > 4.88$, t = 21.98, *P*-value is close to 0, so we can reject the null hypothesis. There is strong evidence that hotel managers have a significantly higher average masculinity score than the general male population.

7.116 $H_0 : \mu = 5.19$ and $H_a : \mu > 5.19$, t = 1.62, 0.05 < *P*-value < 0.10, so we cannot reject the null hypothesis. There is not enough evidence to say that hotel mangers have a significantly higher average femininity score than the general male population.

7.117 **a)** No outliers, slightly skewed right but fairly symmetric. See the stemplot below. **b)** (12.9998, 13.3077).

```
alcohol Stem-and-Leaf Plot

Frequency     Stem &  Leaf

    5.00      12 .  22234
   16.00      12 .  5556777888888899
   14.00      13 .  01111223344444
   10.00      13 .  5556677788
    3.00      14 .  113

Stem width:   1.00
Each leaf:    1 case(s)
```

7.118 This is a two-sample comparison of means situation. See the SPSS output below. If equal variances are not assumed, the 90% confidence interval for the summer – winter difference is (869.707, 2989.293). There is a significant difference between the average summer and winter CPUs at the 10% significance level.

Group Statistics

	season	N	Mean	Std. Deviation	Std. Error Mean
CFUs	summer	4	2138.50	906.429	453.215
	winter	4	209.00	136.575	68.287

Independent Samples Test

		Levene's Test for Equality of Variances		t-test for Equality of Means						90% Confidence Interval of the Difference	
		F	Sig.	t	df	Sig. (2-tailed)	Mean Difference	Std. Error Difference	Lower	Upper
CFUs	Equal variances assumed	9.801	.020	4.210	6	.006	1929.500	458.330	1038.882	2820.118
	Equal variances not assumed			4.210	3.136	.022	1929.500	458.330	869.707	2989.293

7.119 $\bar{x}_C = 48.9513$, $s_C = 0.21537$, $\bar{x}_R = 41.6488$, $s_R = 0.39219$. Side-by-side boxplot shows cotton much higher than ramie. $H_0 : \mu_C = \mu_R$ and $H_a : \mu_C > \mu_R$. t = 46.162, *P*-value is very close to 0 so reject the null hypothesis. There is strong evidence that cotton has a significantly higher mean lightness than ramie.

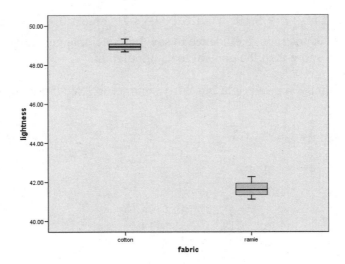

7.120 $H_0 : \mu_P = \mu_H$ and $H_a : \mu_P \neq \mu_H$, t = 3.331, *P*-value = 0.018 (if equal variances not assumed, see SPSS output below), reject the null hypothesis. There is good evidence that the two processes result in significantly different mean breaking strengths.

Independent Samples Test

		Levene's Test for Equality of Variances		t-test for Equality of Means						
		F	Sig.	t	df	Sig. (2-tailed)	Mean Difference	Std. Error Difference	95% Confidence Interval of the Difference	
									Lower	Upper
strength	Equal variances assumed	4.999	.056	3.331	8	.010	4.3400	1.3029	1.3355	7.3445
	Equal variances not assumed			3.331	5.476	.018	4.3400	1.3029	1.0765	7.6035

7.121   (1.0765, 7.6035) if equal variances not assumed; see SPSS output above.

7.122   See the SPSS output below for the two-sample comparison of means t test. Permafresh 55 is fabric #1, and Hylite LF is fabric #2. Hylite has the better wrinkle resistance. The difference is statistically significant with a very small *P*-value.

Group Statistics

	fabricNum	N	Mean	Std. Deviation	Std. Error Mean
wrinkle recovery angle	1	5	134.80	1.924	.860
	2	5	143.20	2.280	1.020

Independent Samples Test

		Levene's Test for Equality of Variances		t-test for Equality of Means					95% Confidence Interval of the Difference	
		F	Sig.	t	df	Sig. (2-tailed)	Mean Difference	Std. Error Difference	Lower	Upper
wrinkle recovery angle	Equal variances assumed	.385	.552	-6.296	8	.000	-8.400	1.334	-11.477	-5.323
	Equal variances not assumed			-6.296	7.779	.000	-8.400	1.334	-11.492	-5.308

7.123 2.555 ± 0.0623.

7.124 **Female Earnings**

```
   1 2
   1 455
   1 6667777777
   1 8888999999
   2 001
   2 2
   2 445
   2 66
   2 8
   3 1
```

Male Earnings

```
   1 5
   1 6666777
   1 88889999
   2 01
   2 2223
   2 4
   2 6
   2 89
   3 0
```

```
Two sample T for Female vs Male

            N      Mean     St Dev    SE Mean
Female     35     19789      4121        697
Male       27     20626      4196        808

95% CI for mu Female - mu Male: (-2974,  1300)
T-Test mu Female = mu Male (vs not =): T = -0.78   P = 0.44   DF = 55
```

These results do not indicate that there is a significant difference between the average male salary and the average female salary. Even if the findings were significant, it would not mean the difference is due to discrimination.

7.125 The 95% confidence interval on percentage of lower priced products at the alternate supplier is (64.55, 92.09). This suggests that more than half of the products at the alternate supplier are priced lower than the original supplier.

7.126   Testing the two-sided test that there is no difference between owners who did evacuate some pets and owners who did not evacuate pets results in a t = 3.65 and a *P*-value < 0.0005. This indicates there is a significant difference in average scores between the two groups.

7.127   **a)** This study used a matched pairs design therefore they used a single sample t test. **b)** The average weight loss in this program was significantly different from zero and we can conclude that the program is effective. **c)** The P-value is approximately equal to zero.

7.128 H_0: $\mu_1 = \mu_2$ H_a: $\mu_1 < \mu_2$, t = -0.76, 0.20 < *P*-value < 0.25. Conclude that there is no strong evidence to indicate that nitrites decrease amino acid uptake.

7.129   **a)** H_0: $\mu_1 = \mu_2$ H_a: $\mu_1 < \mu_2$, t = −8.954, *P*-value ≈ 0. Conclude that the workers were faster than the students. **b)** The t procedures are robust for large sample sizes even when the distributions are slightly skewed. **c)** The middle 95% of scores would be from 29.66 to 44.98. **d)** The scores for the first minute are clearly much lower than the scores for the 15th minute.

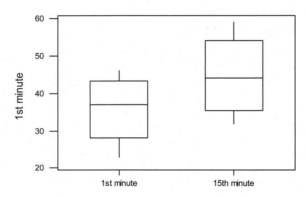

7.130   **a)** "se" stands for standard error.

$\bar{x}$	Drivers	Conductors
Total calories	2821	2844
Alcohol	0.24	0.39

s	Drivers	Conductors
Total calories	435.6	437.3
Alcohol	0.594	1.002

b) t = −0.35, P-value = 0.3636. There is no evidence that conductors consume more calories than drivers. **c)** t = −1.197, *P*-value = 0.1174. This is not strong evidence that conductors use more alcohol than drivers.

7.131   **a)** (0.207, 0.573). **b)** (-0.312, 0.012).

7.132   Since the sample standard deviations are close in value, using the pooled two-sample t test is justified. The t value is -0.35, which is the same as the value in 7.103.

7.133   **a)** No, the t test is robust to skewness. **b)** Yes, the F test is not robust to skewness.

7.134   It is not proper to apply the one-sample t method to this data set. The data describe a population, not a sample.

7.135   **a)** The coding for sex is 1 = men, 2 = women.

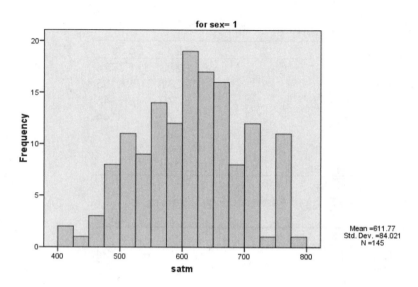

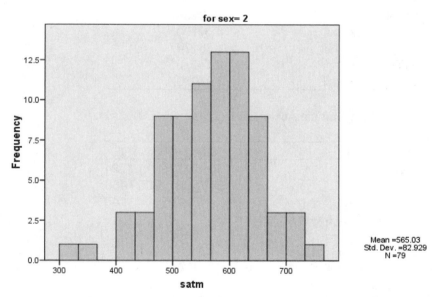

The tables below give the Excel output for the F test used to compare variances, the two-sample t test assuming equal variances and assuming unequal variances. The F test result shows that there is no reason to believe the variances of the two sexes are unequal. Results of the t tests show that there is a significant difference in the average SATM scores between the two sexes. The *P*-values were both approximately zero.

Sex2 avg SATM	Sex1 avg SATM
565.0253165	611.7724
82.92937599	84.02056

F-Test Two-Sample for Variances

	Sex 2	*Sex 1*
Mean	565.0253	611.7724
Variance	6877.281	7059.455
Observations	79	145
df	78	144
F	0.974194	
P(F<=f) one-tail	0.455695	
F Critical one-tail	0.713212	

t-Test: Two-Sample Assuming Equal Variances

	Sex 2	*Sex 1*
Mean	565.0253	611.7724
Variance	6877.281	7059.455
Observations	79	145
Pooled Variance	6995.448	
Hypothesized Mean Difference	0	
df	222	
t Stat	-3.99687	
P(T<=t) one-tail	4.37E-05	
t Critical one-tail	1.651747	
P(T<=t) two-tail	8.74E-05	
t Critical two-tail	1.970707	

t-Test: Two-Sample Assuming Unequal Variances

	Sex 2	*Sex 1*
Mean	565.0253	611.7724
Variance	6877.281	7059.455
Observations	79	145
Hypothesized Mean Difference	0	
df	162	
t Stat	-4.01237	
P(T<=t) one-tail	4.58E-05	
t Critical one-tail	1.654314	
P(T<=t) two-tail	9.16E-05	
t Critical two-tail	1.974718	

7.136

Difference in means	Power
0.5	0.339
0.75	0.746
1	0.959
1.25	0.997

Note that, as the difference in means increases, the power increases.

7.137 As the degrees of freedom increase for small values of n, the value of t rapidly approaches the Z-score. As sample sizes get larger, the t values are close to $Z = 1.96$ but never become greater than 1.96.

7.138 The margin of error is a function of the sample size. Graphing the margin of error as a function of n, shows that the margin of error decreases quite rapidly for smaller values of n, and then the decrease becomes less pronounced.

Case Study 7.1

	Mean	St. dev.	95% CI	5 # summary
1998 billings	3.688	2.8295	(2.520, 4.856)	1.3, 1.65, 2.2, 5.2, 11.5
1997 billings	3.088	2.0547	(2.240, 3.936)	0.7, 1.45, 2.4, 4.15, 8.8
Architects	10.04	8.677	(6.46, 13.62)	2, 4, 5, 15.5, 31
Engineers	7.08	9.622	(3.11, 11.05)	0, 0, 2, 12.5, 35
Staff	60.60	44.706	(42.15, 79.05)	7, 16, 61, 103, 155

Group Statistics

	Old = Pre1970, New = 1970 or later	N	Mean	Std. Deviation	Std. Error Mean
Bill98	new	14	3.907	3.1745	.8484
	old	11	3.409	2.4415	.7361
Bill97	new	14	3.086	2.0512	.5482
	old	11	3.091	2.1594	.6511
Architects	new	14	10.57	8.838	2.362
	old	11	9.36	8.846	2.667
Engineers	new	14	3.07	5.567	1.488
	old	11	12.18	11.435	3.448
Staff	new	14	44.71	43.563	11.643
	old	11	80.82	39.074	11.781

Since the pooled procedures require that the two populations have equal variances, this is probably a safe assumption for Bill98, Bill97, and Architects, but not for Engineers and Staff, based on the differences in the standard deviations in the samples for these variables. We also need to assume that the "new" and "old" groups are independent. (For example, none of the "new" firms are branches of the "old" firms.)

The results of the two-sample comparison of means tests (new – old) from SPSS follow. There is a significant difference for Engineers and Staff for old vs. new companies, but not for any of the other variables.

Note that for Bill97, Bill98, and Architects, Firm #8 (Gibralt) is a high outlier for the old firms. Also note that for Engineers and Staff, Firm #15 (Plus4) is a high outlier for the new firms. Many of these boxplots show either skewness or outliers, and for groups with such small sample sizes (11 for the old firms, 14 for the new firms), that is a problem. The t procedures are not necessarily appropriate here.

Independent Samples Test

		Levene's Test for Equality of Variances		t-test for Equality of Means					95% Confidence Interval of the Difference	
		F	Sig.	t	df	Sig. (2-tailed)	Mean Difference	Std. Error Difference	Lower	Upper
Bill98	Equal variances assumed	1.158	.293	.429	23	.672	.4981	1.1599	-1.9014	2.8975
	Equal variances not assumed			.443	22.997	.662	.4981	1.1233	-1.8256	2.8217
Bill97	Equal variances assumed	.472	.499	-.006	23	.995	-.0052	.8457	-1.7546	1.7442
	Equal variances not assumed			-.006	21.062	.995	-.0052	.8511	-1.7749	1.7645
Architects	Equal variances assumed	.175	.680	.339	23	.738	1.208	3.562	-6.162	8.577
	Equal variances not assumed			.339	21.611	.738	1.208	3.563	-6.189	8.604
Engineers	Equal variances assumed	5.102	.034	-2.622	23	.015	-9.110	3.475	-16.298	-1.922
	Equal variances not assumed			-2.426	13.706	.030	-9.110	3.755	-17.181	-1.040
Staff	Equal variances assumed	.046	.833	-2.150	23	.042	-36.104	16.790	-70.836	-1.372
	Equal variances not assumed			-2.180	22.536	.040	-36.104	16.564	-70.407	-1.801

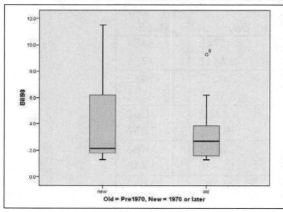

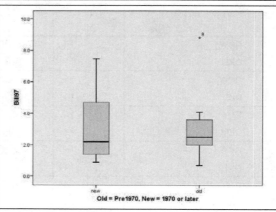

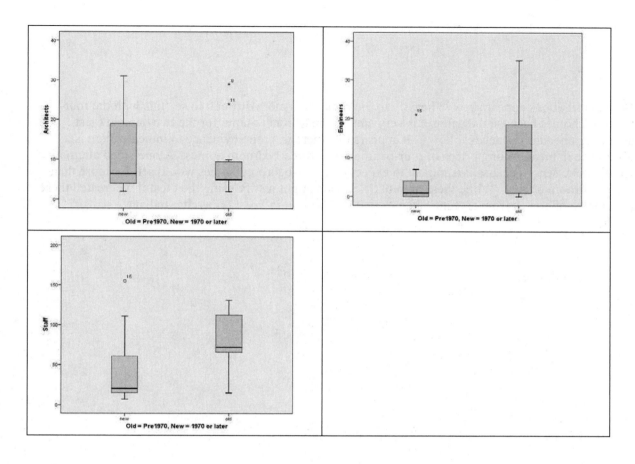

Case Study 7.2

```
Stem-and-leaf of 4 BR      N = 9
Leaf Unit = 10000


        1  23
        1  55
        1  7
        1
        2
        2  23
        2  4
        2
        2  9


Stem-and-leaf of 3 BR      N = 28
Leaf Unit = 10000


        0  6777
        0  8899
        1  01111
        1  22222223
        1  445
        1
        1  9
```

```
2 0
2
2 5
2 6
```

Both distributions appear skewed heavily to the right. It is more difficult to see this with the four-bedroom homes because the data set is very small. The Minitab output for the two-sample t test assuming unequal variances follows. It appears that there is strong evidence to indicate there is a difference in mean selling prices of four-bedroom and three-bedroom homes. A one-sided alternative would make sense because it is logical to expect that four-bedroom homes would sell for more than three-bedroom homes. While these are not SRSs, one might justify using the t test if we treated these as samples of homes from all future homes that will be sold in West Lafayette, Indiana.

```
Two sample T for 4 BR vs 3 BR

          N      Mean      St Dev    SE Mean
4 BR      9     194944     57204      19068
3 BR     28     129546     49336       9324

95% CI for mu 4 BR - mu 3 BR: (19152, 111644)
T-Test mu 4 BR = mu 3 BR (vs not =): T = 3.08   P = 0.0095   DF = 12
```

Chapter 8: Inference for Proportions

Note: Some of the calculations in this chapter were done on Minitab. You may see small differences in numerical values if you use a different software package. The conclusions, however, should all be consistent. The Wilson estimate was used for confidence intervals only when the exercise specifically asked for it.

8.1   (0.21, 0.47).

8.2   (0.566, 0.634).

8.3   (0.22, 0.48). This plus four interval is shifted slightly to the right of the original interval of (0.21, 0.47).

8.4   **a)** $\hat{p} = 0.778$. **b)** $m = 0.272$. **c)** No, this result applies only to this salesperson and her customer base.

8.5   Smaller samples sizes will make a bigger difference when the sample proportion is close to 0. An example would be 1/100.

8.6   **a)** H_0: $p = 0.2$ H_a: $p > 0.2$. Use a one-sided alternative because we will decide to go with the upgrade only if more than 20% agree to the additional cost. **b)** $Z = 2.47$. P-value = 0.0068. **c)** Yes, the sample does give strong evidence to conclude that more than 20% are willing to pay for the upgrade.

8.7   **a)** (0.23, 0.41). This interval could be found from the interval on proportion of employees who would answer "yes" by subtracting the interval endpoints from 1. This is because P (an employee says "yes") = $1 - $ P (an employee says "No"). Also, the standard errors are the same for each proportion, which results in the same interval widths. **b)** H_0: $p = 0.25$ H_a: $p \neq 0.25$. $z = 1.62$. Fail to reject H_0. The reasoning is the same as in part (a).

8.8   Need to sample at least 151.

8.9   Need to sample at least 601 people if a p* of 0.5 is used.

8.10   **a)** The confidence level cannot be above 100%. **b)**   No, the confidence interval takes into account only random sampling error. **c)** No, the P-value is the probability, calculated assuming the null hypothesis is true, that we would get results as unusual as (or more unusual than) our sample results simply due to random variation.

8.11   **a)** $\hat{p} \pm z^* SE_{\hat{p}}$ (forgot the z*). **b)** Hypotheses need population parameters, not the sample statistics. $H_0 : p = 0.3$ is appropriate. **c)** The Z test statistic should be used, not t, for population proportion significance tests.

8.12   **a)** $\mu_{\hat{p}} = 0.4$, $\sigma_{\hat{p}} = 0.0632$. **b)** See the sketch below. **c)** Using the 68-95-99.7% rule, the middle 95% of the distribution will be within 2 standard deviations of the mean, or between $\mu_{\hat{p}} \pm 0.1264$. See the sketch below.

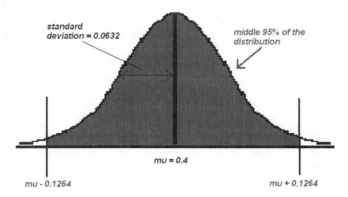

8.13   **a)** 0.634 ± 0.0126. If we were to repeat our sampling many times and compute a confidence interval from each sample, over the long run, approximately 95% of these intervals would contain the population proportion. **b)** No, a high nonresponse rate would skew the results. Those most likely not to reply are the cheaters.

8.14   **a)** 0.417 ± 0.0164. **b)** The margin of error depends on the confidence level (the same for 8.13 as in 8.14), the proportion of successes (not the same for males and females in these stories), and the sample size (not the same for these stories).

8.15   **a)** m = 0.00132. **b)** Students most likely not to respond are the cheaters, and a 15% response rate is very low. What about the schools that can't afford the fee? Just because the sample size is large doesn't mean that good data was collected. The response rate and other issues may be larger sources of error here than pure statistical variation quantified by the margin of error.

8.16   See the table below for the confidence intervals for each rat. The number of successes and the number of failures both need to be above 10 for the large-sample estimates to be valid. The number of failures for each of these cases is less than 10. Since the sample size is at least 5, the plus four estimate is appropriate in this case.

Rat	# of successes, X	# of failures, $80 - X$	$\hat{p} = \dfrac{X}{n}$	$\tilde{p} = \dfrac{X+2}{n+4}$
1, 2, 4, 6	80	0	$\dfrac{80}{80} = 1$	$\dfrac{82}{84} = 0.9762$
3	73	7	$\dfrac{73}{80} = 0.9125$	$\dfrac{75}{84} = 0.8929$
5	74	6	$\dfrac{74}{80} = 0.9250$	$\dfrac{76}{84} = 0.9048$

8.17   **a)** $(0.300, 0.354)$. **b)** $(0.301, 0.355)$. The methods have the same margin of error = 0.027, but the plus four method shifts the interval slightly higher. **c)** Nonresponse rate is only 3.64%, which is small, so we can trust these results. **d)** Yes, the person delivering the sermon probably thinks the sermon is shorter than it actually is, and the congregation would probably think the sermons are longer than they actually are.

8.18 **a)** (0.566, 0.622). **b)** (0.565, 0.621). **c)** Same as in previous exercise. **d)** Theological orientation is a very subjective measure. "More conservative" than what? A congregation leader may have a different view of the orientation than a typical congregation member or an outsider might have. It might be more helpful to ask a series of questions on particular social and religious topics to these leaders, and then the researcher could assign a theoretical orientation score to each congregation based on how these questions are answered.

8.19 (0.324, 0.376).

8.20 (0.160, 0.206).

8.21 99% confidence interval is wider because the z* is bigger. (0.316, 0.384).

8.22 The 90% confidence interval is narrower because the z* is smaller. (0.163, 0.203).

8.23 (0.635, 0.745).

8.24 (0.524, 0.642).

8.25 (0.218, 0.251)

8.26 **a)** (0.547, 0.585). **b)** Income is a very personal quality. People are more likely to imply that they make more money than they actually do if they are going to lie about their income in order to not be embarrassed. Therefore the sample proportion is probably lower than 0.566, and the true population proportion could be lower than the confidence interval predicts. **c)** Pet ownership is a much less embarrassing question than income, so the response bias is probably less for the pet ownership question than for the income question.

8.27 **a)** (0.359, 0.401). **b)** Teens 16 to 19 years old may have jobs, 18- and 19-year olds may be living on their own. It would make more sense to group the teens as 12- to15-year olds, 16- to17-year olds, and 18- to 19-year olds.

8.28 **a)** $\hat{p} = 0.179$, SE = 0.0418. **b)** (0.097, 0.261).

8.29 No, it is possible an applicant attended college but did not graduate. Therefore it may be possible that some applicants lied about which major they studied in college and having graduated.

8.30 **a)** $\hat{p} = 0.842$. **b)** 0.0163. **c)** (0.810, 0.874).

8.31 (0.768, 0.912).

8.32 (0.146, 0.234).

8.33 (0.642, 0.768).

8.34 (0.186, 0.202).

8.35   **a)** $\hat{p} = 0.317$, $SE_{\hat{p}} = 0.0112$. **b)** (0.295, 0.339). **c)** No, these data do not explain cause-and-effect relationships.

8.36   (0.206, 0.246).

8.37   **a)** No, we do not have 10 or more observations of successes and failures. **b)** Yes. **c)** Yes. **d)** Yes.

8.38 H_0: $p = 0.36$ H_a: $p \neq 0.36$. $Z = 0.9317$. *P*-value = 0.3524. There is no evidence to believe the sample does not represent the population with respect to rural versus urban residence.

8.39   **a)** H_0: $p = 0.64$ H_a: $p \neq 0.64$. **b)** $Z = -0.9317$. *P*-value = 0.3524. **c)** The results are the same as in the previous exercise. Fail to reject H_0.

8.40   Need at least 764 in the sample.

8.41   (0.106, 0.294).

8.42 H_0: $p = 0.48$ H_a: $p \neq 0.48$. $Z = -1.79$. *P*-value = 0.0734. The results are significant at the 10% level but not at the 5% level.

8.43   **a)** H_0: $p = 0.5$ H_a: $p \neq 0.5$. $Z = 1.34$. *P*-value = 0.1802. There is no significant evidence that Kerrich's coin does not have probability 0.5 of coming up heads. **b)** (0.4969, 0.5165).

8.44   **a)** H_0: $p = 0.5$, H_a: $p > 0.5$. $Z = 1.58$. *P*-value = 0.0571. No, there is not enough evidence to say that the majority of people prefer fresh-brewed coffee. **b)** (0.496, 0.704).

8.45   Need at least 451 in the sample.

8.46   **a)** Higher. **b)** Higher. **c)** Lower. **d)** No influence on sample size.

8.47   Need at least 201 in the sample, $m = 0.0691$.

8.48   Need at least 2655 in the sample, $m = 0.0179$.

8.49   See the table below.

$\hat{p}$	m
0.1	0.0537
0.2	0.0716
0.3	0.0820
0.4	0.0877
0.5	0.0895
0.6	0.0877
0.7	0.0820
0.8	0.0716
0.9	0.0537

8.50   If the survey uses a sample size of 500 rather than 120, the margin of error will be reduced by almost half. This will give a much better estimate for the true proportion of students who support an increase in fees.

8.51 **a)** $\mu_{\hat{p}_1} = p_1, \mu_{\hat{p}_2} = p_2, \sigma_{\hat{p}_1} = \dfrac{p_1(1-p_1)}{n_1}, \sigma_{\hat{p}_2} = \dfrac{p_2(1-p_2)}{n_2}$. **b)** $\mu_D = \mu_{\hat{p}_1} - \mu_{\hat{p}_2}$.

    c) $\sigma_D^2 = \dfrac{p_1(1-p_1)}{n_1} + \dfrac{p_2(1-p_2)}{n_2}$.

8.52 $(0.025, 0.263)$.

8.53 $(0.0301, 0.0788)$.

8.54 The plus four method gives a 95% confidence interval of $0.104 \pm 0.061 = (0.043, 0.165)$. This is very similar to the Z confidence interval given in the example: $0.105 \pm 0.060 = (0.045, 0.165)$.

8.55 Plus four interval: $0.071 \pm 0.196 = (-0.125, 0.267)$, Z interval: $0.080 \pm 0.192 = (-0.112, 0.272)$. The plus four interval has a slightly lower sample proportion and a slightly larger margin of error.

8.56 H_0: $p_1 = p_2$ H_a: $p_1 \neq p_2$. $Z = 1.83$. *P*-value $= .0672$. The results of this study are significant at the 10% level but not at the 5% level. At the 10% significance level, this study gives evidence different types of companies offer different types of benefits.

8.57 H_0: $p_1 = p_2$ H_a: $p_1 > p_2$. $z = 4.46$. *P*-value ≈ 0. Yes, it appears that more customers who complain leave the HMO.

8.58 **a)** The hypotheses need to use the population proportions, not sample proportions. **b)** This is true only if the sample sizes are true for the two groups. **c)** No, the confidence interval only represents random variation from sampling, not sampling errors such as nonresponse, undercoverage, or response bias.

8.59 **a)** $\mu_{\hat{p}_1-\hat{p}_2} = -0.1$ and $\sigma_{\hat{p}_1-\hat{p}_2} = 0.0947$. **b)** See the sketch below. **c)** Using the 68-95-99.7% rule tells us that this range is $\mu \pm 2\sigma = -0.1 \pm 0.189 = (-0.289, 0.089)$. See the sketch below.

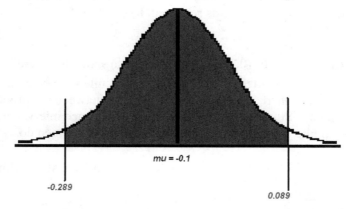

mu = -0.1

-0.289   0.089

8.60 **a)** $\hat{p}_F \sim N(0.83, 0.0188)$, $\hat{p}_M \sim N(0.85, 0.0179)$. **b)** $(\hat{p}_M - \hat{p}_F) \sim N(0.02, 0.0259)$.

8.61 **a)** $H_0 : p_{\text{Impulse}} = p_{\text{Planned}}$ and $H_a : p_{\text{Impulse}} \neq p_{\text{Planned}}$, $Z = -1.02$, *P*-value $= 0.3078$. Do not reject the null hypothesis. There is not enough evidence to say the difference in credit card use between impulse and planned purchases is statistically significant. **b)** $0.111 \pm 0.211 = (-0.100, 0.322)$.

8.62 $H_0 : p_1 = p_2$ $H_a : p_1 < p_2$, z = -1.24, *P*-value = 0.1075. No, there is not enough evidence to say that current users of the standard detergent are less likely than nonusers to prefer the new detergent.

8.63 $H_0 : p_S = p_H$ and $H_a : p_S \neq p_H$, Z = 1.14, *P*-value = 0.2542. Do not reject the null hypothesis. There is not enough evidence to say that the detergent preferences are significantly different for people with hard water and people with soft water.

8.64 H_0: $p_1 = p_2$ H_a: $p_1 > p_2$. Z = 1.82. *P*-value = 0.0344. Yes, the proportion of birth defects observed during the period of time that residents drank from the contaminated well is higher than the proportion after. We need to assume that the observations are independent and represent an SRS.

8.65   **a)** $\hat{p}_1 = 0.511, \hat{p}_2 = 0.408$. **b)** $SE_D = 0.0294$. **c)** (0.0273, 0.1787).

8.66   **a)** H_0: $p_1 = p_2$ H_a: $p_1 \neq p_2$. **b)** $\hat{p} = 0.454$. **c)** $SE_D = 0.0295$. **d)** Z = 3.47, *P*-value = 0.0006. Yes, it appears that Tippecanoe County has a different proportion of producers in favor of the check-off program than Benton County.

8.67   **a)** H_0: $p_1 = p_2$ H_a: $p_1 \neq p_2$. **b)** Z = 1.22, *P*-value = 0.2224. There is no evidence to suggest that there is a difference in tree preference between rural and urban populations. **c)** (-0.0209, 0.1389).

8.68   **a)** H_0: $p_1 = p_2$ H_a: $p_1 \neq p_2$, Z = 2.62, *P*-value = 0.0088. These data provide evidence that the proportion of men college students employed during the summer is different than women college students employed during the summer. **b)** (0.0105, 0.0735). The lower end of this confidence interval for the difference does not seem very large, but the upper end of 7% can translate into hundreds of unemployed women from a large campus. Notice that the difference of 0 is not included in the confidence interval.

8.69   **a)** H_0: $p_1 = p_2$ H_a: $p_1 \neq p_2$, Z = 5.33, P-value ≈ 0. There is a statistically significant difference in the proportion of the two types of shields removed. **b)** (0.2125, 0.4115). I would recommend the new tractors have a flip-up shield.

8.70   **a)** $\hat{p}_F = 0.800, \hat{p}_M = 0.394$. **b)** (0.275, 0.537). The data show that there is gender bias in the text because women are more often referred to with a juvenile reference. Zero is not included in the confidence interval, so there is a significant difference between the proportions of female and male juvenile references. Since both endpoints of the confidence interval are positive, women have a significantly higher proportion of juvenile references than men do.

8.71   **a)** $\hat{p}_F = 0.141, \hat{p}_M = 0.339$. (0.1432, 0.2528). **b)** The quantity that contributes the most to the standard error is $\dfrac{\hat{p}_F(1 - \hat{p}_F)}{n_F}$ because n_F is a smaller sample size.

8.72 H_0: $p_1 = p_2$ H_a: $p_1 \neq p_2$, z = 5.22, *P*-value = 0. Based on this *P*-value there is gender bias.

8.73 H_0: $p_1 = p_2$ H_a: $p_1 > p_2$, z = 5.53, *P*-value = 0. Yes, the gender bias is significant.

8.74   (−0.131, 0.093). It does not appear that the proportion of applicants lying is changing over time because 0 is included in the confidence interval.

8.75 $H_0: p_1 = p_2$ $H_a: p_1 \neq p_2$, Z = -0.34, P-value = 0.733. The results do not give strong evidence that applicants are lying in different proportion than they did 6 months ago.

8.76   **a)** $\hat{p}_1 = 0.8$, $\hat{p}_2 = 0.557$, where population 1 represents the patients who took aspirin. **b)** Using the plus four method, (0.1027, 0.3833). **c)** $H_0: p_1 = p_2$ $H_a: p_1 > p_2$, Z = 3.34, P-value = 0. The proportion of patients with favorable outcomes out of those who took aspirin is significantly greater than the proportion of patients with favorable outcomes who did not take aspirin.

8.77 $H_0: p_1 = p_2$ $H_a: p_1 < p_2$, where p_1 represents the proportion of men without the abnormal chromosome who had criminal records. Z = -3.48, P-value = 0.001. The data supports the belief that abnormality in chromosomes is associated with increased criminality.

8.78   **a)** Z = 1.62, P-value = 0.106. Based on this P-value, it does not suggest that male college students are employed at a higher rate than female college students. **b)** Sample size plays a role in the significance of data. The larger the sample size, the more significant the results can be.

8.79   **a)** (-0.038, 0.482). **b)** $H_0 : p_g = p_{pl}$ $H_a : p_g < p_{pl}$, z = -1.37, P-value = 0.0853. We could conclude that there is strong evidence that the proportion of cockroaches that will die on glass is less than the proportion that will die on plasterboard at the 10% significance level (but not at the 5% level).

8.80   **a)** Using the hypotheses from part (b) above, z = -1.93, P-value = 0.0268. We could conclude that there is reasonably strong evidence that the proportion of cockroaches that will die on glass is less than the proportion that will die on plasterboard. The conclusion is the same as in the previous exercise with smaller sample sizes, but the evidence is stronger for rejecting the null hypothesis with the larger sample sizes.

8.81 $H_0 : p_1 = p_2$, $H_a : p_1 \neq p_2$, Z = 14.8, P-value is approximately 0, so reject the null hypothesis. There is evidence of a significant difference between the proportion of male athletes who admit to cheating and the proportion of female athletes who admit to cheating. The 95% confidence interval (male − female) is (0.1963, 0.2377). Someone who gambles will be less likely to respond to the survey. Do you think men or women are more likely to report that they do not gamble when, in fact, they do gamble?

8.82.1   **a)** $\hat{p}_{congested} = 0.060$, $\hat{p}_{bypass} = 0.212$. **b)** (bypass − congested) difference = 0.152, SE_D = 0.0348. **c)** A two-sided alternative hypothesis would be appropriate because it was not specifically stated what type of difference is expected between the two groups. However, a one-sided alternative hypothesis would also be reasonable because it is common sense that the researchers expected a larger proportion of residents to report improvement in the bypass area. **d)** Z = 4.85. The P-value is close to 0 with either the one- or two-sided hypothesis test, so the null hypothesis would be rejected. See the sketches that follow.

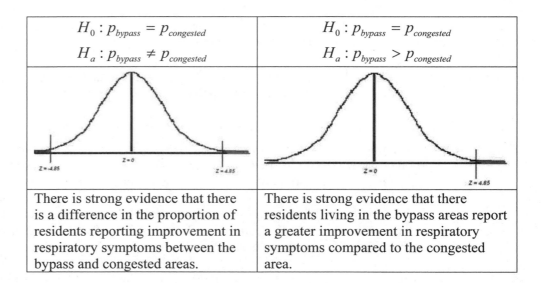

$H_0 : p_{bypass} = p_{congested}$	$H_0 : p_{bypass} = p_{congested}$
$H_a : p_{bypass} \neq p_{congested}$	$H_a : p_{bypass} > p_{congested}$
There is strong evidence that there is a difference in the proportion of residents reporting improvement in respiratory symptoms between the bypass and congested areas.	There is strong evidence that there residents living in the bypass areas report a greater improvement in respiratory symptoms compared to the congested area.

8.83   **a)** and **b)**

Category	$\hat{p}$ (in %)	n	m (in %)
Download less	38	247	3.09
Peer-to-peer	33.3	247	3.00
E-mail and IM	24	247	2.72
Web sites	20	247	2.55
iTunes	17	247	2.39
Overall use of new services	7	1371	0.69
Overall use paid services	3	1371	0.46

c) Argument for (A): Readers should understand that the population percent is not guaranteed to be at the sample percent, there is variability involved in taking a sample. Argument for (B): Listing each individual margin of error does seem excessive, so you could summarize by saying that the margin of error was no greater than 3.09% for each of these questions. You could also separate out the last 2 questions by saying their margin of error was less than 1%.

8.84   Since these measurements represent the improvement over time of particular symptoms, perhaps not all the people from a group had all of the symptoms to begin with. The larger sample sizes will produce smaller margins of error for the confidence intervals and perhaps smaller P-values in significance tests; however, the sample sizes are still fairly close and probably will not have a large impact on the results. The difference in sample sizes between the bypass and congested groups are much larger than the differences within the bypass or within the congested groups. **b)** See the table below. **c)** A two-sided alternative hypothesis would be appropriate because it was not specifically stated what type of difference is expected between the two groups. However, a one-sided alternative hypothesis would also be reasonable because it is common sense that the researchers expected a larger proportion of residents to report improvement in the bypass area. The results below will be based on a two-sided alternative hypothesis for each test. **d)** Only "wheezing disturbs sleep" shows a significant difference between the proportion of bypass and proportion of congested area residents reporting improvement. Only this confidence interval for the difference does not include 0, which would represent "no difference."

Symptom	$\hat{p}_{bypass}$	$\hat{p}_{congested}$	$\hat{p}_{bypass} - \hat{p}_{congested}$	95% CI	Conclusion to two-sided test
Wheezing disturbs sleep	0.160	0.073	0.087	(0.029, 0.145)	Reject null
# wheezing attacks	0.160	0.129	0.031	(-0.036, 0.098)	Do not reject null
Wheezing limits speech	0.043	0.024	0.019	(-0.014, 0.052)	Do not reject null
Wheezing affects activities	0.093	0.079	0.014	(-0.039, 0.067)	Do not reject null
Consulted doctor	0.117	0.129	-0.012	(-0.080, 0.056)	Do not reject null
Winter phlegm	0.047	0.069	-0.022	(-0.071, 0.027)	Do not reject null
Winter cough	0.057	0.090	-0.033	(-0.086, 0.020)	Do not reject null

e) See the table below for the bypass group. Every symptom for the bypass group showed a difference (actually all positive differences) in the improvement of symptoms. Someone looking only at the table below would conclude that putting in the bypass was an excellent idea that made a big difference to respiratory symptoms for the residents in that area. However, when comparing the bypass group to the congested area group in the table above, which could be considered a control group, we found only a significant difference between the groups for "wheezing disturbs sleep."

Symptom	$\hat{p}_{bypass}$	95% CI	Conclusion to test $H_a : p_{bypass} \neq 0$
# wheezing attacks	0.160	(0.117, 0.203)	Reject null
Wheezing disturbs sleep	0.160	(0.117, 0.203)	Reject null
Consulted doctor	0.117	(0.077, 0.157)	Reject null
Wheezing affects activities	0.093	(0.059, 0.127)	Reject null
Winter cough	0.057	(0.029, 0.085)	Reject null
Winter phlegm	0.047	(0.021, 0.073)	Reject null
Wheezing limits speech	0.043	(0.019, 0.067)	Reject null

8.85 **a)** $H_0 : p_1 = p_2$, $H_a : p_1 \neq p_2$, $Z = 6.97$ with a *P*-value near 0, so reject the null hypothesis. There is strong evidence that the users and nonusers differ significantly in the proportion of college graduates. **b)** 95% CI (users – nonusers) = (0.1141, 0.2019)

8.86 CI for internet users – nonusers income < \$50,000: (-0.168, -0.080). CI for internet users – nonusers income ≥ \$50,000: (0.059, 0.139). Using the confidence intervals to do the two-sided hypothesis test, there is a significance difference between internet users and nonusers for both the income < \$50,000 and income ≥ \$50,000 questions.

8.87

	Users (total number)	Nonusers (total number)
Analysis of education	1132	852
Analysis of income	871	677

For users, the proportion of "rather not say" is 0.231. For nonusers, the proportion of "rather not say" is 0.205. $H_0 : p_1 = p_2$, $H_a : p_1 \neq p_2$, $Z = 1.38$, *P*-value = 0.1676, so do not reject the null hypothesis. There is not much evidence of a significant difference in the proportion of "rather not say" answers between users and nonusers. The 95% CI (users – nonusers) is (-0.0106, 0.0626). Since the nonresponse rate is not significantly different for the two groups, it is not a serious limitation for this study.

8.88   **a)** 32 orders were completed in 5 days or less before the changes. The confidence interval is (0.109, 0.211). **b)** 180 orders were completed in 5 days or less after the changes. The confidence interval is (0.858, 0.942). **c)** (0.674, 0.806) (67.4%, 80.6%).

8.89   **a)** $\hat{p}_{repeat} = 0.783$, $\hat{p}_{norepeat} = 0.517$, 95% CI (repeat – no repeat) is (0.102, 0.430).

   b) $H_0 : p_1 = p_2$, $H_a : p_1 \neq p_2$, Z = 3.05, P-value = 0.0022, so reject the null hypothesis. There is strong evidence of a significant difference in the proportion of tips received between servers who repeat the customer's order and those who do not repeat the order. **c)** Cultural differences, personalities of the servers, gender differences could all play a role in interpreting these results. Did one server only do the repeating while the other server did no repeating, or did they switch off? **d)** Answers will vary.

8.90   **a)** Diehard: 121, Less loyal: 161. **b)** z = 4.85, P-value = 0. The diehard fans are more likely to have watched the Cubs as children. **c)** (0.146, 0.302).

8.91 $H_0: p_1 = p_2$ $H_a: p_1 \neq p_2$, where p_1 represents the proportion of diehard fans that attend a Cubs game at least once a month. Z = 9.07, P-value = 0. A 95% confidence interval on the difference is (0.3755, 0.5645). Diehard fans are more likely to attend games at least once a month than the less loyal fans.

8.92   The confidence interval is (0.734, 0.786), and the margin of error is 0.0275.

8.93   779 people responded that they had at least one credit card. $0.41 \times 779 = 319$. The margin of error for a 95% confidence interval on the proportion of credit card holders who do not pay off the balance each month is 0.054.

8.94 $H_0: p = 0.485$ $H_a: p \neq 0.485$, z = 4.03, P-value = 0. The proportion of heavy players who are men is significantly different from the proportion of men in the US population.

8.95   The 95% confidence interval is (0.5524, 0.6736).

8.96 $H_0: p_1 = p_2$ $H_a: p_1 < p_2$ where p_1 represents the proportion of 4- to 5-year olds who sort correctly. The alternative hypothesis means that we expect older children to be better at sorting. A two-sided hypothesis test would also be appropriate because it was not specifically stated in the researcher's story whether the older children were expected to sort more successfully. Z = -3.45, P-value $\approx$ 0. Based on this P-value, it appears that the 6- to 7-year age group has a higher proportion of children who sort correctly. The 90% confidence interval (younger – older) to describe the difference in proportions is (−0.474, −0.182).

8.97 $H_0: p = 0.11$ $H_a: p < 0.11$, Z = −3.14, P-value = 0.001. The results indicate there has been a significant decrease in the proportion of nonconformities. We are assuming the sample used is a SRS from the process.

8.98   95% confidence interval for the new proportion of nonconformities is (0.028, 0.078). Assuming a sample size of 300 for the old proportion, the 95% confidence interval on the difference between the new proportion and the old proportion is (-0.101, -0.013).

8.99 $\hat{p}_M = 0.227$, $\hat{p}_F = 0.1698$, H_0: $p_M = p_F$ and H_a: $p_M \neq p_F$, where the proportions represent the proportion of male and female students who engage in binge drinking. $Z = 9.34$, P-value $= 0$. The sample data provides strong statistical evidence in favor of the alternative hypothesis. The difference between the proportion of men who engage in binge drinking and the proportion of women is estimated to be (0.045, 0.0694) with a 95% confidence level.

8.100   **a)** (0.425, 0.509). **b)** (42.5%, 50.9%). **c)** (12750, 15,270).

8.101   **a)** (−0.014, −0.003). (Example 8.8 calculated a positive interval with the same magnitudes by taking the difference between those with high blood pressure and those without.) **b)** H_0: $p_1 = p_2$ H_a: $p_1 < p_2$, $z = -2.98$, P-value $= 0.001$. This study leads us to believe that death rates are higher among men with high blood pressure.

8.102   The hypotheses for each set of study data would be: H_0: $p_1 = p_2$ H_a: $p_1 \neq p_2$. For each study, p_1 represents the proportion of deaths among those taking aspirin and p_2 represents the proportion of deaths among those not taking aspirin. For the British study: $Z = -0.50$ and the P-value $= 0.309$. This does not give conclusive evidence that taking aspirin reduces deaths due to cardiovascular disease. For the American study: $Z = -5.0$ and the P-value $= 0$. This study gives statistically significant evidence that taking aspirin reduces death due to cardiovascular disease. These conclusions differ in two important ways: The British study had the doctors taking aspirin daily and the deaths included deaths due to stroke. The American study had the doctors taking aspirin every other day and the deaths counted were only those due to heart attack. This may explain the different outcomes.

8.103

n	10	25	50	100	150	200	400	500
m	0.438	0.277	0.196	0.139	0.113	0.098	0.069	0.062

As sample size increases, the margin of error decreases.

8.104   **a)** A sample size of at least 1201 is needed for each group. **b)** $n = 0.5 \left[\dfrac{z*}{m} \right]^2$.

8.105   Starting with a sample size of 25 for the first sample, it is not possible to guarantee a margin of error of 0.15 or less. $m = 1.960 \sqrt{\dfrac{(0.5)(0.5)}{25} + \dfrac{(0.5)(0.5)}{n_2}}$. This leads to a negative value for n_2, which is not feasible.

8.106   This proposal would not lead to trustworthy results using the techniques we have seen in this chapter. The sample sizes are too small to give the desired margin of error. In Exercise 104, we found that at least 1201 subjects are needed for each group to achieve the desired margin of error.

8.107 **a)** $p_0 = 0.791$. **b)** $\hat{p} = 0.3897$, $Z = -29.11$, *P*-value $= 0$. The proportion of Mexican-Americans on juries in this county is significantly lower than their proportion in the population. **c)** $Z = -28.96$, *P*-value $= 0$. The results agree with the results in part (b).

Case Study 8.1

When comparing proportions of "girl" references to proportion of "boy" references, there does not appear to be any pattern that differentiates the male authors from the female authors. Texts 2, 3, 6, and 10 showed a significant difference between the two proportions (with *P*-value < 0.05) with proportion of "girl" references greater than proportion of "boy" references.

Case Study 8.2

$\hat{p}_1$	$\hat{p}_2$	n	z	P-value for two-sided test	Conclusion at 5% significance level
0.7	0.5	10	0.912871	0.3576	Do not reject null
0.7	0.5	20	1.290994	0.1970	Do not reject null
0.7	0.5	50	2.041241	0.0414	Reject null
0.7	0.5	75	2.5	0.0124	Reject null
0.7	0.5	100	2.886751	0.0038	Reject null
0.7	0.5	200	4.082483	≈ 0	Reject null
0.7	0.5	500	6.454972	≈ 0	Reject null

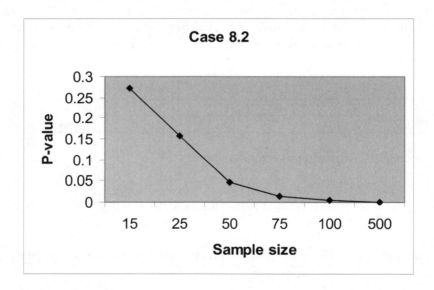

$\hat{p}_1$	$\hat{p}_2$	n	SE	Margin of Error	CI lower bound	CI upper bound
0.7	0.5	10	0.214476	0.420373	-0.22037	0.620373
0.7	0.5	20	0.151658	0.297249	-0.09725	0.497249
0.7	0.5	50	0.095917	0.187997	0.012003	0.387997
0.7	0.5	75	0.078316	0.153499	0.046501	0.353499
0.7	0.5	100	0.067823	0.132934	0.067066	0.332934
0.7	0.5	200	0.047958	0.093998	0.106002	0.293998
0.7	0.5	500	0.030332	0.05945	0.14055	0.25945

As the sample size increases, the significance of the hypothesis test increases (*P*-value decreases) and the margin of error decreases.

Chapter 9: Inference for Two-Way Tables

9.1 **a)**

	French music playing	French music not playing
Purchased French wine		
Did not purchase French wine		

b) Yes, having French music playing would be the explanatory variable. This is something the storeowner can control in an attempt to influence a customer's purchase, which is the response variable. This influences the outline with the explanatory variable as the columns and the response as the rows.

9.2

	40 years or less	Over 40 years	Totals
Terminated	35	85	120
Not terminated	515	665	1180
Totals	550	750	1300

9.3 $108/123 = 87.8\%$ of successful firms and $34/47 = 72.3\%$ of unsuccessful firms were offered exclusive territories.

9.4 $123/170 = 72.3\%$ of firms were successful, and $142/170 = 83.5\%$ of firms were offered exclusive contracts.

9.5 28 firms lacked exclusive territories, and 27.6% were unsuccessful firms. The expected count is $28(47/170) = 7.74$. If there is no association between success of a firm and having an exclusive contract, then we would expect the count of unsuccessful firms without exclusive contracts to be equal to the number of unsuccessful firms times the percent of all firms that did not have an exclusive contract.

9.6 $123(142/170) = 102.74$; the total number of successful firms is 123, the percent of firms that have exclusive territories is the total of "yes" exclusive territories, 142, the product of these numbers is divided by the overall total, 170. This gives you an expected count of 102.74.

9.7 $(6 - 1)(3 - 1) = 10$ degrees of freedom.

9.8 $0.005 < P\text{-value} < 0.01$.

9.9 **a)** $\chi^2 = 10.95$. The value of $Z^2 = (3.31)^2 = 10.95$. **b)** $(3.291)^2 = 10.83$. **c)** The statement of no relation between gender and label use is equivalent to stating that the proportion of female label users is equal to the proportion of male label users.

9.10 **a)** The null hypothesis should be that there is *no* association between the two categorical variables. **b)** The *P*-value is a probability and must be between 0 and 1. **c)** Expected cell counts are computed under the assumption the *null* hypothesis is true.

9.11 Answers will vary, but one example would be:

	X	**Y**	**Z**	**Totals**
A	10	10	10	30
B	10	10	10	30
C	10	10	10	30
Totals	30	30	30	90

9.12 All *P*-values are from Excel. **a)** df = 12, *P*-value = 0.009957. **b)** df = 6, *P*-value = 0.000202. **c)** df = 12, *P*-value = 0.009957. **d)** df = 30, *P*-value = 0.663342.

9.13 **a)** Two-way table:

	Admit		
Gender	**Yes**	**No**	**Total**
Male	490	310	800
Female	400	300	700
Total	890	610	1500

b) Percent of males who are admitted: 490 / 800 = 61.25%; percent of females who are admitted: 400 / 700 = 57.14%. **c)** H_0: There is no association between gender and admission, H_a: There is an association between gender and admission. $\chi^2 = 2.610$, *P*-value = 0.106 from SPSS. Do not reject the null hypothesis. There is not enough evidence to say that there is an association between gender and admission. **d)** Percent of males who are admitted to business school: 400 / 600 = 66.67%; percent of females who are admitted to business school: 200 / 300 = 66.67%. Percent of males who are admitted to law school: 90 / 200 = 45%; percent of females who are admitted to law school: 200 / 400 = 50%. **e)** Business: $\chi^2 = 0$, *P*-value = 1 from SPSS. Do not reject the null hypothesis. There is not enough evidence to say that there is an association between gender and admission in business school. Law: $\chi^2 = 1.335$, *P*-value = 0.248 from SPSS. Do not reject the null hypothesis. There is not enough evidence to say that there is an association between gender and admission in law school. **f)** Simpson's paradox: Because the business school has so many more students both admitted and rejected (and 600 men apply, more than any gender to any program), it changes the overall results when business and law are combined.

9.14 Answers will vary. Students should show that for each school, the percent of males admitted is higher than the percent of females admitted and then show that the overall percent of males admitted is lower than the percent of females admitted. A large difference in the number of students applying to each school will make this work, with the school having the closest percent of males and females admitted having the larges number of total applicants.

9.15 Percent of Department A's classes that are small: 32 / 52 = 61.54%. Percent of Department B's classes that are small: 42 / 106 = 39.62%. Percent of Department A's classes that are for third- and fourth-year students: 40 / 52 = 76.92%. Percent of Department B's classes that are for third- and fourth-year students: 36 / 106 = 33.96%. Department A teaches a much larger percentage of small classes, but Department A teaches more than twice the percentage of third- and fourth-year students as Department B.

9.16 **a)** The marginal distribution for model dress is: not sexual 73.8%, sexual 26.2%. The marginal distribution for magazine readership is: women 38.2%, men 41.0%, general 20.8%. The marginal and joint distributions are shown in the table from SPSS below with the counts.

Model dress * Magazine readership Crosstabulation

			Magazine readership			
			general	men	women	Total
Model dress	not sexual	Count	248	514	351	1113
		% of Total	16.4%	34.1%	23.3%	73.8%
	sexual	Count	66	105	225	396
		% of Total	4.4%	7.0%	14.9%	26.2%
Total		Count	314	619	576	1509
		% of Total	20.8%	41.0%	38.2%	100.0%

The conditional distributions for model dress are shown on the bar chart below. For not sexual, the conditional percent of ads is largest for men's magazines and smallest for general magazines. For sexual, the conditional percent of ads is largest for women's magazines and smallest for general magazines.

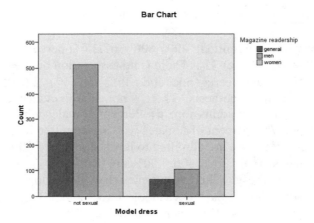

For each type of magazine, the conditional percentage of Not sexual ads is higher than the percentage of Sexual ads. **b)** The hypotheses are H_0: There is no association between model dress and magazine readership. H_a: There is an association between model dress and magazine readership. The SPSS output follows. The test statistic is 80.874 with 2 degrees of freedom and a very small P-value close to 0. Reject the null hypothesis. There is strong evidence that there is an association between model dress and magazine readership.

Chi-Square Tests

	Value	df	Asymp. Sig. (2-sided)
Pearson Chi-Square	80.874[a]	2	.000
Likelihood Ratio	79.796	2	.000
N of Valid Cases	1509		

a. 0 cells (.0%) have expected count less than 5. The minimum expected count is 82.40.

c) Just six magazines (probably two from each group) is not a very good representation. What counted as a "women's" magazine? *Vogue? Oprah? Cosmo? Good Housekeeping?* A sexual ad is much more likely to be seen in *Cosmo* than in *Good Housekeeping* or *Redbook*. What counted as a "general interest" magazine? A fitness magazine? *T.V. Guide? People? Newsweek?* How was the decision made whether an ad was sexual or not sexual? It is good that three different times of year were used. I would want more information before I had full confidence in the validity of the results.

9.17 $\chi^2 = 2.591$, *P*-value = 0.107 from SPSS. Do not reject the null hypothesis. There is not enough evidence to say that there is an association between model dress and magazine readership age group. The marginal percentages for model dress were 73.6% of the ads had models dressed not sexually and 26.4% had models dressed sexually. The marginal percentages for age group were 33.3% in the young adult category and 66.7% in the mature adult category. The conditional distribution of model dress for age shows that not sexual has a higher percentage than sexual for both age groups. A bar chart of this conditional distribution is shown below.

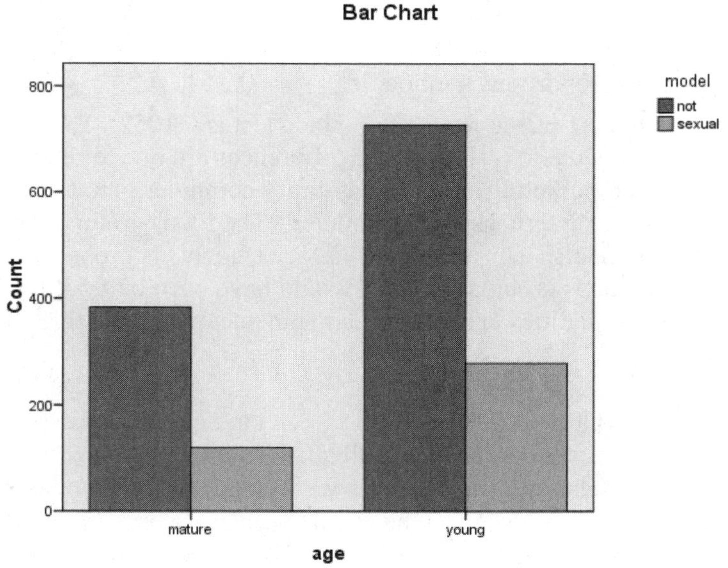

Bar Chart

9.18   **a)** The SPSS output for the joint and marginal counts and percentages is below.

Password question response * Student status Crosstabulation

			Student status		Total
			nonstudent	student	
Password question response	agree	Count	30	22	52
		% of Total	25.0%	18.3%	43.3%
	disagree	Count	29	39	68
		% of Total	24.2%	32.5%	56.7%
Total		Count	59	61	120
		% of Total	49.2%	50.8%	100.0%

The chi-squared test (output below) gives a test statistic of 2.669 with 1 degree of freedom and P-value of 0.102. Do not reject the null hypothesis. There is not enough evidence to say that there is an association between the student's status and the password question response.

Chi-Square Tests

	Value	df	Asymp. Sig. (2-sided)	Exact Sig. (2-sided)	Exact Sig. (1-sided)
Pearson Chi-Square	2.669[b]	1	.102		
Continuity Correction[a]	2.101	1	.147		
Likelihood Ratio	2.678	1	.102		
Fisher's Exact Test				.140	.073
N of Valid Cases	120				

a. Computed only for a 2x2 table

b. 0 cells (.0%) have expected count less than 5. The minimum expected count is 25. 57.

b) Using the two-sample proportions method, $\hat{p}_{student} = 0.361$, $\hat{p}_{Nonstudent} = 0.508$. The test statistic is $Z = -1.62$, and the P-value for the two-sided test is 0.1052. The chi-square test statistic of 2.669 is approximately equal to $(-1.62)^2$. The differences are due to rounding. **c)** Students taking a course in Internet marketing are probably fairly computer literate and may even have been instructed in matters of internet security policies. The focus group did not have any type of computer literacy requirements. The age of the college students is probably younger than the age of the participants in the focus group as well. It would have been better if the participants had been better matched in all qualities except for their student status to do this comparison.

9.19   **a)** $\chi^2 = 76.675$, P-value is close to 0 from SPSS. Reject the null hypothesis. There is very strong evidence that there is an association between collegiate sports division and report of cheating. **b)** Answers will vary, but here is one possibility: If we change all the sample sizes to 1000 but keep the percentages the same, $\chi^2 = 15.713$ and the P-value remains very close to 0. If we change all the "yes" answer counts to 100 but keep the percentages the same, then $\chi^2 = 7.749$ and the P-value increases to 0.021. **c)** The people most likely not to respond are those who gamble, so the results may be biased towards "no" answers. **d)** If one member of a team is cheating, it may be more likely that others are cheating, too. The teammates also may have had a discussion about how to fill out the form.

9.20 **a)** The missing values are 66 and 127. **b)** A table of the joint and marginal distributions is listed below in both percents and counts. For both the rural location and the steel mill location, the conditional percent for "no" mutation is higher than for "yes" mutation. (For rural: No is 84.6% and Yes is 15.3%. For steel mill: No is 68.7% and Yes is 31.3%.) There is a bigger difference between the conditional percentages of No and Yes for rural than for steel mill air.

mutation * location Crosstabulation

| | | | location | | |
			rural	steel mill	Total
mutation	no	Count	127	66	193
		% of Total	51.6%	26.8%	78.5%
	yes	Count	23	30	53
		% of Total	9.3%	12.2%	21.5%
Total		Count	150	96	246
		% of Total	61.0%	39.0%	100.0%

c) The chi-square test gives a test statistic of 8.773 with 1 degree of freedom and a *P*-value of 0.003. There is strong evidence of an association between location and occurrence of mutation.

Chi-Square Tests

	Value	df	Asymp. Sig. (2-sided)	Exact Sig. (2-sided)	Exact Sig. (1-sided)
Pearson Chi-Square	8.773[b]	1	.003		
Continuity Correction[a]	7.857	1	.005		
Likelihood Ratio	8.591	1	.003		
Fisher's Exact Test				.004	.003
N of Valid Cases	246				

a. Computed only for a 2x2 table

b. 0 cells (.0%) have expected count less than 5. The minimum expected count is 20.68.

9.21 $\chi^2 = 12$, *P*-value = 0.001 from SPSS. Reject the null hypothesis. There is strong evidence to say that there is an association between gender and visits to the *H. bihai* flowers. The 0 cell count does not invalidate the significance test. It is the expected counts that need to be 5 or greater for a 2×2 table in order for the chi-square test to be appropriate.

Gender	Visits *H. bihai* Yes	No	Total
Female	20	29	49
Male	0	21	21
Total	20	50	70

9.22   The table with joint and marginal distributions in counts and percents is given below.

domain * journal Crosstabulation

			journal			
			JAMA	NEJM	Science	Total
domain	com	Count	17	6	14	37
		% of Total	2.5%	.9%	2.1%	5.5%
	edu	Count	8	4	47	59
		% of Total	1.2%	.6%	7.0%	8.8%
	gov	Count	103	41	111	255
		% of Total	15.3%	6.1%	16.5%	37.9%
	org	Count	46	37	162	245
		% of Total	6.8%	5.5%	24.1%	36.5%
	other	Count	15	9	52	76
		% of Total	2.2%	1.3%	7.7%	11.3%
Total		Count	189	97	386	672
		% of Total	28.1%	14.4%	57.4%	100.0%

For *JAMA* and *NEJM*, the most common domain was ".gov" with ".org" in second place and ".edu" in last place. For *Science*, the most common domain was ".org" with ".gov" in second place and ".com" in last place.

A bar chart with the conditional distribution of journal for each domain follows. All the domains except ".com" had Science as the highest number of references (usually by quite a big difference) out of these three journals. All of the domains had *NEJM* as the lowest number of references of these three journals.

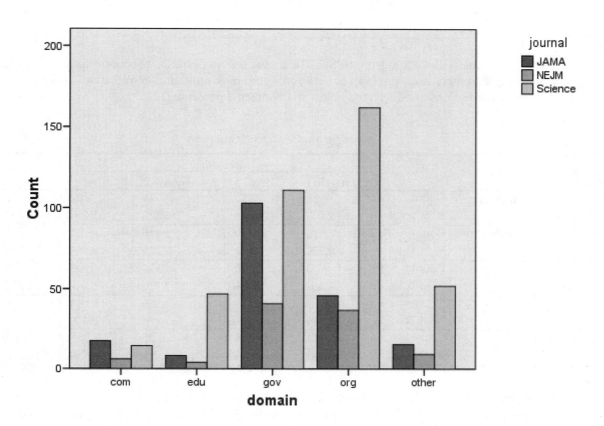

Bar Chart

The chi-square hypothesis test gives a test statistic of 56.120 with 8 degrees of freedom and a *P*-value that is close to 0. Therefore there is strong evidence of an association between the domain reference and the journal.

Chi-Square Tests

	Value	df	Asymp. Sig. (2-sided)
Pearson Chi-Square	56.120[a]	8	.000
Likelihood Ratio	57.044	8	.000
N of Valid Cases	672		

a. 0 cells (.0%) have expected count less than 5. The minimum expected count is 5.34.

9.23

Initial major	Transferred to other
Biology	202
Chemistry	64
Mathematics	38
Physics	33

$\chi^2 = 50.527$, *P*-value is close to 0 from SPSS. Reject the null hypothesis. There is strong evidence to say that there is an association between initial major and transferred area. The joint and marginal distributions are displayed below in counts and percentages.

major * transfer Crosstabulation

			transfer				
			engineering	liberal	management	other	Total
major	biology	Count	13	158	25	202	398
		% of Total	2.0%	24.5%	3.9%	31.3%	61.7%
	chemistry	Count	16	19	15	64	114
		% of Total	2.5%	2.9%	2.3%	9.9%	17.7%
	math	Count	3	20	11	38	72
		% of Total	.5%	3.1%	1.7%	5.9%	11.2%
	physics	Count	9	14	5	33	61
		% of Total	1.4%	2.2%	.8%	5.1%	9.5%
Total		Count	41	211	56	337	645
		% of Total	6.4%	32.7%	8.7%	52.2%	100.0%

The bar graph for the conditional distributions for initial majors is shown below. For every initial major, the students were most likely to transfer to some area other than engineering, management, or liberal arts. The second most likely area to transfer to for each initial major was liberal arts. Students with initial majors of physics and chemistry were more likely to go into engineering than management, but students with initial majors of biology and mathematics were more likely to go into management than engineering.

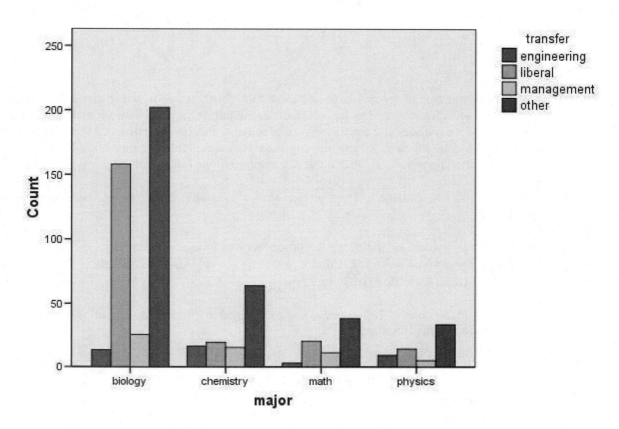

9.24 **a)**

	Not over 40	**Over 40**	**Totals**
Released	7	41	48
Not released	504	765	1269
Totals	511	806	1317

7 / 511 = 1.40% not over 40 was released. 41 / 806 = 5.1% over 40 was released. There appears to be a relationship. **b)** $\chi^2 = 12.29$, df = 1, and $P < .0005$. There is significant evidence that there is a relationship between employee's age and being released.

9.25 $\chi^2 = 50.81$, df = 2, $P < .0005$. The older employees appear to receive lower performance evaluations. They are twice as likely to fall into the lower performance category but only 1/3 as likely to fall in the highest category.

9.26 **a)** $\chi^2 = 10.77$, df = 3, $.01 < P < .02$. There is strong evidence that there is a relationship between majors and gender.

b)

	Female	Male
Accounting	30.22%	34.78%
Administration	40.44%	24.84%
Economics	2.22%	3.73%
Finance	27.11%	36.65%

A larger percentage of women have administration for their major, while men have a larger proportion with finance. **c)** The largest terms are in administration for both male and female genders. More females and fewer men are enrolled than expected. **d)** Even though the expected count of 4.6 is less than 5, we can still say the test is acceptable because it is such a small deviation. **e)** 386 responded; 46.5% did not respond to the questionnaire.

9.27 $\chi^2 = 3.277$, df $= 4$, P-value $> .25$. The data shows no evidence that the response rates are related to industry.

9.28 **a)** H_0: $p_1 = p_2$, where p_1 and p_2 are the proportions of women in each city. p_1: $203/241 = .842$; p_2: $150/218 = .688$. $Z = 3.92$, P-value $< .0004$. **b)** $\chi^2 = 15.33$, which equals $(3.92)^2 = 15.33$. With a df $= 1$, P-value $< .0005$. **c)** $(.0764, .2299)$.

9.29 With a df $= 4$, P-value $> .25$. There is not enough statistical evidence to tell if the two stores have different income distributions.

9.30 **a)**

	Black %
Household	7%
Nonhousehold	14%
Teachers	13%

b)

	Black	Other	Total
Household	172	2283	2455
Nonhousehold	167	1024	1191
Teachers	86	573	659
Total	425	3880	4305

c) Yes, because expected counts are all 5 or more.
H_0: There is no relationship between racial background and being a childcare worker.
H_a: There is a relationship between race and being a childcare worker.
d) With a df $= 2$ the P-value $< .0005$. **e)** There is statistical evidence that there is an association between being a childcare worker and racial background.

9.31 **a)**

	Response Rate %
Letter	43.70%
Phone Call	68.20%
None	20.60%

b) H_0: There is no relationship between intervention type and response rate. H_a: There is a relationship. **c)** $\chi^2 = 163.413$, df = 2, *P*-value is essentially 0. There is significant evidence that intervention is related to response rate with a phone call being more effective than a letter.

9.32 **a)** Those who received letters positively responded 51.2% of the time. Those who received no letter positively responded 52.6%. **b)** H_0: There is no relationship between a prenotification letter and physicians' responding. $\chi^2 = 1.914$, df = 1, and $.15 < P\text{-value} < .20$. There is no relation between prenotification letters and physicians' response rate due to a lack of statistical evidence.

9.33 Based on the information from the two previous studies, recognize there will be considerable nonresponse, so an initial survey must have a larger sample size so the number of respondents will be large enough to have reliable results. Also recognize that by making some contact with the survey individuals, one can increase the response rate.

9.34 $\chi^2 = 38.41$, df = 1, *P*-value $< .0005$. There is a relationship between doing well in one year and doing well again in the next. Conclude that the fund performance is persistent.

9.35 $Z = 6.1977$, *P*-value $< .0004$. $(6.1977)^2 = \chi^2$ or 38.41.

9.36 A retrospective study will give the same difference in proportions as a prospective study and will also give the same standard error for use in calculating the z statistic. For a prospective study, the two proportions are 85/120 and 37/120. For the retrospective study the proportions are 85/122 and 35/118.

9.37 $\chi^2 = 19.683$, df = 1, *P*-value $< .0005$. There is strong evidence of a relationship between winning or losing this year and winning or losing next year. The difference between the study in exercise 9.20 and this study shows that, in the current study, winning last year means there is a higher chance of losing next year. This result is opposite of the results in Exercise 9.20.

9.38

	Men %	Women
Completed	81.2%	18.8%
Still enrolled	80.2%	19.8%
Dropped out	70.8%	29.2%

H_0: There is no relationship between gender and status in college. H_a: There is a relationship. $\chi^2 = 13.40$, df = 2, and $.001 < P\text{-value} < .0025$. There is strong evidence that there is a relationship between gender and status in college. Other factors that may influence drop out rates are age of students, degree subject, and job prospects (both within academia and outside academia).

9.39 **a)** For the data set comparing on-time flights and delayed flights for Alaska Airlines and America West, the χ^2 statistic is 13.572 with a *P*-value ≈ 0. This is a statistically significant result showing that America West has fewer delayed flights. **b)** When running the test for the five different cities the following results are found. For L.A., $\chi^2 = 3.241$, *P*-value $= 0.072$. For

Phoenix, $\chi^2 = 2.346$, *P*-value = 0.126. For San Diego, $\chi^2 = 4.845$, *P*-value = 0.028. For San Francisco, $\chi^2 = 21.223$, *P*-value = 0. For Seattle, $\chi^2 = 14.903$, *P*-value = 0. **c)** The effect of city where flights originate, which illustrates Simpson's Paradox, shows statistically significant results.

9.40 $\chi^2 = 6.525$, df = 6, *P*-value = 0.367. The results of this study show no relationship between receiving a student loan and type of field studied.

9.41   Minitab calculates $\chi^2 = 43.487$, df = 12, *P*-value is essentially 0. There is strong evidence of a relationship between the PEOPLE score and field of study. Science has a much larger percentage of students scoring low on the PEOPLE score than other fields. Liberal arts and education has a much larger percentage of students scoring high on the PEOPLE score than other fields.

9.42 $\chi^2 = 359.677$, df = 8, and the *P*-value is essentially 0.

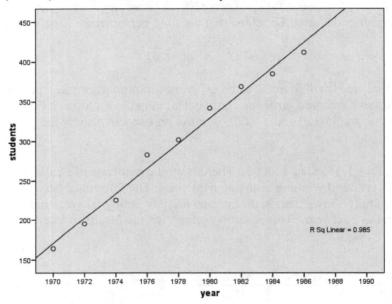

There is a statistically significant relationship between time and the percentage of women enrolled as pharmacy students. This is seen as an increasing trend over time. Yes, the plot is roughly linear. Least squares line: $\hat{y} = -31136.2 + 15.892x$.

9.43

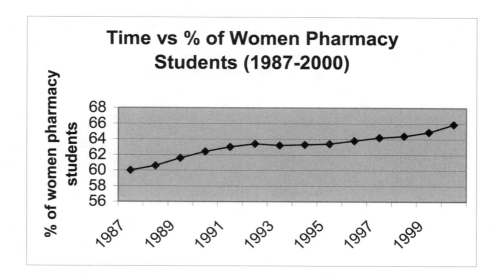

From 1970 to 2000, the percent of women pharmacy students has been increasing. However, when analyzing the data from 1987 through 2000, the statistical evidence shows a significant increase ($\chi^2 = 9.969$, df = 13, P-value = 0.696), but the percentage increase does not seem very high. From 1970 to 1986, the sample results showed an increase from approximately 24% to 59%. From 1987 to 2000, the increase rose from 60% to 66%. Using a regression line based on the 1987 to 2000 data, $\hat{y} = -660.765 + 0.363x$, a prediction for the percent of women pharmacy students in 2004 would be 66.7%.

9.44 $\chi^2 = 852.433$ df = 1, P-value = 0.000. Exercise 8.81 gave a Z statistic equal to 29.11. $(29.11)^2 = 847.4$. The error is due to round off.

9.45 **a)** It makes sense to compare percentages by source of pet because this is the explanatory variable and the more interesting statistics. Use column percents.

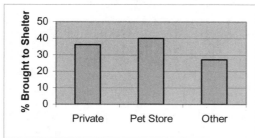

b) $\chi^2 = 6.61$, df = 2, .025 < P-value< .05. There is significant evidence that there is a relationship between the source of the cat and whether or not the cat is brought to the shelter.

9.46 $\chi^2 = 26.942$, df = 2, and P = 0. There is significant evidence that there is a relationship between the source of the dog and whether or not the dog is brought to the shelter.

9.47   Comparing the source variable for the two control groups of cats and dogs, $\chi^2 = 90.624$, df = 2, *P*-value = 0. It appears that there is a statistically significant relationship between type of pet and the source of the pet. The following column chart shows the different sample percentages for the source of the two pet types: cat or dog.

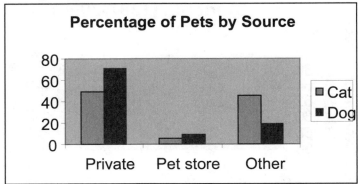

9.48   Minitab calculates $\chi^2 = 8.41$, df = 4, and a *P*-value = .077 for cats. Minitab calculates $\chi^2 = 33.21$, df = 4, and *P*-value < .0005 for dogs. The *P*-value for the test on cats has increased with more cells. The result is no longer significant at the 5% level. It is significant at the 10% level. The *P*-value for dogs has stayed very small.

9.49   For Exercise 9.26–independence using data from a single sample (model 2); 9.27–many samples (model 1); 9.28–two different samples (model 1); 9.30 – model 2.

9.50   **a)** There is strong evidence that a higher proportion of men die in such situations with $\chi^2 = 332.205$, df = 1, and *P*-value essentially 0. This probably occurred because women and children are usually instructed to go first. **b)** $\chi^2 = 103.76$, df = 2, and the *P*-value is essentially 0. There is significant evidence of a relationship between women's deaths and social class.

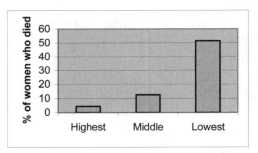   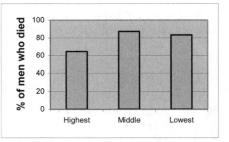

   c) $\chi^2 = 34.621$, df = 2, and the *P*-value is essentially 0. There is significant evidence of a relationship between men's deaths and social class; however, it is not quite as strong as women's relationship.

9.51   **a)** $\chi^2 = 24.9$, df = 3, *P*-value < .0005. There is a relationship between gender and sports goals. It appears that men have a higher percentage in both of the HSC categories, while women have a higher percentage in both of the LSC categories. **b)** $\chi^2 = 23.45$, df =1, *P*-value < .0005. This result shows that the percentages of females and males in the HSC and LSC categories are different. **c)** $\chi^2 = .03$, df =1, *P*-value = .863. This shows no evidence of a relationship between the HM and LM categories and gender. **d)** With regard to sports goals, there is evidence of a relationship between gender and sports goals. The relationship appears to exist between the variable *social comparison* goal, but no relationship exists between gender and *mastery* goals.

9.52   a)

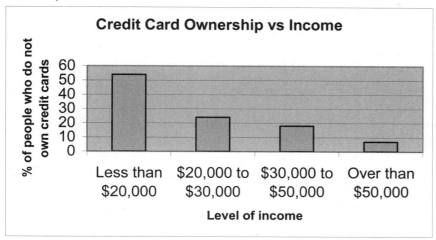

b) A much higher percentage of lower-income people do not own credit cards. As income level increases, the percentage that does not own credit cards decreases. **c)** The percentages do not add up to 100%. Also, we do not know how many out of 1025 people answered the income questions. It is expected that some people may not give out information about their income. Without sample sizes for each income category, we cannot perform a significance test.

Case Study 9.1

Characteristic	Chi-square Value	P-value
Age	26.711	0.00
Gender	2.178	0.14
Education	72.929	0.00
Income	71.576	0.00
Occupation	67.835	0.00
Race	4.329	0.363

The table above shows the Chi-square values and *P*-values for the six different demographic characteristics in the problem. Students may choose many different ways to graphically display the data. Note that there is a significant relationship between age, education level, household income, and occupational category and whether or not the individual chooses to use the World Wide Web for their travel information source or some other source. Gender and race do not show significant results.

Case Study 9.2

Gender of owner/manager: In both countries, there is a higher percentage of male owner/managers than female managers. However according to the chi-square test there is not enough evidence to say that there is an association between country and gender of owner/managers.

gender * country Crosstabulation

			country		Total
			Korea	US	
gender	female	Count	14	19	33
		% of Total	12.2%	16.5%	28.7%
	male	Count	39	43	82
		% of Total	33.9%	37.4%	71.3%
Total		Count	53	62	115
		% of Total	46.1%	53.9%	100.0%

Chi-Square Tests

	Value	df	Asymp. Sig. (2-sided)	Exact Sig. (2-sided)	Exact Sig. (1-sided)
Pearson Chi-Square	.250[b]	1	.617		
Continuity Correction[a]	.086	1	.769		
Likelihood Ratio	.251	1	.617		
Fisher's Exact Test				.682	.386
N of Valid Cases	115				

a. Computed only for a 2x2 table

b. 0 cells (.0%) have expected count less than 5. The minimum expected count is 15. 21.

Age of owner/manager: For Korea, 41 to 50 years of age is the most common group by far for owner/managers. For the U.S., 51 and over is the most common group for owner/managers, and as age decreases, so does the percent of owner/managers. For both groups, the under-30 group is the one with the fewest owner/managers. With the chi-square test, there is evidence that there is an association between age of owner/manager and country.

age * country Crosstabulation

| | | | country | | |
			Korea	US	Total
age	0 to 30	Count	2	2	4
		% of Total	1.7%	1.7%	3.5%
	31 to 40	Count	7	12	19
		% of Total	6.1%	10.4%	16.5%
	41 to 50	Count	33	17	50
		% of Total	28.7%	14.8%	43.5%
	51 and over	Count	11	31	42
		% of Total	9.6%	27.0%	36.5%
Total		Count	53	62	115
		% of Total	46.1%	53.9%	100.0%

Chi-Square Tests

	Value	df	Asymp. Sig. (2-sided)
Pearson Chi-Square	15.349[a]	3	.002
Likelihood Ratio	15.759	3	.001
N of Valid Cases	115		

a. 2 cells (25.0%) have expected count less than 5. The minimum expected count is 1.84.

Major at college of owner/manager: For Korea, the most common major for owner/managers is engineering with equal (lesser) percents for business and other majors. For the U.S., the most common major for owner/managers is other with equal (lesser) percents for business and engineering. The chi-square test shows strong evidence for association between country and major of owner/manager.

major * country Crosstabulation

| | | | country | | |
			Korea	US	Total
major	business	Count	12	12	24
		% of Total	10.4%	10.4%	20.9%
	engineering	Count	29	12	41
		% of Total	25.2%	10.4%	35.7%
	other	Count	12	38	50
		% of Total	10.4%	33.0%	43.5%
Total		Count	53	62	115
		% of Total	46.1%	53.9%	100.0%

Chi-Square Tests

	Value	df	Asymp. Sig. (2-sided)
Pearson Chi-Square	19.987[a]	2	.000
Likelihood Ratio	20.768	2	.000
N of Valid Cases	115		

a. 0 cells (.0%) have expected count less than 5. The minimum expected count is 11.06.

Education of owner/manager: For both countries, the highest percentage of owner/managers have undergraduate degrees, and the lowest percentage have only high school diplomas. For Korea, doctoral degrees are second and master's degrees are third, but for the U.S. these are reversed. The chi-square test shows that at the 5% significance level (but not 1%), there is evidence that there is an association between country and education of owner/managers.

education * country Crosstabulation

			country		Total
			Korea	US	
education	doctoral	Count	7	13	20
		% of Total	6.1%	11.3%	17.4%
	high school	Count	3	3	6
		% of Total	2.6%	2.6%	5.2%
	master's	Count	6	20	26
		% of Total	5.2%	17.4%	22.6%
	undergraduate	Count	37	26	63
		% of Total	32.2%	22.6%	54.8%
Total		Count	53	62	115
		% of Total	46.1%	53.9%	100.0%

Chi-Square Tests

	Value	df	Asymp. Sig. (2-sided)
Pearson Chi-Square	10.620[a]	3	.014
Likelihood Ratio	11.007	3	.012
N of Valid Cases	115		

a. 2 cells (25.0%) have expected count less than 5. The minimum expected count is 2.77.

Previous area of work of owner/manager: For both countries, the most common area of previous work is "other", and the 4th and 5th most common areas are research and technical, respectively. For Korea, marketing is 2nd and administrative is 3rd, but this trend is reversed for the U.S. The chi-square test shows there is not enough evidence to say that there is an association between country and previous area of work for owner/managers.

work * country Crosstabulation

			country		
			Korea	US	Total
work	administrative	Count	12	14	26
		% of Total	10.4%	12.2%	22.6%
	marketing	Count	14	11	25
		% of Total	12.2%	9.6%	21.7%
	other	Count	17	27	44
		% of Total	14.8%	23.5%	38.3%
	research	Count	6	6	12
		% of Total	5.2%	5.2%	10.4%
	technical	Count	4	4	8
		% of Total	3.5%	3.5%	7.0%
Total		Count	53	62	115
		% of Total	46.1%	53.9%	100.0%

Chi-Square Tests

	Value	df	Asymp. Sig. (2-sided)
Pearson Chi-Square	2.095[a]	4	.718
Likelihood Ratio	2.103	4	.717
N of Valid Cases	115		

a. 2 cells (20.0%) have expected count less than 5. The minimum expected count is 3.69.

Previous job position of owner/manager: For both countries Employee is the most common previous job position and owner is the least common previous job position for owner/managers. For Korea, director is 2nd, CEO is 3rd, and manager is 4th. For the U.S., manager is 2nd, director is 3rd, and CEO is 4th. The chi-square test shows there is not enough evidence to say that there is an association between country and previous job position of owner/managers.

position * country Crosstabulation

			country		Total
			Korea	US	
position	CEO	Count	11	8	19
		% of Total	9.6%	7.0%	16.5%
	director	Count	14	14	28
		% of Total	12.2%	12.2%	24.3%
	employee	Count	15	20	35
		% of Total	13.0%	17.4%	30.4%
	manager	Count	10	16	26
		% of Total	8.7%	13.9%	22.6%
	owner	Count	3	4	7
		% of Total	2.6%	3.5%	6.1%
Total		Count	53	62	115
		% of Total	46.1%	53.9%	100.0%

Chi-Square Tests

	Value	df	Asymp. Sig. (2-sided)
Pearson Chi-Square	2.023[a]	4	.731
Likelihood Ratio	2.028	4	.731
N of Valid Cases	115		

a. 2 cells (20.0%) have expected count less than 5. The minimum expected count is 3.23.

Years of experience of owner/manager in current business: For Korea, less than 1 year of experience is the most common, with 1 to 2 years in second, 5 or more years" in third, and 3 to 4 years in fourth. For the U.S., 5 or more years is the most common, and as years of experience decreases, so does the percent of managers in that group. The trends are almost exactly opposite! The chi-square test shows that there is strong evidence of an association between country and years of experience of owner/manager in the current business.

experience * country Crosstabulation

			country		Total
			Korea	US	
experience	0 to 1	Count	31	1	32
		% of Total	27.0%	.9%	27.8%
	1 to 2	Count	14	5	19
		% of Total	12.2%	4.3%	16.5%
	3 to 4	Count	2	14	16
		% of Total	1.7%	12.2%	13.9%
	5 +	Count	6	42	48
		% of Total	5.2%	36.5%	41.7%
Total		Count	53	62	115
		% of Total	46.1%	53.9%	100.0%

Chi-Square Tests

	Value	df	Asymp. Sig. (2-sided)
Pearson Chi-Square	68.101[a]	3	.000
Likelihood Ratio	79.692	3	.000
N of Valid Cases	115		

a. 0 cells (.0%) have expected count less than 5. The minimum expected count is 7.37.

Type of business: For both countries, general (opportunistic) business is slightly more common than technical (craftsman) business. The chi-square test does not show enough evidence to say there is an association between country and type of business.

type * country Crosstabulation

			country		Total
			Korea	US	
type	general	Count	30	33	63
		% of Total	26.1%	28.7%	54.8%
	technical	Count	23	29	52
		% of Total	20.0%	25.2%	45.2%
Total		Count	53	62	115
		% of Total	46.1%	53.9%	100.0%

Chi-Square Tests

	Value	df	Asymp. Sig. (2-sided)	Exact Sig. (2-sided)	Exact Sig. (1-sided)
Pearson Chi-Square	.132[b]	1	.717		
Continuity Correction[a]	.031	1	.861		
Likelihood Ratio	.132	1	.717		
Fisher's Exact Test				.851	.431
N of Valid Cases	115				

a. Computed only for a 2x2 table

b. 0 cells (.0%) have expected count less than 5. The minimum expected count is 23.
97.

Ownership type: For both countries, the most common ownership type is corporation. For Korea, sole proprietorship is 2nd, other is 3rd, and partnership is 4th. For the U.S., partnership is 2nd, and other and sole proprietorship tie for 3rd. The chi-square test shows that there is evidence of an association between country and ownership type.

ownership * country Crosstabulation

			country		Total
			Korea	US	
ownership	corporation	Count	36	56	92
		% of Total	31.3%	48.7%	80.0%
	other	Count	5	1	6
		% of Total	4.3%	.9%	5.2%
	partner	Count	2	4	6
		% of Total	1.7%	3.5%	5.2%
	sole	Count	10	1	11
		% of Total	8.7%	.9%	9.6%
Total		Count	53	62	115
		% of Total	46.1%	53.9%	100.0%

Chi-Square Tests

	Value	df	Asymp. Sig. (2-sided)
Pearson Chi-Square	14.429[a]	3	.002
Likelihood Ratio	15.816	3	.001
N of Valid Cases	115		

a. 4 cells (50.0%) have expected count less than 5. The minimum expected count is 2.77.

Type of site: For both countries, general (free) location is the most common. For Korea, industrial is least common. For the U.S. other is least common. The chi-square test gives strong evidence that there is an association between country and type of site.

site * country Crosstabulation

| | | | country | | |
			Korea	US	Total
site	general	Count	43	30	73
		% of Total	37.4%	26.1%	63.5%
	industrial	Count	2	17	19
		% of Total	1.7%	14.8%	16.5%
	other	Count	8	15	23
		% of Total	7.0%	13.0%	20.0%
Total		Count	53	62	115
		% of Total	46.1%	53.9%	100.0%

Chi-Square Tests

	Value	df	Asymp. Sig. (2-sided)
Pearson Chi-Square	15.679[a]	2	.000
Likelihood Ratio	17.340	2	.000
N of Valid Cases	115		

a. 0 cells (.0%) have expected count less than 5. The minimum expected count is 8.76.

Chapter 10: Inference for Regression

10.1   Predicted wages = $404.91. Residual = -$15.91.

10.2   The smallest LOS data point is 7, and the largest LOS data point is 228. Therefore the predictions based on LOS = 100 and 200 are appropriate, but the LOS = 1 and 400 yield extrapolations, not predictions.

LOS	1	100	200	400
Wages	$349.99	$408.45	$467.50	$585.60

10.3   **a)** $\beta_0 = 4.6$. This number means that when the U.S. market is flat, the average overseas return will be 4.7%. **b)** $\beta_1 = 0.67$. This number means that for every 1% increase in the U.S. market, the overseas return will increase 0.67%. **c)** $y_i = 4.6 + 0.67x_i + \varepsilon_i$. ε_i is the error term that represents variation in overseas returns.

10.4   **a)** Total cost = $\beta_0 + \beta_1 \times$ Number of Units + ε. β_0 represents the fixed cost for setting up the production line. **b)** $\beta_1 > 0$. **c)** ε.

10.5   **a)** Yes, there is a strong, positive, linear relationship between year and spending. **b)** $\hat{y} = -2651.400 + 1.340x$. **c)**

Year	1995	1996	1997	1998	1999
residual	0.30	-0.24	-0.18	-0.12	0.24

d) $SPENDING = \beta_0 + \beta_1 \cdot YEAR + \varepsilon$, with estimates $\beta_0 = -2651.400$, $\beta_1 = 1.340$, $\varepsilon = 0.2898$. **e)** For 2001, the predicted spending is $29.94. The residual is $2.76. This is an extrapolation. The trend might not stay the same beyond 1999.

10.6   The scatterplot shows a fairly strong linear relationship in the positive direction. $\hat{y} = 2.666 + 0.627x$.

10.7 $b_1 = 0.627$, $SE_{b1} = 0.0992$, $H_0: \beta_1 = 0$ $H_a: \beta_1 > 0$, $t = 6.32$, df = 49, P-value ≈ 0. There is significant evidence to conclude that β_1 is greater than 0.

10.8   (0.4277, 0.8263).

10.9   Chance plays a role in the performance of a fund. The group of mutual funds that performed well last year will be influenced by chance this year and will likely see a smaller return than last year.

10.10   Since chance influenced the performance of those companies that did extremely well or extremely poorly, chance will also influence their performance in coming years. This means that, over time, companies that did extremely well will likely have a year or two when they are not considered the best. Likewise, companies that did very poorly will see an improvement in their performance.

10.11   **a)** r = 0.67, t = 6.318, df = 49, P-value < 0.0005. Based on this *P*-value, it is reasonable to conclude that there is a positive correlation between return on treasury bills and inflation.

b) Verify.

10.12 **a)** $\hat{y} = -12.24 + 0.212x$. **b)** Average wages = \$391, average length of service = 70.5 months. **c)** Use t = 2.853.

10.13 **a)**

variable	Area	IBI
mean	28.29	65.94
s	17.714	18.280
min	2	29
max	70	91
	Fairly symmetric and Normally distributed except for 2 high outliers.	Skewed left but no outliers.

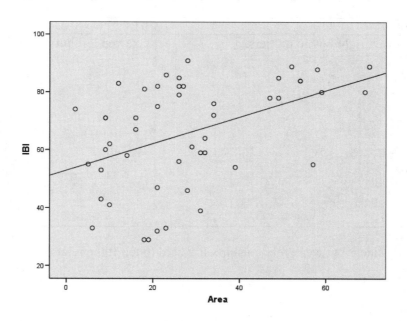

b) Scatterplot looks weak, positive, and linear. It's very hard to tell if there are any outliers or unusual patterns because the relationship is so weak.

c) $IBI = \beta_0 + \beta_1 \cdot AREA + \varepsilon$. **d)** $H_0 : \beta_1 = 0$, $H_a : \beta_1 \neq 0$. **e)** $\hat{y} = 52.923 + 0.460x$. From SPSS, the hypothesis test in part (d) has t = 3.415 and a *P*-value of 0.001, so we can reject the null hypothesis. There is strong evidence that Area and IBI have a linear relationship. $R^2 =$ 19.9%, and the regression standard error is $s = 16.535$. **f)** The residual plot shows that the residuals get slightly less spread out as Area increases, but overall, it doesn't look too bad. **g)** Yes, the Normal probability plot looks good.

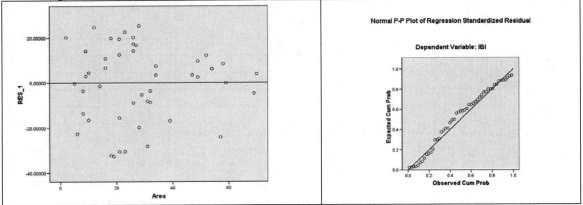

h) The assumptions are reasonable—we are assuming a simple random sample from the population, there is a fairly linear (although weak) relationship between IBI and Area, there is approximately the same spread above and below the regression line on the scatterplot, which is fairly uniform for all Area values on the plot, and the Normal probability and residual plots look good.

10.14   a)

variable	Forest	IBI
mean	39.39	65.94
s	32.204	18.280
min	0	29
max	100	91
	Skewed right but no outliers.	Skewed left but no outliers.

b) Fairly linear but weak relationship. It's hard to tell if the relationship is positive or negative.

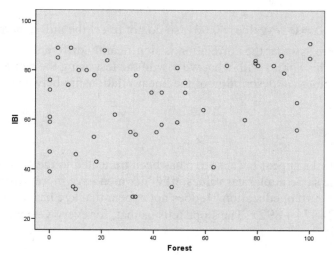

c) $IBI = \beta_0 + \beta_1 \cdot FOREST + \varepsilon$. **d)** $H_0 : \beta_1 = 0$, $H_a : \beta_1 \neq 0$. **e)** $\hat{y} = 52.907 + 0.153x$.
From SPSS, the hypothesis test in part (d) has t = 1.921 and a *P*-value of 0.061, so we cannot reject the null hypothesis. There is not enough evidence to say that Forest and IBI have a linear relationship. $R^2 = 7.3\%$, and the regression standard error is $s = 17.788$. **f)** The residual plot looks fairly random. **g)** Yes, the Normal probability plot looks pretty good.

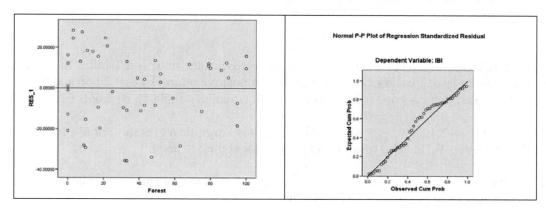

h) The assumptions are reasonable—we are assuming a simple random sample from the population, there is a fairly linear (although weak) relationship between IBI and Forest, there is approximately the same spread above and below the regression line on the scatterplot which is fairly uniform for all Area values on the plot, and the Normal probability and residual plots look good.

10.15 Area is the better explanatory variable for regression with IBI. IBI and Forest have a much weaker relationship than IBI and Area.

10.16 $H_0 : \rho = 0$, $H_a : \rho \neq 0$, *P*-value = 0.001, so do reject the null hypothesis. There is strong evidence that the correlation is significantly different from 0 if a significance level of 0.05 is used. This agrees with what we saw in the test using the slope in the 10.13. The correlation is a numerical description of the linear relationship between Area and IBI, which is fairly weak but still clearly linear and positive.

10.17 $H_0 : \rho = 0$, $H_a : \rho \neq 0$, P-value = 0.061, so do not reject the null hypothesis. There is not enough evidence to say that the correlation is significantly different from 0 if a significance level of 0.05 is used. This agrees with what we saw in the test using the slope in the 10.14. The correlation is a numerical description of the linear relationship between Forest and IBI, which is very weak.

10.18 Answers will vary.

10.19 **a)** The vertical stacks appear because age has been truncated to the nearest year. This results in many x's with the same numerical values. **b)** Older men have more experience. Younger men may have a more current education. It does not appear that age has a strong relationship with income. **c)** $\hat{y} = 24874 + 892x$ The slope tells us that, for every year a man is older, his income increases by $892.

10.20 **a)** The large sample size almost guarantees that there will be a statistically significant result. **b)** (771, 1013). **c)** (732, 1052).

10.21 **a)** The close cluster of values between 0 and 100,000 and the scattered points above 100,000 indicate a distribution skewed to the right for each value of x. **b)** Large sample sizes help make up for any skewness in the sample data.

10.22 $349.38 \pm (1.676)(18.10) = (319.0, 379.7)$.

10.23 **a)** If there is no inflation in a particular year, β_0 represents the return on T-bills. In order for the government to issue treasury bills, there must be a positive return. **b)** $b_0 = 2.666$ and $SE_{b_0} = 0.5039$. **c)** Yes, there is good evidence that $\beta_0 > 0$. (P-value < 0.0001). **d)** $2.666 \pm 2.009(0.5039)$.

10.24 For n = 20, t = −2.45, 0.01 < P-value < 0.02. This is a significant result. For n = 10, t = −1.633, 0.05 < P-value < 0.10. This result is not significant at the 5% level.

10.25 **a)** There is a moderate, positive, linear relationship between size and price. The R^2 is 43.1%. Yes, size is helpful in predicting selling price.

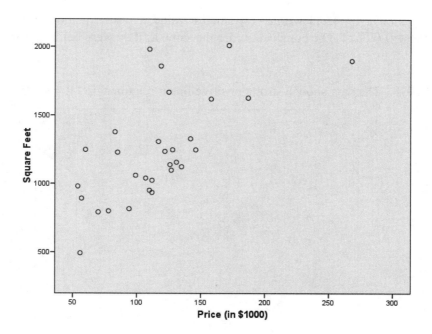

b) $\hat{y} = 21.398 + 0.077x$, t = 4.601, *P*-value < 0.0001. The small *P*-value means that there is a significant linear relationship between size and selling price.

10.26 **a)**

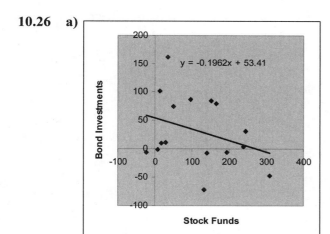

The data suggest a negative linear relationship between stock funds and bond investments. **b)** H_o: $\beta_1 = 0$ H_a: $\beta_1 < 0$, t = −1.27, *P*-value = 0.113. Conclude that there is not enough evidence to say that the slope is less than zero. **c)** The scatterplot does not show any kind of relationship between the two variables.

10.27 r = 0.656, t = 4.601, *P*-value < 0.0001. Conclude that the population correlation is greater than zero, and therefore larger houses have higher prices.

10.28 r = −0.321, t = −1.27, *P*-value = 0.113. There is no significant evidence that the correlation is less than zero.

10.29 **a)** The R^2 is 39.6%, t = 4.211 with a very small P-value, and the equation of the line is $\hat{y} = 20.596 + 0.077x$. The conclusions are the same as they were before, so this outlier is not influential.

10.30 **a)** $R^2 = 0.7998$. The data show a strong positive linear relationship. $\hat{y} = -0.013 + 0.018x$

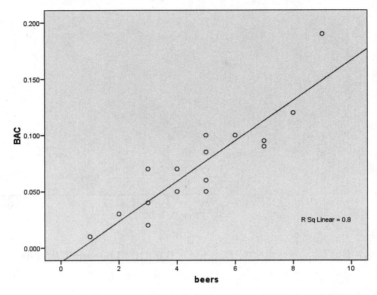

b) H_0: $\beta_1 = 0$ H_a: $\beta_1 > 0$, t = 7.48, *P*-value < 0.0001. Conclude that drinking more beers increases blood alcohol on the average.

10.31 **a)**

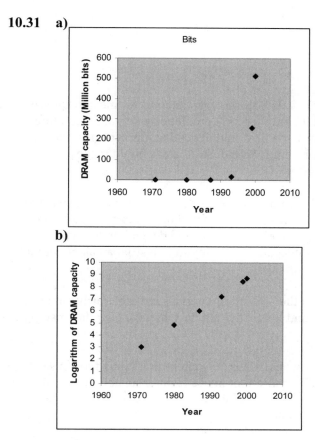

c) $\hat{y} = -379 + 0.194x$. (0.18765, 0.20035).

10.32 **a)** Yes, this student has the largest residual. No, it does not appear extreme in the x direction.
b) The regression line (shown with the dotted line on the scatterplot below), the R^2 value (76.8%), and the *P*-value for a test on slope do not change greatly. $\hat{y} = 0.0000248 + 0.015x$. This was not an influential observation.

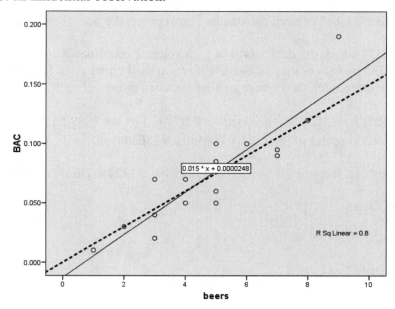

10.33　**a)** Verify. **b)** 423.2 ± 26.1456.

10.34　**a)** Verify. **b)** $(0.561, 9.410)$.

10.35　**a)** $(62.379, 71.996)$. **b)** $(33.579, 100.797)$. **c)** A 95% confidence interval for mean response is the interval for the average IBI for all areas of 31 km^2. A 95% prediction interval for a future response estimates a single IBI for a 31 km^2 area. **d)** It would depend on the type of terrain and the location. Mountain regions, latitude, and proximity to industrial areas might make a difference.

10.36　**a)** $(62.07, 72.75)$. **b)** $(31.23, 103.59)$. **c)** A 95% confidence interval for mean response is the interval for the average IBI for all areas of 49% forest. A 95% prediction interval for a future response estimates a single IBI for an area of 49% forest. **d)** It would depend on the type of terrain and the location. Mountain regions, latitude, and proximity to industrial areas might make a difference.

10.37　The confidence intervals for mean response and the prediction intervals are both fairly similar. They are not exactly the same because the IBI and Forest did not have as strong a relationship as IBI and Area.

10.38　**a)** The predicted selling price is $144,598, so I would advise the client to *not* buy the house because the asking price of $180,000 for a 1600-square-foot house is unreasonably high. **b)** The predicted selling price is $113,798, so I would advise my client that this is a good deal because the asking price of $80,000 is cheap for a 1200-square-foot house.

10.39　**a)** Verify. **b)** $(49780, 53496)$. **c)** $(-41735, 145010)$. This interval is not very useful.

10.40　The narrow interval describes an average. The wider interval predicts an individual's income. There is more variation in individual incomes than in average income.

10.41　$(58918, 62200)$.

10.42　**a)** $(4.4715, 5.5005)$. **b)** We need the standard error on y. We don't have that in this output.

10.43　**a)** $(44446, 55314)$. **b)** More data was used to develop the confidence interval in exercise 10.27 than was used in part (a) of this problem. Since standard errors are a function of sample size, when we have large samples we have smaller standard errors.

10.44　**a)** $\bar{x} = 1239.53$, $\bar{y} = 116330$, $\hat{y} = 21.398 + 0.077x$. For x = 1239.53, y = 116842 (The difference is due to round-off error.) **b)** $(\$45894, \$186844)$.

10.45　The 90% prediction interval for Steve's BAC is $(.04, .11424)$. He should not drive.

10.46　$(\$140223, \$178295)$.

10.47　$SE_{b1} = 0.0994$.

10.48　$s_x^2 = 9.6123$, $(0.563, 9.409)$.

10.49 H_0: $\beta_1 = 0$ H_a: $\beta_1 \neq 0$, t = 6.3177, F = 39.914, t^2 = F, *P*-value = 7.563E-08.

10.50 **a)** 189.705 + 232.89 = 422.596. **b)** Total: 51 – 1 = 50, Residual: 51 – 2 = 49. **c)** MS_{Reg} = 189.705/1, MS_{Res} = (232.89/49) = 4.753. **d)** F = (189.705/4.753) = 39.913.

10.51 **a)** R^2 = (189.705/422.596) =0.4489. **b)** $s = \sqrt{\dfrac{232.89}{49}} = 2.1801$.

10.52 The row reads:

	DF	SS	MS
	28	10152.4	362.586

10.53 R^2 = (3445.9/13598.3) = 0.2534, $s = \sqrt{\dfrac{10152.4}{28}} = 19.042$.

10.54 SE_{b1} = 0.215, (0.297, 1.029).

10.55 **a)** H_0: $\beta_1 = 0$ H_a: $\beta_1 \neq 0$, t = 6.041, *P*-value = 0.0001. Yes, these data give a statistically significant result. Reputation helps explain profitability. **b)** R^2 = 0.1936. 19.36% of the variation in profit can be explained by the reputation of the company. **c)** Statistical significance does not always translate in practical significance. While there is some relationship between reputation and profitability, reputation explains a small percentage of the variation in profitability. There are likely many more variables that would help predict profitability of a company.

10.56 Slope tells how much the profitability will increase for every one point increase in a company's reputation. (0.022, 0.056).

10.57 The 95% confidence interval for mean profitability for companies with a reputation of 7 is (0.110604, 0.141804) with appropriate round-off error.

10.58 A prediction interval will be wider than the confidence interval. There is much more variation in a single company's profitability than in the average profitability for all companies with a reputation score of 7. The 95% prediction interval is (-0.01766, 0.27006).

10.59 The F statistic is equal to the t statistic squared. The P-values will be the same. F = 36.492 = $(6.041)^2$.

10.60 s^2 = (SS_{error}/df) = (.78963/152) = 0.005195, s = $(0.005195)^{1/2}$ = 0.072076.

10.61 R^2 = (SS_{model}/SS_{total}) = 0.1936

10.62 r = 0.44, t = 6.041, *P*-value = 0.0001. Yes, these data provide good evidence that the population correlation is positive.

10.63 Answers will vary.

10.64 The *P*-value < 0.001, so we would reject H_0, and 0 would not be in the confidence interval.

10.65 **a)** For more expensive items, the pharmacy would be charging less of a markup. **b)** $\hat{y} = 2.885 - 0.295x$, where $\hat{y}$ is the predicted (log) markup and x is the (log) cost. **c)** df = 137, but using the t table, we would use df = 100 to be conservative. For testing $H_0 : \beta_1 = 0$, $H_a : \beta_1 < 0$, the *P*-value is less than 0.005, so we can reject the null hypothesis. There is strong evidence that (log) markup and (log) cost have a negative linear relationship (evidence that charge compression is taking place).

10.66 **a)** The degrees of freedom will be 1411, but using Table D, we will use degrees of freedom 1000 to be conservative. A significance level of 5% and a two-sided test would give a critical t value of 1.962. Any |t| > 1.962 will yield a significant correlation. Below is a table of the test statistics for the correlations. A * marks significant correlations. The only correlations that are not significant are Table with Check and Table with SPM.

	Check	Minutes	Table	Party
Minutes	9.74*			
Table	1.69	3.13*		
Party	-12.07*	5.19*	15.38*	
SPM	35.71*	-16.25*	-1.16	-16.39*

b) The strongest correlation is positive and shows the relationship spending per minute (SPM) with check divided by minutes (check). SPM is also strongly negatively correlated with minutes spent dining and the number of people in the party. The next strongest correlation is positive and represents the relationship between number of people in the party and the size of the table (which makes sense because the larger tables are where the larger parties are seated). **c)** A significance level of 0.05/9 is 0.0056. For a two-sided test, this corresponds to a critical t value of approximately 2.813. Therefore, any |t| > 2.813 will yield a significant correlation. All the same correlations are significant as in part (a).

10.67 **a)** Answers will vary. Some questions to consider: Is this a national chain or an independent restaurant? What kind of food is prepared? Do the restaurants have similar staffing and experience? **b)** Answers will vary.

10.68 **a)** There is a significant linear relationship between brand equity and sales. The correlation is positive, which means as brand equity increases sales also increase. **b)** The nonresponse rate is 58.5%, which is high. Mall shoppers might not be typical of the general population, and attitudes in Korea may be different than in other parts of the world. The question referred only to quick-service restaurants, so the results not apply to other businesses such as clothing or doctors or schools. Answers will vary.

10.69 **a)** The relationship looks positive, linear, and moderately strong except for potential outliers for the two largest hotels (1388 and 1590 rooms each).

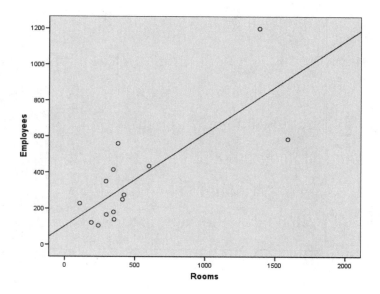

b) The moderately strong linear relationship is good, but the outliers are not.

c) $\hat{y} = 101.981 + 0.514x$, where $\hat{y}$ is the predicted number of employees and x is the number of rooms. **d)** $H_0 : \beta_1 = 0$, $H_a : \beta_1 \neq 0$ with t = 4.287 and *P*-value from SPSS of 0.001, so reject the null hypothesis. There is strong evidence that there is a significant linear relationship between the number of rooms and the number of employees working at hotels in Toronto. **e)** (0.253, 0.775).

10.70 **a)** 51.4. **b)** (25.3, 77.5). **c)** It probably would generalize well to other hotels in Toronto, less well to hotels in other parts of Canada (for example, in less crowded cities), and even less well to hotels in other countries.

10.71 a) Hotel 1 (1388 rooms) and Hotel 11 (1590 rooms) are the two outliers. (b) The R^2 drops from 60.5% in the original model to just 26.3% in the model without the outliers. The s drops from 188.774 in the original model to 129.151 in the model without the outliers. The new equation of the line is $\hat{y} = 72.526 + 0.589x$. The new t test statistic is 1.891, and the *P*-value is now 0.088, so we cannot reject the null hypothesis. There is not enough evidence to say that the slope is significantly different from 0. The 95% confidence interval for the slope is (-0.105, 1.284), which contains 0. The 95% confidence interval for the slope from the original model did not contain 0.

10.72 **a)** Estimate = 47.38, prediction interval = (43.495, 51.265). **b)** The regression line fits the data pretty well in the 1990s, and the overall R^2 = 90.3%, which is pretty good. However, the line doesn't fit the data nearly as well in the later years, so the prediction for 2003 is probably not a good prediction.

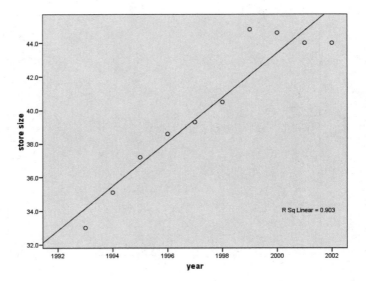

10.73   The scatterplot shows a strong, linear, and positive relationship between the number of students and the total yearly expenditures.

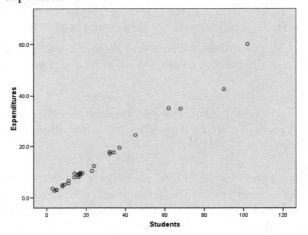

The least-squares regression line is $\hat{y} = 0.526 + 0.530x$, where $\hat{y}$ is the predicted total yearly expenditure and x is the number of students. R^2 is very good at 98.4%, and the regression standard error is $s = 1.70$. A two-sided test of the slope gives a t = 41.623 and a *P*-value close to 0. These results sound very promising; however, the Normal probability plot does not look good, and the residual plot has a distinct funnel shape. The assumptions for regression may not be appropriate here.

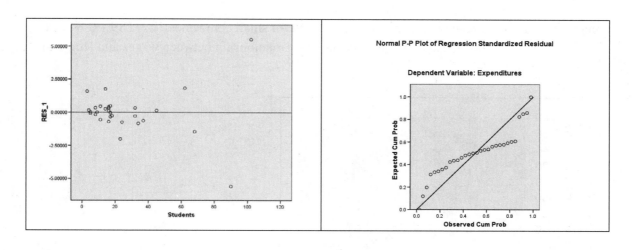

10.74 With just x = 137 thousand students added in: $\hat{y} = -0.205 + 0.565x$, $R^2 = 98.6\%$, s = 2.1788. The normal probability plot still looks bad, and the residual plot still looks funnel shaped.

With just x = 0 thousand students added in: $\hat{y} = 1.409 + 0.512x$, $R^2 = 95.1\%$, s = 2.9241. The normal probability plot still looks bad, and the residual plot still looks funnel-shaped and now has an outlier at x = 0.

With both x = 137 and x = 0 added in: $\hat{y} = 0.609 + 0.552x$, $R^2 = 96.6\%$, s = 3.2921. The scatterplot looks pretty good, except x = 0 is an outlier. The Normal probability plot still looks bad, and the residual plot still looks funnel-shaped and now has an outlier at x = 0.

10.75

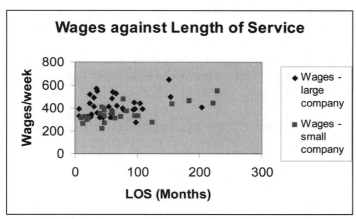

It appears that women who work for large companies generally have higher wages. It is probably easier to predict wages from LOS for the group of women who work for small companies.

10.76 H_0: $\mu_{\text{wages-large}} = \mu_{\text{wages-small}}$ and H_a: $\mu_{\text{wages-large}} \neq \mu_{\text{wages-small}}$, t = 3.02, P-value = 0.0038. There is a significant difference in wages. H_0: $\mu_{\text{LOS-large}} = \mu_{\text{LOS-small}}$ and H_a: $\mu_{\text{LOS-large}} \neq \mu_{\text{LOS-small}}$, t = -0.819, P-value = 0.4177. There is no significant difference in wages.

10.77 For regressing wages on length of service for large companies, $\hat{y} = 390 + 0.425x$, t = 1.27, P-value = 0.2134. There is not a significant linear relationship between LOS and wages for large companies. For regressing wages on length of service for small companies, $\hat{y} = 289 + 0.84x$, t = 4.49, *P*-value = 0.00017. There is a significant linear relationship between wages and length of service for small companies.

10.78   **a)**

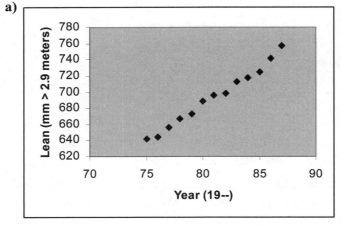

The plot shows a strong positive linear relationship. The lean is increasing at a positive rate. **b)** The regression line is: $\hat{y} = -61.12 + 9.32x$. 98.8% of the variation in lean is explained by year. **c)** (8.636, 10.0).

10.79   **a)** The predicted amount of lean for 1918 would be 106.64 mm. **b)** The plot of data from 1975 through 1987 shows a very strong linear relationship. However, it is not appropriate to extrapolate that relationship for earlier years or later years. Using the 1918 data point (lean = 71) and its predicted value (lean = 106.64), we have a residual of –35.64. This residual is clearly an outlier, and therefore, the prediction formula should not be used for earlier years. It may be the case that the lean was increasing at a much slower rate in the early part of the century.

10.80   **a)** The predicted lean in 2000 would be 870.9 mm. **b)** A prediction interval would be appropriate for estimating the lean in 2000. We want to know the amount of lean for that year, not the average lean over the course of the year.

10.81 H_0: $\beta_1 = 0$ H_a: $\beta_1 \neq 0$, t = 2.16, 0.02 < *P*-value < 0.04. Yes, there is a significant linear relationship between pretest and final exam scores.

Case Study 10.1

a)

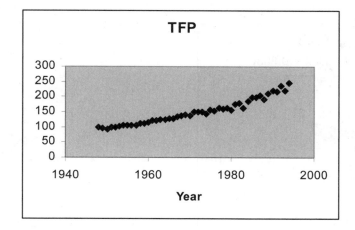

Around 1980, the rate of increase of TFP started to go up. TFP started to increase at a faster rate. The variation also appears to have increased.

b) $\hat{y} = -5689.168 + 2.962x$

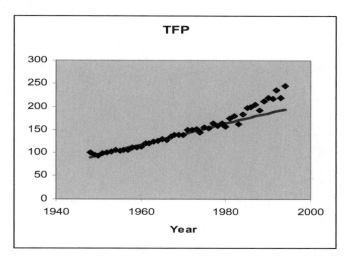

c) (2.127, 2.411).

d) $\hat{y} = -10201.7 + 5.235x$, (3.974, 6.496).

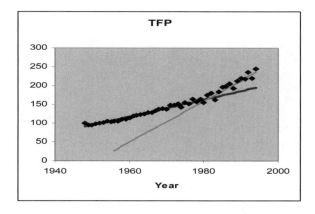

Case Study 10.2

a)

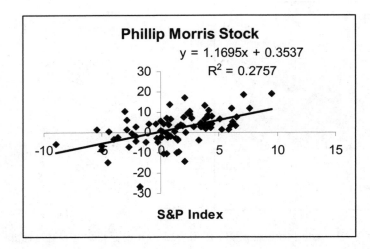

b) (0.82, 1.52). **c)** Data points 33 and 73 have large negative residuals. These are not likely to be influential because many other data points anchor them above. **d)** Aside from the two low outliers, the residuals appear fairly Normal. **e)** (6.653, 11.597).

Chapter 11: Multiple Regression

11.1 $\hat{y} = 210 + 160(45.24) + 160(17.00) + 150(38.00) + 65(315.00) + 120(43.25) = 41,533.4 \text{ ft}^2$

11.2   **a)** $32,475 \text{ ft}^2$. **b)** The residual is -9436 ft^2. According to the model in the previous exercise, the math department needs 9436 ft^2 more space than it actually has.

11.3   **a)** The response variable is bank assets. **b)** The explanatory variables are the number of banks and deposits. **c)** There are two explanatory variables; therefore, $p = 2$. **d)** The sample size is 54; therefore, $n = 54$.

11.4

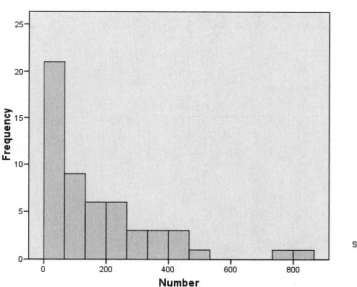

Histogram

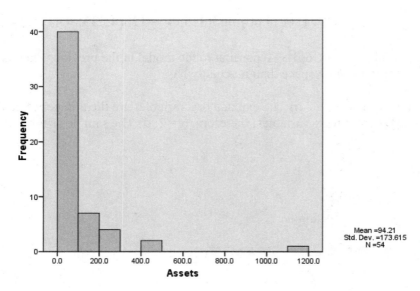

Histogram

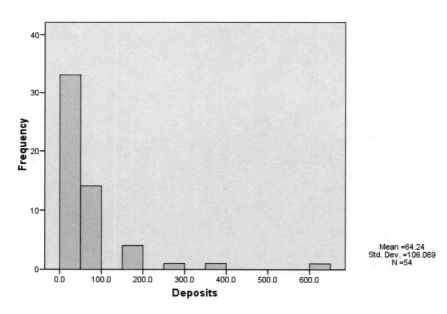

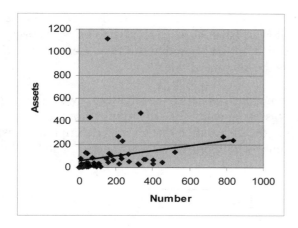

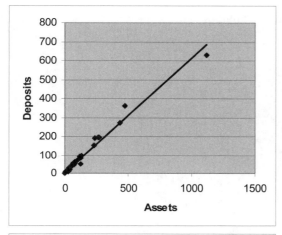

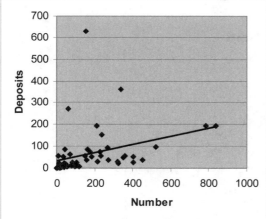

The distribution of the number of banks, the assets, and the deposits each appear to be skewed to the right with at least one outlier. Texas and Illinois each have a significantly higher number of banks than any other state or area. The state of New York has a significantly larger amount of deposits and assets than any other state or area. New York is by far the most significant outlier of the data set.

11.5 The distribution of the sales of DJIA companies is skewed to the right with two possible outliers when considering the sales of Wal-Mart and General Motors compared to the other DJIA companies. No, there are no companies that are outliers in assets that are also outliers in the form of sales. We should not be surprised that Wal-Mart has high sales relative to its assets because Wal-Mart's primary business function is the distribution of products to final users. This would require less in the form of assets and increase the amount of sales.

11.6   The distribution of the profits of the DJIA companies appears to be slightly skewed to the right; however, they certainly are not as skewed as assets or sales. The distribution for profits also does not appear to have any outliers. One aspect of the distribution that Excel's descriptive statistics fails to capture is the large number of companies whose profits were between $7 and 8 billion.

11.7

Correlation	Assets	Sales	Profits
Assets	1		
Sales	0.642513	1	
Profits	0.526326	0.569048	1

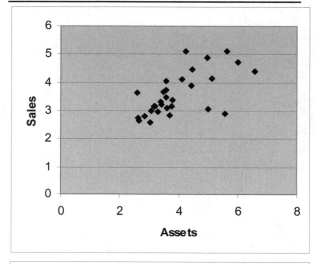

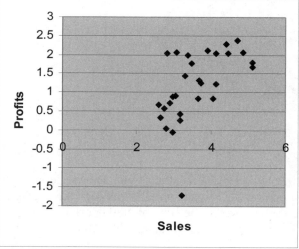

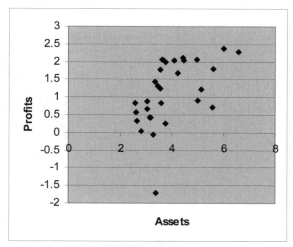

The largest difference between the analysis of the original variables and the logarithmic variables is the difference between the correlation of assets and sales. With the original analysis, the correlation was r = 0.45, and once adjusted, the correlation increased to r = 0.64. The correlation between profits and assets decreased slightly after the new analysis, while the correlation between sales and profits increased slightly. Using the logarithm transformation did indeed reduce the skew of the distributions while also decreasing the spread of the data points in the scatter plots.

11.8

Excel
$b_0 = 2.340454802$
$b_1 = 0.007406337$
$b_2 = 0.026100013$

SPSS
$b_0 = 2.340$
$b_1 = 7.406E-03$
$b_2 = 2.610E-02$

Minitab
$b_0 = 2.3405$
$b_1 = 0.007406$
$b_2 = 0.02610$

SAS
$b_0 = 2.34045$
$b_1 = 0.00741$
$b_2 = 0.02610$

11.9 Regression equation:
log (profits) = −1.49842 + 0.238021 × log (Assets) + 0.478135 × log (Sales)

11.10 New regression coefficients: $b_0 = 2.345977$, $b_1 = 0.007127$, $b_2 = 0.026381$
Once Citigroup was removed from the regression analysis, the regression coefficients changed to the new values above. b_0 and b_2 both slightly increased, while b_1 was slightly decreased.

11.11 New regression coefficients: $b_0 = 1.554698$, $b_1 = 0.004965$, $b_2 = 0.055349$
Once General Motors and Wal-Mart were removed from the regression analysis, the regression coefficients changed to the new values above. b_0 and b_2 both increased, while b_1 decreased.

11.12
```
-2  5
-2
-1
-1
-0  76
-0  44444332200
 0  011112223
 0  55679
 1  23
```

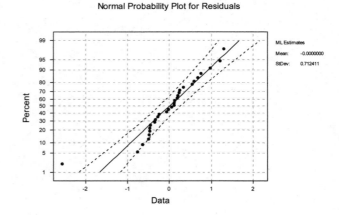

Normal Probability Plot for Residuals

11.13

Excel	SPSS
s = 2.449581635	s = 2.44958
s^2 = 6.000450185	s^2 = 6.000
name for s: Standard Error	name for s: Standard Error of the Estimate
Minitab	SAS
s = 2.450	s = 2.44958
s^2 = 6.000	s^2 = 6.00045
name for s: S	name for s: Root Mean Square Error (MSE)

11.14 s_y = 3.036641161. We expect s to be smaller than s_y because we expect assets and sales to have some effect on profits. Although there are many variables that affect the response variable profits, a smaller value for s when considering the effects of sales and assets demonstrates their contribution toward explaining the response in the variability of profits.

11.15   **a)** See table below. **b)** See stemplots below. **c)** Price: fairly Normally distributed, no outliers. Weight: fairly Normally distributed, one low outlier. Amps: very left-skewed, no outliers. Depth: fairly Normally distributed, one low outlier (depth of 2.2).

Variable	$\bar{x}$	s	Min	Q1	M	Q3	Max
Price	91.84	43.308	30	50	90	140	150
Weight	11.21	1.032	9	11	11	12	13
Amps	13.53	1.744	10	12	14	15	15
Depth	2.416	0.0765	2.2	2.4	2.4	2.5	2.5

```
Price Stem-and-Leaf Plot              Weight Stem-and-Leaf Plot

Frequency     Stem & Leaf            Frequency     Stem & Leaf

    4.00      0 . 3344                   1.00  Extremes    (=<9.0)
    6.00      0 . 557889                 3.00      10 . 000
    6.00      1 . 011344                  .00      10 .
    3.00      1 . 555                    8.00      11 . 00000000
                                          .00      11 .
Stem width:        100                   5.00      12 . 00000
                                          .00      12 .
                                         2.00      13 . 00

                                     Stem width:        1
Amps Stem-and-Leaf Plot              Depth Stem-and-Leaf Plot

Frequency     Stem & Leaf            Frequency     Stem & Leaf

    2.00      10 . 00                     1.00  Extremes    (=<2.20)
     .00      11 .                        1.00      23 . 0
    4.00      12 . 0000                    .00      23 .
    2.00      13 . 00                    11.00      24 . 00000000000
    2.00      14 . 00                      .00      24 .
    9.00      15 . 000000000             6.00      25 . 000000

Stem width:        1                 Stem width:       .1
```

11.16 **a)** See the scatterplots that follow. Price and Weight: positive, linear, weak. Price and Amps: positive, linear, moderate. Price and Depth: negative, linear, weak. Amps and Weight: positive, linear, moderate. Weight and Depth: negative, linear, weak. Amps and Depth: negative, linear, moderate. **b)** See the correlation table that follows.   **c)** It's hard to say whether there are any unusual observations or outliers because the relationships are fairly weak. **d)** Amps is most strongly correlated with Price, but Weight and Depth have significant correlations with Amps, too.

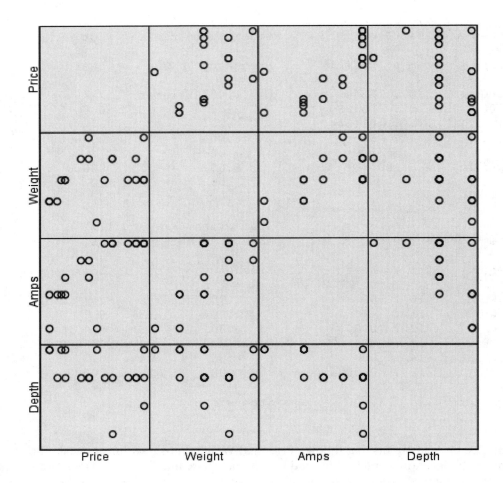

Correlations

		Price	Weight	Amps	Depth
Price	Pearson Correlation	1	.401	.785**	-.420
	Sig. (2-tailed)		.089	.000	.073
	N	19	19	19	19
Weight	Pearson Correlation	.401	1	.676**	-.326
	Sig. (2-tailed)	.089		.001	.173
	N	19	19	19	19
Amps	Pearson Correlation	.785**	.676**	1	-.607**
	Sig. (2-tailed)	.000	.001		.006
	N	19	19	19	19
Depth	Pearson Correlation	-.420	-.326	-.607**	1
	Sig. (2-tailed)	.073	.173	.006	
	N	19	19	19	19

**. Correlation is significant at the 0.01 level (2-tailed).

11.17 **a)** $\hat{y} = -303.445 - 10.808 \cdot \text{weight} + 25.674 \cdot \text{amps} + 70.030 \cdot \text{depth}$

  b) $27.831 = \sqrt{774.574}$.

11.18 **a)** \$71.64. **b)** \$127.04. **c)** -\$36.44. **d)** Part (c) is unreliable. This is an extrapolation. You are unlikely to be paid for purchasing a saw! Twenty pounds is much heavier than the other saws in the sample.

11.19 **a)** A histogram shows that the residuals are fairly Normally distributed with no outliers. The Normal probability plot also looks good. See the graphs below.

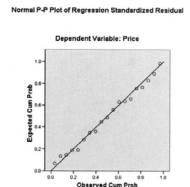

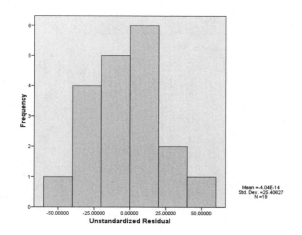

b) See the residual plots that follow. Residuals vs. Weight plot looks good with possibly an outlier at Weight = 9. Residuals vs. Amps looks good with possibly an outlier at Amps = 10. Residuals vs. Depth looks funnel shaped.

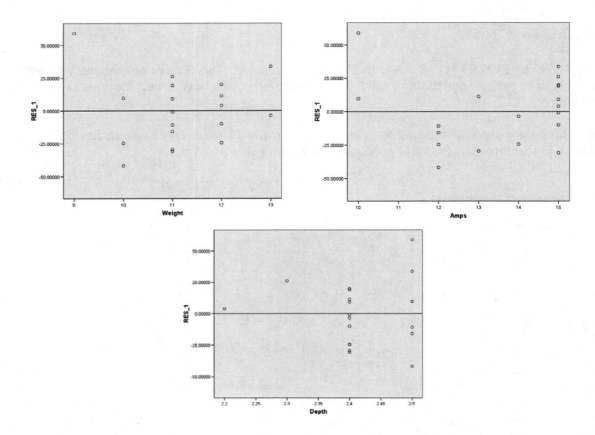

11.20   **a)** See the residual plot below. There is a downhill trend. As the rankings increase, the residuals go negative.

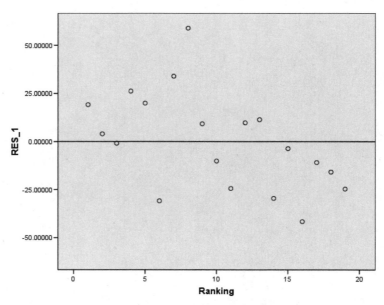

b) Yes, there is information in the ranks that is not contained in the explanatory variables used or the multiple regression analysis. Otherwise, the residuals would look more randomly distributed

on the residual plot. **c)** The regression line equation is
$$\hat{y} = -349.269 + 0.72 \cdot weight + 12.799 \cdot amps + 127.784 \cdot depth - 4.878 \cdot ratings.$$ The P-values for the coefficients for Rank and Amps are significant, but not for Weight and Depth (See SPSS output below). All the residual plots look good except for possibly an outlier for Depth = 2.2. The new residual plot for residuals vs. Rank is given below. The value of the regression standard error is now 19.049, which is lower than it was when Rank was not included.

Model Summary[b]

Model	R	R Square	Adjusted R Square	Std. Error of the Estimate
1	.922[a]	.850	.807	19.049

a. Predictors: (Constant), Ranking, Weight, Depth, Amps

b. Dependent Variable: Price

ANOVA[b]

Model		Sum of Squares	df	Mean Square	F	Sig.
1	Regression	28680.671	4	7170.168	19.761	.000[a]
	Residual	5079.856	14	362.847		
	Total	33760.526	18			

a. Predictors: (Constant), Ranking, Weight, Depth, Amps

b. Dependent Variable: Price

Coefficients[a]

Model		Unstandardized Coefficients		Standardized Coefficients			95% Confidence Interval for B	
		B	Std. Error	Beta	t	Sig.	Lower Bound	Upper Bound
1	(Constant)	-349.269	208.476		-1.675	.116	-796.406	97.868
	Weight	.720	6.558	.017	.110	.914	-13.345	14.785
	Amps	12.799	5.182	.515	2.470	.027	1.683	23.914
	Depth	127.784	75.916	.226	1.683	.114	-35.039	290.608
	Ranking	-4.878	1.149	-.634	-4.245	.001	-7.342	-2.413

a. Dependent Variable: Price

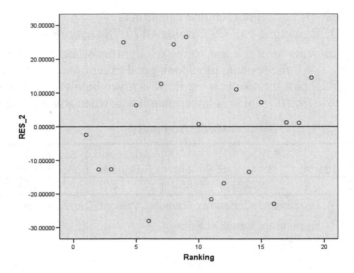

11.21   Saw 6 has the most negative residual of all, and Saws 2 and 11 both have negative residuals. However Saw 8 has a positive residual. Therefore, we cannot say that there is a relationship between rank and the residuals. A scatterplot of Residuals vs. Rank looks completely random.

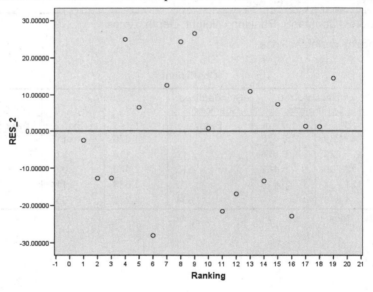

11.22   a) 8.3. **b)** The values do not need to correspond to a case in the data set to be valid, but these values should be in the range of the values in the original data to be considered prediction instead of extrapolation. **c)** The predicted value of y decreases by 3.2 units.

11.23   a)

Market Share	
Column1	
Mean	8.96
Standard deviation	7.74
Median	8.85
Minimum	1.3
Maximum	27.50
Q1	2.80
Q3	11.60

Assets	
Column1	
Mean	48.91
Standard deviation	76.16
Median	15.35
Minimum	1.30
Maximum	219.00
Q1	5.90
Q3	38.80

Accounts	
Column1	
Mean	794
Standard deviation	886
Median	509
Minimum	125
Maximum	2500
Q1	134
Q3	909

b) Market Share   **Accounts**   **Assets**

```
0 | 1  2  3  4        0 | 1  1  1  2  4     0 | 0  0  0  0  1  2  2  4
0 | 8  9              0 | 6  6  9           0 |
1 | 0  2  3           1 |                   1 |
1 |                   1 |                   1 | 6
2 |                   2 | 3                 2 | 2
2 | 8                 2 | 5                 2 |
```

c) All three stem plots are skewed to the right. The market share data set has one outlier, and both Accounts and Assets each have two outliers within the distribution of the data set.

11.24   a)

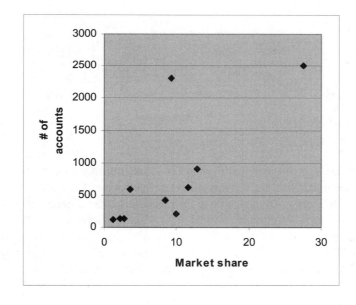

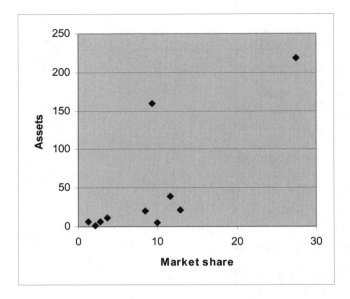

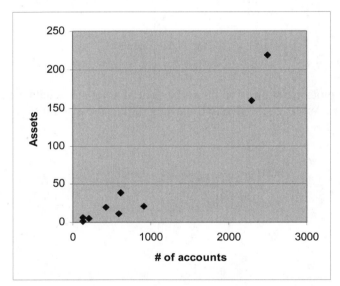

b) Each of the relationships between the market share, number of accounts, and assets appears to be positively correlated, with the strongest being assets versus number of accounts. There also appears to be two outliers with each of the three scatterplots. These outliers are the online brokerage firms of Charles Schwab and Fidelity. Charles Schwab is an obvious outlier in each of the examined variables; however, Fidelity is an outlier only in the number of accounts and assets. The market share for Fidelity seems lower than it should be. This factor could be responsible for a lower correlation between market share and the other variables.

c)

	Market share	Accounts	Assets
Market share	1		
Accounts	0.75318288	1	
Assets	0.7801696	0.968272	1

11.25 **a)** Market share = 5.159 + −0.000312 × Accounts + 0.08277 × Assets.
b) Regression standard error (s) = 5.4876.

11.26 **a)**

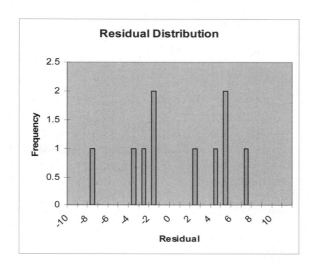

There may be one possible outlier with regard to Fidelity, or observation #5, which has a residual value of −8.

b)

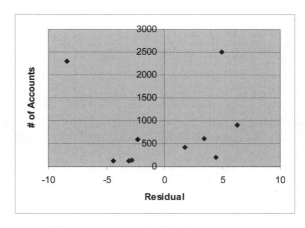

Again, the two outliers are Charles Schwab and Fidelity.

c)

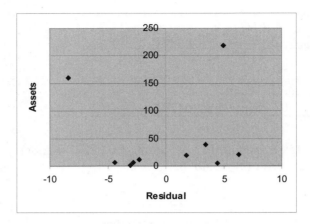

Again, the two outliers are Charles Schwab and Fidelity.

11.27   a)

	Market share	Accounts	Assets
Mean	6.6	392	13.8
Standard deviation	4.6	292	12.3
Median	6.0	317	9.0
Minimum	1.3	125	1.3
Maximum	12.9	909	38.8
Q1	2.5	132	5.7
Q3	10.8	603	19.8

b)

Market share				Accounts					Assets			
0	1 2 3 4			**0**	1 1 1 2 4				**0**	1 6 6 7		
0	8			**0**	6 6 9				**1**	1		
1	0 2 3			**1**					**2**	0 1		
1				**1**					**3**	9		

c) The distribution of brokerage firms without the data for Schwab and Fidelity has a much shorter range and no outliers compared to the results of 11.13. The largest effect was on the mean and standard deviation.

11.28 **a)**

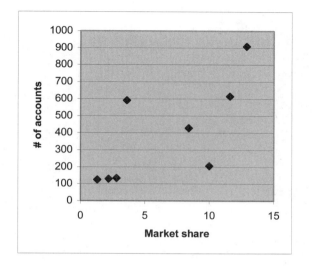

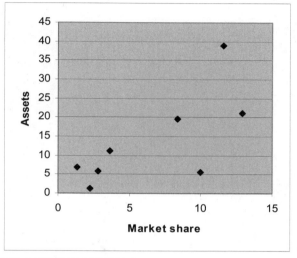

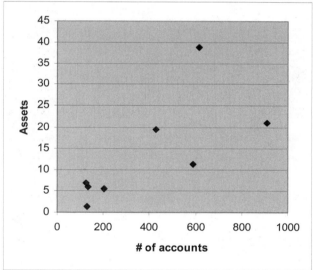

b) There appears to be moderate positive correlation among all three pairs of variables. In the absence of Schwab and Fidelity it is much easier to see the relative position of the brokerage firms to each other with respect to the different variables.

c) The correlation between the variables has been reduced compared to the values obtained in Exercise 11.14, and the values are consistently around (r = 0.7).

11.29 **a)** Market Share = 1.845 + 0.00663 × Accounts + 0.1566 × Assets.

b) Regression standard error (s) = 3.50. The coefficients of the regression equation have all changed when a regression analysis was done without Schwab and Fidelity. The standard error (s) was also reduced.

11.30   a)

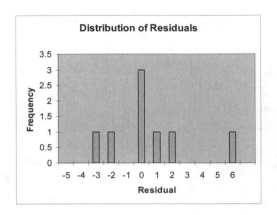

There is a possible outlier for Datek with a residual value of 6.

b)

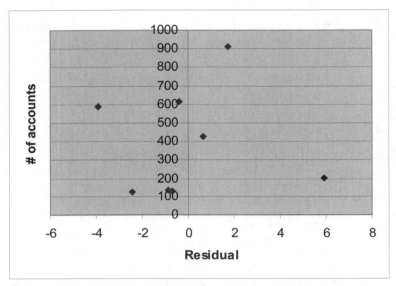

The distribution appears well spread out with no obvious trend.

	Market share	*Accounts*	*Assets*
Market share	1		
Accounts	0.711784	1	
Assets	0.710687	0.707353	1

c)

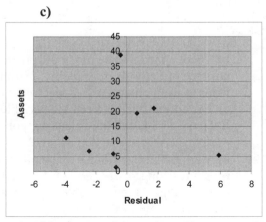

This distribution also appears to have no obvious trend, with one possible outlier, TD Waterhouse.

11.31   a)

Gross Total Sales	
Mean	320.30
Standard error	36.02
Median	263.29
Standard deviation	180.09
Skewness	1.66
Range	798.20
Minimum	92.30
Maximum	890.50

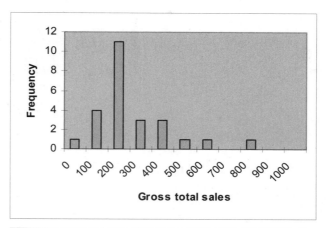

Cash Items	
Mean	20.52
Standard error	2.36
Median	19.00
Standard deviation	11.80
Skewness	1.26
Range	50.00
Minimum	5.00
Maximum	55.00

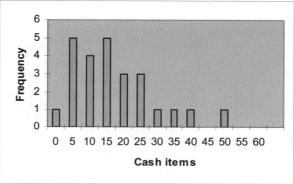

Check Items	
Mean	20.04
Standard error	2.82
Median	15.00
Standard deviation	14.07
Skewness	1.45
Range	54.00
Minimum	3.00
Maximum	57.00

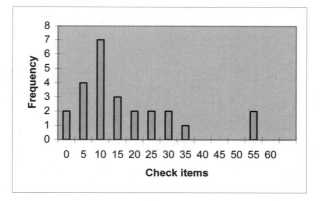

Credit Card Items	
Mean	7.68
Standard error	1.60
Median	5.00
Standard deviation	7.98
Skewness	1.33
Range	28.00
Minimum	0
Maximum	28.00

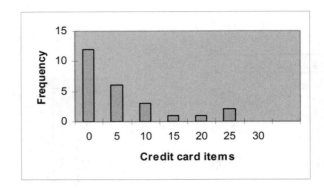

Each of the distributions of the variables is skewed to the right. Both Gross Total Sales and Cash Items appear to have potential outliers. The distribution for Check Items has two obvious outliers.

b)

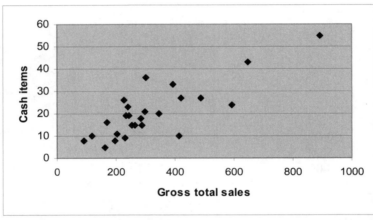

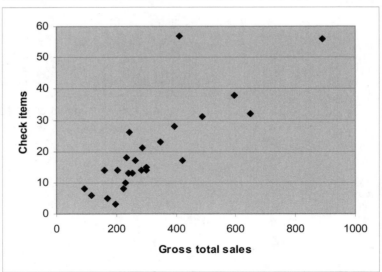

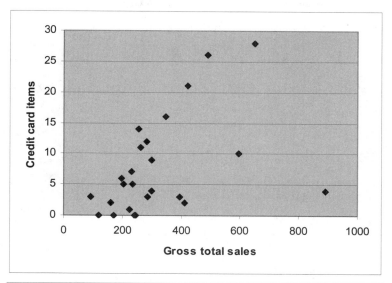

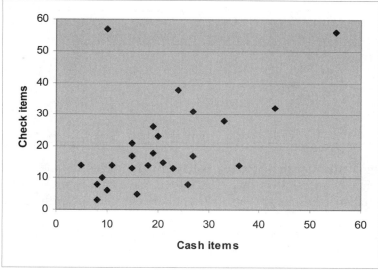

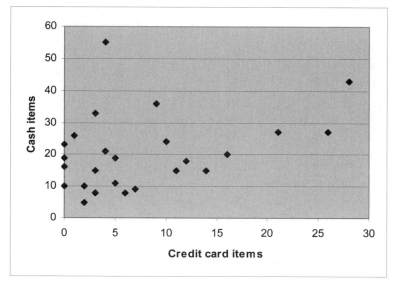

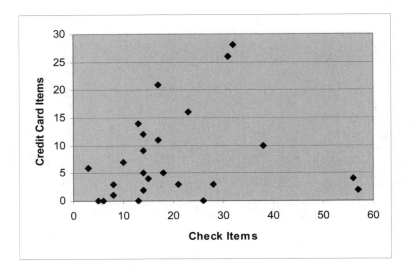

	Gross Total Sales	Cash Items	Check Items	Credit Card Items
Gross Total sales	1			
Cash items	0.816956	1		
Check items	0.821062	0.516425	1	
Credit card items	0.457943	0.352708	0.176447	1

After observing the relationship between each pair of variables and the correlation analysis, it can be concluded that both Cash Items and Check Items have a fairly strong correlation with Gross Total Sales. Credit Card Items appears to have a weak correlation with all the other variables.

11.32 **a)** Gross Total Sales = 0.3412 + 7.1003 × Cash Items + 6.987 × Check Items + 4.4579 × Credit Card Items. **b)** Regression Standard Error (s) = 54.8476.

11.33

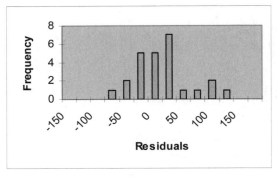

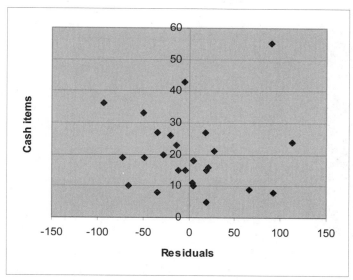

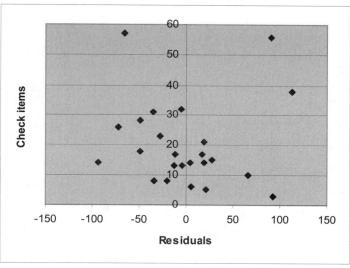

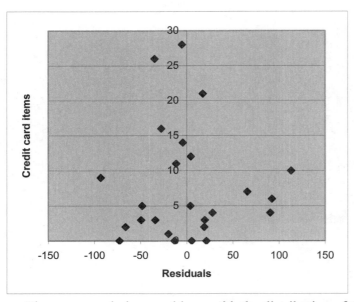

There are no obvious problems with the distribution of the residuals or the plots against the three explanatory variables.

11.34   a)

Total billing	
Mean	6.30
Standard error	0.85
Median	6.30
Mode	2.70
Standard deviation	4.26
Skewness	0.54
Range	13.40
Minimum	1.60
Maximum	15.00

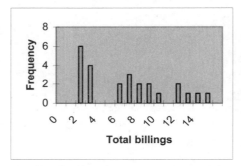

The distribution is skewed to the right and has no obvious outliers.

Architects	
Mean	10.04
Standard error	1.74
Median	5.00
Mode	5.00
Standard deviation	8.68
Skewness	1.26
Range	29.00
Minimum	2.00
Maximum	31.00

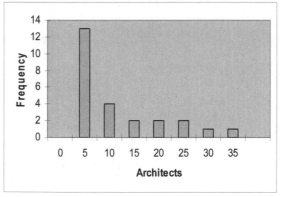

The distribution is skewed to the right and has no obvious outliers.

Engineers	
Mean	7.08
Standard error	1.92
Median	2.00
Mode	0
Standard deviation	9.62
Skewness	1.49
Range	35.00
Minimum	0
Maximum	35.00

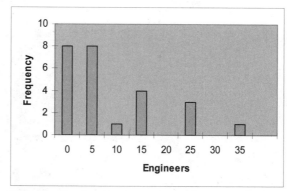

The distribution is skewed to the right and has one possible outlier.

Staff	
Mean	60.6
Standard error	8.94
Median	61.00
Mode	15.00
Standard deviation	44.71
Skewness	0.51
Range	148.00
Minimum	7.00
Maximum	155.00

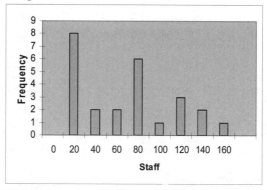

The distribution is skewed to the right and has no obvious outliers.

b)

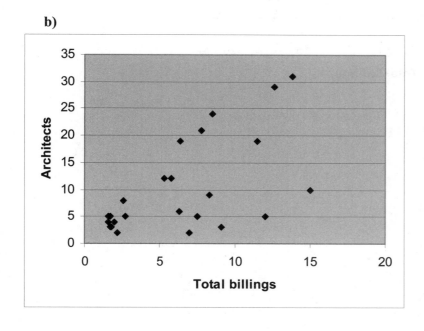

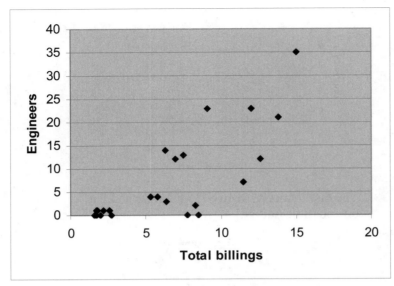

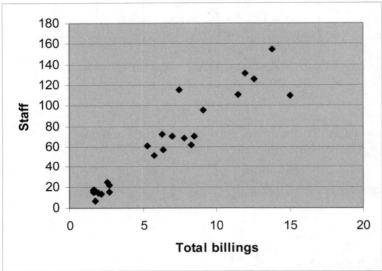

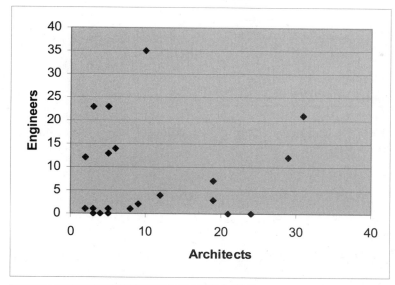

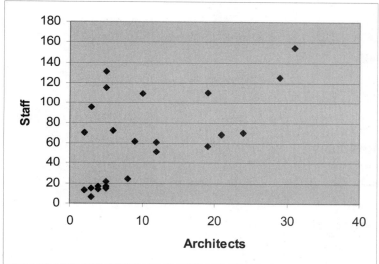

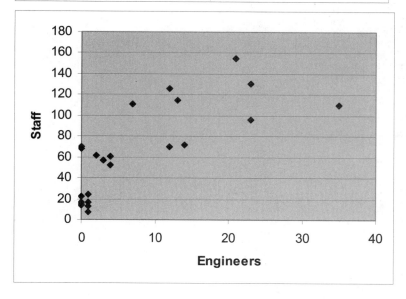

	TBill98	Arch	Eng	Staff
TBill98	1			
Arch	0.618034	1		
Eng	0.788269	0.125229	1	
Staff	0.947341	0.580601	0.778777	1

11.35 **a)** Total Billings = 0.8832 + 0.1378 × Architects + 0.16008 × Engineers + 0.04783 × Staff.
b) Regression standard error (s) = 1.1617.

11.36

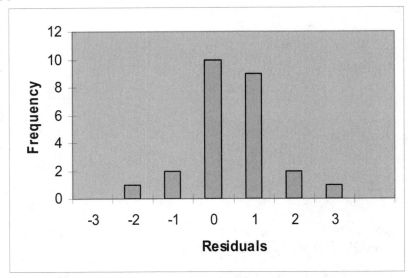

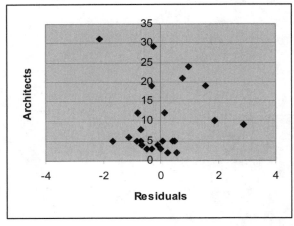

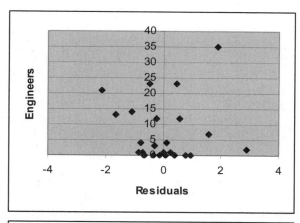

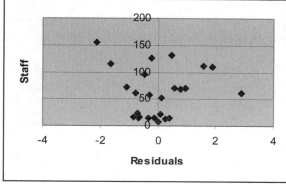

The distribution of the residuals and the plots against the explanatory variables does not appear to have any problems.

11.37   Excel
Regression coefficient for HSS: 0.034315568
Standard error for HSS: 0.03755888
t-stat for HSS: 0.913647251
DOF: 223
P-value: 0.361902429

SPSS
Regression coefficient for HSS: 3.432E-02
Standard error for HSS: 0.038
t-stat for HSS: 0.914
DOF: 223
P-value: 0.362

Minitab
Regression coefficient for HSS: 0.03432
Standard error for HSS: 0.03756
t-stat for HSS: 0.91
DOF: 223
P-value: 0.362

SAS
Regression coefficient for HSS: 0.03432
Standard error for HSS: 0.03756
t-stat for HSS: 0.91
DOF: 223
P-value: 0.3619

From this information, we can conclude that HSS does not help predict GPA, given that HSM and HSE scores are also available.

11.38 *P*-value = 4.55E-07. Though science grades are not significant when math and English grades are also in the model, when regression analysis is performed on HSS alone, it can be highly significant in predicting college GPA. This is a good demonstration of how the inference of any one explanatory variable depends on what other explanatory variables are in the model. Alone, high school science grades are helpful in predicting future performance; however, when coupled with math and English grades in the model, science grades are not as helpful in predicting future performance.

11.39 GPA = 0624 + 0.183 × HSE + 0.0607. HSM is still the most important explanatory variable in predicting college GPA with a P-value = 3.51E-08, which is smaller than the model including HSS. HSE also became more helpful in predicting GPA in the absence of HSS in the model with a smaller *P*-value = 0.0820.

11.40 **a)** (1.58875, 2.07084). **b)** (0.42964, 3.22995)

11.41 **a)** 95% confidence interval for the mean college GPA = (1.60108, 2.08062). 95% prediction interval = (0.44146, 3.24024). The models give similar values, but the intervals in this exercise are both shifted slightly higher.

11.42 F = 27.89, df = 223, *P*-value = 1.577E-11. When HSS is removed from the model, the F-statistic is increased from a previous value of 18.86 and the *P*-value is also significantly reduced. From these data, we can conclude that there is no evidence to suggest that the remaining variables HSM and HSE are equal to zero.

11.43 **a)** HSM, HSS, HSE (20.5%). **b)** HSM, HSE (20.2%). **c)** HSM, HSS (20%). **d)** HSS, HSE (12.3%). **e)** HSM (19.1%). Almost all the information used to predict GPA is contained in HSM scores.

11.44 **a)** Yes, R^2 is equal to 21.15% according to the model.

b)

All var. in	Coefficients	Standard error	t Stat	P-value
SATM	0.000943593	0.000686	1.37618690	0.17017578
SATV	−0.000407850	0.000592	−0.68905989	0.49151830

Just SAT var.	Coefficients	Standard error	t Stat	P-value
SATM	0.002282834	0.000663	3.44363406	0.00068651
SATV	−2.45619E-05	0.000618	−0.03971405	0.96835695

When the scores from HSM, HSS, and HSE are included in the model, it becomes apparent from examining the data that the SATM scores are somewhat more helpful in predicting college GPA than SATV scores. When an analysis is performed with only the SAT data, this distinction between the two different scores becomes even greater. SATV scores are terrible at predicting future college GPAs for computer science majors, while SATM scores become a better predictor in the absence of the other explanatory variables.

11.45 $R^2_1 = 21.15\%$, $R^2_2 = 6.34\%$. $F = 13.65$, $df = n - p - 1 = 218$, $q = 3$. Software provides a *P*-value < 0.0001. High school grades contribute significantly to explaining GPA, even when SAT scores are included in the model.

11.46 **a)** $t = 3.31$, $df = 40 - 30 - 1 = 9$, $0.005 < $ *P*-value < 0.01. Reject the null hypothesis. There is evidence that the coefficient of P5 is not zero. **b)** (0.1975, 1.0525). Since we rejected the null hypothesis in part (a), we did not expect the confidence interval to include 0, and it does not include zero.

11.47 **a)** $t = -8.917$, $df = 40 - 30 - 1 = 9$, *P*-value < 0.001. There is strong evidence that the coefficient of P5 is not 0. **b)** (-1.487, -0.885). Since we rejected the null hypothesis in part (a), we did not expect the confidence interval to include 0.

11.48 In Exercise 11.46, the change in proportion of DC plans is positive. In Exercise 11.47, the change in proportion of DB plans is negative. This makes sense because employees have been switching from DB to DC plans.

11.49 The difference in signs makes sense because employees generally sign up for either the DC or the DB plan. The total number of dual-earner couples available to sign up for a plan probably stays about the same from year to year, however as more dual-earner couples sign up for DB plans, fewer would be signing up for DC plans.

11.50 **a)** x_1: (-2.83, 27.03). x_2: (8.80, 25.80). **b)** x_1: (-2.18, 26.38). x_2: (-0.83, 15.43). **c)** In part (a), do not reject the null hypothesis for the coefficient for x_1, but do reject the null hypothesis for x_2. In part (b), do not reject the null hypothesis for the coefficients for either x_1 or x_2.

11.51 **a)** The squared multiple correlation, R^2, gives the proportion of the variation in the response variable that is explained by the explanatory variables. **b)** The null hypothesis should be $H_0 : \beta_2 = 0$. **c)** One of the assumptions for multiple regression is that the deviations ε_i are independent Normal random variables with mean 0 and a common standard deviation σ. Another possible correction would be: in each subpopulation, *y* varies Normally with a mean given by the population regression equation.

11.52 **a)** F-statistic: $df = 6$ and 60. **b)** Standard deviation is equal to the square root of the mean standard error (MSE) = 6. **c)** Using Table D with t(60): (7.7, 17.3). **d)** $t = 5.21$, $df = 60$, *P*-value is close to 0, so reject the null hypothesis. There is evidence that the regression coefficient for the first explanatory variable is not zero.

11.53 **a)** $F = 4$, which has the F(2, 60) distribution. *P*-value = 0.023403 from software. **b)** $R^2 = $ SSR / SST. SST = SSR + SSE = 16 + 120 = 136. $R^2 = 16 / 136 = 0.1176$.

11.54 **a)** H_0: All 13 explanatory variables have a coefficient of zero. H_a: At least one of the variables has a nonzero coefficient. df are (13,2215). *P*-value = 0. Conclude that at least one of the coefficients is not zero. **b)** 29.7% of the variation in interest rates is explained by the 13 explanatory variables.

11.55 **a)** The hypotheses for each of the explanatory variables are $H_0 : \beta = 0$ and $H_a : \beta \neq 0$. The degrees of freedom for the t statistics are 2215. Values that are less than -1.96 or greater than 1.96 will lead to rejection of the null hypothesis. **b)** The significant explanatory variables are loan size, length of loan, percent down payment, cosigner, unsecured loan, total income, bad credit report, young borrower, own home and years at current address. If an explanatory variable is concluded to be insignificant, then that means the variable does not contribute significantly to the prediction of the response variable. **c)** After examining the signs of each of the 13 explanatory variables with regards to the nature of the variable, it is obvious that a favorable interest rate is awarded to variables that demonstrate some form of lower risk. The interest rate is lower for larger loans, lower for longer length loans, lower for a higher percent down payment; cosigner, lower when there is a cosigner, higher for an unsecured loan, lower for those with higher total income, higher when there is a bad credit report, higher when there is a young borrower, lower when the borrower owns a home and lower when the years at current address is higher.

11.56 **a)** The hypotheses about the explanatory variables are $H_0 : \beta_j = 0$ and $H_a : \beta_j \neq 0$. The degrees of freedom for the F statistic are 5650 and 13. P-value = 0. At least one of the explanatory variables has a coefficient that is not zero. **b)** 14.1% of the variation in interest rates is explained by the 13 explanatory variables.

11.57 **a)** The hypotheses about the jth explanatory variable are $H_0: \beta_j = 0$ and $H_a: \beta_j \neq 0$. The degrees of freedom for the t statistics are 5650. At the 5% level, values of that are less than -1.96 or greater than 1.96 will lead to rejection of the null hypothesis. **b)** The statistically significant explanatory variables are loan size, length of loan, percent down payment and unsecured loan. **c)** The interest rate is lower for larger loans, lower for longer length loans, lower for a higher percent down payment and higher for an unsecured loan. Again, these results indicate banks' tendency to give lower interest rates to loans that demonstrate lower risk of default. For example, an unsecured loan is more risky than a secured loan.

11.58 Less than half of the variance in the interest rates is explained by the explanatory variables in the indirect loan analysis than the explanatory variables in the direct loan analysis. This means that the borrower's characteristics examined through the explanatory data has much more weight when determining the interest rate through a direct loan.

11.59 **a)** y varies Normally with a mean $\mu_{\text{GPA}} = \beta_0 + 8\beta_1 + 9\beta_2 + 7\beta_3$.
b) $\mu_{\text{GPA}} = 0.59 + 8(0.169) + 9(0.034) + 7(0.045)$. The GPA of students with a B+ in math, A- in science and B in English have a normal distribution with an estimated mean of 2.563.

11.60 **a)** y varies normally with a mean $\mu_{\text{GPA}} = \beta_0 + 7\beta_1 + 6\beta_2 + 9\beta_3$.
b) $\mu_{\text{GPA}} = 0.59 + 7(0.169) + 6(0.034) + 9(0.045)$. The GPA of students with a B in math, B- in science and A- in English have a normal distribution with an estimated mean of 2.382.

11.61 **a)** $y_i = \beta_0 + \beta_{2002}x_{2002i} + \beta_{\text{years}}x_{\text{years}i} + \varepsilon_i$. **b)** $\beta_0, \beta_{2002}, \beta_{\text{years}}, \sigma$. **c)** $b_0 = 30236.981$, $b_{2002} = 0.865$, $b_{\text{years}} = 57.392$, $s = 9035.243$. **d)** F = 20.177 with degrees of freedom 2 and 13, and P-value = 0.000 from software. We conclude years in rank and 2002 salary contain information that can be used to predict 2005 salary. **e)** $R^2 = 75.6\%$. **(f)** For 2002 salary, $t = 2.750$, *P*-value = 0.017, reject the null hypothesis. For years in rank, $t = 0.109$, *P*-value = 0.915, do not reject the null hypothesis. Both tests use df = 13. There is evidence the coefficient for 2002 salary is significantly different from zero, but the coefficient for years in rank is not.

11.62 **a)** The stemplot shows residuals fairly Normally distributed with one high outlier at years = 10, 2002 salary = $102,300. See the histogram and Normal probability plot below. **b)** The residual plots look fairly good except for that one outlier mentioned in part (a).

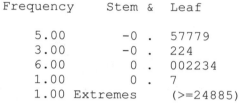

```
Unstandardized Residual
Stem-and-Leaf Plot

  Frequency      Stem &   Leaf

     5.00        -0 .  57779
     3.00        -0 .  224
     6.00         0 .  002234
     1.00         0 .  7
     1.00  Extremes     (>=24885)

  Stem width:    10000.00
  Each leaf:        1 case(s)
```

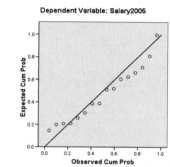

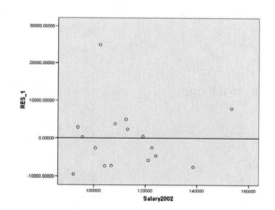

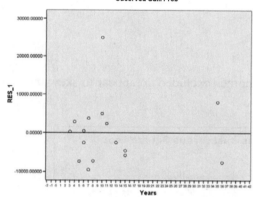

11.63 **a)** 2005 Predicted Salary = 112,518.7 + 1351.837 (years in rank). **b)** $t = 4.725$, df = 14, and *P*-value is close to 0. Years in rank is a useful variable for predicting 2005 salary. **c)** Years in rank included with 2002 salary produced these results, coefficient = 57.392, $t = 0.109$, df = 13 and *P*-value = 0.915. When included with the data concerning 2002 salary, years in rank is not very useful in predicting 2005 salary; however, rank in years is useful when performing the same regression analysis without the data from 2002 salary.

11.64 $F = [(n-p-1)/q] [(R^2_1 + R^2_2)/(1-R^2_1)]$, $F = [(82-10-1)/4] [(0.77-0.06)/(1-0.77)]$
$F = 54.8$, df = 71 and 10, *P*-value = 0. The conclusion is that the human capital variables do provide significant prediction of bank branch manager salaries.

11.65   Price (leaf unit $1000)

```
 5 22
 6 2459
 7 2233566
 8 01124444779999
 9 234469
10 4
11 449
12 4499
13
14
15
16
17 39
18
19 9
```

Sq Ft (leaf unit 100sf)

```
0 67777
0 88899999
1 000011
1 22223333
1 455555
1 66666
1 89
2 01
2 22
```

The seven homes excluded do appear to skew the distributions to the right.

11.66

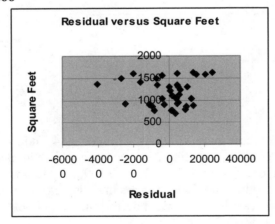

11.67   a) Price = 45,298 + 34.32 (Sq Ft). For Sq Ft = 1000, Predicted Price = $79,622. For Sq Ft = 1500, Predicted Price = $96,783.

11.68

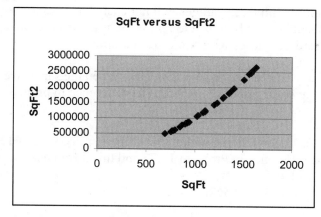

	Sq Ft	Sq Ft2
Sq Ft	1	
SqFt2	0.995168	1

11.69 Price = 81273.37 + −30.14 (Sq Ft) + 0.027 (Sq Ft2). For Sq Ft = 1000, Predicted Price = $78,253. For Sq Ft = 1500, Predicted Price = $97,042. Overall, the two sets of predictions are fairly similar.

11.70 **a)** Mean Price for houses with 3 or more bedrooms = $90,845.83. Mean Price for houses with fewer than 3 bedrooms = $75,700. **b)** $90,845.83 − $75,700 = $15,145.83. This is indeed the value of the coefficient in Example 11.21.

11.71 From Minitab, t = -2.88 *P*-value = 0.0068 df = 35.   These values agree with Example 11.21.

11.72 **a)** Homes with 1 bathroom: Price = $77,504 + 20,533(0) + 12,616(0) + 44,896(0) = 77,504. **b)** Homes with 1.5 bathrooms: Price = 77,504 + 20,533 (1) + 12,616(0) + 44,896(0). **c)** Homes with 2 bathrooms: Price = 77,504 + 20,533 (0) + 12,616(1) + 44,896(0) = 90,120. **d)** Homes with 2.5 bathrooms: Price = 77,504 + 20,533 (0) + 12,616(0) + 44,896(1) = 122400. **e)** We can say that homes with two bathrooms are sold for $12,616 more than houses with only one bathroom on average.

11.73

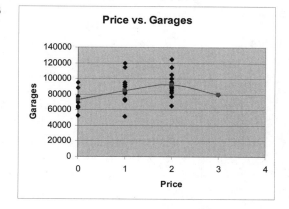

The trend is increasing and roughly linear as one examines from 0 to 2 garages and then levels off.

11.74   Though the inclusion of the price of the house with three garages will not change the results of the scatter plot significantly, it would probably be the best idea to remove it as an unusual data point and only examine the scatterplot regarding houses with two or fewer garages.

11.75   When a 1400 ft^2 home has an extra half bath the average price is $99,719. When the same size home does not have an extra half bath, the average price is $84,585. The difference in price is $15,134.

11.76   For a home with a half bath, price = $113,311. For a home without a half bath, price = $87,615. The difference is $25,696. Comparing the difference in Problem 11.75 and this difference we see it can be found using the difference in the square footage:
$(1600 - 1400) \times 52.81 = 10,562$. $25,696 - 15,134 = 10,562$.

11.77   No, it does not make sense to compare homes with whole and half baths less than 700 ft^2 because in this study no homes that small have a half bath.

11.78   **a)**

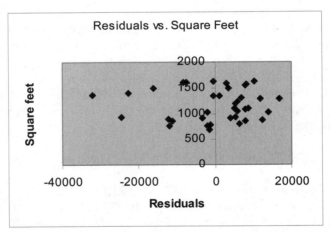

The residuals seem to be on the positive side rather than evenly distributed between positive and negative. There is a greater spread in values on the negative side than on the positive side.
b) These low residuals correspond to homes 1, 8, and 24. These are lower priced homes with larger square footage than would be expected. **c)** The histogram shows that the residuals are not Normally distributed but heavily skewed to the left.

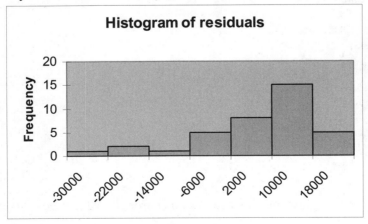

11.79

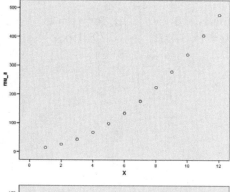

a) The relationship is increasing and curved.

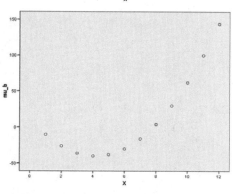

b) The relationship is curved and decreases up to x = 4 and then begins to increase.

c) The relationship is decreasing and slightly curved.

11.80 **a)** For Group A the mean response is 10, and for Group B the mean response is 13. **b)** For Group A, the mean response is 10, and for Group B, the mean response is 40. **c)** For Group A, the mean response is 10, and for Group B, the mean response is 310.

11.81 For each equation, the difference in means is equal to the coefficient of x. This will be true in general.

11.82

Part	Graph	μ_y for $x_1 = 0$	μ_y for $x_1 = 1$
a)	The relationships are both increasing, with the values of μ_y greater for $x_1 = 1$ than for $x_1 = 0$.	$80 + 7x_2$	$120 + 19x_2$

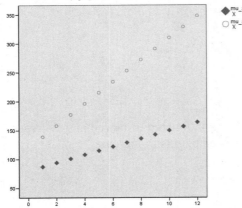

Part	Graph	μ_y for $x_1 = 0$	μ_y for $x_1 = 1$
b)	The relationship for $x_1 = 1$ is fairly horizontal, while the line representing $x_1 = 0$ is increasing.	$60 + 7x_2$	$52 - x_2$

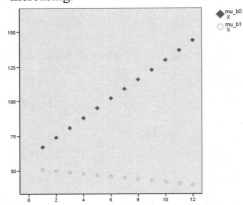

Part	Graph	μ_y for $x_1 = 0$	μ_y for $x_1 = 1$
c)	The relationships are opposite of each other. For $x_1 = 0$ the relationship is increasing, for $x_1 = 1$, the relationship is decreasing.	$200 + 7x_2$	$203 - 7x_2$

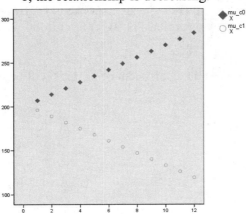

11.83 For part (a), the difference in slopes is $19 - 7 = 12$. This is the coefficient of x_1x_2. The difference in intercepts is $120 - 80 = 40$, which is the coefficient of x_1. This is true in general.

11.84 **a)** $\mu_y = \beta_o + \beta_1 x_1 + \beta_2 x_2 + \beta_3 x_3 + \beta_4 x_4$, where $x_1 = 0$ or 1, $x_2 = 0$ or 1, $x_3 = 0$ or 1, and $x_4 = 0$ or 1. $x_1 = 1$, $x_2 = 0$, $x_3 = 0$, and $x_4 = 0$ corresponds to the first value of the categorical variable. $x_1 = 0$, $x_2 = 1$, $x_3 = 0$, and $x_4 = 0$ corresponds to the second value of the categorical variable. $x_1 = 0$, $x_2 = 0$, $x_3 = 1$, and $x_4 = 0$ corresponds to the third value of the categorical variable. $x_1 = 0$, $x_2 = 0$, $x_3 = 0$, and $x_4 = 1$ corresponds to the fourth value of the categorical variable. $x_1 = 0$, $x_2 = 0$, $x_3 = 0$, and $x_4 = 0$ corresponds to the fifth value of the categorical variable.

b) $\mu_y = \beta_o + \beta_1 x_1 + \beta_2 x_2 + \beta_3 x_3 + \beta_4 x_4 + \beta_5 x_1 x_4$. $x_1 = 0$ or 1, and corresponds to the first categorical variable, $x_2 = 0$ or 1 and $x_3 = 0$ or 1, and both correspond to the second categorical value with $x_2 = 1$, $x_3 = 0$ corresponding to the first value of this categorical variable; $x_2 = 0$, $x_3 = 1$ corresponding to the second value of this categorical variable, and $x_2 = 0$, $x_3 = 0$ corresponding to the third value of this categorical variable. x_4 is the quantitative variable.

c) $\mu_y = \beta_0 + \beta_1 x + \beta_2 x^2 + \beta_3 x^3 + \beta_4 x^4$.

11.85 **a)** Assets $= 7.6 - 0.00457 \times$ Account $+ 3.36 \times 10^{-5} \times$ Account^2 **b)** $(1.25 \times 10^{-5}, 5.47 \times 10^{-5})$ **c)** $t = 3.76$, df $= 7$, P-value $= 0.007$. The squared term lends predictive power to the model. **d)** Since the variables account and account^2 are dependent (or correlated) the model without the squared term will give a different coefficient on the account variable.

11.86 The regression model with the squared term is:
Salary $= 104,229 + 2706 \times$ Years $- 33.7 \times$ Years^2. The F statistic is 11.7 with a P-value of 0.001. The t statistic for the squared term is $t = -1.013$, df $= 13$, and the P-value $= 0.329$. The squared term does not contribute significantly to the prediction of salaries. The t statistic for Years is $t = 1.980$ with a P-value of 0.069. The R^2 is 0.643.

11.87 **a)** $R_1^2 = 0.643$, $R_2^2 = 0.615$. **b)** $F = 1.02$, df $= 1$ and 13, P-value is bigger than 0.100. The squared term does not add significant prediction of salaries. **c)** $(-1.013)^2 = 1.026$ (dfference due to rounding).

11.88 Let b_0 be the constant and b_1, b_2, and b_3 represent the coefficients on acetic acid, hydrogen sulfide, and lactic acid, respectively.

b_0	b_1	b_2	b_3	R^2
-61.50	15.65*	0	0	0.3020
-9.79	0	5.78*	0	0.5712
-29.86	0	0	37.72*	0.4960
-26.94	3.80	5.15*	0	0.5822
-27.59	0	3.95*	19.89*	0.6517
-51.37	5.57	0	31.39*	0.5203
-28.88	0.33	3.91*	19.67*	0.6518

The results above show that hydrogen sulfide and lactic acid concentration positively influence the taste variable in cheese. The best model would be the one with the highest R^2 value (0.6517). The model is: $\hat{y} = -27.59 + 3.95 \times$ hydrogen sulfide $+ 19.89 \times$ lactic acid.

11.89 **a)** Price vs. Promotions: negative, moderate, linear. Price vs. Discount: negative, weak, fairly linear. See the scatterplots below.

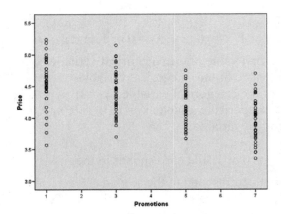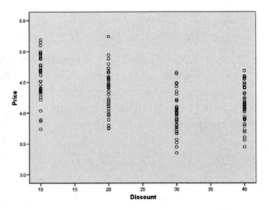

b) The table below shows the mean and standard deviation for expected price for each combination of promotion and discount.

		Discount		
Promotions	**10**	**20**	**30**	**40**
1	4.920, 0.1520	4.689, 0.2331	4.225, 0.3856	4.423, 0.1848
3	4.756, 0.2429	4.524, 0.2707	4.097, 0.2346	4.284, 0.2040
5	4.393, 0.2685	4.251, 0.2648	3.89, 0.1629	4.058, 0.1760
7	4.269, 0.2699	4.094, 0.2407	3.76, 0.2618	3.780, 0.2144

(b) and **(c)** At every promotion level, the 10% discount yields the highest expected price, then 20%, then 40%, then 30%. For every discount level, the 1 promotion yields the highest expected price, then 3, then 5, then 7.

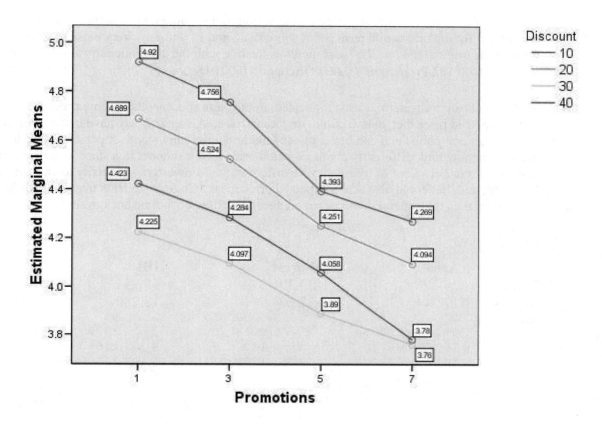

Estimated Marginal Means of Price

11.90 $\hat{y} = 5.118 - 0.102 \cdot promotions - 0.017 \cdot discount$ with F = 102.449 and *P*-value very close to 0. Both the coefficients for Promotions and Discount are significant. $R^2 = 56.6\%$ and s = 0.2644.

11.91 In the previous exercise, the residual plot for promotions looks okay, but the residual plot for discount seems to have a curved shape. See the plots below.

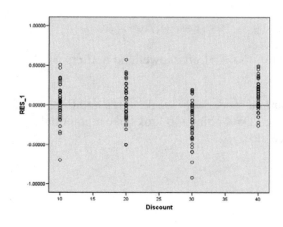
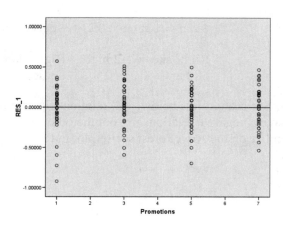

Therefore, try the quadratic term for discount and the interaction of discount and promotion. If the quadratic term for discount is used, the R^2 increases to 61.1%, the s decreases to 0.2511, the F test statistic is 81.809, and the *P*-value is still very close to 0. All coefficients are significantly different from 0.

If the quadratic term is removed and the interaction of discount and promotion is used instead, the coefficient for the interaction term is not significant, and R^2 and s are very close to what they were in the original model. The best model is the one with the quadratic term for discount:
$\hat{y} = 5.540 - 0.102 \text{ Promotion} - 0.060 \text{ Discount} + 0.001 \text{ Discount}^2$.

11.92 The subjects are trained, or at least interested, in business and may have some preconceived ideas about expected price the general public might not have. Also, they may have better math skills than the general public and can better understand how discounts work. A person sitting in a classroom may think differently about expected price than a shopper in a store with the item in front of him or her. Cost of living may be different in a Midwestern university town than in other locations, and that could also affect expected price ideas. College students may have different price ideas than the general pubic based on age, education, economic background, etc.

11.93 **a)**

	Area	**Forest**	**IBI**
Mean	28.29	39.39	65.94
St. dev.	17.714	32.204	18.280

```
Stemplot    0 .  2              0 .  00000033789     2 .  99
            0 .  5688999        1 .  0014778         3 .  2339
            1 .  0024           2 .  125             4 .  1367
            1 .  66889          3 .  123339          5 .  34556899
            2 .  111133         4 .  133799          6 .  01247
            2 .  66667889       5 .  229             7 .  1112456889
            3 .  112244         6 .  38              8 .  001222344556899
            3 .  9              7 .  599             9 .  1
            4 .                 8 .  069
            4 .  799            9 .  055
            5 .  244           10 .  00
            5 .  789

            2.00 Extremes
            (>=69)


Stem width: 10    Stem width: 10    Stem width: 10
```

Right-skewed, 2 high   Right-skewed, no   Left-skewed, no outliers.
outliers   outliers

b) See scatterplots below. All relationships are linear and moderately weak. Area and Forest have a negative relationship, but the others are positive. Data point #40 looks like a potential outlier on the Area/Forest scatterplot but not anyplace else.

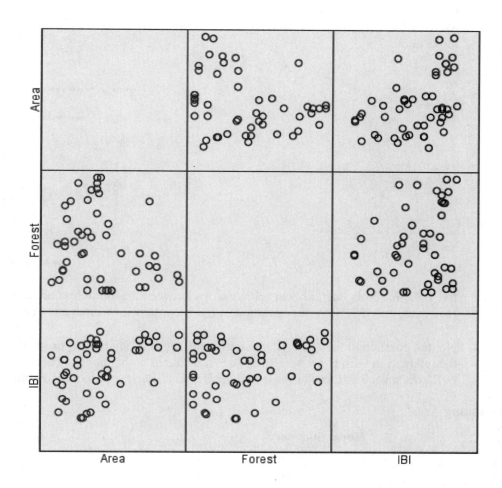

c) $y_i = \beta_0 + \beta_{\text{Area}} x_{\text{Area}i} + \beta_{\text{Forest}} x_{\text{Forest}i} + \varepsilon_i$ **d)** $H_0 : \beta_{\text{Area}} = \beta_{\text{Forest}} = 0$, H_a : The coefficients are not both 0. **e)** $R^2 = 35.7\%$, s = 14.972, F = 12.776, *P*-value = 0.000. All coefficients are significant. $\hat{y} = 40.629 + 0.569 \text{ Area} + 0.234 \text{ Forest}$. **f)** Residual plots look good—random and no outliers. See below.

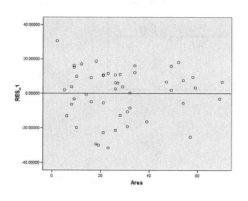

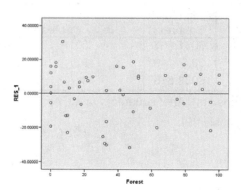

g) A histogram of the residuals looks somewhat skewed left, but the normal probability plot looks good.

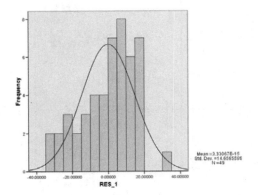

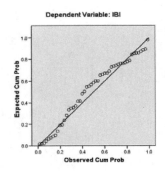

h) Yes. We had general linear relationships between the variables and the residuals look good. However, only 35.7% of the variation in IBI is explained by Area and Forest.

11.94 No, the coefficient for Area^2 is not significant, the coefficient for Forest^2 is not significant, and the interaction term is not significant when included in the model. There is not much difference in R^2 when each of these terms is included, either. See the output below for details.

Including Area^2:

Model Summary[b]

Model	R	R Square	Adjusted R Square	Std. Error of the Estimate
1	.613[a]	.376	.334	14.912

a. Predictors: (Constant), Area squared, Forest, Area

b. Dependent Variable: IBI

ANOVA[b]

Model		Sum of Squares	df	Mean Square	F	Sig.
1	Regression	6031.667	3	2010.556	9.041	.000[a]
	Residual	10007.149	45	222.381		
	Total	16038.816	48			

a. Predictors: (Constant), Area squared, Forest, Area

b. Dependent Variable: IBI

Coefficients[a]

Model		Unstandardized Coefficients		Standardized Coefficients	t	Sig.	95% Confidence Interval for B	
		B	Std. Error	Beta			Lower Bound	Upper Bound
1	(Constant)	46.268	7.270		6.364	.000	31.625	60.912
	Area	.035	.474	.034	.073	.942	-.921	.990
	Forest	.252	.071	.445	3.555	.001	.109	.395
	Area squared	.008	.007	.545	1.169	.249	-.006	.022

a. Dependent Variable: IBI

Including Forest[2]:

Model Summary[b]

Model	R	R Square	Adjusted R Square	Std. Error of the Estimate
1	.616[a]	.379	.338	14.875

a. Predictors: (Constant), Forest squared, Area, Forest

b. Dependent Variable: IBI

ANOVA[b]

Model		Sum of Squares	df	Mean Square	F	Sig.
1	Regression	6082.042	3	2027.347	9.163	.000[a]
	Residual	9956.774	45	221.262		
	Total	16038.816	48			

a. Predictors: (Constant), Forest squared, Area, Forest

b. Dependent Variable: IBI

Coefficients[a]

Model		Unstandardized Coefficients		Standardized Coefficients	t	Sig.	95% Confidence Interval for B	
		B	Std. Error	Beta			Lower Bound	Upper Bound
1	(Constant)	44.970	6.419		7.005	.000	32.041	57.898
	Area	.545	.127	.528	4.291	.000	.289	.800
	Forest	-.063	.245	-.111	-.258	.797	-.556	.429
	Forest squared	.003	.002	.538	1.265	.212	-.002	.008

a. Dependent Variable: IBI

Including interaction of Area and Forest:

Model Summary[b]

Model	R	R Square	Adjusted R Square	Std. Error of the Estimate
1	.617[a]	.380	.339	14.863

a. Predictors: (Constant), Interaction of area and forest, Area, Forest

b. Dependent Variable: IBI

ANOVA[b]

Model		Sum of Squares	df	Mean Square	F	Sig.
1	Regression	6097.298	3	2032.433	9.200	.000[a]
	Residual	9941.518	45	220.923		
	Total	16038.816	48			

a. Predictors: (Constant), Interaction of area and forest, Area, Forest

b. Dependent Variable: IBI

Coefficients[a]

Model		Unstandardized Coefficients		Standardized Coefficients	t	Sig.	95% Confidence Interval for B	
		B	Std. Error	Beta			Lower Bound	Upper Bound
1	(Constant)	34.719	7.091		4.896	.000	20.437	49.000
	Area	.759	.193	.736	3.933	.000	.370	1.148
	Forest	.431	.167	.759	2.575	.013	.094	.768
	Interaction of area and forest	-.007	.006	-.380	-1.293	.202	-.019	.004

a. Dependent Variable: IBI

11.95 a)

	Mean	St. dev.	Description of distribution
PCB	68.4674	59.3906	Skewed right, 5 high outliers

```
0 .  0001111
0 .  2222222222233333333333333
0 .  44444455555
0 .  6666677
0 .  888999999
1 .  1111
1 .  23
1 .
1 .  7

5.00 Extremes    (>=199)
Stem width:  100.0000
```

PCB52 0.9580 1.5983 Skewed right, 6 high outliers

```
0 .  0000011111111111
0 .  22222233333333
0 .  4444444555555
0 .  667777
0 .  888899
1 .
1 .  22
1 .  44
1 .  677
1 .  8

6.00 Extremes    (>=2.1)

Stem width:      1.000
```

PCB118 3.2563 3.0191 Skewed right, 5 high outliers

```
0 .  234577889
1 .  0113334445555556778899
2 .  1334456679
3 .  133455566889
4 .  0078
5 .  046
6 .  0289

5.00 Extremes    (>=8.2)

Stem width:      1.00
```

PCB138 6.8268 5.8627 Skewed right, 5 high outliers

```
0 .  000111
0 .  22222222222333333333333333
0 .  444444555555
0 .  67777
0 .  888888999
1 .  011
1 .  22333

5.00 Extremes    (>=18)

Stem width:      10.00
```

PCB180   4.1584   4.9864   Skewed right, 7 high outliers

```
0 .  345667889
1 .  0000111123334578
2 .  111233466678
3 .  011344666779
4 .  1446
5 .  0034
6 .  2
7 .  06
8 .  8
9 .  3

7.00 Extremes    (>=9.5)

Stem width:     1.000
```

b) All the variables are positively correlated with each other. All the explanatory variables are significantly correlated with PCB, although PCB52 is the most weakly correlated with PCB and with the other explanatory variables. Only the correlation between PCB52 and PCB180 is not significant (P-value = 0.478).

Correlations

		PCB	PCB52	PCB118	PCB138	PCB180
PCB	Pearson Correlation	1	.596**	.843**	.929**	.801**
	Sig. (2-tailed)		.000	.000	.000	.000
	N	69	69	69	69	69
PCB52	Pearson Correlation	.596**	1	.685**	.301*	.087
	Sig. (2-tailed)	.000		.000	.012	.478
	N	69	69	69	69	69
PCB118	Pearson Correlation	.843**	.685**	1	.729**	.437**
	Sig. (2-tailed)	.000	.000		.000	.000
	N	69	69	69	69	69
PCB138	Pearson Correlation	.929**	.301*	.729**	1	.882**
	Sig. (2-tailed)	.000	.012	.000		.000
	N	69	69	69	69	69
PCB180	Pearson Correlation	.801**	.087	.437**	.882**	1
	Sig. (2-tailed)	.000	.478	.000	.000	
	N	69	69	69	69	69

**. Correlation is significant at the 0.01 level (2-tailed).

*. Correlation is significant at the 0.05 level (2-tailed).

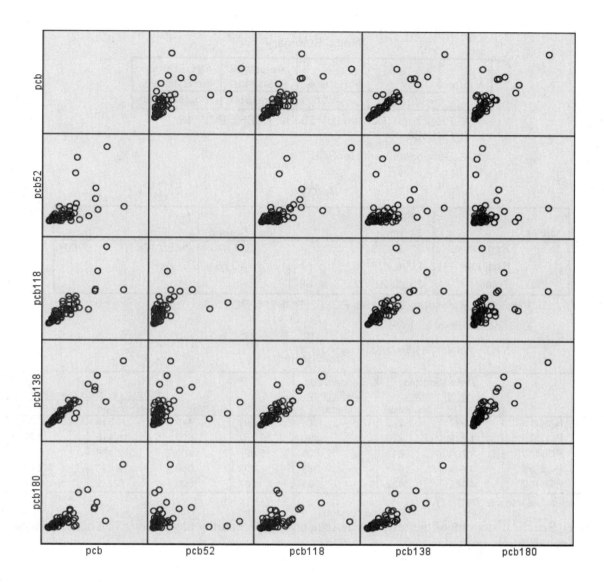

11.96 **a)** $\mu_y = \beta_0 + \beta_1 \cdot PCB52 + \beta_2 \cdot PCB118 + \beta_3 \cdot PCB138 + \beta_4 \cdot PCB180$. Assume the deviations

are independent and Normally distributed with a mean 0 and standard deviation σ, that is the deviations are an SRS from the $N(0, \sigma)$ distribution. Assume that the standard deviation of the responses is the same in all subpopulations and that the subpopulation means are related to the regression coefficients by the equation given above. **b)** See the SPSS output below.
$\hat{y} = 0.937 + 11.873 \cdot PCB52 + 3.761 \cdot PCB118 + 3.884 \cdot PCB138 + 4.182 \cdot PCB180$. $R^2 =$
98.9%, s = 6.3821, F = 1456.178, *P*-value is very close to 0. All the coefficients are significant.

Model Summary[b]

Model	R	R Square	Adjusted R Square	Std. Error of the Estimate
1	.995[a]	.989	.988	6.3820755

a. Predictors: (Constant), PCB180, PCB52, PCB118, PCB138

b. Dependent Variable: PCB

ANOVA[b]

Model		Sum of Squares	df	Mean Square	F	Sig.
1	Regression	237245.8	4	59311.442	1456.178	.000[a]
	Residual	2606.777	64	40.731		
	Total	239852.5	68			

a. Predictors: (Constant), PCB180, PCB52, PCB118, PCB138

b. Dependent Variable: PCB

Coefficients[a]

Model		Unstandardized Coefficients		Standardized Coefficients	t	Sig.	95% Confidence Interval for B	
		B	Std. Error	Beta			Lower Bound	Upper Bound
1	(Constant)	.937	1.229		.762	.449	-1.519	3.393
	PCB52	11.873	.729	.320	16.287	.000	10.416	13.329
	PCB118	3.761	.642	.191	5.855	.000	2.478	5.044
	PCB138	3.884	.498	.383	7.803	.000	2.890	4.879
	PCB180	4.182	.432	.351	9.687	.000	3.320	5.045

a. Dependent Variable: PCB

c) See the histogram of the residuals and the normal probability plot below. The residuals look approximately normal.

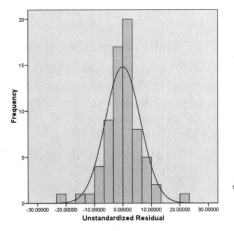

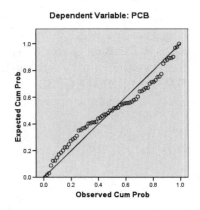

Normal P-P Plot of Regression Standardized Residual

The residual plots below show no obvious patterns except for possible outliers at #50 and #65.

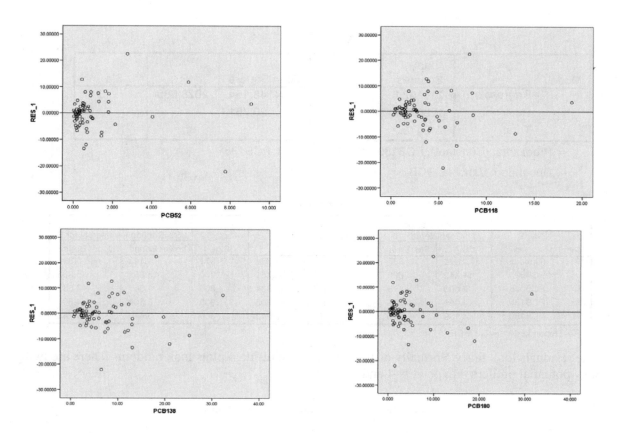

11.97 **a)** #50 and #65 are the two potential outliers. #50 (residual = -22.0864) is the overestimate.

b) $\hat{y} = 1.628 + 14.442$ PCB52 $+ 2.600$ PCB118 $+ 4.054$ PCB 138 $+ 4.109$ PCB 180. All coefficients are significant again. $R^2 = 99.4\%$, s = 4.555, F = 2628.685, *P*-value = 0.

Model Summary[b]

Model	R	R Square	Adjusted R Square	Std. Error of the Estimate
1	.997[a]	.994	.994	4.5553398

a. Predictors: (Constant), PCB180, PCB52, PCB118, PCB138

b. Dependent Variable: PCB

ANOVA[b]

Model		Sum of Squares	df	Mean Square	F	Sig.
1	Regression	218192.6	4	54548.154	2628.685	.000[a]
	Residual	1286.569	62	20.751		
	Total	219479.2	66			

a. Predictors: (Constant), PCB180, PCB52, PCB118, PCB138

b. Dependent Variable: PCB

Coefficients[a]

Model		Unstandardized Coefficients		Standardized Coefficients	t	Sig.	95% Confidence Interval for B	
		B	Std. Error	Beta			Lower Bound	Upper Bound
1	(Constant)	1.628	.886		1.838	.071	-.143	3.398
	PCB52	14.442	.696	.342	20.751	.000	13.051	15.833
	PCB118	2.600	.516	.135	5.034	.000	1.567	3.632
	PCB138	4.054	.375	.407	10.805	.000	3.304	4.804
	PCB180	4.109	.317	.356	12.942	.000	3.474	4.743

a. Dependent Variable: PCB

The residuals look fairly Normally distributed, and the residual plots look random. There are two new potential outliers though at #44 and #58.

Normal P-P Plot of Regression Standardized Residual

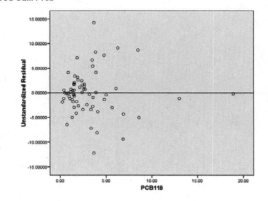

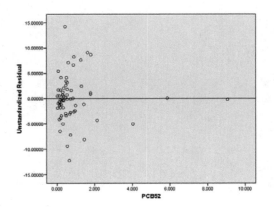

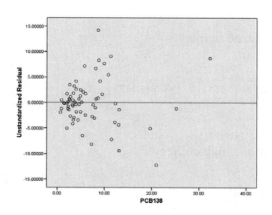

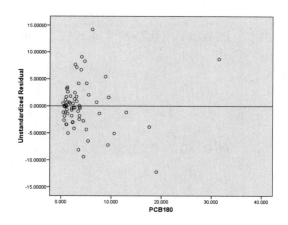

11.98 **a)** $\hat{y} = -1.018 + 12.644 \cdot PCB52 + 0.313 \cdot PCB118 + 8.255 \cdot PCB138$. $R^2 = 97.3\%$, s = 9.9450, F = 786.709, *P*-value is close to 0. The coefficient for PCB118 is not significant, but the other coefficients are. **b)** $b_{PCB118} = 0.313$, *P*-value = 0.708. **c)** $b_{PCB118} = 3.761$, *P*-value is close to 0. **d)** Multiple regression is complicated. Apparently, the relationship between PCB180 and PCB118 makes the coefficient for PCB118 significant if PCB180 is included in the model, but not if PCB180 is left out of the model.

11.99 **a)** $\beta_0 = 0$, $\beta_1 = \beta_2 = \beta_3 = 1$ because TEQ = TEQPCB + TEQDIOXIN + TEQFURAN. **b)** The error terms are all 0, so $\sigma = 0$. **c)** Software confirms what we did in (a) and (b).

11.100 Model is $\mu_y = \beta_0 + \beta_1 \cdot PCB52 + \beta_2 \cdot PCB118 + \beta_3 \cdot PCB138 + \beta_4 \cdot PCB180$. Assume the deviations are independent and Normally distributed with a mean 0 and standard deviation σ, that is the deviations are an SRS from the N(0, σ) distribution. Assume that the standard deviation of the responses is the same in all subpopulations and that the subpopulation means are related to the regression coefficients by the equation given above. The regression line equation is $\hat{y} = 1.060 - 0.097 \cdot PCB52 + 0.306 \cdot PCB118 + 0.106 \cdot PCB138 - 0.004 \cdot PCB180$. $R^2 =$ 67.7%, s = 0.9576, F = 33.527, *P*-value is close to 0. The only coefficient which is significant is PCB118. The coefficients for PCB52 (P-value 0.377), PCB138 (P-value 0.162), and PCB180 (*P*-value 0.952) are not significant.

11.101 **a)** Results will vary with software. SPSS results for logPCB126 are given below. **b)** Most software should ignore these data points, but ignoring data is not a good idea. **c)** Table below uses Base 10 logs. Minitab and SPSS give mean = -2.1044 and standard deviation = 0.3325 when using 0.0026 for all the 0 values.

Log of variable	Mean	St. dev.	Description of stemplot
PCB138	0.7009	0.3494	Fairly symmetric, 1 low outlier

```
1.00 Extremes    (=<-.2)

-0 .  00
 0 .  11233333334444
 0 .  5555555555556666666677777788888999999999
 1 .  000001112234
 1 .  5

Stem width:    1.0000
```

PCB153   0.7397   0.3914   Fairly symmetric, no outliers

```
-0 .  000
 0 .  01222333444444
 0 .  55555555555556666677778888888899999
 1 .  00000011123344
 1 .  556

 Stem width:     1.0000
```

PCB180   0.4235   0.4028   Fairly symmetric, 1 high outlier

```
-0 .  000112234
 0 .  00000000011112223333333344444444
 0 .  555555556666677777889999
 1 .  0122

1.00 Extremes      (>=1.5)

 Stem width:     1.0000
```

PCB28   -0.5793   0.4918   Fairly symmetric, 1 low and 1 high outlier

```
1.00 Extremes      (=<-2.2)

-1 .  6
-1 .  0000011222
-0 .  55555555556666666777778888899999
-0 .  0001222223333344444
 0 .  122333

1.00 Extremes      (>=.8)

 Stem width:     1.0000
```

PCB52   -0.3354   0.5167   Fairly symmetric, 1 low and 2 high outliers

```
1.00 Extremes      (=<-1.7)

-1 .  5
-1 .  112
-0 .  55555666677778888999
-0 .  00000011111122222233333334444444
 0 .  1111222234
 0 .  67

2.00 Extremes      (>=.9)

 Stem width:     1.0000
```

PCB126
With 0
values

-1.96   0.228   Right-skewed

```
-22 .  0223568
-21 .  02333444466688
-20 .  146889
-19 .  012359
-18 .  001369
-17 .  00247
-16 .  668
-15 .  55899
-14 .  9

 Stem width:      .1000
```

PCB 126   -2.104   0.3325   Fairly symmetric, no outliers.
With
0.0026
for the 0
values

```
-2 .  5555555555555555
-2 .  2222222
-2 .  00000011111111111111
-1 .  888888999999
-1 .  66677777
-1 .  455555

Stem width:    1.0000
```

PCB118   0.3717   0.3592   Fairly symmetric, 1 low and 1 high outlier

```
1.00 Extremes     (=<-.6)

-0 .  00011234
 0 .  000111111111111122222223333344444
 0 .  5555555555556666677778888999
 1 .  1

1.00 Extremes     (>=1.3)

Stem width:    1.0000
```

PCB   1.701   0.3483   Fairly symmetric, no outliers

```
0 .  799
1 .  1223333334444444
1 .  55555555555566666667777777888888999999999
2 .  00000122333
2 .  5

Stem width:    1.0000
```

TEQ   0.3495   0.2591   Right-skewed, no outliers

```
-0 .  0012
 0 .  011245667899
 1 .  0333446789
 2 .  22345888
 3 .  135777
 4 .  03488899
 5 .  135788
 6 .  01358
 7 .  001556799
 8 .  1

Stem width:     .1000
```

11.102 a) See the correlations and scatterplots that follow. The strongest correlation is logPCB vs. logPCB138 (0.956). All the correlations are significant except logPCB28 with logPCB180, logPCB28 with logPCB126, and logPCB126 with logPCB52. All the scatterplots look fairly linear.

Correlations

		logpcb138	logpcb153	logpcb180	logpcb28	logpcb52	logpcb126	logpcb118	logpcb	logteq
logpcb138	Pearson Correlation	1	.922**	.896**	.388**	.540**	.792**	.890**	.956**	.728**
	Sig. (2-tailed)		.000	.000	.001	.000	.000	.000	.000	.000
	N	69	69	69	69	69	69	69	69	69
logpcb153	Pearson Correlation	.922**	1	.867**	.326**	.519**	.647**	.780**	.905**	.583**
	Sig. (2-tailed)	.000		.000	.006	.000	.000	.000	.000	.000
	N	69	69	69	69	69	69	69	69	69
logpcb180	Pearson Correlation	.896**	.867**	1	.227	.302*	.695**	.654**	.829**	.592**
	Sig. (2-tailed)	.000	.000		.060	.012	.000	.000	.000	.000
	N	69	69	69	69	69	69	69	69	69
logpcb28	Pearson Correlation	.388**	.326**	.227	1	.795**	.272*	.534**	.570**	.422**
	Sig. (2-tailed)	.001	.006	.060		.000	.024	.000	.000	.000
	N	69	69	69	69	69	69	69	69	69
logpcb52	Pearson Correlation	.540**	.519**	.302*	.795**	1	.331**	.671**	.701**	.463**
	Sig. (2-tailed)	.000	.000	.012	.000		.005	.000	.000	.000
	N	69	69	69	69	69	69	69	69	69
logpcb126	Pearson Correlation	.792**	.647**	.695**	.272*	.331**	1	.739**	.729**	.854**
	Sig. (2-tailed)	.000	.000	.000	.024	.005		.000	.000	.000
	N	69	69	69	69	69	69	69	69	69
logpcb118	Pearson Correlation	.890**	.780**	.654**	.534**	.671**	.739**	1	.906**	.752**
	Sig. (2-tailed)	.000	.000	.000	.000	.000	.000		.000	.000
	N	69	69	69	69	69	69	69	69	69
logpcb	Pearson Correlation	.956**	.905**	.829**	.570**	.701**	.729**	.906**	1	.720**
	Sig. (2-tailed)	.000	.000	.000	.000	.000	.000	.000		.000
	N	69	69	69	69	69	69	69	69	69
logteq	Pearson Correlation	.728**	.583**	.592**	.422**	.463**	.854**	.752**	.720**	1
	Sig. (2-tailed)	.000	.000	.000	.000	.000	.000	.000	.000	
	N	69	69	69	69	69	69	69	69	69

**. Correlation is significant at the 0.01 level (2-tailed).

*. Correlation is significant at the 0.05 level (2-tailed).

b) All the correlations are stronger using the logs. There is less scatter in the top right corner of the scatterplots when logs are used.

11.103 Answers will vary depending on the method used.

If you start with the full model and then drop one variable at a time, one good possibility is leaving out logPCB126 because all the remaining coefficients are significant at the 5% level. This model has $R^2 = 97.5\%$ and s = 0.0581. The least-squares regression line is $\hat{y} = 1.287 + 0.400$ logPCB138 + 0.144 logPCB153 + 0.132 logPCB180 + 0.088 logPCB28 + 0.101 logPCB52 + 0.151 logPCB118.

If you choose a lower significance level, a good model with only 4 variables would be $\hat{y} = 1.212$ + 0.668 logPCB138 + 0.152 logPCB153 + 0.108 logPCB28 + 0.087 logPCB52. This model has an $R^2 = 97.2\%$ and s = 0.0600.

A model with 3 variables would be $\hat{y} = 1.214 + 0.821$ logPCB138 + 0.091 logPCB28 + 0.103 logPCB52. This model has an $R^2 = 96.8\%$ and s = 0.0638.

If you build the model up from just one variable or use software to choose the best model, results will be different. Multiple regression is very complicated.

11.104 Answers may vary depending on the method used. If you leave all the log TEQ variables in the model, $R^2 = 88.3\%$ and $s = 0.0894$. All the coefficients are significant (P-values < 0.001), so there is no reason to drop any of the variables. The model for logTEQ is

$$\hat{y} = 0.476 + 0.440 \cdot \log TEQPCB + 0.192 \cdot \log TEQDIOX + 0.118 \cdot \log TEQFURAN .$$

If you build the model up from just one variable or use software to choose the best model, results will be different. Multiple regression is very complicated.

11.105 Answers will vary depending on the method used. Ideally, a good model will have a high R^2, low s, high F test statistic, low P-value from the F test, and coefficients which are all significant in t tests. It may not be possible to achieve all of these features in a single model however.

11.106 a) x_1 and x_2 are strongly negatively correlated, but they don't seem to have an association with y.

Correlations

		x1	x2	y
x1	Pearson Correlation	1	-.989**	.180
	Sig. (2-tailed)		.000	.342
	N	30	30	30
x2	Pearson Correlation	-.989**	1	-.040
	Sig. (2-tailed)	.000		.832
	N	30	30	30
y	Pearson Correlation	.180	-.040	1
	Sig. (2-tailed)	.342	.832	
	N	30	30	30

. Correlation is significant at the 0.01 level (2-tailed).

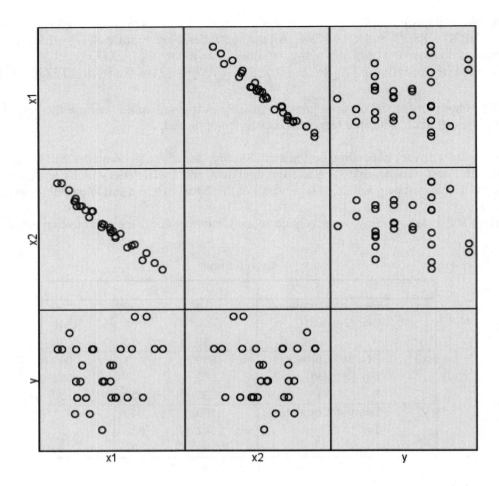

b) $\hat{y} = 0.830 + 0.107x_1 + 0.108x_2$, $R^2 = 88.5\%$, $s = 0.0629$, all coefficients are significant.

Model Summary

Model	R	R Square	Adjusted R Square	Std. Error of the Estimate
1	.941[a]	.885	.877	.0629

a. Predictors: (Constant), x2, x1

ANOVA[b]

Model		Sum of Squares	df	Mean Square	F	Sig.
1	Regression	.825	2	.413	104.181	.000[a]
	Residual	.107	27	.004		
	Total	.932	29			

a. Predictors: (Constant), x2, x1

b. Dependent Variable: y

Coefficients[a]

Model		Unstandardized Coefficients		Standardized Coefficients	t	Sig.
		B	Std. Error	Beta		
1	(Constant)	.830	.156		5.329	.000
	x1	.107	.007	6.333	14.421	.000
	x2	.108	.008	6.223	14.169	.000

a. Dependent Variable: y

c) It may be better in this case to start with all explanatory variables in the model and then eliminate the insignificant ones.

11.107 a) $R^2 = 18.9\%$, $s = 1.1421$, $F = 3.152$, *P*-value = 0.059. Neither the coefficient for x_1 or for x_2 is significant.

Model Summary

Model	R	R Square	Adjusted R Square	Std. Error of the Estimate
1	.435[a]	.189	.129	1.1421

a. Predictors: (Constant), x2, x1

ANOVA[b]

Model		Sum of Squares	df	Mean Square	F	Sig.
1	Regression	8.223	2	4.111	3.152	.059[a]
	Residual	35.216	27	1.304		
	Total	43.439	29			

a. Predictors: (Constant), x2, x1

b. Dependent Variable: y

Coefficients[a]

Model		Unstandardized Coefficients		Standardized Coefficients	t	Sig.
		B	Std. Error	Beta		
1	(Constant)	.906	.337		2.691	.012
	x1	.027	.032	.209	.857	.399
	x2	.211	.197	.262	1.075	.292

a. Dependent Variable: y

b) All correlations are significant. The scatterplots show that both x_1 and x_2 have positive linear relationships with y and with each other.

Correlations

		x1	x2	y
x1	Pearson Correlation	1	.703**	.393*
	Sig. (2-tailed)		.000	.032
	N	30	30	30
x2	Pearson Correlation	.703**	1	.409*
	Sig. (2-tailed)	.000		.025
	N	30	30	30
y	Pearson Correlation	.393*	.409*	1
	Sig. (2-tailed)	.032	.025	
	N	30	30	30

**. Correlation is significant at the 0.01 level (2-tailed).

*. Correlation is significant at the 0.05 level (2-tailed).

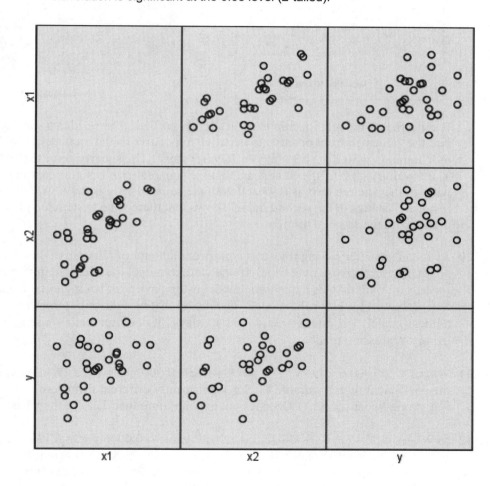

If just x_1 is used, its coefficient is significant (*P*-value 0.032). If just x_2 is used, its coefficient is significant (*P*-value 0.025). **c)** This isn't always the best approach either. Multiple regression is complicated.

11.108 a) A 95% confidence interval would be (2.11, 2.16). **b)** Based on the previous confidence interval, the value 2.13 falls within the interval, so the logical conclusion is that the price is within the expected range of variability. I agree with the court ruling.

11.109 a) Vitamin C = 46 – 6.05 x days, t = –10.62, df = 8, *P*-value = 0. It appears there is a significant linear relationship between vitamin C level and the number of days after baking. **b)**

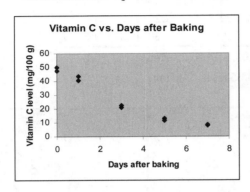

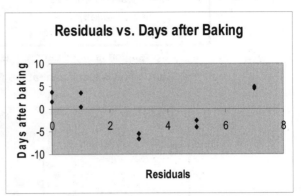

It appears that the relationship may be slightly curved. The residuals show a systematic pattern in that the values go from positive to negative to positive as the number of days increases.
c) Vitamin C = 50.1 – 11.3 × days + 0.763 × days^2. The squared term t statistic is 6.08 and df = 7. The *P*-value = 0.000503. It appears that the squared term is significant in the model. **d)** R^2 without the squared term is 0.93 and with the squared term is 0.99. A look at a scatterplot of residuals vs days in the second model shows that there is no systematic pattern. Choose the model with the squared term.

11.110 As bread sits after baking it loses a significant amount of Vitamins C and A, but Vitamin E does not appear to decrease over time. If one were to model the decrease in vitamins, the best model for loss of Vitamin C is a quadratic model using days after baking as the explanatory variable. See problem 11.109 for the model. The model that best describes the loss of Vitamin A would be a linear model: Vitamin A = 3.34 – 0.04 × days. It does not make sense to predict Vitamin E loss using a regression model.

11.111 Wages = 349 + 0.6 × LOS, t = 2.86, *P*-value = 0.006. $R^2 = 0.12$. While the t statistic shows that the coefficient on the variable LOS is significantly different from zero, it does not appear that this is a strong linear model. LOS does not explain more than 12% of the variation in wages.

11.112 a) Wages = 354.2 + 63.9 × Size, t = 2.96, *P*-value = 0.0046. $R^2 = 0.133$. While the t statistic shows that the coefficient on the variable Size is significantly different from zero, it does not appear that this is a strong linear model. Company size does not explain more than 14% of the variation in wages. **b)** t = 2.96, df = 57, *P*-value = 0.0045. Since size takes on only two values, 0 or 1, it makes sense that the t statistics would be the same. **c)** The plot of residuals vs. LOS shows a slight increasing trend. This is confirmed by r, the correlation, which is 0.35. Adding LOS to the model using Size may be beneficial.

11.113 Wages = 302.5 + 0.67 LOS + 71.8 Size, $R^2 = 0.29$, t statistics have small *P*-values.

11.114 a) Corn Yield = $-3572 + 1.85 \times$ Year, $R^2 = 0.858$, t = 15.916, *P*-value = 0. **b)** The residuals appear fairly Normal on the Normal quantile plot. **c)** The residuals plotted against soybean yield do not show an increasing trend. The correlation between the two is positive. There may be some benefit to using soybean yield in addition to year to predict corn yield.

11.115 a) Corn Yield = $-43.8 + 4.7 \times$ Soybean Yield, $R^2 = 0.89$, t = 18.733, *P*-value = 0. **b)** The residuals appear fairly Normal. **c)** It appears that there is an increasing and then decreasing effect when looking at the residuals plotted against year. It makes sense to include year in the regression model.

11.116 a) H_0: All coefficients equal zero. H_a: At least one coefficient is not equal to zero. F = 242, df = 2 and 37, *P*-value = 0. This model provides significant prediction of corn yield. **b)** $R^2 = 0.922$, compared to 0.86 with only year as the explanatory variable and 0.89 with only soybean yield as the explanatory variable. **c)** Corn yield = $-1553 + 0.789 \times$ Year + 2.913 x Soybean yield, Year and Soybean yield are dependent on each other, so one would expect the coefficients to be different when both variables are used in the regression model. **d)** For the coefficient on Year, t = 3.880 and the *P*-value = 0. For the coefficient on Soybean yield, t = 5.795 and the *P*-value = 0. Both of these results tell us that the coefficients are significantly different from zero. **e)** For β_1: (0.338, 1.200). For β_2: (1.898, 3.928). **f)** The residual plot against soybean yield shows no pattern. The residual plot against year shows an increasing and then decreasing trend with time. This indicates it might make sense to include the year squared as an additional term in the model.

11.117 a) Corn yield = $-1049.5 + 0.526 \times$ Year $- 0.031 \times$ Year^2 + 3.631 $\times$ Soybean Yield **b)** H_0: All coefficients are equal to zero. H_a: At least one coefficient is not equal to zero. F = 245, df = 3 and 36, *P*-value = 0. This indicates that the model provides significant prediction of corn yield. **c)** R^2 = 0.95, compared to 0.92 from previous model. **d)** In the order they appear in the model, the t statistics for the coefficients are t = 2.973 with a *P*-value = 0.005, t = -4.536, *P*-value = 0, t = 8.20, *P*-value = 0. **e)** The residuals all appear random when plotted against the explanatory variables.

11.118 a) The t statistic for the coefficient on year2 is -1.061 with a *P*-value = 0.295. This indicates the term is not significant in the model with only year and year2. **b)** Since year and year2 are highly correlated, if these are the only two explanatory variables, we can obtain just as good predictions using year only. **c)** Note that the two fits differ toward the end of the data sets, in the early and late years.

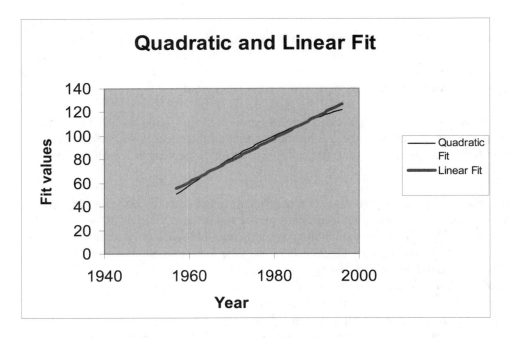

11.119 For the linear model, predicted yield for 2001 was 136.82 with a 95% prediction interval of (116.11, 157.52) and a residual of 1.38. For the quadratic model, predicted yield for 2001 was 133.07 with a 95% prediction interval of (111.18, 154.95) and a residual of 5.13. The linear model gave a closer prediction to actual.

11.120 The 2002 predicted value using the linear model is 138.67 with a 95% prediction interval of (117.91, 159.44). For the quadratic model, predicted yield is 134.42 with a 95% prediction interval of (112.15, 156.69).

11.121

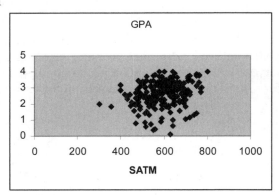
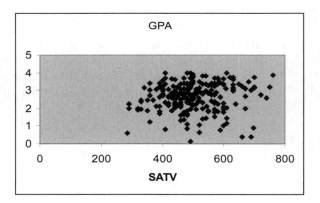

The scatterplots do not show strong relationships. The plot of SATM vs. GPA shows two possible outliers on the left side. The plot of SATV vs. GPA does not show any obvious outliers.

11.122

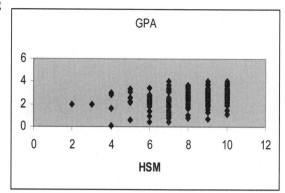

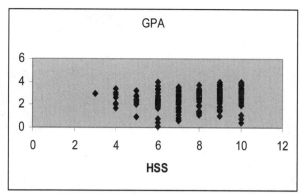

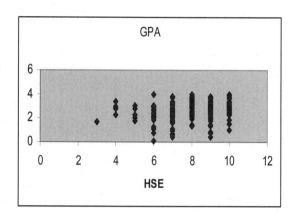

The scatterplots show a possibly increasing trend in GPA as high school grades increase. The variability in GPA also increases with high school grades.

11.123

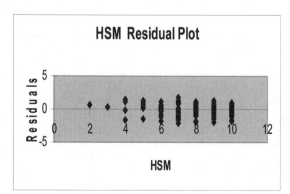

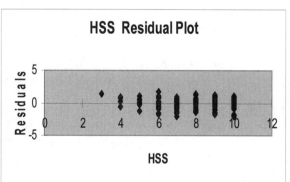

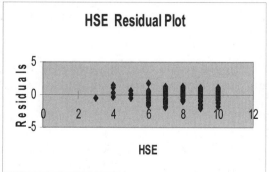

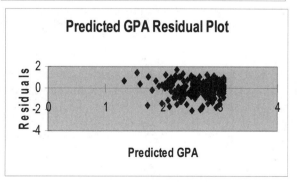

The residuals do not show any obvious patterns.

11.124

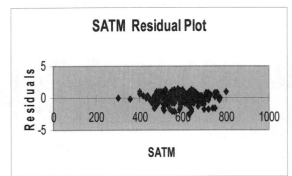

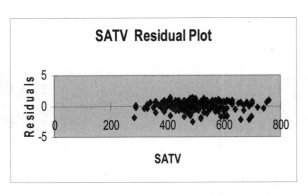

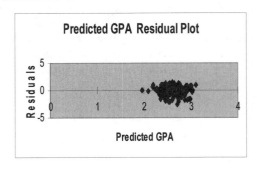

There are no obvious patterns in the residual plots.

11.125 **a)** GPA = 0.666 + 0.193 × HSM + 0.00061 × SATM. **b)** H_0: All coefficients in the regression model are zero. H_a: At least one coefficient is not zero. This means that we assume the model is not a significant predictor of GPA and let the data provide evidence that the model is a significant predictor. F = 26.63 and the *P*-value = 0. This model provides significant prediction of GPA. **c)** HSM: (0.1295, 0.2565) SATM: (−0.00059, 0.001815). Yes, the interval describing the SATM coefficient does contain zero. **d)** HSM: t = 5.99, *P*-value = 0. SATM: t = 0.999, *P*-value = 0.319. Based on the large P-value associated with the SATM coefficient one should conclude that SATM does not provide significant prediction of GPA. **e)** s = 0.703. **f)** R^2 = 0.1942.

11.126 While the model with HSE and SATV does provide some prediction of GPA, it is not much. R^2 = 0.086. The explanatory variable SATV is not a significant predictor with HSE in the model. This parallels the results found in 11.125. Note that the model with the math scores: HSM and SATM is a much stronger model than the model with verbal scores.

11.127 Looking at the sample of males only shows the same results when compared to the sample of all students. R^2 = 0.184 (compared to 0.20) and, while HSM is a significant predictor, HSS and HSE are not.

11.128 The analysis of the female students also shows similar results to all students. The R^2 value is slightly higher (0.25), but the same explanatory variables are considered insignificant (HSS and HSE).

11.129 **a)** GPA = 0.582 + 0.155 HSM + 0.050 HSS + 0.044 HSE + 0.067 Gender + 0.05 GHSM − 0.05 GHSS − 0.012 GHSE. The t statistics for each coefficient have *P*-values greater than 0.10 for all except the explanatory variable HSM. **b)** Verify. **c)** Verify. **d)** F = 0.143, *P*-value = 0.966. This indicates there is no reason to include gender and the interactions.

Case Study 11.1

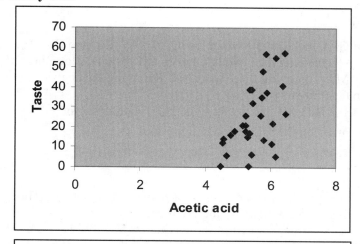

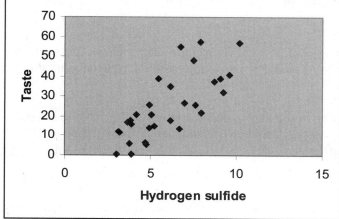

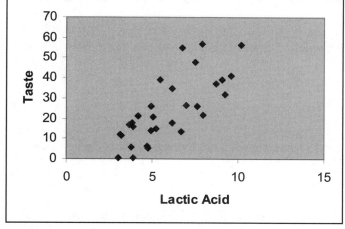

The relationships between Taste and Hydrogen sulfide and Taste and Lactic acid appear slightly stronger than the relationship between Taste and Acetic acid. The correlation coefficient values support this. The values for r are 0.7558, 0.7042, and 0.5500, respectively. After running the analysis with interaction effects, it was found that the strongest model in terms of R^2 was the model with both the hydrogen sulfide term and the lactic acid term. Interaction did not seem to significantly improve the model's predictive ability. The best model for predicting taste would be:
$\hat{y} = -27.50 + 3.95 \times$ hydrogen sulfide $+ 19.89 \times$ lactic acid.

Case Study 11.2

The model chosen as the best predictor of GPA includes the variables IQ, SC, C1, C3, and C5. The original analysis included all 10 variables. Reviewing the residuals scores and residual plots showed that there were two outliers: cases 51 and 22. After removing these cases and rerunning the analysis with only the variables that appeared significant the resulting model is

$\hat{y} = -4.0 + 0.09IQ - 0.08SC + 0.29C1 + 0.17C3 + 0.13C5$. $R^2 = 0.62$ and standard error $= 1.186$.

There does not appear to be any reason to question the regression assumptions.

Case Study 11.3

The mean earnings for females is $20,708.56, and the mean earnings for males is $20,569.16. The side-by-side boxplots look fairly similar for both genders with many high outliers. The average earnings for part-time workers is $19,033.25, and the mean earnings for full-time workers is $21,291.12. The side-by-side boxplots for status show that the distribution of full-time workers is higher than that of part-time workers.

The correlation between Earnings and Gender is -0.012 and is not significant. The correlation between Earnings and Status is 0.224 and is significant. Gender is also significantly correlated with Status (r = 0.081).

The ANOVA F test concludes that at least one of the explanatory variables will be able to tell us something about salary. With both gender and salary included in the model, the equation is

$\hat{y} = 19077.147 - 354.928x_{gender} + 2282.401x_{status}$. R^2 is 5.1% (which is very low), and the standard error of the estimate is 4361.671. The coefficient for gender is not significantly different from 0.

Using just Status, the model is $\hat{y} = 19033.254 + 2257.867x_{status}$. R^2 didn't change much and is now 5.0%. The standard error of the estimate has stayed much the same at 4362.486. The coefficient of Status is significantly different from 0.

The model that uses just Status is the better model. Therefore, gender is not significantly related to salary for hourly employees.

Case Study 11.4

Both Job Level (r = 0.798) and Gender (r = 0.157) are significantly correlated with Salary. Job Level and Gender are also significantly correlated with each other (r = 0.141).

Using both Job Level and Gender to predict Salary, the model is
$\hat{y} = -18113.2 + 6114.266x_{joblevel} + 1278.652x_{gender}$ with an R^2 of 63.9% and a standard error of the estimate of 8391.326. The coefficient for gender is not significant.

With gender dropped out of the model, the equation of the line is: $\hat{y} = -17905.7 + 6163.957x_{joblevel}$. The new R^2 is 63.7%, and the new standard error of the estimate is 8404.060. There is not much of a change in either of these values, and the coefficient for Job Level is still significant. Therefore the model using only Job Level is the better model. Gender is not a good predictor variable for Salary.

Case Study 11.5

The zip code chosen for analysis was 47905. There were 158 homes in this zip code. After looking at the data, four homes were removed as outliers. Two of the homes had high square footage with very low home prices and two homes had high prices for the square footage. There were two homes that had very high square footage, but their prices reflected this and the observations fit the linear trend. The scatterplot below shows the linear trend between price and square footage. The residual plots did not show any reason to believe the relationship was not linear.

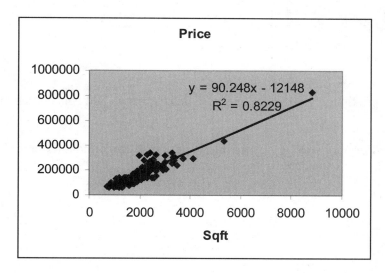

Further analysis was done with the bedroom and bathroom variables. It was found that the number of bedrooms was not a significant predictor of price. This is consistent with the results found in case 11.3. The number of bathrooms did contribute significantly to the price of a home. The indicator variables used were bath25 and bath3. Bath25 was equal to 1 if the home had 2.5 bathrooms and 0 otherwise. Bath3 was equal to 1 if the home had more than 2.5 bathrooms and 0 otherwise. When bath25 and bath3 were both zero this indicated that the home had either one or two bathrooms. The model with SqFt, bath25, and bath3 gave the best fit.

$\hat{y} = \$7,539 + 4.234Sqft + 7,532Bath25 + 10,496Bath3$.

$R^2 = 0.8334$ and standard error $= 37,202$.

Chapter 12: Statistics for Quality: Control and Capability

12.1 Answers will vary.

12.2 Answers will vary.

12.3

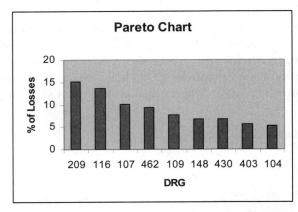

These 9 DRGs account for approximately 80.5% of losses. The hospital should concentrate on DRG 209 first.

12.4 Special causes might be illness or poor weather. A tire blowout or mechanical failure of her bike during a training ride would also be considered a special cause.

12.5 Answers will vary.

12.6 CL = 75, UCL = 75.75, LCL = 74.25.

12.7 **a)** CL = 11.5, UCL = 11.8, LCL = 11.2. **b)**

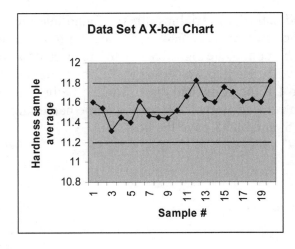
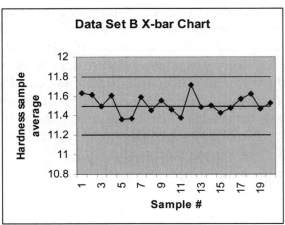

Points 12 and 20 are above the UCL for Data Set A. Data Set B has all points inside the control limits. Data set C shows points 19 and 20 above the UCL.

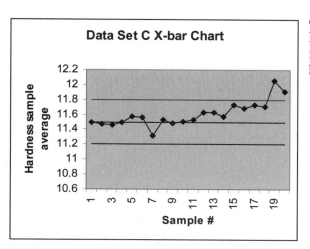

c) Data Set B comes from a process in control. Data Set C shows a process with a gradual drift in the mean. Data Set A shows a process that has shifted suddenly.

12.8 **a)** Number of applications received that day, time of day the application is reviewed. **b)** Hiring freeze (no applications reviewed and response time is quick), new employee in human resources (their review time is longer; therefore, response time is longer than other HR employees). **c)** New procedures for review could either increase or decrease the average time, time of year (there may be many applications in May when college graduates hit the job market).

12.9 CL = 0.4607, UCL = 1.044, LCL = 0.

12.10 **a)**

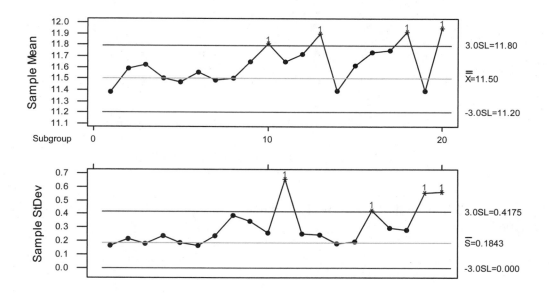

b) It appears that the standard deviation started to move up between sample #10 and #11. The x-bar chart also shows an out of control situation. **c)** The s chart does not reflect the increase in the process mean. The x-bar chart clearly shows the shift in the mean and the increase in the variation by having more scatter in the sample means and several out of control points.

12.11   Answers will vary.

12.12   Answers will vary.

12.13   Answers will vary.

12.14

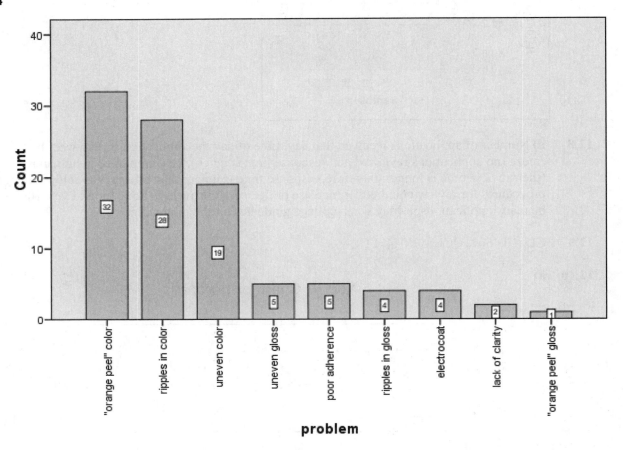

Cases weighted by percent

We should look at the "orange peel" texture in color first. It is contributing to 32% of the problems.

12.15   x-bar chart: CL = 0.875, UCL = 0.87661, LCL = 0.87339. s chart: CL = 0.00113, UCL = 0.00236, LCL = 0.

12.16   **a)** CL = 0.1194, UCL = 0.2494, LCL = 0. **b)** CL = 4.22, UCL = 4.39, LCL = 4.05.

12.17

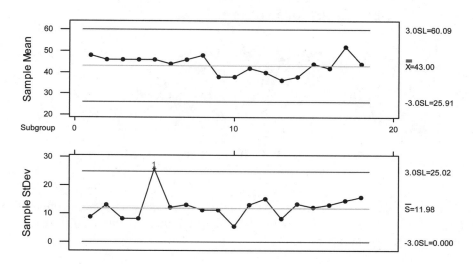

Xbar/S Chart for Distance

The process appears to be running out of control with respect to variation. Sample five is just above the upper control limit.

12.18 The new type of yarn most likely showed up on the $\bar{x}$ chart. The leaky valve most likely showed up on the s chart.

12.19 $P(\bar{x} > 713 \mid \mu = 693) + P(\bar{x} < 687 \mid \mu = 693) = 0.0004 + 0.1587 = 0.1591.$

12.20 3.1 standard deviations.

12.21 **a)** $UCL_{\bar{x}} = \mu + 2\dfrac{\sigma}{\sqrt{n}}, LCL_{\bar{x}} = \mu - 2\dfrac{\sigma}{\sqrt{n}}$ **b)** $UCL_s = (c_4 + 2c_5)\sigma, LCL_s = (c_4 - 2c_5)\sigma.$

12.22 **a)** This would likely show up as a run out on the $\bar{x}$ chart as the solution becomes less effective over time. **b)** This would most likely show up as a run on the $\bar{x}$ chart if the buildup continues over a long period of time or as a point out on the s chart. **c)** This would likely show up as single point out on the s chart whenever this representative answers a call if she works with other representatives also taking calls. If the representative is the only representative taking calls, then it would probably appear as a run on the $\bar{x}$ chart. **d)** This would likely show up as a single point out on the s chart.

12.23

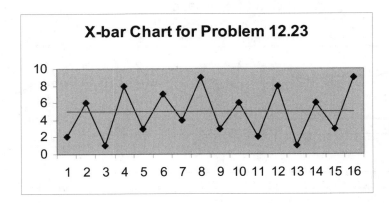

The chart above shows a process that is actually two processes in one. Note that each point alternates above and below the mean of 5. This is an unusual pattern if the process were being operated the same by all operators.

12.24 $\bar{x}$ chart: CL = 48.7, UCL = 50.2, LCL = 47.2. s chart: CL = 0.92, UCL = 2.085, LCL = 0.

12.25 **a)** $\mu = 275$, $\sigma = 37.5$. **b)** Referring to Figure 12.7, almost all of the 20 s values plot below or just slightly above the centerline of the chart. This indicates that σ has most likely decreased.

12.26   a)

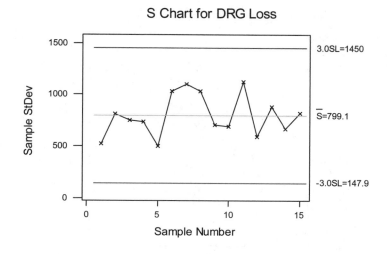

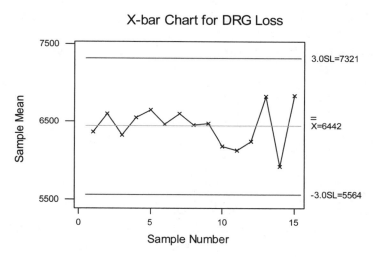

The process appears to be in control with respect to process mean.

12.27   If the computer maker is confident that their monitor manufacturer is operating in control, then they can safely predict the tension on the screens and no longer have to perform incoming inspection.

12.28   Natural tolerances are: $6442 \pm 3(811)$ or $(4009, 8875)$.

12.29

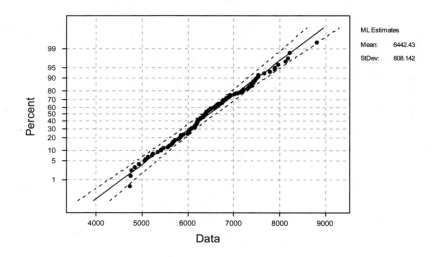

Normal Probability Plot for DRG Losses

The data appear to have a fairly Normal distribution.

12.30   **a)** 99.94%. **b)** 97.38%.

12.31   99.06%.

12.32   **a)** Verify.
             b)

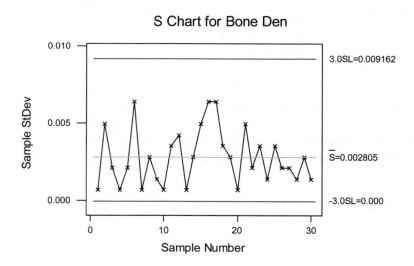

S Chart for Bone Den

This chart shows process or short run variation. The process appears to be in control with respect to standard deviation.

c)

X-bar Chart for Bone Den

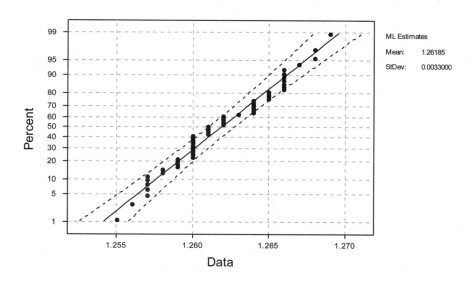

Day to day variation will be visible on this chart. It appears that this machine is staying in control with respect to both the variation and the average.

12.33 With data point #5 removed, $\hat{\mu} = \overline{\overline{x}} = 43.41$, $\overline{s} = 11.647$, $\hat{\sigma} = \dfrac{\overline{s}}{c_4} = \dfrac{11.647}{0.9400} = 12.390$. The natural tolerances are $\hat{\mu} \pm 3\hat{\sigma} = 43.41 \pm 3(12.39) = 43.41 \pm 37.17 = (6.24, 80.58)$.

12.34 (1.25191, 1.2719).

12.35 43.16%.

12.36

Normal Probability Plot for Bone Density

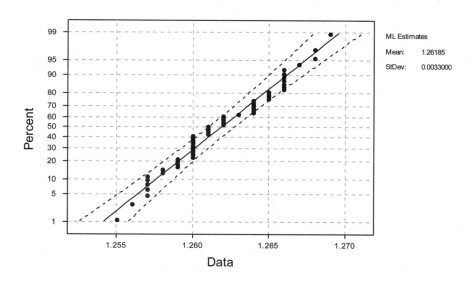

The data are approximately Normal.

12.37

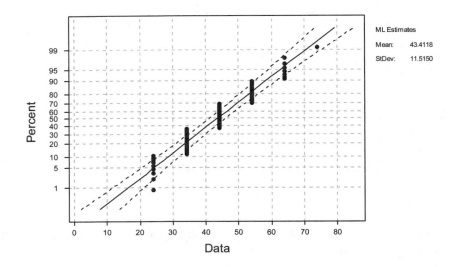

Normal Probability Plot for Distance

There are no serious departures from Normality. The stacks of data appear because of the lack of precision in the measurement.

12.38 a)

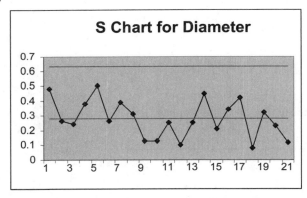

The short-term process variation appears to be in control.

b)

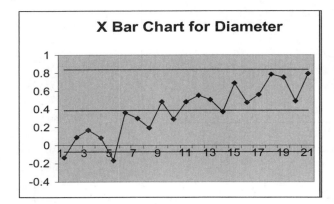

The process average is rising steadily and appears out of control. Tool wear could explain the lack of control.

12.39 a) This would show up as a sudden increase in $\bar{x}$. **b)** This would show up as a sudden change in s or R. **c)** This would show up as a gradual shift in $\bar{x}$.

12.40 a) This speaks to the fact that processes in control may not always be capable but operators can only work with the process management gives them. **b)** Bringing a process into control does not make it capable. **c)** Again, operators can only work with the process that has been provided by management. Pep talks do not make high quality. Capable processes do.

12.41 The control limits include times from the beginning of the Boston Marathon that were highly variable. Since then, the variation has decreased and remained steady. Rick should calculate the variation from 1980 on and look at winning times over the past 20 years.

12.42

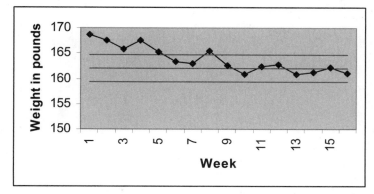

Joe's weight begins well above the UCL but then appears to stabilize towards the end of the 16 weeks.

12.43 Specifications limits start with the customer. When the customer states their product or service requirements, the product/service designer translates those requirements into product/service specifications. These specifications define limits within which the product can function as intended. Control limits, on the other hand, are derived from process behavior. They are independent of product/service specifications. Control limits tell us what the expected variability is in the process with respect to certain product, process, or service characteristics.

12.44 a)

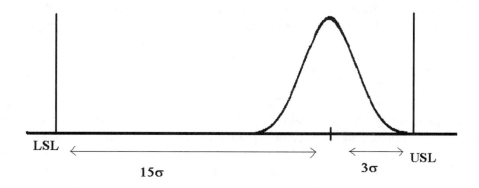

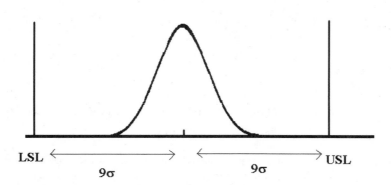

12.45   **a)** $C_p = 1.3$, $C_{pk} = 1.09$. **b)** $\hat{C}_p = 0.87, \hat{C}_{pk} = 0.65$.

12.46   **a)** $\hat{C}_p = 1.3, \hat{C}_{pk} = 1.3$. **b)** $\hat{C}_p = 0.87, \hat{C}_{pk} = 0.87$.

12.47   **a)** $C_{pk} = 1$, 50% meet specifications. **b)** 99.74%. **c)** The capability index formulas make sense for Normal distributions, but for distributions that are clearly not Normal they will give misleading results.

12.48 $\hat{\sigma} = 37.5, \hat{C}_{pk} = 0.89$.

12.49 C_p is referred to as the potential capability index because it measures process variability against the standard provided by external specifications for the output of the process. It estimates what the process is capable of producing if the process could be centered. C_{pk} is referred to as the actual capability index because it considers both the center and the variability against the standard provided by external specifications for the output of the process. It estimates what the process is capable of if the process target is centered between the specification limits.

12.50 Estimated nonconformance rate is 0.0164. This comes from $0.80 = \dfrac{USL - LSL}{6\sigma}$, which when simplified tells us that the USL and LSL are 2.4 standard deviations away from the target. Using the Normal table, this means that a proportion of 0.0082 of the area falls in the tails below Z = -2.4 and above Z = 2.4. Therefore, the total area in these tails is 0.0164, which represents the nonconformance.

12.51 **a)** $\hat{\mu} = 43.4, \hat{\sigma} = 11.6$

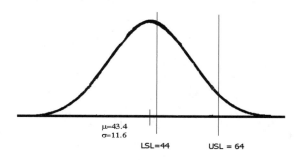

b) $\hat{C}_p = 0.29, \hat{C}_{pk} = 0.02$. The process capability is very poor. Not only is the process average below the lower specification, but the variability of the process is almost 3 times greater than the width of the specification limits.

12.52 **a)** 97.49%. **b)** $\hat{C}_p = 0.821$ (using a standard deviation of 811.530 for the whole data set). **c)** $\hat{C}_{pk} = 0.640$.

12.53 **a)** 97.43%. **b)** $\hat{C}_{pk} = 0.73$.

12.54 **a)** This may show an initial improvement but it won't be lasting. **b)** This will likely show improvements if the operators are trained on the new equipment properly. **c)** This is also a viable solution if in fact the issue is one of not understanding the equipment. **d)** This solution will introduce more variation than is already in the process. **e)** This could be a viable solution also.

12.55   A process is said to be at six-sigma quality when the distance between the mean of the process and each of the specification limits is equal to six times the standard deviation of the process.

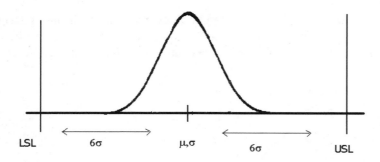

12.56   a)

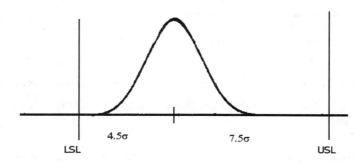

b) $C_{pk} = 1.5$. No, six-sigma quality is not as strong as requiring $C_{pk} \geq 2$. **c)** The probability of an outcome outside the specification limit is 0.0000034. This means 3.4 parts per million will fail to meet specification.

12.57   The choice to choose six calls at random from each shift makes sense because there are many different people working the call center. The different people add to the common cause variation in the process and we want to include this in our estimate of the process standard deviation. If we did not want to include the variation arising from different workers, then we could choose six consecutive calls.

12.58 a)

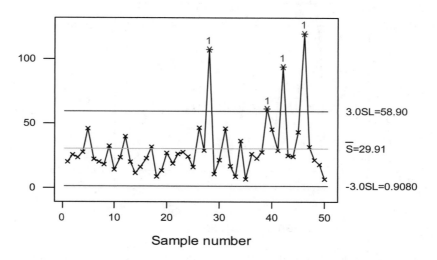

b)

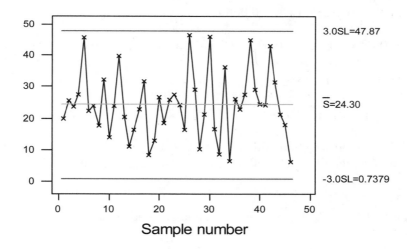

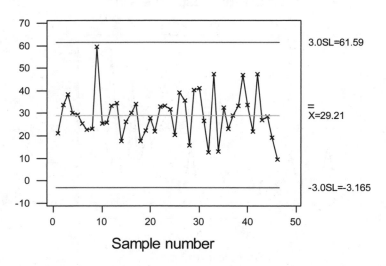

X-bar Chart for Response Time

c) It appears that the process is in control with respect to the process average.

12.59 From sample 28, the outlier is 276. Removing the outlier results in an $s = 9.28$. From sample 42, the outlier is 244 and the resulting $s = 6.71$. From sample 46, the outlier is 333 and the resulting $s = 31.01$.

12.60 CL = 0.0972, UCL = 0.1255, LCL = 0.0689.

12.61 **a)** 28750, $\bar{p} = 0.0334$. **b)** CL = 0.0334, UCL = 0.0435, LCL = 0.0233.

12.62 CL = 0.005, UCL = 0.0117, LCL = 0.

12.63 CL = 0.006, UCL = 0.0131, LCL = 0.

12.64 For a day with 75,000 prescriptions filled, CL = 0.01, UCL = 0.0111, LCL = 0.0089. For a day with 50,000 prescriptions filled, CL = 0.01, UCL = 0.0113, LCL = 0.0087.

12.65 **a)** $\bar{p} = 0.3555$, $\bar{n} = 922$.
   b) UCL = 0.403, LCL = 0.308. The process appears to be in control.

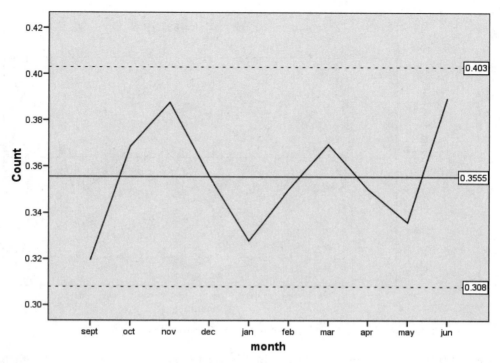

Cases weighted by Proportion absent

c) Adding exact limits does not affect the conclusions. The process remains in control. For October, UCL = 0.402 and LCL = 0.309. For June, UCL = 0.404 and LCL = 0.307.

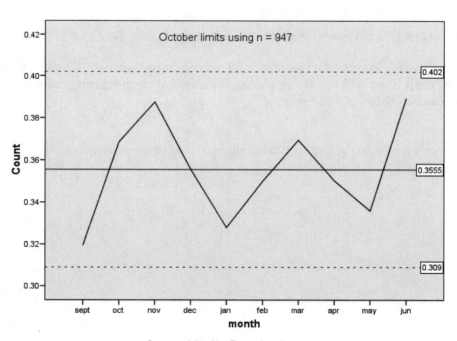

Cases weighted by Proportion absent

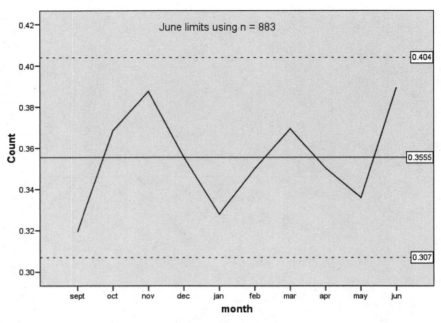

Cases weighted by Proportion absent

12.66 **a)** $\bar{p} = 0.0000035$. One would expect to see 0.0175 defects per day or 0.42 defects per month.
b) CL = 0.0000035, UCL = 0.000083, LCL = 0. **c)** A p chart is not useful in this circumstance because it will not detect subtle changes in product quality. The probability of observing a defect on any given day is extremely small.

12.67 **a)** $\bar{p} = 0.008$. One would expect to see 4 bad orders per month. **b)** CL = 0.008, UCL = 0.02, LCL = 0.11 bad orders would result in an out of control situation.

12.68 When a process is in control it means that the process is predictable. We can anticipate what the output of the process will be. Being predictable does not mean meeting customer requirements. A process can be predictably bad or good.

12.69 **a)** The percents do not add up to 100 because some customers have more than one complaint.

b)

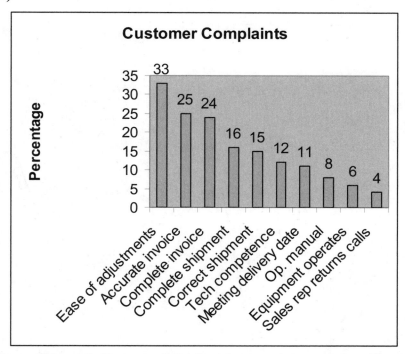

Choose "Ease of adjustments" for focusing your improvement efforts.

12.70 **a)** $\overline{x} - s$ charts. Time is a continuous variable. **b)** p charts are used for percents. **c)** A p chart would make sense here as well. We can calculate the percentage of employees participating in health screening.

12.71 **a)** If computer availability is measured as time available, then $\overline{X} - s$ charts make sense because time is a continuous variable. If we measure computer availability as a percentage of total time open for business, then a p chart makes sense. **b)** Again, because time is a continuous variable, $\overline{x} - s$ charts make sense. **c)** Percentages are shown on p charts.

12.72 Use a p chart. CL = 0.005, UCL = 0.0172, LCL = 0.

12.73 CL = 7.65, UCL = 19.65, LCL = 0. Sample number 1 is above the UCL and sample number 10 is very close to the UCL.

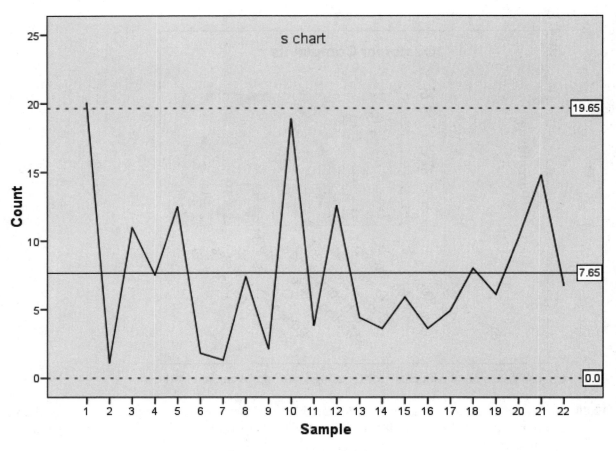

Cases weighted by StdDev

12.74 The new UCL = 16.615.

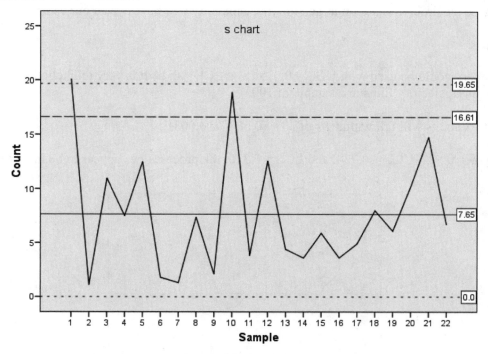

Cases weighted by StdDev

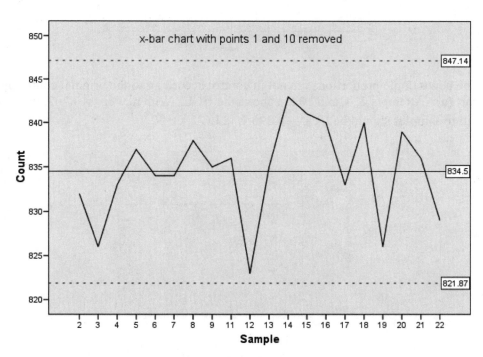

Cases weighted by Mean

For the $\bar{x}$ chart, the center line = 834.50, UCL = 847.14, LCL = 821.87. The chart above shows sample means with samples 1 and 10 removed. The process appears to be in control with respect to process average.

12.75 a) $\hat{\sigma} = 7.3$, $C_p = 1.14$. **b)** C_p describes the potential process capability if the process is on target. **c)** Because the process is not on target, the true capability will be less than our estimate for C_p.

12.76 0.0626%.

12.77 a) A p chart would be used with UCL = 0.0194 and LCL = 0. **b)** It is very unlikely that we will observe unsatisfactory films in a sample of 100.

12.78 P(next 15 points will fall within 1σ of μ) = $(0.68)^{15}$ = 0.0031.

12.79 a) With $\bar{p} = 0.522$, UCL = 0.734, and LCL = 0.310, the process does appear to be in control.

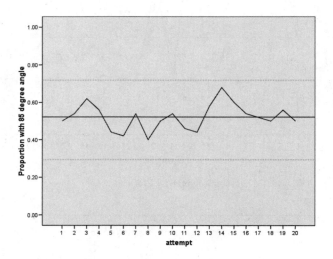

b) The new sample proportions are not in control according to the original control limits from part **(a)**. Attempts 2, 4, and 10 are above the UCL. With new $\bar{p} = 0.702$, the new limits for future samples should be UCL = 0.896, and LCL = 0.50.

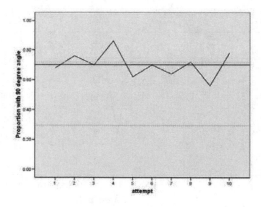

Chapter 13: Time Series Forecasting

13.1   **a)** Fourth-quarter sales are the highest quarter. The sales also are increasing year by year.
   b)

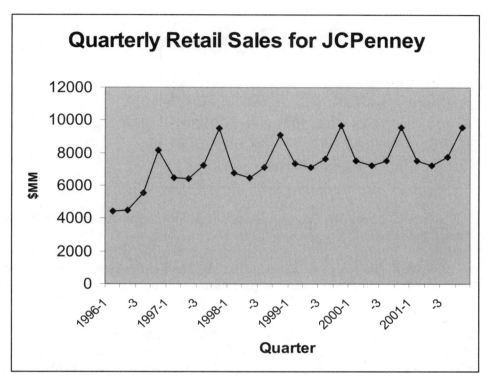

c) There seems to be a positive trend with spikes at every fourth quarter. **d)** The pattern can be seen on a yearly basis. Quarters 1, 2, and 3 are close in value with a slight dip in second-quarter sales. Quarter 4 shows a strong increase.

13.2   **a)**

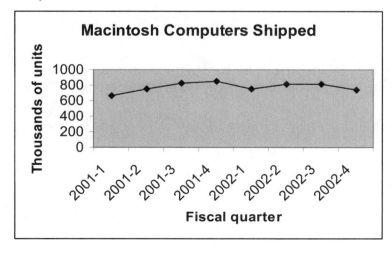

b) y = 7.9048x + 737.93. **c)** No, the linear model does not seem appropriate here.

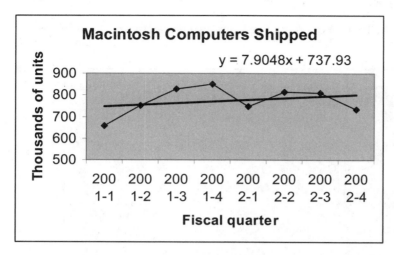

13.3 **a)** y = 118.75x + 5903.22. **b)** The intercept is a prediction for fourth quarter 1995. **c)** The slope tells how much the sales will increase each quarter.

13.4 **a)** $y = 786.75 + 0.88x - 86.88x_1 - 8.25x_2 + 26.38x_3$. **b)** The fourth quarter is represented by $x_1 = 0$, $x_2 = 0$, and $x_3 = 0$. **c)** The F test indicates that this model is not a good predictor of units shipped.

13.5 **a)** $y = 7858.8 + 99.54x - 2274.21x_1 - 2564.58x_2 - 2022.79x_3$. **b)** The fourth quarter is represented by $x_1 = 0$, $x_2 = 0$, and $x_3 = 0$. **c)** Yes, fourth quarter 1995. The estimate for the intercept for the second model is 7858. This is greater than the estimate from the first model – 5903. The second estimate is a better estimate.

13.6 **a)**

1st Q	0.921557
2nd Q	1.015779
3rd Q	1.052191
4th Q	1.010351

b) The average of the four factors is 0.99997. This is close to one. The factor for the first quarter is 0.921557, which means that the seasonal forecast for the number of Macs shipped in the first quarter is approximately 8% below the amount forecasted by the trend model alone.

c)

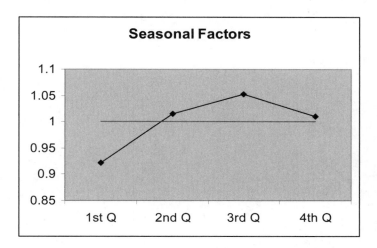

13.7   a)

1st Q	0.922881
2nd Q	0.883456
3rd Q	0.959464
4th Q	1.231493

b) The average of the four factors is 0.99923. This is close to one. The fourth quarter factor is 1.2315, which means that the seasonal forecast for fourth quarter sales is 123% of the trend only forecast.

c)

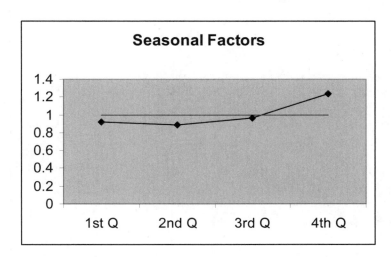

13.8   **a)** The seasonal pattern shows a steady but small increase during the first three quarters of the year. The sales show a dramatic increase in the fourth quarter. **b)** Using an x = 63 and a seasonality factor of 0.989, $29,523.65e^{0.068941(63)} / 0.989 = 2,297,405$.

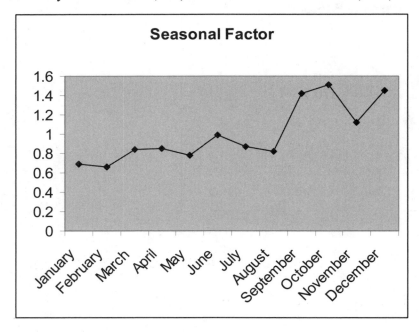

13.9   **a)**

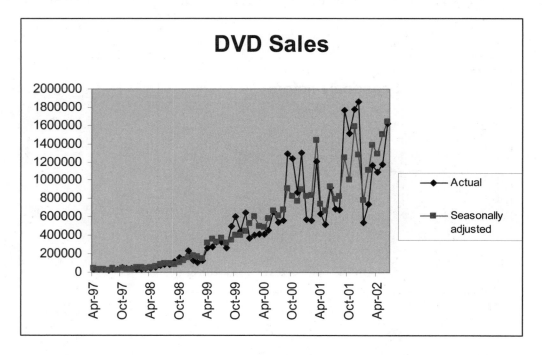

b) No, the seasonal adjustments did not smooth out the time series. The seasonal pattern does not appear to be as strong as the trend.

13.10 **a)** and **b)** See the table below.

Month	Predicted units	Resdiual	Month	Predicted units	Residual
1 (April 1997)	26822.9535	7778.0465	32	301059.3173	148182.6827
2	26466.8633	584.1367	33	417616.2782	228673.7218
3	35907.7694	-6870.7694	34	213248.9702	156782.0298
4	33880.5917	-14464.5917	35	217919.3844	183115.6156
5	34173.3363	-152.3363	36	295284.9940	117274.0060
6	63312.6446	-28941.6446	37	320901.4267	88290.5733
7	72041.0263	-15634.0263	38	316641.2748	136793.7252
8	57553.9813	-19896.9813	39	429589.3231	225097.6769
9	79836.3581	-37261.3581	40	405336.8034	132116.1966
10	40767.1397	-6740.1397	41	408839.1075	148777.8925
11	41659.9901	-7423.9901	42	757452.6788	538827.3212
12	56450.0949	-18114.0949	43	861876.3082	374781.6918
13	61347.2284	-18458.2284	44	688557.8328	177949.1672
14	60532.8085	-12727.8085	45	955137.2202	347953.7798
15	82125.2639	-3081.2639	46	487725.3096	84305.6904
16	77488.8717	7220.1283	47	498407.0925	57448.9075
17	78158.4126	3011.5874	48	675351.2806	532137.7194
18	144803.4152	-31245.4152	49	733939.0550	-102586.0550
19	164766.2440	-1692.2440	50	724195.5901	-200970.5901
20	131632.6795	5275.3205	51	982520.9726	-61681.9726
21	182595.0786	50909.9214	52	927052.6267	-234039.6267
22	93239.2115	32296.7885	53	935062.8052	-261136.8052

23	95281.2647	14117.7353	54	1732382.7728	36438.2272
24	129107.9623	-5641.9623	55	1971211.8137	-455000.8137
25	140308.2789	128798.7211	56	1574812.2107	206235.7893
26	138445.6054	141310.3946	57	2184510.4153	-321738.4153
27	187830.0735	138837.9265	58	1115484.7662	-572786.7662
28	177226.1029	147924.8971	59	1139915.2516	-403797.2516
29	178757.4213	81467.5787	60	1544607.2829	-382039.2829
30	331182.3285	170318.6715	61	1678604.3681	-587837.3681
31	376839.6504	226208.3496	62	1656319.9254	-484335.9254
			63 (June 2002)	2247140.2566	-630042.2566

c) The residuals appear to be autocorrelated. The residuals are strictly positive from months 26 to 48 and then become mostly negative for the rest of the data set. We should see random scatter around the zero line. It appears that the residuals are positively autocorrelated. **d)** Yes, there is evidence of positive autocorrelation between the residuals. The scatterplot shows a positive trend.

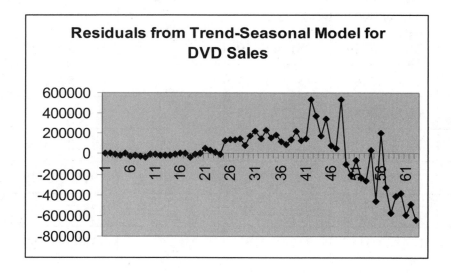

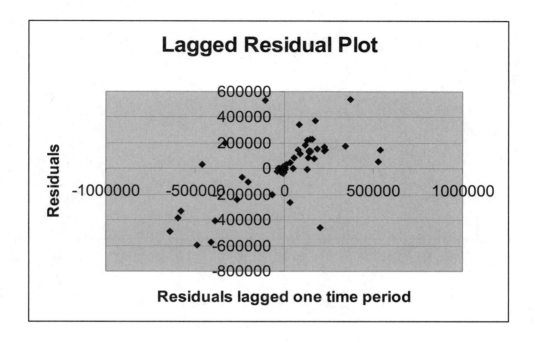

13.11   **a)** See time plot that follows. **b)** There is a positive, fairly linear trend over time. **c)** There is usually a peak in January, a drop until April, and then an increase until the next January each year. **d)** There are two temporary troughs: a big one from January 1991 to November 1994 and a smaller one from January 1998 to January 2003. There could also be considered a temporary peak at the very end of the data set where there is a steep increase.

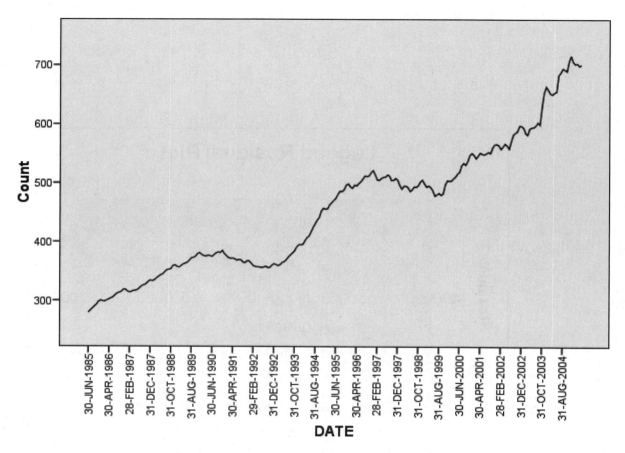

Cases weighted by Consumer-Loans(Billions-of-Dollars)

13.12   **a)** $\hat{y} = 270.840 + 1.537x$ **b)** For every month that passes, the amount of money held in consumer loans at all commercial banks in the U.S. increases by $1.537 billion.   **c)** Overestimates: March 1991 to November 1994 and February 1998 to November 2002. Underestimates: July 1985 to February 1991, December 1994 to January 1998, and November 2003 to June 2005.   **d)** The forecasted amount of money in consumer loans for July 2005 would be 641.257 billion dollars. This is expected to be less than the actual amount because all the residuals in that period of time are all very big and positive.

13.13   **a)** See time plot that follows.   **b)** There is no obvious increase or decrease overall, but there is lots of month-to-month variability.   **c)** The biggest dips come in August each year, and then there is another major (but not quite as big) dip in December each year. There are smaller dips in June each year. In August 2002, there is a dip, but it's just not as dramatic as for all the other years. However, the June 2002 dip was bigger than all the other June dips, so that might help explain why the August dip isn't as big as expected.

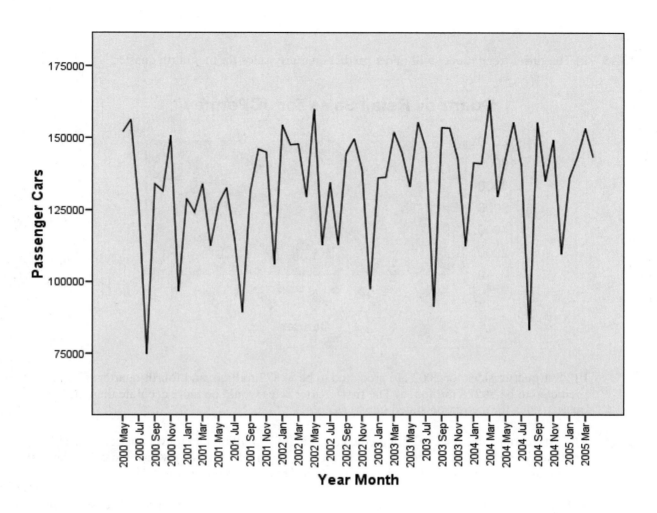

13.14 **a)** $\hat{y} = 126265.2 + 245.231x$ **b)** See time plot of the residuals and lagged residual plot below. On the time plot of the residuals, in general each residual seems to be followed by a smaller residual. On the lagged residual plot, there is a downward trend, so there is a negative autocorrelation. **c)** The correlation between successive residuals is -0.121. There is a weak, negative autocorrelation.

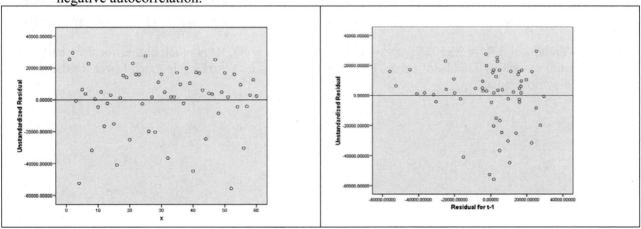

13.15 **a)** The linear trend model will under predict quarterly sales for the fourth quarter.

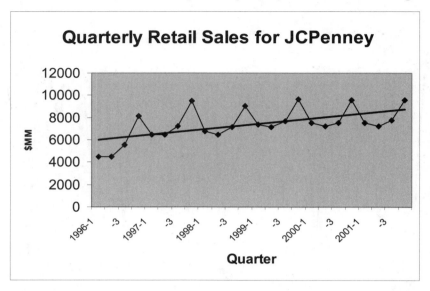

b) First-quarter sales for 2002 are predicted to be $8872 million, and fourth-quarter sales are predicted to be $9228 million. **c)** The first-quarter sales would be more accurate than the fourth quarter sales for the reason stated in part (**a**).

13.16 **a)** First-quarter sales for 2002 are predicted to be $8072 million and fourth quarter sales are predicted to be $10,644 million. **b)** The trend-seasonal model gives a lower forecast for the first-quarter and a higher forecast for the fourth-quarter than the trend-only model.

13.17 **a)** First-quarter sales for 2002 are predicted to be $8,187 million and fourth-quarter sales are predicted to be $11,364 million. **b)** The model using seasonality factors gives a lower forecast for the first quarter and a higher forecast for the fourth quarter than the trend only model. **c)** The model using seasonality factors gives a higher forecast for both periods than the trend-and-season model using indicator variables.

13.18 **a)** First quarter: $y = 5584.6 + 99.5x$. Second quarter: $y = 5294.2 + 99.5x$. Third quarter: $y = 5836 + 99.5x$. Fourth quarter: $y = 7858.8 + 99.5x$. **b)** The slopes are the same. **c)** The lines are parallel.

13.19 **a)** Trend-only: $R^2 = 0.3501$. Trend-and-season: $R^2 = 0.8683$. R^2 is much higher for the trend-and-season model. **b)** Trend-only: $s = 1170$. Trend-and-season: $s = 567$. s is much lower for the trend-and-season model.

c)

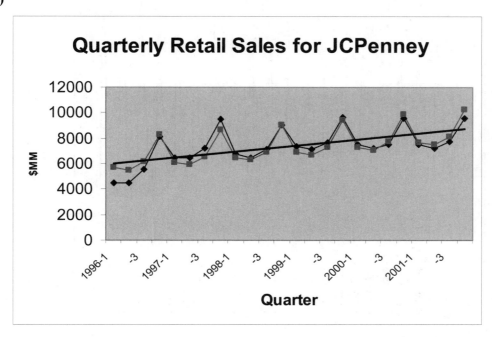

d) The trend-and-season model is a big improvement over the trend-only model.

13.20 **b)** There is a regular, repeating pattern. June and July are low, then there is a steady, linear increase through August and September. There is a further increase to a maximum in January, then a sharp decrease to a minimum in April. There is a brief small increase in May, then a small drop to June and July.

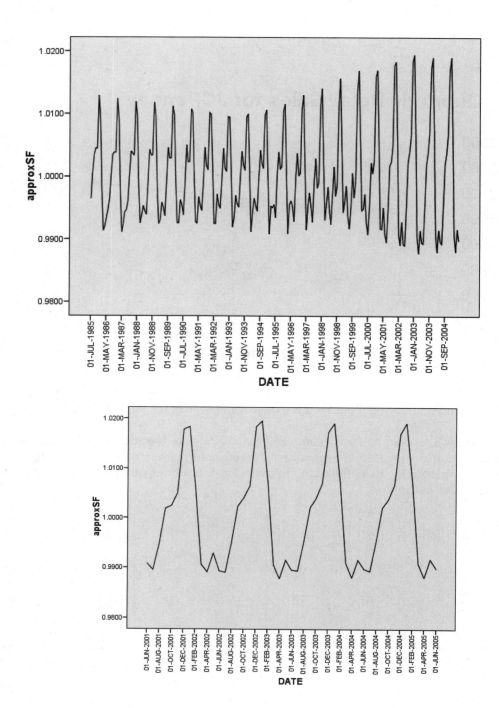

13.21 **a)** There are two very large temporary troughs (approximately) between July 1990 and July 1995 and then between April 1997 and November 2003. At the end of the data, there is a sharp rise. See the time plot of the residuals that follows. **b)** A closer look at the time plot suggests a positive autocorrelation. The majority of pairs of successive residuals shows the first residual lower than the second residual in the pair. **c)** The lagged residual plot shows a beautiful, positive, linear relationship between e_{t-1} and e_t. The correlation between e_{t-1} and e_t is 0.985. Yes, we have strong evidence of autocorrelation. See the lagged residual plot that follows.

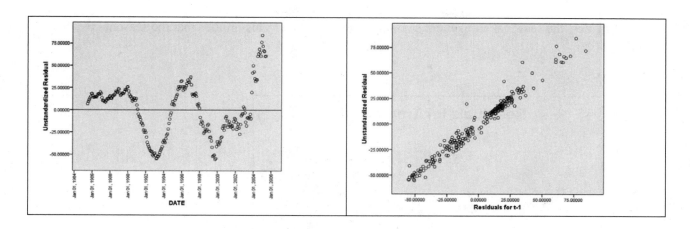

13.22 **a)** Using SF = 1.231 for the fourth-quarter seasonal adjustment, the seasonally adjusted value for 4th quarter 2001 is 9542 / 1.231 = $7751.42. **b)**

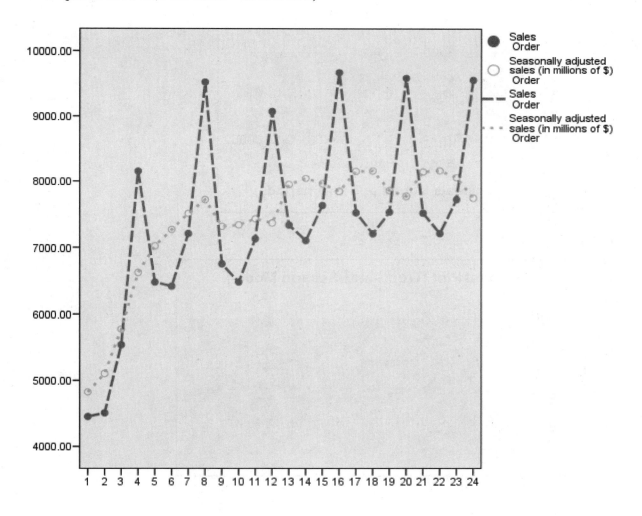

c) Yes, the seasonal adjustment smoothed the sales data. This implies that the seasonal pattern is strong.

13.23   a)

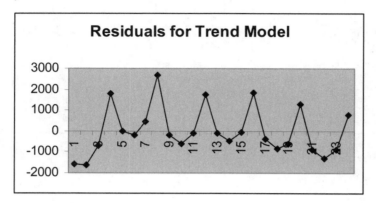

b) It is difficult to detect any autocorrelation from this scatterplot.

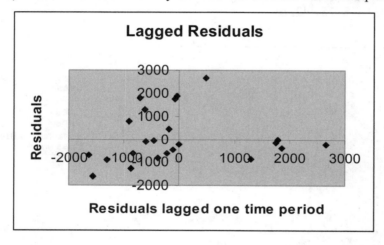

13.24   a)

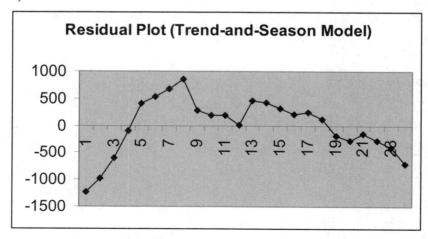

b) There does not appear to be any autocorrelation.

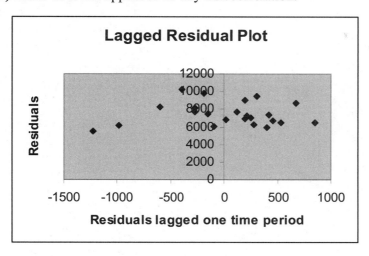

13.25 a) The upper group of ten points would have December sales as the *y*-coordinate. **b)** Yes, the increase in the correlation value indicates a strong autocorrelation in the time series. **c)** We would expect the correlation between the seasonally adjusted time series to be closer to 0.9206. By adjusting the data for seasonal influences, we are smoothing out the time series, which should result in a higher correlation.

13.26 a)

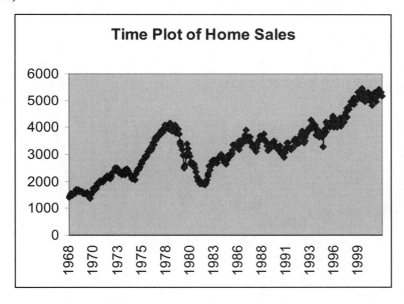

b) There appears to be an increasing trend with an obvious departure between the years 1978 and 1983. There may be seasonal influences. **c)** The plot that follows suggests that an AR(1) model is appropriate because there is a strong linear trend between the actual sales and the previous period's sales.

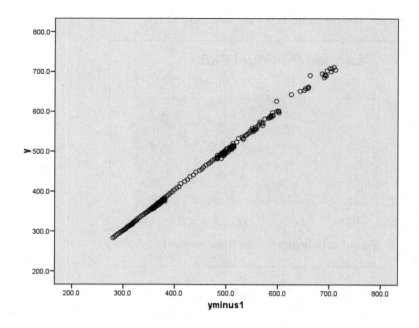

13.27 **a)** $\hat{y}_t = 34.044 + 0.9924 y_{t-1}$, 5165. **b)** $\hat{y}_t = 25.7022 + 0.995 y_{t-1}$, 5170. **c)** The preferred model would be the AR(1) model. The estimates of the slopes are similar but the intercept is smaller for the AR(1) model. Because of the strong correlation between actual sales for period t and the previous period sales it is appropriate to have a strong weight on the previous period's sales.

13.28 **a)**

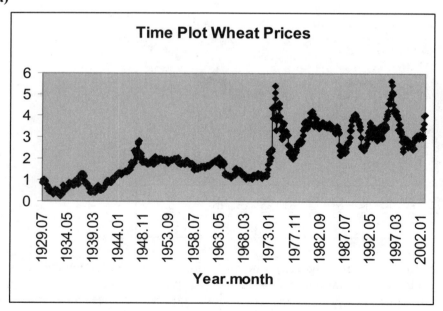

b) The time series shows a steady price with an increase between the years 1938 and 1948, followed by a drop and then a fairly slow decrease until 1974 when the prices jump dramatically. The prices stay high for a few years then drop again. We see ups and downs with another dramatic high in 1996.

c)

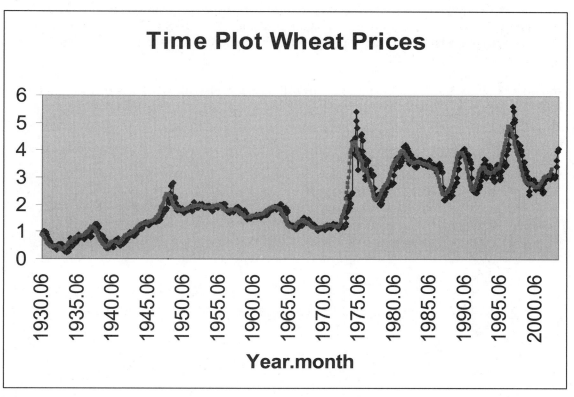

d)

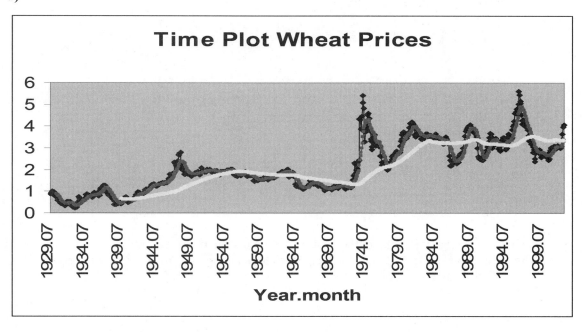

e) We see that the 120-month moving average is much smoother, as expected. It shows the overall increasing trend without the "noise" or constant ups and downs we see in the time series or the 12-month moving average.

13.29   **a)** The 12-month moving average forecast predicts the November 2002 price by the average of the preceding 12 months. The 12-month moving average forecast is $3.31. The 120-month moving average forecast predicts the November 2002 price by the average of the preceding 120 months. The 12-month moving average forecast is $3.39. **b)** $4.28. The 120-month moving average gave a slightly better forecast, but neither captures the sharp rise in price that occurred over the latter part of 2002.

13.30   **a)** 3, 3, 2.13, 2.037. **b)** Software confirms the values. **c)** 3.707. **d)** $y_{135} = 0.1(-8.1) + 0.9(3.707)$.

13.31

a)	b)	c)
0.1000	0.5000	0.9000
0.0900	0.2500	0.0900
0.0810	0.1250	0.0090
0.0729	0.0625	0.0009
0.0656	0.0313	9E-05
0.0590	0.0156	9E-06
0.0531	0.0078	9E-07
0.0478	0.0039	9E-08
0.0430	0.0020	9E-09
0.0387	0.0010	9E-10

d)

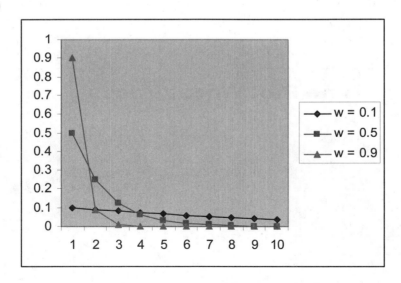

e) The curve that starts the highest, at w = 0.9, puts the more weight on the most recent value of the time series. **f)** 0.0349, 0.0005, 9×10^{-11}. These are smaller than the first ten coefficients. w = 0.1 puts the most weight on y_1.

13.32 **a)** $\hat{y}_t = -0.021 + 1.004y_{t-1}$. Using this model, $\hat{y}_{July\,2005} = 703.5822$. **b)**

$\hat{y}_t = -2.454 + 1.00877y_{t-1}$. Using this model $\hat{y}_{July\,2005} = 704.492$. **c)** The slope is very similar for the two models, but the intercept is more negative for the AR(1) model. The estimates are very close though. The assumptions necessary for the regression model are no longer valid, so it is better to use the AR(1) model.

13.33 From 13.32, $\hat{y}_t = -0.021 + 1.004y_{t-1}$, $\hat{y}_{July\,2005} = 703.5822$. **a)** $\hat{y}_t = -2.45385 + 1.00877y_{t-1}$,

$\hat{y}_{July\,2005} = 704.49217$. **b)** The slope is very similar for both equations, however the y-intercept is not the same. The estimates are fairly close. The assumptions necessary for the regression model are no longer valid, so it is better to use the AR(1) model.

13.34 **a)** See lagged time series plot below. **b)** The correlation is -0.065. **c)** No, there is an extremely weak association.

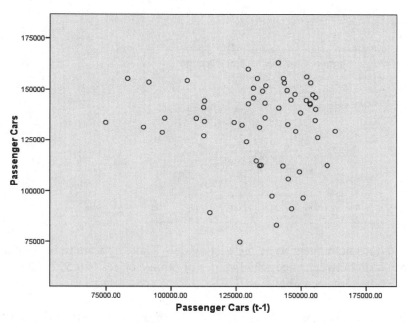

13.35 **a)** There is a moderate positive linear relationship. See the lagged time series plot below. **b)** 0.692. **c)** Yes, the relationship is strong enough to make production 12 months ago a good predictor or this month's production. The correlation is large and the relationship looks strong.

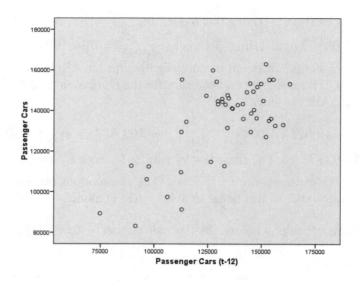

13.36 a)

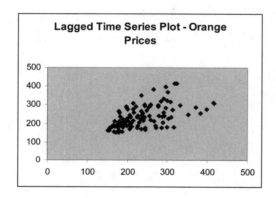

b) An AR(1) does not appear to be the best model. There appears to be a moderate linear trend.
c) The correlation between successive values of orange prices is 0.572. This value makes sense based on the time plot seen above.

13.37 a) $\hat{y}_t = 100.42 + 0.5716 y_{t-1}$, $R^2 = 0.327$, s = 47.86. **b)** $\hat{y}_t = 100.9 + 0.568 y_{t-1}$, $R^2 = 0.327$, s = 47.74. **c)** The equations are almost identical. **d)** There is very little difference between the values of R^2 and s in this example. Therefore, there is no clear indication which fitting method is preferred, although in general maximum likelihood is preferred to least-squares in time series models.

13.38 a) See the time series plot that follows. **b)** k = 5 follows the trend of the time plot the best because the upward trend lasted about 5 months and the downward trend lasted about 5 months.
c) The actual amount of consumer loans = 700.8. $\hat{y}_5 = 705.24$, $\hat{y}_{12} = 694.81$, $\hat{y}_{20} = 675.02$.
The k = 5 prediction is closest.

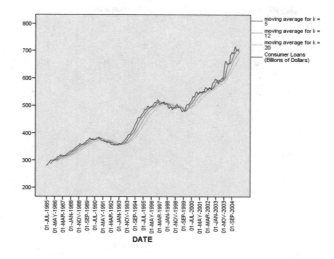

13.39   a) The moving averages do appear to be fairly linear. See the plot below.

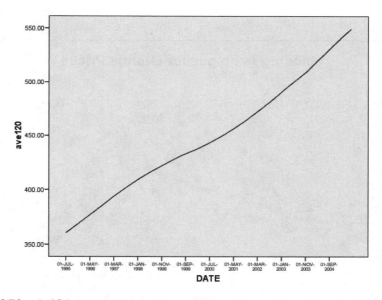

b) $\hat{y} = 181.372 + 1.481x$.   **c)** The moving average line and predicted value line completely overlap until about 1996. From 1996 on until the end of the data, there is a slight spiraling of the moving averages around the predicted value line, but he lines are still very close.

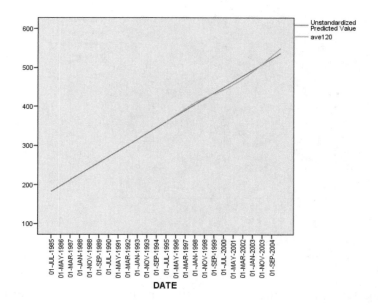

13.40   a)

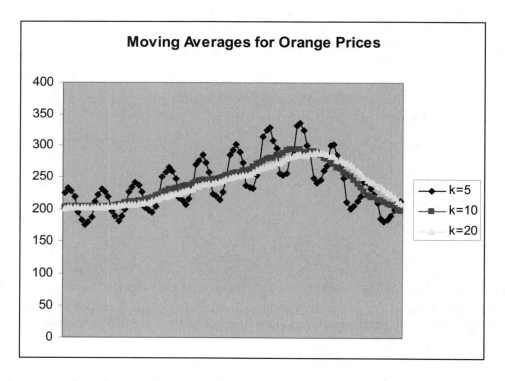

b) As expected, as the span increases the model becomes smoother. To predict monthly ups and downs in orange prices, the moving average model with a span of k=5 would be best. **c)** 270 (k = 5), 260 (k = 10), and 298 (k = 20). The model using k = 5 gave the best forecast.

13.41 a)

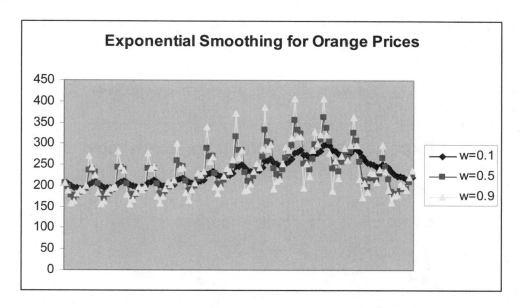

b) As expected, the model with the smallest value of w gives the smoothest forecasts. The model with w = 0.5 might be a good choice because it shows the monthly ups and downs but does not over respond to random variation. An analysis of the forecast errors should be done to determine the best model to use. Without that analysis, one would most likely choose the model with w = 0.9 because it is most responsive to monthly ups and downs. **c)** 219.48 (w = 0.1), 223.96 (w = 0.5), 237.46 (w = 0.9). The model that used w=0.9 gave the most accurate forecast.

13.42 a) $\hat{y}_t = -0.0021 + 1.0015 y_{t-1}$, s = 0.0055. **b)** 0.9909. **c)** $\hat{y}_t = -0.0004 + y_{t-1}$. **d)** 1.0114. Both forecasts were below the actual for that day.

13.43 a) $\hat{y}_t = y_{t-1}$

b) and c)

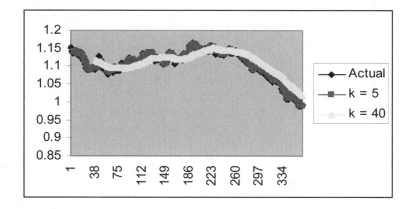

d) The moving average model with a span of 40 is smoother than the model with a span of 5. This is to be expected.

13.44   **a)** 0.9915. **b)** 0.9889. **c)** 1.01902 **d)** The forecast equation would simply be the annual average. 1.1072. **e)** Actual = 1.0114. The model in part (c) performed the best and the model in part (d) performed the worst.

13.45   **a)** For w = 1, $\hat{y}_t = y_{t-1}$. For w = 0, $\hat{y}_t = \hat{y}_{t-1}$. **b)** w = 0.2. **c)** w = 0.8. **d)**

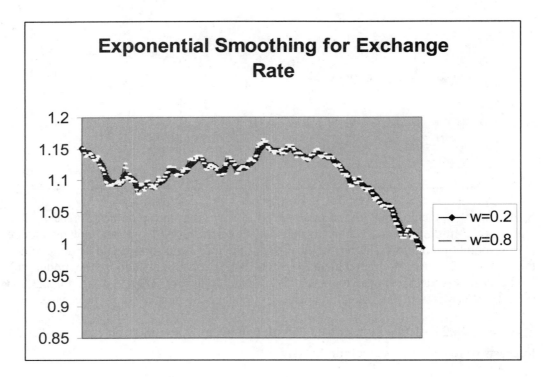

As expected, the model that puts a greater weight on the most recent observation is less smooth than the model that used a weight of 0.2. **e)** 0.9935 and 0.9907. Both forecasts underestimate the actual exchange rate.

13.46   **a)** $\beta_o = 0$, $\beta_1 = 1$. **b)** k = 1. **c)** w = 1. **d)** No, a better forecasting model might use more than one past period. Using forecast errors, one could find an optimal forecasting model.

13.47 a)

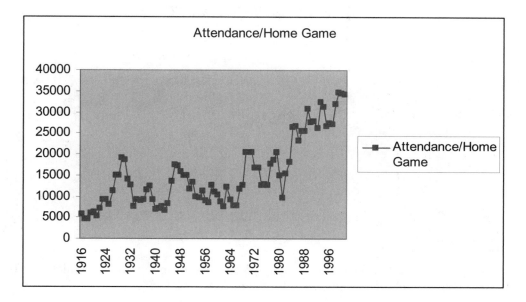

b) $\hat{y} = -487429.824 + 256.735x$, $R^2 = 0.62$, s = 5048.

c) $\hat{y} = 20082384.1 - 20752.332x + 5.363558x^2$, $R^2 = 0.753$, s = 4091.

d) $\hat{y} = -1102185875 + 1698652.29x - 872.6402x^2 + 0.14943473x^3$, $R^2 = 0.802$, s = 3684.

e) Based on the regression statistics, the third degree polynomial looks like the best fit.

13.48 a) 26,553, 33,397, and 38,486. **b)** The model from part (b) provided the best forecast. This is not the model we selected.

13.49 a) The estimated trend-and-season model is:

$$\hat{y} = 9.298 + 0.0695x - 0.0244x_1 + 0.2015x_2 + 0.2170x_3 + 0.1288x_4$$
$$+0.3899x_5 + 0.2365x_6 + 0.2279x_7 + 0.7205x_8 + 0.8192x_9 + 0.5361x_{10} + 0.7613x_{11}$$

b) No indicator variable is needed for December because setting x_1 through x_{11} equal to zero indicates that the month is December. **c)** 2,356,716.75. **d)** This forecast is less than the one found in example 13.5. **e)** This forecast is greater than the one found in example 13.10.

13.50 a) The time series plot of coffee prices shows that prices stay fairly constant for long periods of time, and then it appears that some event causes the price to spike. After the spike in price, the prices drop rapidly back to some steady value. It would not make sense to use a trend or trend-and-season model to forecast coffee prices.

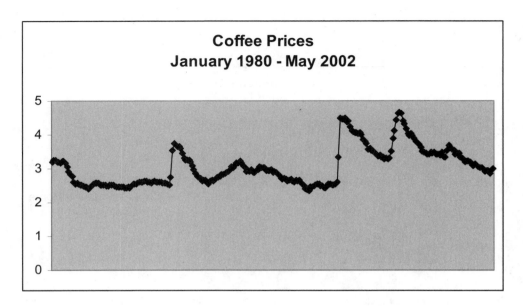

13.51   After comparing several values of k, a span of 5 appears to smooth the ups and downs but still captures the spikes in price. The forecast for June 2002 is 2.9456.

13.52   An exponential smoothing model with a weight of 0.7 was chosen. The forecast for June 2002 is 2.9922.

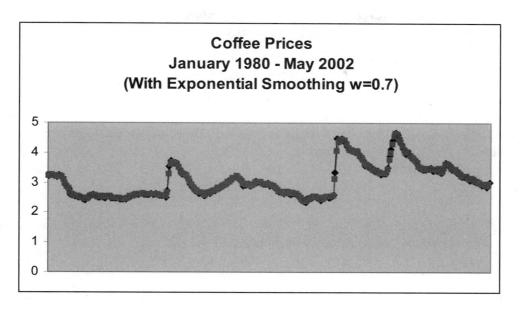

13.53 The AR(1) model does not smooth the minor ups and downs in the data, although it does capture the major jump in the series that occurs two-thirds of the way through the values. Using the AR(1) model, Minitab forecasts the June 2002 average price per pound of coffee as 3.01245.

13.54 The actual average price for a pound of coffee in June 2002 was 2.938. This value is less than the forecast found in problems 13.39 and 13.40. The forecast in problem 13.39 was closer to actual than the one found in 13.40.

Chapter 14: One-Way Analysis of Variance

14.1 $x_{ij} = \mu_i + \varepsilon_{ij}$, $i = 1, 2$, and $3, j = 1, \ldots, 60$. $I = 3$. The n_i are all equal to 60, and the parameters are μ_1, μ_2, μ_3, and σ.

14.2 $x_{ij} = \mu_i + \varepsilon_{ij}$, $i = 1, 2, 3, 4$, and $5, j = 1, \ldots, 50$. $I = 5$. The n_i are all equal to 50, and the parameters are μ_1, μ_2, μ_3, μ_4, μ_5, and σ.

14.3 **a)** Yes, $120 < 2 \times 80$. **b)** $\hat{\mu}_1 = 75, \hat{\mu}_2 = 125, \hat{\mu}_3 = 100, \hat{\sigma} = 101.32$.

14.4 **a)** Check: Is largest s $< 2 \times$ smallest s? These data are right on the borderline, but technically it is not reasonable to pool the standard deviations. $14 = 2 \times 7$.
b) $\hat{\mu}_A = 35, \hat{\mu}_B = 42, \hat{\mu}_C = 20, \hat{\mu}_D = 22, \hat{\mu}_E = 46, \hat{\sigma} = 10.3$.

14.5

0 46	0 6	0 445666
0 7888999	0 777888889999	0 777889
1 012222222	1 00022	1 11122
1 345	1 335	1 33344
1 6	1 6	1

There do not appear to be any systematic differences between the groups.

14.6 It appears that the residuals have a Normal distribution with a mean equal to zero.

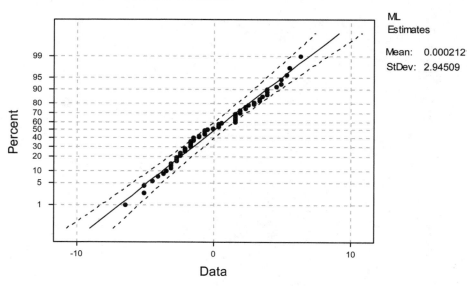

14.7 $20.58 + 572.45 = 593.03$.

14.8 $I = 3, N = 66$. DFG $= 2$, DFE $= 63$, and DFT $= 65$.

14.9 $2 + 63 = 65$.

14.10 $MSG = 20.58/2 = 10.29$. $MSE = 572.45/63 = 9.09$.

14.11 $MST = 9.1235$. This is the value of the sample variance of all 66 responses.

14.12 Verify that $MSE = 9.09$.

14.13 **a)** 3 and 20. **b)** 3.10.

14.14 **a)** 3 and 100. **b)** 2.70. The degrees of freedom in the numerator are the same for both situations, but the degrees of freedom in the in the denominator is much larger with the increased sample size. As the denominator degrees of freedom increase, the critical F value becomes smaller (it is easier to reject the null hypothesis with a larger sample size).

14.15 **a)** SAS labels the standard error as Root MSE because the value can be found by taking the square root of the mean square error. **b)** $\sqrt{0.616003} = 0.7849$.

14.16 Applet.

14.17 Applet.

14.18

$$\frac{1}{2}(\mu_1 + \mu_2) = \frac{1}{2}(\mu_4 + \mu_5), \ 0 = \frac{1}{2}(\mu_4 + \mu_5) - \frac{1}{2}(\mu_1 + \mu_2), \ a_1 = a_2 = \ -\frac{1}{2}, \ a_4 = a_5 = \ \frac{1}{2}.$$

14.19 $SE_c = s_p \sqrt{\sum \frac{a^2_i}{n_i}} = 10 \sqrt{\frac{1}{25} \left[\left(\frac{1}{2}\right)^2 + \left(\frac{1}{2}\right)^2 + \left(\frac{1}{2}\right)^2 + \left(\frac{1}{2}\right)^2 \right]} = 2$.

14.20 $C = 15$. H_o: $\frac{1}{2}(\mu_1 + \mu_2) = \frac{1}{2}(\mu_4 + \mu_5)$, H_a: $\frac{1}{2}(\mu_1 + \mu_2) \neq \frac{1}{2}(\mu_4 + \mu_5)$. $t = 15/2 = 7.5$ with 120 df.

The *P*-value for this result is less than 0.0005. The contrast is significant.

14.21 (11.032, 18.968).

14.22 $t_{13} = \dfrac{\overline{x}_1 - \overline{x}_2}{s_p \sqrt{\dfrac{1}{n_1} + \dfrac{1}{n_2}}} = \dfrac{41.0455 - 44.2727}{6.31\sqrt{\dfrac{1}{22} + \dfrac{1}{22}}} = -1.693$.

14.23 $t_{23} = \dfrac{\overline{x}_2 - \overline{x}_3}{s_p \sqrt{\dfrac{1}{n_2} + \dfrac{1}{n_3}}} = \dfrac{46.7273 - 44.2727}{6.31\sqrt{\dfrac{1}{22} + \dfrac{1}{22}}} = 1.29$.

14.24 We would fail to reject the null hypothesis.

14.25 We would fail to reject the null hypothesis.

14.26   –3.2273 / 1.90378 = –1.69.

14.27   2.4545 / 1.90378 = 1.29.

14.28   Mark groups 1, 2, and 3 with the letter A and mark groups 4 and 5 with the letter B. Groups 1, 2, and 3 do not differ significantly from each other. Groups 4 and 5 do not differ significantly from each other.

14.29   Mark groups 1 and 4 with A, groups 2, 3, and 5 with B, and groups 3 and 4 with C. Groups 1 and 4 do not differ significantly. Groups 2, 3, and 5 do not differ significantly. Groups 3 and 4 do not differ significantly.

14.30   (–7.91, 1.46). Yes, the interval includes 0.

14.31   (–2.23, 7.14). Yes, the interval includes 0.

14.32 a)

n	F*	DFG	DFE	λ	PROBF	Power
10	2.866	3	36	3.135	0.74060	0.2594
20	2.725	3	76	6.27	0.48518	0.51482
30	2.683	3	116	9.405	0.28382	0.71618
40	2.663	3	156	12.54	0.15234	0.84766
50	2.651	3	196	15.675	0.076369	0.923631
100	2.627	3	396	31.35	0.001231645	0.9987684

b) As sample size increases, power increases. See the graph below.

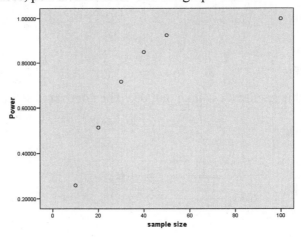

c) Based on the values of *n* selected, I would choose a sample size of 50. The power is fairly high at 0.9236. Increasing the sample size to 100 increases the power so it is very close to one, but to get there the sample size was doubled.

14.33 a)

n	F*	DFG	DFE	λ	PROBF	Power
10	2.866	3	36	0.9042	0.89757	0.10243
20	2.725	3	76	1.8084	0.83012	0.16988
30	2.683	3	116	2.7126	0.75683	0.24317
40	2.663	3	156	3.6168	0.68113	0.31887
50	2.651	3	196	4.521	0.60573	0.39427
100	2.627	3	396	9.042	0.29117	0.70883

b) As sample size increases, power increases. See the graph below.

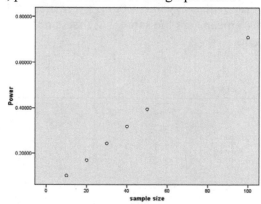

c) Of the sample sizes selected in the table above, 100 would be best since the power is fairly low at smaller sample sizes.

14.34 a) The ANOVA test is for the population means, not the sample means. **b)** The sum of squares (not the mean squares) in an ANOVA table will add, that is SST = SSG + SSE. **c)** Between-group variation (not within-group) is the variation in the data due to the differences in the sample means.

14.35 a) The response variable needs to be quantitative, not categorical. **b)** You do want to use one-way ANOVA when there are at least three means to be compared. **c)** The pooled estimate s_p is an estimate for σ, which is a parameter.

14.36 a) $F(5, 6) = 4.387$. **b)** $F(5, 18) = 2.773$. **c)** $F(5, 60) = 2.368$. **d)** As DFE increases (or as N increases) for the same number of groups, the F needed to reject the null hypothesis decreases.

14.37 a) $F(3, 40)$

p	0.100	0.050	0.025	0.010	0.001
$F*$	2.23	2.84	3.46	4.31	6.59

b) See sketches that follow for $F* = 2.23$ and 2.84. The sketches for the other $F*$ values will look very similar, but the $F*$ cut-off will move further to the right.

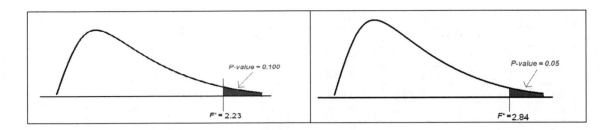

c) The *P*-value would be between 0.010 and 0.025. **d)** You can never conclude from an F test that all the means are different. The alternative hypothesis is that "not all the means are the same." In this case with a *P*-value < 0.05, reject the null hypothesis. We have evidence that not all the pairs of means are the same, but that is not the same thing as saying that all the pairs are different.

14.38

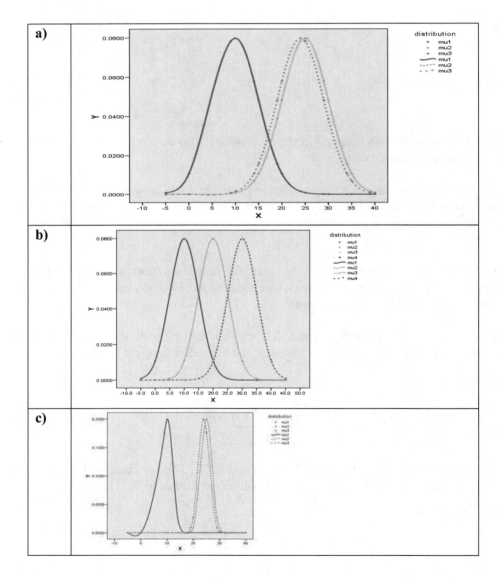

14.39 **a)** $F(4, 35)$, $F = 1.14$, P-value = 0.3538 (from software).

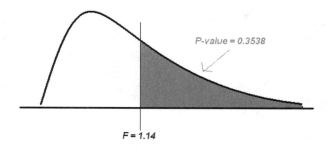

b) $F(2, 18)$, $F = 4$, P-value = 0.0365 (from software).

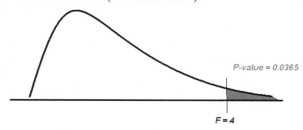

14.40 **a)** $I = 6$, $n_i = 20$, $N = 120$, response variable = breaking strength. **b)** $I = 3$, $n_i = 10$, $N = 30$, response = amount of tips. **c)** $I = 4$, $n_i = 5$, $N = 20$, response = sales.

14.41 **a)** $I = 3$, $n_1 = 220$, $n_2 = 145$, $n_3 = 76$, $N = 441$, response variable = 1 to 5 rating of "Did you discuss the presentation with any of your friends?" **b)** $I = 3$, $n_i = 5$, $N = 15$, response = cholesterol level. **c)** $I = 3$, $n_i = 25$, $N = 75$, response = 1 to 10 rating of the game.

14.42 **a)** $H_0 : \mu_1 = \mu_2 = \mu_3 = \mu_4 = \mu_5 = \mu_6$ and H_a: Not all the means are the same. DFG = 5, DFE = 114, DFT = 119, F(5, 114). **b)** $H_0 : \mu_1 = \mu_2 = \mu_3$ and H_a: Not all the means are the same. DFG = 2, DFE = 27, DFT = 29, F(2, 27). **c)** $H_0 : \mu_1 = \mu_2 = \mu_3 = \mu_4$ and H_a: Not all the means are the same. DFG = 3, DFE = 16, DFT = 19, F (3, 16).

14.43 For parts a, b, and c: $H_0 : \mu_1 = \mu_2 = \mu_3$ and H_a: Not all the means are the same. **a)** DFG = 2, DFE = 438, DFT = 440, F(2, 438). **b)** DFG = 2, DFE = 12, DFT = 14, F(2, 12). **c)** DFG = 2, DFE = 72, DFT = 74, F (2, 72).

14.44 Answers will vary.

14.45 Answers will vary.

14.46 **a)** No, the biggest s (21) is not less than twice the smallest s (10). **b)** $s_1^2 = 400$, $s_2^2 = 441$, $s_3^2 = 100$, $s_2^2 = 361$. **c)** $s_p^2 = 187.45$. **d)** $s_p = 13.69$. **e)** The third group had the largest sample size so it has the heaviest weight in the pooled standard deviation.

14.47   **a)** Yes, it is reasonable. $20 < 2 \times 15$. **b)** $s_1^2 = 48400$, $s_2^2 = 36100$, $s_3^2 = 40000$. **c)** $s_p^2 = 41866$. **d)** $s_p = 204.61$.

14.48   **a)** Matched pairs if each subject was measured twice: once on duty and once off-duty. **b)** Not really because the researchers aren't comparing the 4 tasks to each other. Each task is studied separately, comparing off-duty to on-duty averages for each.

14.49   **a)** In general, as the number of accommodations increased, the mean grade decreased, but it is not a steady decline.

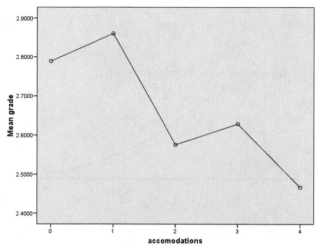

b) So many decimal places are not necessary. No additional information is gained by having so many. Using 2 decimal places would be fine. **c)** The biggest s is not exactly less than 2 times the smallest s (1.66233 vs. 2 x 0.82745), but it is close. Pooling should not be used (s_p would be 0.86). **d)** It is never a good idea to eliminate data points without a good reason. Since the mean grade is affected similarly for 2, 3, and 4 accommodations, it is not unreasonable to group these data together. **e)** These data do not represent 245 independent observations. Some students were measured multiple times. **f)** Answers will vary. University policies, teacher policies, student backgrounds might not be the same from school to school. **g)** There is no control group, so it is impossible to comment on the effectiveness of the accommodations.

14.50   **a)** With only a 1-to-7 discrete rating scale for the responses, the results will probably not be exactly Normally distributed. However, it is also unlikely that there will be any outliers, so ANOVA is still probably appropriate. There is also a bigger difference in sample sizes than we would like. **b)** The largest standard deviation (1.26) is less than twice the smallest standard deviation (1.03), so it is reasonable to use the pooled standard deviation for these data. **c)** $F(4, 405)$ will have a P-value of < 0.001 using the table. There is strong evidence that not all of the means are the same (at least one mean is different). **d)** The mean for Hispanic Americans (5.04) seems quite a bit higher than the means for European Americans (4.39), Asian Americans (4.35), and Indians (4.34). European Americans, Asian Americans, and Indians have very similar means. The mean for Japanese is right in the middle (4.72) of the two groups, so it is hard to predict whether it will be significantly different from any of the other groups without doing more analysis.

14.51 **a)** Checking whether the largest s < 2 x smallest s for each group indicates that it is appropriate to pool the standard deviations for intensity and recall but not frequency.
b) $F(4, 405)$. The *P*-value for all three one-way ANOVA tests is < 0.001, so for frequency, intensity, and recall there is strong evidence that not all the means are the same.

p	0.100	0.050	0.025	0.010	0.001
F	1.95	2.42	2.85	3.41	4.81

c) Hispanic Americans were highest in each of the three groups. For Emotion score, the European, Asian, and Indian scores were low but close together. For Frequency and Intensity and Recall, Asian and Japanese were both low, and European and Indian are close together in the middle. **d)** Answers will vary. People near a university might not be representative of all citizens of those countries. **e)** The chi-squared test has a test statistic of 11.353 and a *P*-value of 0.023, so at the 5% significance level, there is enough evidence to say that there is a relationship between gender and culture. In other words, there is evidence that the proportion of men and women is not the same for all of the cultural groups. This may affect how broadly the results can be applied.

14.52 **a)** See the graphs and table below. Age for novelists is fairly symmetric with no outliers. Age for poets is a little left-skewed. Age for nonfiction writers is fairly symmetric except for a low outlier at age 40. **b)** The largest standard deviation (17.297) is less than twice the smallest standard deviation (13.052), so it is appropriate to pool the standard deviations. However, the outlier for the nonfiction group is not ideal.

Group	Novel	Poet	Nonfiction
Histogram			
Mean	71.45	63.19	76.88
St. dev.	13.052	17.297	14.097
Normal quantile plot			

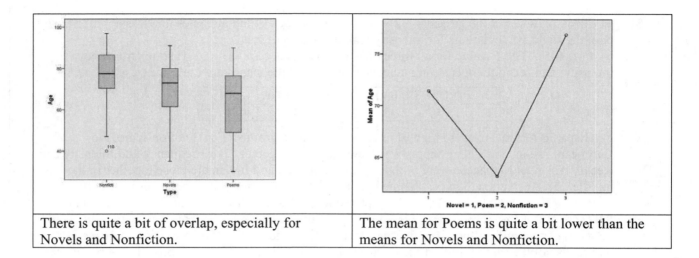

| There is quite a bit of overlap, especially for Novels and Nonfiction. | The mean for Poems is quite a bit lower than the means for Novels and Nonfiction. |

c) The ANOVA F test gives a test statistic of 6.563 with *P*-value of 0.002, so we have evidence that not all of the mean ages are the same (at least one mean is different).

ANOVA

Age

	Sum of Squares	df	Mean Square	F	Sig.
Between Groups	2744.193	2	1372.096	6.563	.002
Within Groups	25088.067	120	209.067		
Total	27832.260	122			

d) Because Yeats thinks the mean age for Poets to die is younger than that for Novelists and Nonfiction writers, use $\psi_1 = \frac{1}{2}(\mu_N + \mu_{NF}) - \mu_P$ with $H_0 : \psi_1 = 0$ and $H_0 : \psi_1 > 0$. SPSS calculates c = 10.97, SE_c = 3.081, t = 3.562, df = 120, and *P*-value of 0.005 for a one-sided test (or 0.001 for a two-sided test). There is evidence that Poets do die younger on average than Novelists or Nonfiction writers.

Contrast Tests

		Contrast	Value of Contrast	Std. Error	t	df	Sig. (2-tailed)
Age	Assume equal variances	1	10.97	3.081	3.562	120	.001
	Does not assume equal	1	10.97	3.472	3.161	48.246	.003

e) A contrast to compare Novelists with Nonfiction writers could use $\psi_2 = \mu_N - \mu_{NF}$ with $H_0 : \psi_2 = 0$ and $H_0 : \psi_2 \neq 0$. SPSS calculates c = -5.43, SE_c = 3.440, t = -1.578, df = 120, and *P*-value = 0.117. There is not enough evidence to say that there is a significant difference between average age of death for Novelists and Nonfiction writers.

Contrast Tests

		Contrast	Value of Contrast	Std. Error	t	df	Sig. (2-tailed)
Age	Assume equal variances	1	-5.43	3.440	-1.578	120	.117
	Does not assume equal	1	-5.43	3.290	-1.650	38.043	.107

f) The Bonferroni multiple comparisons test shows that the average age for Poets to die is significantly different from the age for Novelists and the age for Nonfiction writers. The average age for Novelists is not significantly different from the Nonfiction writers. The conclusion for the Bonferroni multiple comparisons test backs up the contrast tests that were done in the previous parts.

Multiple Comparisons

Dependent Variable: Age

Bonferroni

(I) Novel = 1, Poem = 2, Nonfiction = 3	(J) Novel = 1, Poem = 2, Nonfiction = 3	Mean Difference (I-J)	Std. Error	Sig.	95% Confidence Interval	
					Lower Bound	Upper Bound
1	2	8.260*	3.107	.027	.72	15.80
	3	-5.427	3.440	.352	-13.78	2.92
2	1	-8.260*	3.107	.027	-15.80	-.72
	3	-13.688*	3.904	.002	-23.17	-4.21
3	1	5.427	3.440	.352	-2.92	13.78
	2	13.688*	3.904	.002	4.21	23.17

*. The mean difference is significant at the .05 level.

14.53 a) The histogram of bone density for the control group shows a right-skewed distribution. The histograms for low and high groups show fairly symmetric distributions. There are no outliers for any groups. **b)** The Normal quantile plots for low and high look good, but the plot for control shows some deviation from Normality toward the very low and very high ends. The largest s is < 2 x smallest s, so it is appropriate to pool the standard deviations.

Group	Control	Low	High
Histogram			
Mean	0.219	0.216	0.235
St. dev.	0.0116	0.0115	0.0188

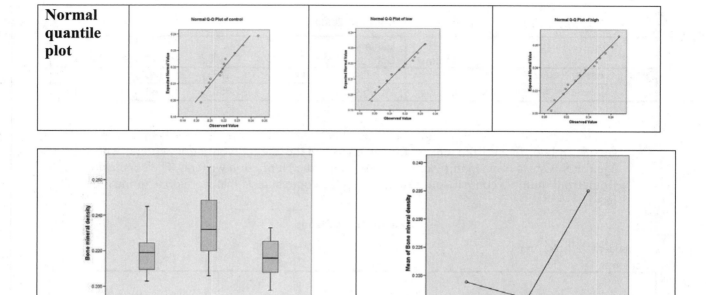

| **Normal quantile plot** | |

| A side-by-side boxplot of the groups shows heavy overlap of control and low, but not much overlap of high with the other two groups. | A means plot shows that control is slightly higher than low, but high is much higher than the other two groups. |

c) F = 7.718, *P*-value = 0.001. There is strong evidence that not all the means are the same.

ANOVA

Bone mineral density

	Sum of Squares	df	Mean Square	F	Sig.
Between Groups	.003	2	.002	7.718	.001
Within Groups	.009	42	.000		
Total	.012	44			

d) Bonferroni multiple comparisons shows that high is significantly different from both control and low groups, but control and low groups are not significantly different from each other.

Multiple Comparisons

Dependent Variable: Bone mineral density

Bonferroni

(I) treatnum	(J) treatnum	Mean Difference (I-J)	Std. Error	Sig.	95% Confidence Interval Lower Bound	95% Confidence Interval Upper Bound
1	2	.002933	.005246	1.000	-.01015	.01601
	3	-.016200*	.005246	.011	-.02928	-.00312
2	1	-.002933	.005246	1.000	-.01601	.01015
	3	-.019133*	.005246	.002	-.03221	-.00605
3	1	.016200*	.005246	.011	.00312	.02928
	2	.019133*	.005246	.002	.00605	.03221

*. The mean difference is significant at the .05 level.

e) The high dose of kudzu isoflavones yields a significantly greater mean bone density for the femur of a rat than the control or low dose does. There is no significant difference in mean bone density between the control and low dose.

14.54 a)

Condition	Vitamin C (mg/100g)		Sample size	Average	Standard deviation
Immediately after baking	47.62	49.79	2	48.71	1.5344
One day after baking	40.45	43.46	2	41.96	2.1284
Three days after baking	21.25	22.34	2	21.80	0.7707
Five days after baking	13.18	11.65	2	12.42	1.0819
Seven days after baking	8.51	8.13	2	8.32	0.2687

b)

ANOVA

Source of Variation	SS	df	MS	F	P-value	F crit
Between Groups	2565.721	4	641.4302	367.742	2.33E–06	5.192163
Within Groups	8.721	5	1.7442			
Total	2574.442	9				

H_o: All μ's are equal. H_a: at least one μ is not equal. $F = 367.742$, P-value $= 2.33E–06$.

c)

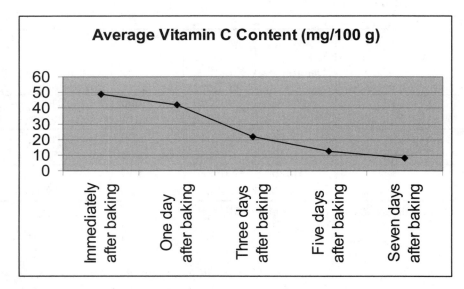

14.55   **a)** Confidence intervals from Minitab output for comparing means:

```
Tukey's pairwise comparisons

Family error rate = 0.0500
Individual error rate = 0.0102

Critical value = 5.67

Intervals for (column level mean) - (row level mean)

          Five day      Immediate      One day       Seven day

Immediate    -41.585
             -30.995

One day      -34.835         1.455
             -24.245        12.045

Seven day     -1.200        35.090       28.340
               9.390        45.680       38.930

Three day    -14.675        21.615       14.865       -18.770
              -4.085        32.205       25.455        -8.180
```

From the confidence intervals above, we can see that there is a significant difference between the Vitamin C content in bread immediately after baking, one day after baking, three days after baking, and five days after baking. The Vitamin C content does not significantly drop between five and seven days after baking.

14.56

```
Analysis of Variance for Vitamin A
Source      DF        SS         MS        F         P
C2           4     0.17894    0.04474    12.09     0.009
Error        5     0.01850    0.00370
Total        9     0.19744
                                       Individual 95% CIs For Mean
                                       Based on Pooled StDev
Level        N      Mean      StDev   --------+---------+---------+--------
Five day     2     3.3050    0.0778                      (----*-----)
Immediate    2     3.3500    0.0141                        (----*-----)
One day      2     3.2400    0.0566                   (-----*-----)
Seven day    2     2.9650    0.0636     (----*-----)
Three day    2     3.2100    0.0707                  (----*-----)
                                       --------+---------+---------+--------
Pooled StDev =     0.0608                3.00      3.20      3.40


Analysis of Variance for Vitamin E
Source      DF        SS         MS        F         P
C2           4      9.09       2.27      0.69      0.630
Error        5     16.48       3.30
Total        9     25.56
                                       Individual 95% CIs For Mean
                                       Based on Pooled StDev
Level        N      Mean      StDev   ---------+---------+---------+-------
Five day     2     96.350     1.909            (------------*-------------)
Immediate    2     95.300     0.990         (------------*-----------)
One day      2     94.450     1.768       (------------*-----------)
Seven day    2     93.700     1.980     (------------*-----------)
Three day    2     95.850     2.192           (------------*-------------)
                                       ---------+---------+---------+-------
Pooled StDev =     1.815                92.5      95.0      97.5
```

The ANOVA procedure shows a significant difference in Vitamin A content: $F = 12.9$ and P-value $= 0.009$. The ANOVA procedure shows there is no significant difference in Vitamin E content: $F = 0.69$ and P-value $= 0.63$.

14.57 **a)** It is not appropriate to perform a multiple comparisons analysis for Vitamin E because the ANOVA procedure showed no significant difference in content after baking.

b) Tukey's pairwise comparisons for Vitamin A content:
```
 Family error rate = 0.0500
 Individual error rate = 0.0102
 Critical value = 5.67
 Intervals for (column level mean) - (row level mean)
```

```
              Five day      Immediate      One day      Seven day

Immediate    -0.28888
              0.19888

One day      -0.17888      -0.13388
              0.30888       0.35388

Seven day     0.09612       0.14112       0.03112
              0.58388       0.62888       0.51888

Three day    -0.14888      -0.10388      -0.21388     -0.48888
              0.33888       0.38388       0.27388     -0.00112
```

Based on the confidence intervals for the mean differences, we can see that there is no significant difference in Vitamin A content between immediately after baking, one day after, three days after, and five days after. Once the bread is seven days old, the level of Vitamin A drops significantly.

14.58   Reports will vary by student. The facts are outlined in Problems 14.44 to 14.47.

14.59 a)

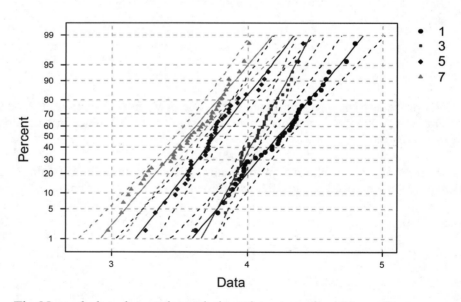

Normal Plot for Expected Price by Promotions

The Normal plots do not show obvious departures from Normality.

b)

Number of promotions	Average	Standard deviation	Sample size
1	4.224	0.2734	40
3	4.063	0.1742	40

5	3.759	0.2526	40
7	3.549	0.2750	40

c) Yes, the assumption of equal standard deviations is appropriate because $0.2750 < 2 \times 0.1742$.
d) H_0: All μ's are equal. H_a: At least one μ is different from the others. The test statistic is the F statistic with 3 and 156 degrees of freedom. F = 59.9 with a *P*-value = 0.0. There is at least one μ that is significantly different than the others.

14.60
```
Tukey's pairwise comparisons
Family error rate = 0.0500
Individual error rate = 0.0104

Critical value = 3.67

Intervals for (column level mean) - (row level mean)

                1              3             5

    3        0.0178
             0.3047

    5        0.3215        0.1603
             0.6085        0.4472

    7        0.5318        0.3705        0.0668
             0.8187        0.6575        0.3537
```

All four means are significantly different from each other.

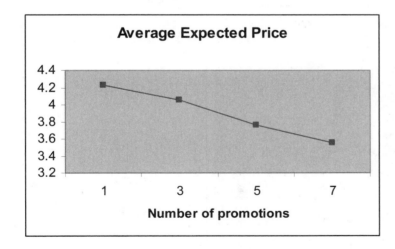

14.61 a)

Type of lesson	Average	Standard deviation	Sample size
Piano	3.62	3.055	34
Singing	-0.30	1.494	10
Computer	0.45	2.212	20
None	0.79	3.072	14

b) H_0: All μ's are equal. H_a: At least one μ is different from the others. The test statistic is the F statistic with 3 and 74 degrees of freedom. F = 9.24 with a *P*-value = 0.000. There is at least one μ that is significantly different than the others.

14.62
```
Tukey's pairwise comparisons
Family error rate = 0.0500
Individual error rate = 0.0104

Critical value = 3.72

Intervals for (column level mean) - (row level mean)

          Computer      None        Piano

None       -2.842
            2.171

Piano      -5.195       -5.116
           -1.140       -0.548

Singing    -2.036       -1.893      1.330
            3.536        4.064      6.505
```

Based on the confidence intervals, we can see that there is a significant difference in scores between the children that took piano lessons and those that did not. There is no significant difference among the children that took singing lessons, computer lessons, or no lessons.

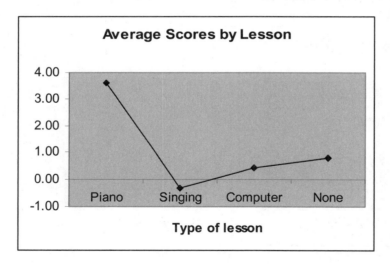

14.63 H_0: $\mu_P = 1/3(\mu_s + \mu_C + \mu_N)$ H_a: $\mu_P > 1/3(\mu_s + \mu_C + \mu_N)$. c = 3.306 and $s_P = 0.6356$. t = 5.20 with 74 degress of freedom. The *P*-value is approximately zero. The conclusion is that the average score with piano lessons is greater than the average of the three means without piano lessons.

14.64 **a)**

Group	n	Average	Standard deviation
Control	10	601.1	27.36
High jump	10	638.7	16.59
Low jump	10	612.5	19.33

Yes, it is reasonable to pool the variances because $27.36 < 2 \times 16.59$. **b)** $F = 7.98$ and P-value = 0.002. There is at least one mean that is significantly different from the rest.

14.65 **a)**

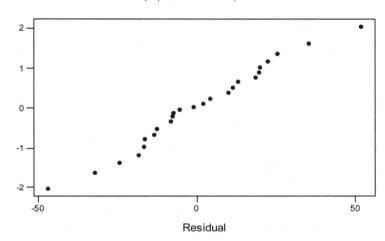

Normal Probability Plot of the Residuals

(response is Bone den)

Residual

b)   **Multiple Comparisons**

Dependent Variable: Bone Density

Bonferroni

(I) Treatment	(J) Treatment	Mean Difference (I-J)	Std. Error	Sig.	95% Confidence Interval	
					Lower Bound	Upper Bound
1	2	-11.400	9.653	.744	-36.04	13.24
	3	-37.600*	9.653	.002	-62.24	-12.96
2	1	11.400	9.653	.744	-13.24	36.04
	3	-26.200*	9.653	.034	-50.84	-1.56
3	1	37.600*	9.653	.002	12.96	62.24
	2	26.200*	9.653	.034	1.56	50.84

*. The mean difference is significant at the .05 level.

There is a significant difference in bone density between the high-jump group (group 3) and the control (group 1) and low-jump (group 2) groups. There is no significant difference between the control and low-jump groups.

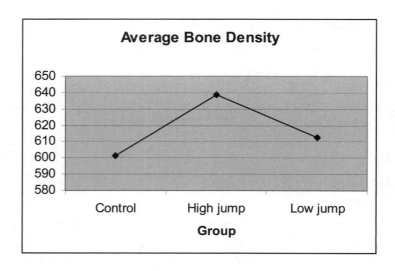

14.66 a)

Type of pot	n	Mean	Standard deviation
Aluminum	4	2.06	0.252
Clay	4	2.18	0.621
Iron	4	4.68	0.628

Because $0.628 < 2 \times 0.252$ it appears unreasonable to pool the standard deviations.
b) $F = 31.16$ with 2 and 9 degrees of freedom. P-value = 0.000. At least one of the means is different from the others.

14.67 a)

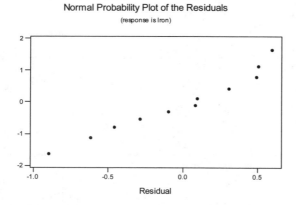

The Normal assumption appears reasonable.

b) Tukey's pairwise comparisons
Family error rate = 0.0500
Individual error rate = 0.0209

Critical value = 3.95

Intervals for (column level mean) - (row level mean)

```
              Aluminum      Clay

Clay            -1.1677
                 0.9277

Iron            -3.6702    -3.5502
                -1.5748    -1.4548
```

There does not appear to be a statistically significant difference in iron content between the aluminum and clay pots. Iron pots appear to have a significantly higher iron content than either aluminum or clay pots.

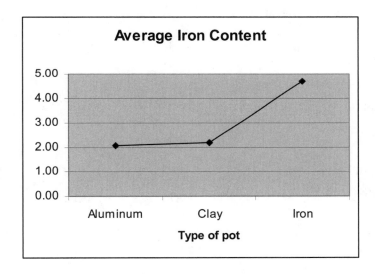

14.68 **a)**

Level	N	Mean	Standard deviation
ECM1	3	65.000	8.660
ECM2	3	63.333	2.887
ECM3	3	73.333	2.887
MAT1	3	23.333	2.887
MAT2	3	6.667	2.887
MAT3	3	11.667	2.887

While the largest standard deviation is more than twice the smallest, due to the small sample sizes and the rounding of the data, it is reasonable to pool the variances. **b)** $F = 137.94$ with 5 and 12 degrees of freedom. *P*-value = 0.000. At least one μ is different from the rest.

14.69   a)

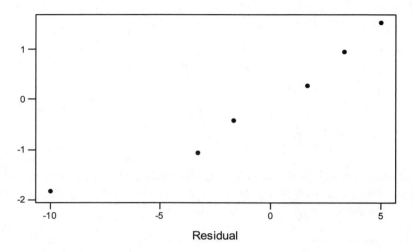

Normal Probability Plot of the Residuals
(response is Gpi(%))

The Normal assumption appears reasonable.

b) Tukey's pairwise comparisons
     Family error rate = 0.0500
     Individual error rate = 0.00569

     Critical value = 4.75

     Intervals for (column level mean) - (row level mean)

	ECM1	ECM2	ECM3	MAT1	MAT2
ECM2	-10.43 13.76				
ECM3	-20.43 3.76	-22.09 2.09			
MAT1	29.57 53.76	27.91 52.09	37.91 62.09		
MAT2	46.24 70.43	44.57 68.76	54.57 78.76	4.57 28.76	
MAT3	41.24 65.43	39.57 63.76	49.57 73.76	-0.43 23.76	-17.09 7.09

There is a significant difference between each of the three ECMs and the MATs. There is a significant difference between MAT1 and MAT2. There is no significant difference between the ECMs or between MAT2 and MAT3 or MAT1 and MAT3.

14.70 $c = 53.333$, $SE_c = 2.079$, $t = 25.653$ with 12 degrees of freedom, and the *P*-value < 0.0005. These results agree with the conclusions found in Problem 14.59.

14.71 **a)**

Level	Mean	Standard deviation
Blue	14.83	5.345
Green	31.50	9.915
Lemon yellow	47.17	6.795
White	15.67	3.327

b) H_0: All μ's are equal and H_a: At least one μ is not equal to the rest. **c)** $s_p = 6.784$, $F = 30.55$, *P*-value $= 0.000$. Conclude that at least one μ is different than the other three. However, please note that the biggest standard deviation (47.17) is *not* less than two times the smallest standard deviation (14.83), so it is really not appropriate to use ANOVA for this data.

14.72 The pairs of colors that are significantly different are: Blue and Green, Blue and Lemon yellow, Lemon yellow and Green, Green and White, and Lemon yellow and White. Blue and White are not significantly different. To attract the most insects choose Lemon yellow.

Group (I)	Group (J)	Mean difference (I - J)	t_{ij}
Blue	Green	-16.667	-4.25532
	LY	-32.334	-8.25533
	White	-0.834	-0.21293
Green	Blue	16.667	4.25532
	LY	-15.667	-4.00001
	White	15.833	4.04239
LY	Blue	32.334	8.25533
	Green	15.667	4.00000
	White	31.500	8.04239
White	Blue	0.834	0.21293
	Green	-15.833	-4.04239
	LY	-31.500	-8.04239

14.73 **a)**

Source	DF	Sum of Squares	Mean square	F
Groups	3	104,855.87	34,951.96	15.86
Error	32	70,500.59	2,203.14	
Total	35	175,356.46	5,010.18	

b) H_0: All μ's are equal and H_a: At least one μ is not equal to the rest. **c)** F with 3 and 32 degrees of freedom. *P*-value $= 0.000$. At least one μ is different from the others. **d)** $s_p^2 = 2{,}203.14$, $s_p = 46.94$.

14.74　a)

Source	DF	Sum of Squares	Mean square	F
Groups	3	476.88	158.96	2.53
Error	32	2009.92	62.81	
Total	35	2486.80	221.77	

b) H_0: All μ's are equal and H_a: At least one μ is not equal to the rest. **c)** F with 3 and 32 degrees of freedom. P-value = 0.0746. There is some evidence that at least one μ is different from the rest. **d)** $s_p^2 = 62.81$, $s_p = 7.925$.

14.75　a) $s_p^2 = 3.8975$, MSE.

b)

Source	Degrees of freedom	Sum of squares	Mean square	F
Groups	2	17.22	8.61	2.2091
Error	206	802.89	3.90	
Total	208			

c) H_0: All μ's are equal and H_a: At least one μ is not equal to the rest. **d)** F with 2 and 206 degrees of freedom. P-value = 0.1124. There is no strong evidence to support the alternative hypothesis.

14.76　a) $s_p^2 = 72{,}412.12$, MSE.

b)

Source	Degrees of freedom	Sum of squares	Mean square	F
Groups	2	6,572,551	3,286276.00	45.383
Error	230	16,654,788	72,412.12	
Total	232			

c) H_0: All μ's are equal and H_a: At least one μ is not equal to the rest. **d)** F with 2 and 230 degrees of freedom. P-value = 0.000. There is strong evidence to support the alternative hypothesis. At least one μ is different from the other two.

14.77　a) $\psi_1 = \frac{1}{2}(\mu_1 + \mu_2) - \mu_3$. **b)** $\psi_2 = -\mu_1 + \mu_2$.

14.78　a) $\psi_1 = -\frac{1}{2}(\mu_1 + \mu_2) + \frac{1}{2}(\mu_3 + \mu_4)$. **b)** $\psi_2 = -\mu_1 + \mu_2$. **c)** $\psi_3 = -\mu_3 + \mu_4$.

14.79　a) H_{01}: $\frac{1}{2}(\mu_1 + \mu_2) = \mu_3$ H_{a1}: $\frac{1}{2}(\mu_1 + \mu_2) > \mu_3$. H_{02}: $\mu_1 = \mu_2$ H_{a2}: $\mu_1 \neq \mu_2$. **b)** $c_1 = 49$ and $c_2 = 10$. **c)** $s_{c1} = 11.27821$ and $s_{c2} = 16.9008$. **d)** $t_1 = 4.3447$ with 253 degrees of freedom and a P-value < 0.0005. $t_2 = 0.5917$ with 253 degrees of freedom and a P-value = 0.5546. It appears that the average SAT math scores for the computer science majors and engineering majors are significantly higher than for the other majors. The computer science and engineering majors do not have significantly different average SAT math scores. **e)** The 95% confidence interval for contrast one is 49 ± 22.59. The 95% confidence interval for contrast two is 10 ± 33.8.

14.80　a) H_{01}: $\frac{1}{2}(\mu_1 + \mu_2) = \mu_3$ H_{a1}: $\frac{1}{2}(\mu_1 + \mu_2) > \mu_3$. H_{02}: $\mu_1 = \mu_2$ H_{a2}: $\mu_1 \neq \mu_2$. **b)** $c_1 = 0.93$ and $c_2 = -0.02$. **c)** $s_{c1} = 0.2299$ and $s_{c2} = 0.3421$. **d)** $t_1 = 4.046$ with 221 degrees of freedom and a P-value

< 0.0005. $t_2 = -0.058$ with 221 degrees of freedom and a P-value $= 0.9534$. It appears that the average high school math grades for the computer science majors and engineering majors are significantly higher than for the other majors. The computer science and engineering majors do not have significantly different average high school math grades. **e)** The 95% confidence interval for contrast one is 0.93 ± 0.4598. The 95% confidence interval for contrast two is -0.02 ± 0.6842.

14.81 **a)** $\psi_1 = \mu_1 - \mu_2$ $H_{01}: \mu_1 = \mu_2$ $H_{a1}: \mu_1 > \mu_2$. $\psi_2 = \mu_1 - \frac{1}{2}(\mu_2 + \mu_4)$ $H_{02}: \mu_1 = \frac{1}{2}(\mu_2 + \mu_4)$ $H_{a2}: \mu_1 > \frac{1}{2}(\mu_2 + \mu_4)$. $\psi_3 = \mu_3 - 1/3(\mu_1 + \mu_2 + \mu_4)$ $H_{03}: \mu_3 = 1/3(\mu_1 + \mu_2 + \mu_4)$ $H_{a3}: \mu_3 > 1/3(\mu_1 + \mu_2 + \mu_4)$. **b)** $t_1 = -0.6635$ with a P-value $= 0.2559$. $t_2 = 1.242$ with a P-value $= 0.1116$. $t_3 = 5.282$ with a P-value $= 0.000$. The average score for the joggers groups is significantly higher than the average of the other three groups. **c)** This study does not show causation. There are many lurking variables that could contribute to a low score.

14.82 **a)** $\psi_1 = \mu_2 - \mu_1$ $H_{o1}: \mu_1 = \mu_2$ $H_{a1}: \mu_1 < \mu_2$. $\psi_2 = -\mu_1 + \frac{1}{2}(\mu_2 + \mu_4)$ $H_{02}: \mu_1 = \frac{1}{2}(\mu_2 + \mu_4)$ $H_{a2}: \mu_1 < \frac{1}{2}(\mu_2 + \mu_4)$. $\psi_3 = -\mu_3 + 1/3(\mu_1 + \mu_2 + \mu_4)$ $H_{o3}: \mu_3 = 1/3(\mu_1 + \mu_2 + \mu_4)$ $H_{a3}: \mu_3 < 1/3(\mu_1 + \mu_2 + \mu_4)$. **b)** $t_1 = 1.2663$ with a P-value $= 0.173$. $t_2 = 1.7785$ with a P-value $= 0.0424$. $t_3 = 2.092$ with a P-value $= 0.0222$. The average depression score for the treatment group is significantly lower than for the average of the control and sedentary groups. The average depression score for the joggers groups is significantly lower than the average of the other three groups. **c)** This study does not show causation. There are many lurking variables that could contribute to a low score.

14.83

Group (I)	Group (J)	Mean difference	Standard error	t_{ij}
T	C	−17.06	25.7101	−0.66355
	J	−74.96	20.5096	−3.65488
	S	65.84	20.9922	3.13640
C	T	17.06	25.7101	0.66355
	J	−57.90	25.3176	−2.28695
	S	82.90	25.7101	3.22441
J	T	74.96	20.5096	3.65488
	C	57.90	25.3176	2.28695
	S	140.80	20.5096	6.86509
S	T	−65.84	20.9922	−3.13640
	C	−82.90	25.7101	−3.22441
	J	−140.80	20.5096	−6.86509

The sedentary group is significantly different from the three other groups. The treatment group is significantly different from the jogger group and the sedentary group. There is no significant difference between the jogger group and the control group or between the treatment group and the control group.

14.84

Group (I)	Group (J)	Mean difference	Standard error	t_{ij}
T	C	−5.50	4.3434	−1.26628
	J	2.17	3.4649	0.62629
	S	−6.30	3.5464	−1.77645
C	T	5.50	4.3434	1.26627
	J	7.67	4.2771	1.79326
	S	−0.80	4.3434	−0.18419
J	T	−2.17	3.4649	−0.62629
	C	−7.67	4.2771	−1.79326
	S	−8.47	3.4649	−2.44454
S	T	6.30	3.5464	1.77645
	C	0.80	4.3434	0.18419
	J	8.47	3.4649	2.44454

There do not appear to be any significant differences between groups.

14.85

```
      Sample
      size    Power
        50    0.2948
       100    0.5449
       150    0.7332
       175    0.8014
       200    0.8545
```

A sample size of 200 would give the highest power for these alternative values of μ.

14.86 The results will be the same because the differences are the same.

14.87 a)

Condition	Vitamin C (% of original)		Sample size	Average	Standard deviation
Immediately after baking	74.4063	77.79688	2	76.1094	2.3975
One day after baking	63.2031	67.90625	2	65.5625	3.3256
Three days after baking	33.2031	34.90625	2	34.0625	1.2042
Five days after baking	20.5938	18.20313	2	19.4063	1.6905
Seven days after baking	13.2969	12.70313	2	13	0.4198

b) You could have performed the transformation directly on the means and standard deviations by using the relationships described in Chapter 4.

c)

ANOVA

Source of Variation	SS	df	MS	F	P-value	F crit
Between Groups	6263.967	4	1565.992	367.742	2.33E-06	5.192163
Within Groups	21.292	5	4.258			
Total	6285.259	9				

The F statistic has the same value as the one found in Problem 14.44.

14.88 In general the F statistic, degrees of freedom, and P-value stay the same when changing the units of measure.

14.89 **a)** $F = 2.0$ with a P-value $= 0.146$. The test does not show a statistically significant result. **b)** The result found in 14.61 did show a statistically significant result. Outliers can change the conclusion of an ANOVA test.

c)

Level	N	Mean	StDev
Blue	6	14.83	5.34
Green	6	31.50	9.91
Lemon yellow	6	114.67	164.42
White	6	15.67	3.33

One can see that the outlier would be in the Lemon Yellow level because the high value of the mean and standard deviation stand out.

14.90 **a)**

Level	n	Mean	StDev
Blue	6	3.7931	0.7312
Green	6	5.5435	0.9613
Lemon yellow	6	6.8533	0.4882
White	6	3.9400	0.4142

b) $F = 27$ with a P-value $= 0.000$. This result indicates there is at least one μ that is significantly different than the rest. This is the same result we found in 14.61.

14.91 **a)**

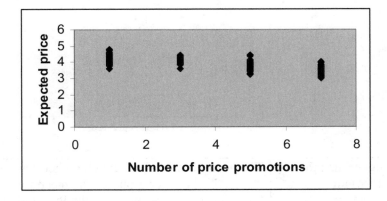

The pattern is roughly linear. **b)** The test for $\beta = 0$ is the test for no linear relationship between explanatory variable and response variable. **c)** The results of the regression analysis show that there is a significant linear relationship between the number of promotions and the expected

price. The ANOVA results state that there is at least one μ that is different from the other three.
Regression analysis gives more information because we know that there is a linear relationship.
ANOVA does not tell us the type of relationship between the variables.

Case Study 14.1 (DANDRUFF)

Variable	PyrI	PyrII	Keto	Placebo
Mean	17.29	17.54	16.04	29.39
St. dev.	1.182	1.290	0.962	1.595
Histogram				
	Fairly symmetric with 2 low outliers and 2 high outliers	Strongly left skewed with no outliers.	Fairly symmetric with no outliers.	Fairly symmetric with no outliers.
Normal quantile plot				

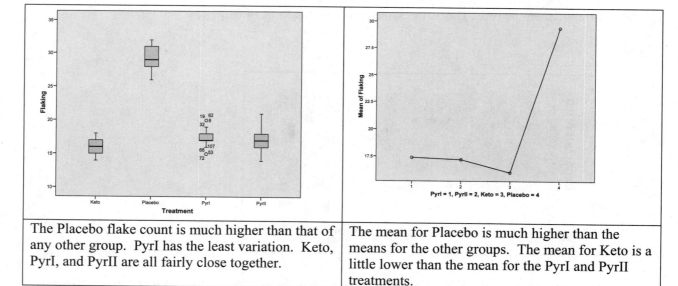

The largest standard deviation (1.595) is less than twice the smallest standard deviation (0.962),
so it is appropriate to pool the standard deviations. The PyrI group does have come outliers,
which is not ideal, and the sample size for the Placebo group is much smaller than the sample size
for the other groups. (The numbers above are from SPSS. Minitab gives slightly different
results.)

The Placebo flake count is much higher than that of any other group. PyrI has the least variation. Keto, PyrI, and PyrII are all fairly close together.	The mean for Placebo is much higher than the means for the other groups. The mean for Keto is a little lower than the mean for the PyrI and PyrII treatments.

The ANOVA test with hypotheses $H_0 : \mu_{PyrI} = \mu_{PyrII} = \mu_{Keto} = \mu_{Placebo}$ and

H_a : Not all of the means are the same. The F test statistic is 967.819, and the P-value is close to 0. Therefore, we have strong evidence that not all the means are the same (at least one mean is different).

ANOVA

Flaking

	Sum of Squares	df	Mean Square	F	Sig.
Between Groups	4151.428	3	1383.809	967.819	.000
Within Groups	501.868	351	1.430		
Total	4653.296	354			

Using the Bonferroni multiple comparisons test, PyrI is not significantly different from PyrII, but Keto is significantly different from all 3 other groups and Placebo is significantly different from all 3 other groups.

Multiple Comparisons

Dependent Variable: Flaking

Bonferroni

(I) PyrI = 1, PyrII = 2, Keto = 3, Placebo = 4	(J) PyrI = 1, PyrII = 2, Keto = 3, Placebo = 4	Mean Difference (I-J)	Std. Error	Sig.	95% Confidence Interval	
					Lower Bound	Upper Bound
1	2	.191	.161	1.000	-.24	.62
	3	1.365*	.162	.000	.93	1.79
	4	-12.000*	.253	.000	-12.67	-11.33
2	1	-.191	.161	1.000	-.62	.24
	3	1.174*	.163	.000	.74	1.61
	4	-12.191*	.253	.000	-12.86	-11.52
3	1	-1.365*	.162	.000	-1.79	-.93
	2	-1.174*	.163	.000	-1.61	-.74
	4	-13.365*	.254	.000	-14.04	-12.69
4	1	12.000*	.253	.000	11.33	12.67
	2	12.191*	.253	.000	11.52	12.86
	3	13.365*	.254	.000	12.69	14.04

*. The mean difference is significant at the .05 level.

Contrast #1: $\psi_1 : \frac{1}{3}(\mu_{PyrI} + \mu_{PyrII} + \mu_{Keto}) - \mu_{Placebo}$ with $H_0 : \psi_1 = 0$ and $H_a : \psi_1 < 0$ (the two-sided hypothesis would also be appropriate, but the researchers probably expect that the treatments will reduce flaking over the Placebo group so a one-sided test is chosen here). The value of the contrast is c = -12.39, $SE_c = 0.233$, t = -53.167, df = 351, and *P*-value close to 0 for either the one-sided or two-sided test. Therefore we have evidence that the average flaking count of the three treatment groups is significantly lower than the average of the Placebo group.

Contrast #2: $\psi_2 : \frac{1}{2}(\mu_{PyrI} + \mu_{PyrII}) - \mu_{Keto}$ with $H_0 : \psi_2 = 0$ and $H_a : \psi_2 \neq 0$. The value of the contrast is c = 1.27, SE_c = 0.141, t = 8.983, df = 351, and P-value close to 0 for either the one-sided or two-sided test. Therefore, we have evidence that the average flaking count of the three treatment groups is significantly different (or higher of if one-sided test is done using a ">" in the alternative hypothesis) in the Keto group than in the average of the PyrI and PyrII groups.

Contrast #3: $\psi_3 : \mu_{PyrI} - \mu_{PyrII}$ with $H_0 : \psi_3 = 0$ and $H_a : \psi_3 \neq 0$. The value of the contrast is c = 0.19, SE_c = 0.161, t = 1.187, df = 351, and P-value is 0.236 for two-sided test. Therefore, we do not have enough evidence to say that the average flaking count is significantly different for the PyrI and PyrII groups.

Contrast Coefficients

Contrast	PyrI = 1, PyrII = 2, Keto = 3, Placebo = 4			
	1	2	3	4
1	.33	.33	.33	-.99
2	.5	.5	-1	0
3	1	-1	0	0

Contrast Tests

		Contrast	Value of Contrast	Std. Error	t	df	Sig. (2-tailed)
Flaking	Assume equal variances	1	-12.39	.233	-53.167	351	.000
		2	1.27	.141	8.983	351	.000
		3	.19	.161	1.187	351	.236
	Does not assume equal variances	1	-12.39	.305	-40.635	29.465	.000
		2	1.27	.124	10.268	266.704	.000
		3	.19	.169	1.133	211.008	.258

Case Study 14.2 (READING)

In the SPSS output below, Group B = 1, Group D = 2, Group S = 3. For each of these tests, it is appropriate to pool the standard deviations because the biggest s for each test is smaller than twice the smallest s.

Descriptives

		N	Mean	Std. Deviation	Std. Error	95% Confidence Interval for Mean		Minimum	Maximum
						Lower Bound	Upper Bound		
Pre1	1	22	10.50	2.972	.634	9.18	11.82	4	16
	2	22	9.73	2.694	.574	8.53	10.92	6	16
	3	22	9.14	3.342	.713	7.65	10.62	4	14
	Total	66	9.79	3.021	.372	9.05	10.53	4	16
Pre2	1	22	5.27	2.763	.589	4.05	6.50	2	13
	2	22	5.09	1.998	.426	4.21	5.98	1	8
	3	22	4.95	1.864	.397	4.13	5.78	2	9
	Total	66	5.11	2.213	.272	4.56	5.65	1	13
Post1	1	22	6.68	2.767	.590	5.46	7.91	2	12
	2	22	9.77	2.724	.581	8.56	10.98	5	14
	3	22	7.77	3.927	.837	6.03	9.51	1	15
	Total	66	8.08	3.394	.418	7.24	8.91	1	15
Post2	1	22	5.55	2.041	.435	4.64	6.45	3	10
	2	22	6.23	2.092	.446	5.30	7.15	0	11
	3	22	8.36	2.904	.619	7.08	9.65	1	13
	Total	66	6.71	2.636	.324	6.06	7.36	0	13
Post3	1	22	41.05	5.636	1.202	38.55	43.54	32	54
	2	22	46.73	7.388	1.575	43.45	50.00	30	57
	3	22	44.27	5.767	1.229	41.72	46.83	33	53
	Total	66	44.02	6.644	.818	42.38	45.65	30	57

The ANOVA F tests results follow.

Neither of the Pretests give evidence for significant differences between the groups. It does seem that the three groups of subjects were similar at the start of the study.

All three Posttests show evidence that not all the means are the same within each test (at least one group has a different mean within each test).

ANOVA

		Sum of Squares	df	Mean Square	F	Sig.
Pre1	Between Groups	20.576	2	10.288	1.132	.329
	Within Groups	572.455	63	9.087		
	Total	593.030	65			
Pre2	Between Groups	1.121	2	.561	.111	.895
	Within Groups	317.136	63	5.034		
	Total	318.258	65			
Post1	Between Groups	108.121	2	54.061	5.317	.007
	Within Groups	640.500	63	10.167		
	Total	748.621	65			
Post2	Between Groups	95.121	2	47.561	8.407	.001
	Within Groups	356.409	63	5.657		
	Total	451.530	65			
Post3	Between Groups	357.303	2	178.652	4.481	.015
	Within Groups	2511.682	63	39.868		
	Total	2868.985	65			

The results of the Bonferroni multiple comparison tests are below. Ignore the results for both Pretests since there are no significant differences to be found there.

Post1: There is a significant difference between Group B and Group D, but there are no other significant differences.

Post2: Group S is significantly different from both Group B and Group D, but Group B and Group D are not significantly different from each other.

Post3: There is a significant difference between Group B and Group D but there are no other significant differences.

Posttest 1 and Posttest 3 indicate that Teaching Method D is more effective than the others.

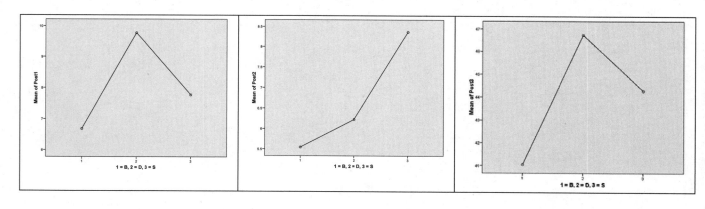

Multiple Comparisons

Bonferroni

Dependent Variable	(I) 1 = B, 2 = D, 3 = S	(J) 1 = B, 2 = D, 3 = S	Mean Difference (I-J)	Std. Error	Sig.	95% Confidence Interval	
						Lower Bound	Upper Bound
Pre1	1	2	.773	.909	1.000	-1.46	3.01
		3	1.364	.909	.416	-.87	3.60
	2	1	-.773	.909	1.000	-3.01	1.46
		3	.591	.909	1.000	-1.64	2.83
	3	1	-1.364	.909	.416	-3.60	.87
		2	-.591	.909	1.000	-2.83	1.64
Pre2	1	2	.182	.676	1.000	-1.48	1.85
		3	.318	.676	1.000	-1.35	1.98
	2	1	-.182	.676	1.000	-1.85	1.48
		3	.136	.676	1.000	-1.53	1.80
	3	1	-.318	.676	1.000	-1.98	1.35
		2	-.136	.676	1.000	-1.80	1.53
Post1	1	2	-3.091*	.961	.006	-5.46	-.73
		3	-1.091	.961	.782	-3.46	1.27
	2	1	3.091*	.961	.006	.73	5.46
		3	2.000	.961	.125	-.36	4.36
	3	1	1.091	.961	.782	-1.27	3.46
		2	-2.000	.961	.125	-4.36	.36
Post2	1	2	-.682	.717	1.000	-2.45	1.08
		3	-2.818*	.717	.001	-4.58	-1.05
	2	1	.682	.717	1.000	-1.08	2.45
		3	-2.136*	.717	.012	-3.90	-.37
	3	1	2.818*	.717	.001	1.05	4.58
		2	2.136*	.717	.012	.37	3.90
Post3	1	2	-5.682*	1.904	.012	-10.36	-1.00
		3	-3.227	1.904	.285	-7.91	1.46
	2	1	5.682*	1.904	.012	1.00	10.36
		3	2.455	1.904	.606	-2.23	7.14
	3	1	3.227	1.904	.285	-1.46	7.91
		2	-2.455	1.904	.606	-7.14	2.23

*. The mean difference is significant at the .05 level.

Chapter 15: Two-Way Analysis of Variance

15.1   Response variable: Effectiveness rating. Factors: Training program and Delivery method. I = 4, J = 2, and N = 100.

15.2   Response variable: Attractiveness rating. Factors: Type of packaging and Color. I = 3, J = 4, and N = 600.

15.3   Response variable: Lotion rating. Factors: Formulation and Fragrance. I = 6, J = 4, and N = 3600.

15.4   Verify.

15.5   The difference increases with age until the age of 65.

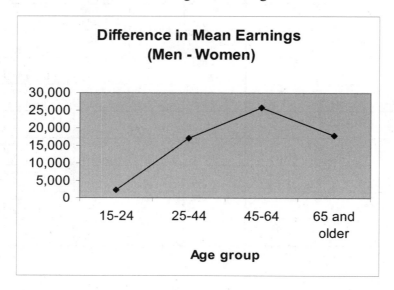

15.6   The two mean plots follow each other. Figure 15.2 shows divergent plots.

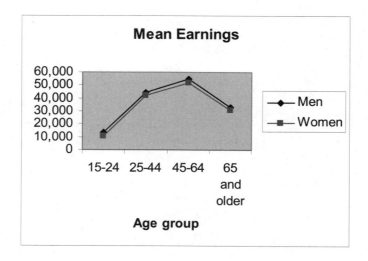

15.7   **a)** Yes, there is an interaction. The effect of factor B decreases as factor A increases.

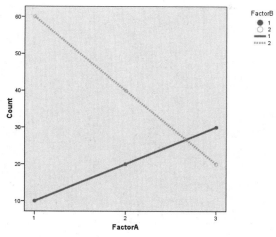

b) No, there is no interaction effect. The lines are fairly parallel.

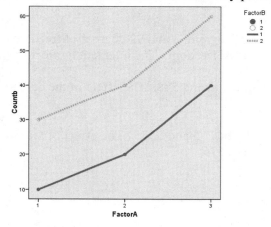

c) Yes, there is an interaction effect. The effect is not apparent until we reach level 3 of factor A.

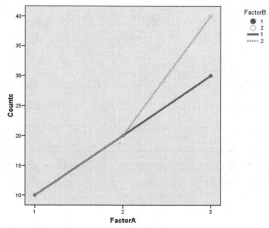

d) Yes, there is an interaction. The lines are not parallel. The effect of factor B increases as factor A increases.

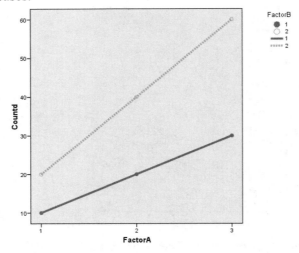

15.8   The effect of the training program: 3 and 92 degrees of freedom. The effect of the delivery method: 1 and 92 degrees of freedom. The interaction effect: 3 and 92 degrees of freedom.

15.9   The effect of the packaging: 2 and 588. The effect of the colors: 3 and 588. The interaction effect: 6 and 588.

15.10   The effect of the formulations: 5 and 3576. The effect of the fragrances: 3 and 3576. The interaction effect: 15 and 3576.

15.11

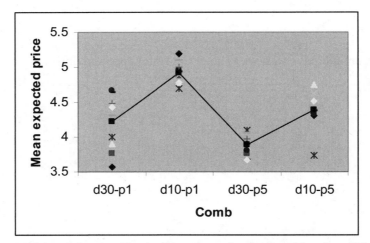

The spread in each group is similar except for the combination d10-p5. There may be an outlier on the low side. The treatment means appear to be different.

15.12

	Discount		
Promotions	20%	40%	Total
1	4.689	4.423	4.556
3	4.524	4.284	4.404
Total	4.6065	4.3535	

Excel agrees with the SPSS output except for one thing. Excel does not give the total mean for the entire set of observations.

15.13

Promo	Discount	Mean	Standard deviation	N
1	30%	4.225	0.385609	10
1	10%	4.920	0.152023	10
	Total	4.573	0.456611	20
5	30%	3.890	0.162891	10
5	10%	4.393	0.268537	10
	Total	4.142	0.336613	20
Total	30%	4.058	0.335463	20
	10%	4.657	0.343791	20
	Total	4.357	0.452113	40

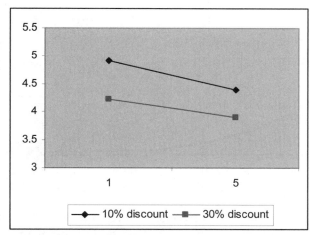

Based on the standard deviations it makes sense to pool the group standard deviations to get MSE. There is a difference in mean expected price as the number of promotions decrease. There may be an interaction effect due to percentage discount but it is not readily apparent from the plot.

15.14   Verify.

15.15   Answers will vary.

15.16   There is a significant drop in expected price when the number of promotions increases from 1 to 5. ($F = 27.47$, df = 1 and 36, $P = 0.0$). When the discount increases from 10% to 30%, there is a significant drop in expected price ($F = 53.07$, df $= 1$ and 36, $P = 0.0$). There is no significant interaction effect ($F = 1.39$, df $= 1$ and 36, $P = 0.2507$).

15.17 **a)** The FIT part of the model in a two-way ANOVA is the population means μ_{ij}. **b)** You should reject the null hypothesis that there is no interaction in a two-way ANOVA when the test statistic is big and the *P*-value is small. **c)** Mean squares are equal to the sums of squares divided by degrees of freedom.

15.18 **a)** The significance tests for the main effects in a two-way ANOVA have an F distribution when the null hypothesis is true. **b)** You can perform a two-way ANOVA with different sample sizes for all cells, but we assume that all populations have the same standard deviation. **c)** The population means μ_{ij} are parameters of the two-way ANOVA model.

15.19 **a)** The degrees of freedom for interaction will be 3 and 32. The corresponding entries from Table E are (using 3 and 30 since 32 is not on the table):

P-value	F
0.100	2.28
0.050	2.92
0.025	3.59
0.010	4.51
0.001	7.05

b) See the picture below.

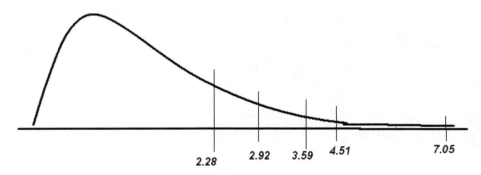

c) $0.050 < P\text{-value} < 0.100$. **d)** Since we cannot reject the null hypothesis at the 5% significance level, we would expect a plot of the means to look fairly parallel, indicating that there is no interaction.

15.20 **a)** The degrees of freedom are 2 and 27. The critical F* value is 3.35.

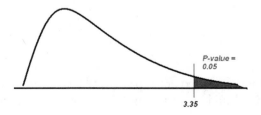

b) The degrees of freedom are 4 and 36. The critical F* value is (from Excel) 2.63.

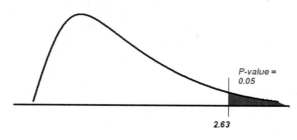

c) The degrees of freedom are 1 and 1000. The critical F* value is 3.85.

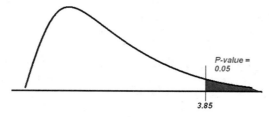

15.21 **a)** The marginal mean for intervention is 11.600, for control 9.967, for baseline 10.000, for 3 months 11.200, and for 6 months 11.150. **b)** See the means plot below. There does appear to be an interaction because the lines are not parallel. The means for the intervention group are higher than the means for the means for the control group in all the different time periods. For the control group (bottom line), the average number of behaviors increases with time. For the intervention group (top line), the average number of behaviors peaks at 3 months from a low of 0 months and then reduces slightly at 6 months.

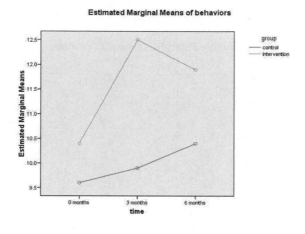

15.22   **a)** Yes, a graphical display is much more effective than a large table with lots of numbers. A means plot could be done for each category of behavior, with separate lines for intervention and control groups and time on the x axis. (See below.) This shows that in virtually every behavior, the intervention group has a greater percent of participation in that positive behavior.

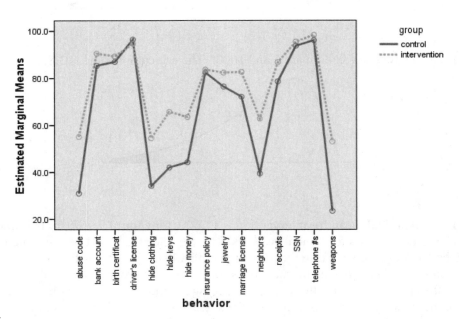

Another option would be a means plot with the 15 behaviors on the x axis and separate lines for the three time periods. (See below.) In general the baseline time period had a lower percentage of participation in the positive behaviors than in the other two time periods, but there is not much difference between the 3-month and 6-month time periods.

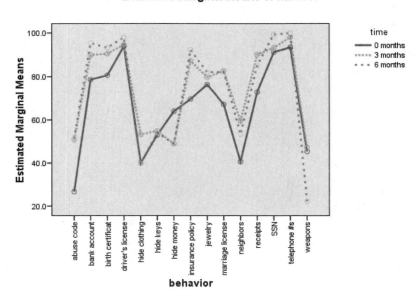

Clustered and paneled bar graphs are shown below. (There are probably other graphs that would be informative, too.)

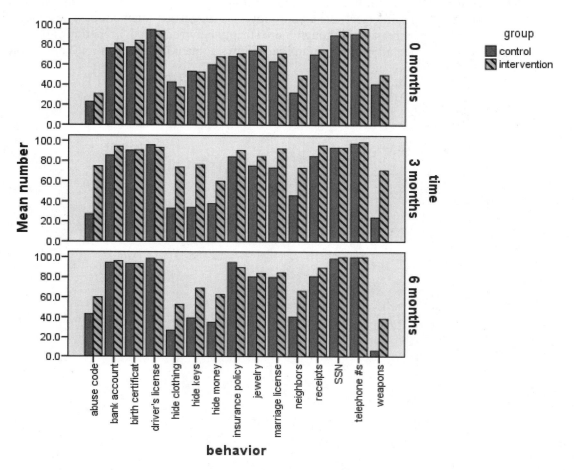

b) Overall, the intervention group showed a higher percent of participation in the positive behaviors than the control group. For most behaviors, there is greater increase in the percent of participation in the positive behaviors between 0 and 3 months, but then not as much of a change between 3 and 6 months. **c)** Small town or rural behavior might not be equivalent. An ethnically diverse area might not have the same results as an area with primarily just one ethnic group in the population.

15.23 With a 5% significance level, neither main effect not the interaction are significant. At the 10% significance level, main effect B is significant. Main effect A (degrees of freedom 2, 24) has *P*-value > 0.100. Main effect B (degrees of freedom 1, 24) has 0.05 < *P*-value < 0.10. The interaction of A and B (degrees of freedom (2, 24) has *P*-value > 0.100.

15.24 **a)** If a significance level of 5% is used, then both main effects and their interaction are significant. If a significance level of 1% is used, then both main effects are significant, but their interaction is not significant. **b)** To prepare a summary, you would also need the means to make a plot and to describe the meaning of the statistically significant results. Standard errors should also be included in the summary. A table with n, mean, and standard deviation for each treatment combination, etc., would be helpful.

15.25   **a)** The means plot below shows that "familiar" has a higher rating than "unfamiliar" for 1 and 3 repetitions, but "unfamiliar" has a higher rating than "familiar" for 2 repetitions.
b) Yes. Since the lines intersect, the means plot does suggest an interaction. The pattern for "familiar" is always increasing (although more steeply between 2 and 3 repetitions than between 1 and 2). The pattern for "unfamiliar" shows a much larger mean for 2 repetitions than for 1 and 3.

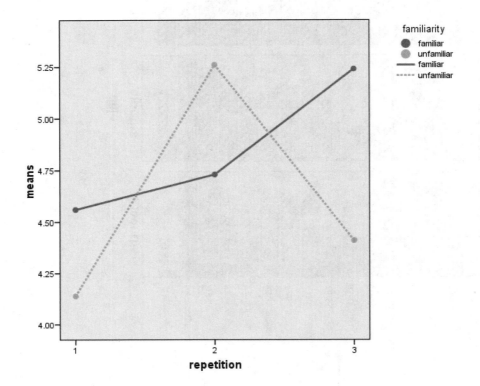

15.26   From the problem above, Attitude to Ad increases with repetition for a familiar brand. For an unfamiliar brand, Attitude to Ad increases sharply between the first and second repetition but then decreases sharply with the 3rd repetition. There does appear to be interaction between repetition and familiarity for Attitude to Ad.

Attitude to Brand: For a familiar brand, there is not much change between the first and second repetition, but then there is a sharp increase with the third repetition. For an unfamiliar brand, there is a sharp increase between the first and second repetition and then a sharp decrease for with the third repetition. Familiar brand has a higher mean than unfamiliar for 1 and 3 repetitions, but unfamiliar brand has the higher mean for 2 repetitions. There does appear to be an interaction between repetition and familiarity for Attitude to Brand.	**Total Thoughts:** The unfamiliar brand has a higher rating than familiar brand at for all three repetitions. For both familiar and unfamiliar brands, there is an increase in total thoughts as repetitions increase. However for familiar brand, there is a steady increase with repetitions. With unfamiliar brand, there is a sharp increase between 1 and 2 repetitions, and then the increase is much shallower between 2 and 3 repetitions. There does appear to be an interaction between repetition and familiarity for Total Thoughts.

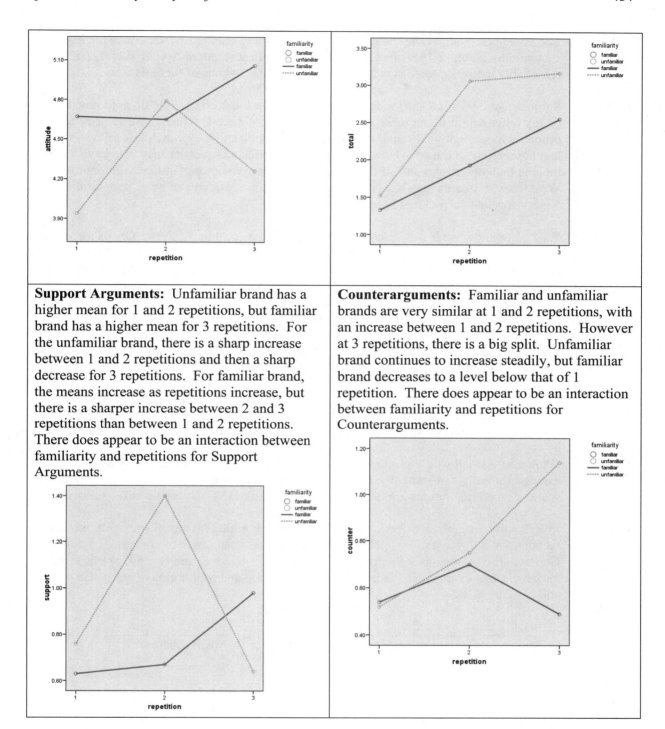

Support Arguments: Unfamiliar brand has a higher mean for 1 and 2 repetitions, but familiar brand has a higher mean for 3 repetitions. For the unfamiliar brand, there is a sharp increase between 1 and 2 repetitions and then a sharp decrease for 3 repetitions. For familiar brand, the means increase as repetitions increase, but there is a sharper increase between 2 and 3 repetitions than between 1 and 2 repetitions. There does appear to be an interaction between familiarity and repetitions for Support Arguments.

Counterarguments: Familiar and unfamiliar brands are very similar at 1 and 2 repetitions, with an increase between 1 and 2 repetitions. However at 3 repetitions, there is a big split. Unfamiliar brand continues to increase steadily, but familiar brand decreases to a level below that of 1 repetition. There does appear to be an interaction between familiarity and repetitions for Counterarguments.

Overall, there is interaction between familiarity and repetition for all of these variables.

15.27 The pooled estimate of the standard deviation for these data is 1.3077. Since the biggest standard deviation (1.46) is less than twice the smallest standard deviation (1.16), it is reasonable to use a pooled standard deviation for the analysis of these data.

15.28   The pooled estimate of the standard deviation for these data is 1.6767. Since the biggest standard deviation (2.16) is less than twice the smallest standard deviation (1.42), it is reasonable to use a pooled standard deviation for the analysis of these data.

15.29   Subjects were 94 adult staff members at a West Coast university: We do not know the ages or any other details about these subjects. If faculty is included, then these subjects are probably more highly educated than the general public and may watch less television or be less susceptible to the ads. However, staff members at a university may also have a higher income than other segments of the population and may be more familiar with brand names. West Coast residents may have different opinions than residents of other parts of the country. Ninety-four is a fairly large sample size, though.

We do not know what was discussed on the half-hour local news show. Choosing an out-of-state news program was good because the material covered during the show would be fairly neutral to all subjects involved. It would be good to know exactly what topics were covered during the program though and what the subjects' reactions were to the show.

The quality of the ads was prejudged by experts to be "good" and by a sample to be "real," so the quality difference in familiar brands vs. unfamiliar brands is probably not an issue, but it would be good to know how those judgments were made. A professional video editor was used to change the brand names, so that work was probably high quality as well.

Most aspects of this research were well done. I would question how well the results will apply to the general public mainly because of how the subjects were selected. It would be good to compare these results to other areas of the country and other types of people.

15.30   Whenever a small whole-number scale is used to measure opinion, the results will not be exactly normally distributed. However, there also won't be any extreme outliers with a 1-7 scale. Since these ratings are the average of three ads, ANOVA would still be fairly safe.

15.31   **a)** Response variable: number of hours of sleep each night. Factors: Type of smoker and Gender. $I = 3$, $J = 2$, and $N = 480$. **b)** Response variable: strength of concrete. Factors: Concrete formula and Number of freezing cycles. $I = 6$, $J = 3$, and $N = 54$. **c)** Response variable: Final exam score. Factors: Teaching method and Major area of study. $I = 4$, $J = 2$, and $N = 32$.

15.32   **a)**

Source	Degrees of freedom	Sum of squares	Mean square	F
A	2			
B	1			
AB	2			
Error	474			
Total	479			

b)

Source	Degrees of freedom	Sum of squares	Mean square	F
A	5			
B	2			
AB	10			
Error	36			
Total	53			

c)

Source	Degrees of freedom	Sum of squares	Mean square	F
A	3			
B	1			
AB	3			
Error	24			
Total	31			

15.33 **a)**

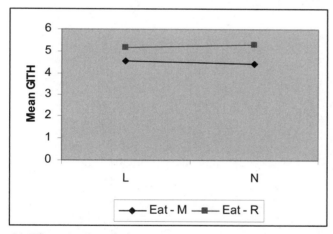

b) The amount of chromium does not seem to affect the mean GITH. Restricting the diet does seem to increase the amount of GITH. No interaction is obvious.

c)

Chromium	Eat - M	Eat - R	Means difference
L	4.545	5.175	0.630
N	4.425	5.317	0.892
Total means	4.485	5.246	0.761

The differences in means are similar. No interaction is obvious.

15.34

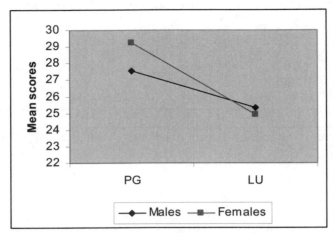

The scores decrease from the PG group to the LU group. The interaction effect is evident, but because of the type of interaction, the main effect of gender does not mean anything without the information about the individuals tested.

15.35

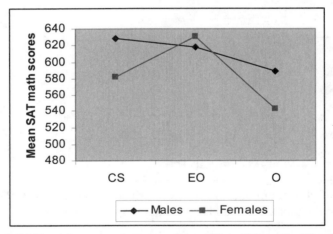

The males' SAT math scores decrease from CS to EO to O. The females' scores increase and then decrease. In fact, the females' scores are greater for the males' only in the group EO.

15.36

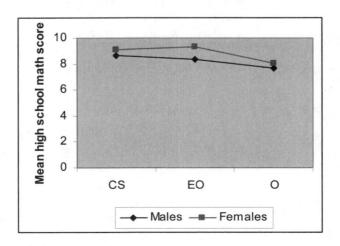

The mean high school math scores decrease from the groups CS to EO to O. The males' scores tend to be slightly lower than the females'. There does not appear to be an interaction.

15.37 Excel output:

ANOVA: Two-Factor with Replication

SUMMARY	4 weeks	8 weeks	Total
ECM1			
Count	3	3	6
Sum	195	190	385
Average	65	63.33333	64.16667
Variance	75	8.333333	34.16667
ECM2			
Count	3	3	6
Sum	190	190	380
Average	63.33333	63.33333	63.33333
Variance	8.333333	33.33333	16.66667
ECM3			
Count	3	3	6
Sum	220	220	440
Average	73.33333	73.33333	73.33333
Variance	8.333333	33.33333	16.66667
MAT1			
Count	3	3	6
Sum	70	65	135
Average	23.33333	21.66667	22.5
Variance	8.333333	33.33333	17.5
MAT2			
Count	3	3	6
Sum	20	20	40
Average	6.666667	6.666667	6.666667
Variance	8.333333	8.333333	6.666667
MAT3			
Count	3	3	6
Sum	35	30	65
Average	11.66667	10	10.83333
Variance	8.333333	25	14.16667

b)

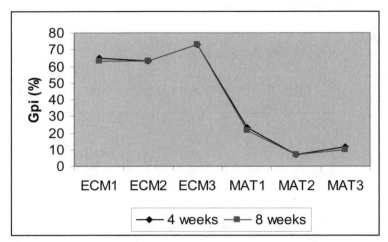

The difference between the ECM and MAT is dramatic. There does not seem to be a difference in mean Gpi between the two times. **c)** For the scaffold material effect: $F = 251.26$ with df = 5 and 24. $P = 0.0$. For the time effect: $F = 0.29$ with df = 1 and 24. $P = 0.595$. For the interaction effect: $F = 0.058$ with df = 5 and 24. $P = 0.998$. The main effect of type of material used as a scaffold was significant. The effect of time and the interaction effect showed no significant differences in means.

15.38   The two main effects, material and time, are both significant now. The interaction effect is also significant. The percent of Gpi drops for each type of material between the 2-week period and the 4-week period. For the ECM groups 1 and 2, the drop is relatively small. For ECM3 there is actually an increase in percent of Gpi. For the MAT groups, the drop in percent Gpi is almost half of what the value is at the 2-week period. Material: $F = 282.847$ with df = 5 and 36. $P = 0.0$. Time: $F = 16.932$ with df = 2 and 36. $P = 0.0$. Interaction: $F = 3.814$ with df = 10 and 36. $P = 0.00061$.

15.39   For the 2-week period: There is a significant difference (using Tukey's comparison with alpha = 0.05) between all three MAT groups and between the MAT groups and each of the ECM groups. There is no significant difference between the three ECM groups. For the 4-week period: There is a significant difference (using Tukey's comparison with alpha = 0.05) between the three MAT groups and the three ECM groups. There is no significant difference among the MAT groups or the ECM groups. For the 8-week period: The same result holds as for the 4-week period.

15.40   **a)** Excel output:

ANOVA: Two-Factor With Replication

SUMMARY	Meat	Legumes	Vegetables	Total
Aluminum				
Count	4	4	4	12
Sum	8.23	9.32	4.93	22.48
Average	2.0575	2.33	1.2325	1.873333
Variance	0.063492	0.012333	0.053492	0.27277
Clay				

Count	4	4	4	12
Sum	8.71	9.89	5.84	24.44
Average	2.1775	2.4725	1.46	2.036667
Variance	0.386025	0.005092	0.211667	0.361606

Iron				
Count	4	4	4	12
Sum	18.72	14.68	11.16	44.56
Average	4.68	3.67	2.79	3.713333
Variance	0.394733	0.0298	0.057533	0.78197

b)

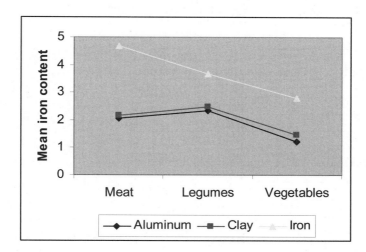

The iron content of foods appears to be much higher for the iron pot when compared to the aluminum and clay pots. There is a noticeable decrease in mean iron content as the food type changes from meat to legumes and vegetables.

c)

ANOVA

Source of Variation	SS	df	MS	F	P-value	F crit
Sample (type of pot)	24.89396	2	12.44698	92.26312	8.53E-13	3.354131
Columns (type of food)	9.296872	2	4.648436	34.45649	3.7E-08	3.354131
Interaction	2.640428	4	0.660107	4.893037	0.004247	2.727766
Within	3.6425	27	0.134907			
Total	40.47376	35				

Both of the main effects and the interaction effect are significant.

15.41   Yes, in general, this data support the hypothesis that foods cooked in iron pots contain a significantly higher iron content than foods cooked in aluminum or clay pots. The interaction effect is small compared to the main effect of type of pot.

15.42   Based on Pooled StDev

```
Level        N      Mean     StDev   ---+---------+---------+---------+---
L-A          4     2.3300   0.1111               (--*---)
L-C          4     2.4725   0.0714               (---*--)
L-I          4     3.6700   0.1726                              (---*--)
M-A          4     2.0575   0.2520           (--*--)
M-C          4     2.1775   0.6213             (--*--)
M-I          4     4.6800   0.6283                                      (--*--)
V-A          4     1.2325   0.2313   (--*--)
V-C          4     1.4675   0.4681     (--*--)
V-I          4     2.7900   0.2399                    (--*--)
```

Based on Tukey's comparison with alpha = 0.05, the clay and aluminum pots do not show significant differences in iron content for meat, legumes, and vegetables. However, there are significant differences between iron and aluminum and iron and clay. There are also significant differences across the three food types.

15.43   **a)**

Tool	Time	Mean	Standard deviation
1	1	25.0307	0.001155
	2	25.0280	0
	3	25.0260	0
2	1	25.0167	0.001155
	2	25.0200	0.002000
	3	25.0160	0
3	1	25.0063	0.001528
	2	25.0127	0.001155
	3	25.0093	0.001155
4	1	25.0120	0
	2	25.0193	0.001155
	3	25.0140	0.004000
5	1	24.9973	0.001155
	2	25.0060	0
	3	25.0003	0.001528

b)

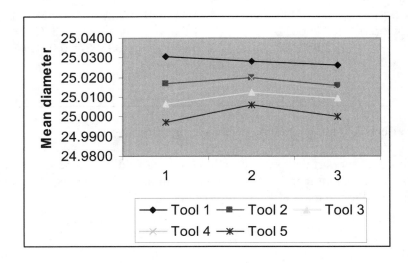

The means change with each tool and with time but the times the measurements were taken does not appear as dramatic. There may be a slight interaction effect.

c)

ANOVA

Source of Variation	SS	df	MS	F	P-value	F crit
Sample	0.003597	4	0.000899	412.9439	9.27E-26	2.689632
Columns	0.00019	2	9.5E-05	43.60204	1.33E-09	3.315833
Interaction	0.000133	8	1.67E-05	7.645409	1.55E-05	2.266162
Within	6.53E-05	30	2.18E-06			
Total	0.003986	44				

Both the main effects of time and tool type were significant, as well as the interaction effect.

15.44

ANOVA

Source of Variation	SS	df	MS	F	P-value	F crit
Sample	5.76E-06	4	1.44E-06	412.9439	9.27E-26	2.689632
Columns	3.04E-07	2	1.52E-07	43.60204	1.33E-09	3.315833
Interaction	2.13E-07	8	2.66E-08	7.645408	1.55E-05	2.266162
Within	1.05E-07	30	3.48E-09			
Total	6.38E-06	44				

The SS values changed but the *F* values, degrees of freedom and *P*-values did not change.

15.45 **a)**

Number of promotions	Percent discount	Mean	Standard deviation
1	40	4.423	0.184755
	30	4.225	0.385609
	20	4.689	0.233069
	10	4.920	0.152023
3	40	4.284	0.204026
	30	4.097	0.234618
	20	4.524	0.270727
	10	4.756	0.242908
5	40	4.058	0.175992
	30	3.890	0.162891
	20	4.251	0.264846
	10	4.393	0.268537
7	40	3.780	0.214372
	30	3.760	0.261789
	20	4.094	0.240749
	10	4.269	0.269916

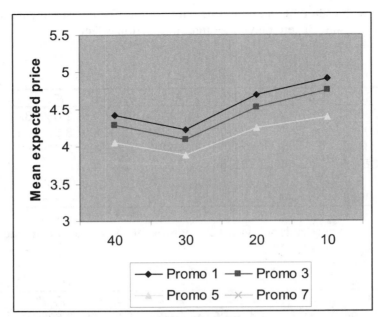

There is a main effect from the number of promotions offered. As the number of promotions offered increases, the expected price decreases. There is also a main effect from the percent discount. As the percent discount increases, the expected price tends to decrease. There does not appear to be an interaction effect.

b)

ANOVA

Source of Variation	SS	df	MS	F	P-value	F crit
Sample	8.360502	3	2.786834	47.72504	1.78E-21	2.667441
Columns	8.306937	3	2.768979	47.41927	2.24E-21	2.667441
Interaction	0.230586	9	0.025621	0.438758	0.9121	1.945452
Within	8.40867	144	0.058394			
Total	25.30669	159				

The main effects of promotions offered ($F = 47.72$ with df = 3 and 144 and $P = 0.0$) and percent discount ($F = 47.42$ with df = 3 and 144 and $P = 0.0$) are both statistically significant. The interaction effect is not statistically significant ($F = 0.4388$ with df = 9 and 144 and $P = 0.9121$).

15.46

```
                                      Individual 95% CIs For Mean
                                      Based on Pooled StDev
Level       N     Mean    StDev    ----------+---------+---------+------
Promo110    10    4.9200   0.1520                              (---*---)
Promo120    10    4.6890   0.2331                         (---*---)
Promo130    10    4.2250   0.3856              (---*--)
Promo140    10    4.4230   0.1848                 (---*--)
Promo310    10    4.7560   0.2429                           (---*---)
Promo320    10    4.5240   0.2707                      (---*---)
Promo330    10    4.0970   0.2346           (--*---)
Promo340    10    4.2840   0.2040              (---*---)
Promo510    10    4.3930   0.2685                (---*---)
Promo520    10    4.2510   0.2648               (---*---)
Promo530    10    3.8900   0.1629         (---*---)
Promo540    10    4.0580   0.1760          (--*---)
Promo710    10    4.2690   0.2699              (---*---)
Promo720    10    4.0940   0.2407          (--*---)
Promo730    10    3.7600   0.2618      (---*---)
Promo740    10    3.7800   0.2144      (---*--)
                                      ----------+---------+---------+------
Pooled StDev =    0.2416              4.00      4.40      4.80
```

The ANOVA tool on Minitab generated the confidence intervals above. One can see a decreasing trend in expected price as the number of promotions increases. It is also possible to see that within each promotion group, the lowest expected price occurs at a 30% discount. (Note: Minitab does not calculate the Bonferroni multiple comparisons.)

15.47 **a)**

ANOVA

Source of Variation	df	SS	MS	F
A (Chromium)	1	0.00121	0.00121	0.04031
B (Eat)	1	5.79121	5.79121	192.91173
AB	1	0.17161	0.17161	5.71652
Error	36	1.08084	0.03002	
Total	39	7.04487		

b) $F = 5.71652$. The distribution has df = 1 and 36. $P = 0.022125$. **c)** Chromium: $F = 0.04031$ with df = 1 and 36. $P = 0.842006$. Eat: $F = 192.91173$ with df = 1 and 36. $P = 0.0$. **d)** $s_p^2 = 0.03002$ and $s_p = 0.17326$. **e)** The results of this ANOVA test are consistent with the observations made in 15.33. The chromium level does not affect the level of GITH. There is a significant difference in GITH between the restricted diet and unrestricted diet. The interaction between Chromium and Eat is statistically significant at the 0.05 level, but not at the 0.01 level. The interaction effect is relatively small compared to the main effect of Eat.

15.48   **a)**

ANOVA

Source of Variation	df	SS	MS	F
A (Gender)	1	62.40	62.40	2.041
B (Group)	1	1,599.03	1,599.03	52.307
AB	1	163.80	163.80	5.358
Error	446	13,633.29	30.57	
Total	449	15,458.52		

b) Interaction: $F = 5.358$. The distribution has df $= 1$ and 446. The P-value is between 0.01 and 0.025. **c)** Gender: $F = 2.041$ with df $= 1$ and 446. The P-value is bigger than 0.10. Group: $F = 52.307$ with df $= 1$ and 446. The P-value is less than 0.001. **d)** $s_p^2 = 30.57$ and $s_p = 5.53$. **e)** The main effect of Group and the interaction of Group and Gender are significant at the 5% level. The main effect of gender is not significant. This is consistent with the observations from problem 15.34.

15.49   **a)** $F = 22.36$ with df $= 1$ and 945: $P = 0.0$. $F = 37.44$ with df $= 1$ and 945: $P = 0.0$. $F = 2.10$ with df $= 1$ and 945: $P = 0.1476$. **b)** The main effects of gender and handedness are significant but the interaction effect is not.

15.50   **a)** $F = 7.02$ with df $= 3$ and 56: $P = 0.00043$. $F = 1.96$ with df $= 1$ and 56: $P = 0.16703$. $F = 1.24$ with df $= 3$ and 56: $P = 0.3039$. **b)** The main effect of series is significant but the effects of holder and interaction are not. The difference in average readings from the four production series was important because it is typically assumed that the detectors are all the same, whereas this study shows that they are not. The different production series actually detected different average levels even though they were exposed to the same level of radon.

15.51   The main effects of group and gender are both significant. The interaction effect is shown to be statistically significant even though it is not apparent in a plot of the means. This is most likely due to the large sample sizes used in the study. One might ask if this interaction effect is of practical significance as well as statistical significance.

Case Study 15.1

SATV: From the two-way ANOVA F tests: main effect major is significant, but main effect sex and the interaction between major and sex is not significant (even though the means plot looks as though there is an interaction). Using Bonferroni, Major 3 is significantly different from Majors 1 and 2, but Majors 1 and 2 are not significantly different from each other. For both genders, SATV decreases from Major 1 to 2 to 3.

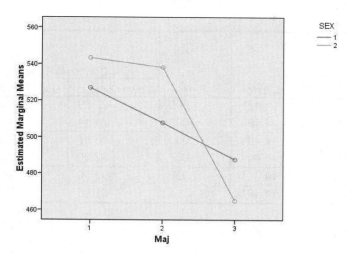

Estimated Marginal Means of SATV

Descriptive Statistics

Dependent Variable: SATV

SEX	Maj	Mean	Std. Deviation	N
1	1	526.95	100.937	39
	2	507.85	57.213	39
	3	487.56	108.779	39
	Total	507.45	92.450	117
2	1	543.38	77.654	39
	2	538.21	102.209	39
	3	465.03	82.184	39
	Total	515.54	94.348	117
Total	1	535.17	89.846	78
	2	523.03	83.692	78
	3	476.29	96.445	78
	Total	511.50	93.291	234

Tests of Between-Subjects Effects

Dependent Variable: SATV

Source	Type III Sum of Squares	df	Mean Square	F	Sig.
Corrected Model	183869.368[a]	5	36773.874	4.547	.001
Intercept	61220923.5	1	61220923.50	7569.701	.000
SEX	3824.427	1	3824.427	.473	.492
Maj	150723.496	2	75361.748	9.318	.000
SEX * Maj	29321.444	2	14660.722	1.813	.166
Error	1843979.128	228	8087.628		
Total	63248772.0	234			
Corrected Total	2027848.496	233			

a. R Squared = .091 (Adjusted R Squared = .071)

Multiple Comparisons

Dependent Variable: SATV

Bonferroni

(I) Maj	(J) Maj	Mean Difference (I-J)	Std. Error	Sig.	95% Confidence Interval Lower Bound	95% Confidence Interval Upper Bound
1	2	12.14	14.401	1.000	-22.59	46.87
	3	58.87*	14.401	.000	24.14	93.60
2	1	-12.14	14.401	1.000	-46.87	22.59
	3	46.73*	14.401	.004	12.00	81.46
3	1	-58.87*	14.401	.000	-93.60	-24.14
	2	-46.73*	14.401	.004	-81.46	-12.00

Based on observed means.

*. The mean difference is significant at the .05 level.

HSM: From the two-way ANOVA F tests: main effect major and main effect sex are significant, but the interaction between major and sex is not significant. Using Bonferroni, Major 3 is significantly different from Majors 1 and 2, but Majors 1 and 2 are not significantly different from each other. For both genders, HSM decreases from Major 2 to 3 and from Major 1 to 3.

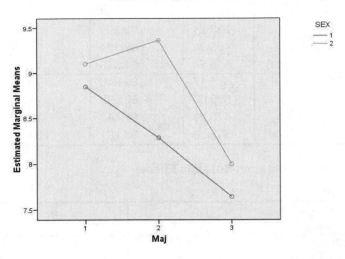

Estimated Marginal Means of HSM

Descriptive Statistics

Dependent Variable: HSM

SEX	Maj	Mean	Std. Deviation	N
1	1	8.85	1.288	39
	2	8.28	1.701	39
	3	7.64	1.614	39
	Total	8.26	1.609	117
2	1	9.10	1.165	39
	2	9.36	.778	39
	3	8.00	1.864	39
	Total	8.82	1.460	117
Total	1	8.97	1.227	78
	2	8.82	1.421	78
	3	7.82	1.741	78
	Total	8.54	1.559	234

Tests of Between-Subjects Effects

Dependent Variable: HSM

Source	Type III Sum of Squares	df	Mean Square	F	Sig.
Corrected Model	87.641[a]	5	17.528	8.352	.000
Intercept	17059.846	1	17059.846	8128.612	.000
SEX	18.615	1	18.615	8.870	.003
Maj	61.231	2	30.615	14.588	.000
SEX * Maj	7.795	2	3.897	1.857	.158
Error	478.513	228	2.099		
Total	17626.000	234			
Corrected Total	566.154	233			

a. R Squared = .155 (Adjusted R Squared = .136)

Multiple Comparisons

Dependent Variable: HSM

Bonferroni

(I) Maj	(J) Maj	Mean Difference (I-J)	Std. Error	Sig.	95% Confidence Interval	
					Lower Bound	Upper Bound
1	2	.15	.232	1.000	-.41	.71
	3	1.15*	.232	.000	.59	1.71
2	1	-.15	.232	1.000	-.71	.41
	3	1.00*	.232	.000	.44	1.56
3	1	-1.15*	.232	.000	-1.71	-.59
	2	-1.00*	.232	.000	-1.56	-.44

Based on observed means.

*. The mean difference is significant at the .05 level.

HSS: From the two-way ANOVA F tests: main effect major, main effect sex, and their interaction are all significant. Using Bonferroni, Major 3 is significantly different from Majors 1 and 2, but Majors 1 and 2 are not significantly different from each other.

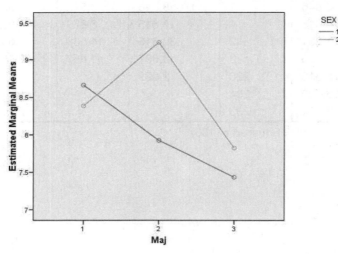

Estimated Marginal Means of HSS

Descriptive Statistics

Dependent Variable: HSS

SEX	Maj	Mean	Std. Deviation	N
1	1	8.67	1.284	39
	2	7.92	2.057	39
	3	7.44	1.714	39
	Total	8.01	1.774	117
2	1	8.38	1.664	39
	2	9.23	.706	39
	3	7.82	1.805	39
	Total	8.48	1.573	117
Total	1	8.53	1.483	78
	2	8.58	1.663	78
	3	7.63	1.759	78
	Total	8.24	1.690	234

Tests of Between-Subjects Effects

Dependent Variable: HSS

Source	Type III Sum of Squares	df	Mean Square	F	Sig.
Corrected Model	82.192[a]	5	16.438	6.430	.000
Intercept	15901.885	1	15901.885	6219.740	.000
SEX	12.927	1	12.927	5.056	.025
Maj	44.410	2	22.205	8.685	.000
SEX * Maj	24.855	2	12.427	4.861	.009
Error	582.923	228	2.557		
Total	16567.000	234			
Corrected Total	665.115	233			

a. R Squared = .124 (Adjusted R Squared = .104)

Multiple Comparisons

Dependent Variable: HSS

Bonferroni

(I) Maj	(J) Maj	Mean Difference (I-J)	Std. Error	Sig.	95% Confidence Interval	
					Lower Bound	Upper Bound
1	2	-.05	.256	1.000	-.67	.57
	3	.90*	.256	.002	.28	1.51
2	1	.05	.256	1.000	-.57	.67
	3	.95*	.256	.001	.33	1.57
3	1	-.90*	.256	.002	-1.51	-.28
	2	-.95*	.256	.001	-1.57	-.33

Based on observed means.

*. The mean difference is significant at the .05 level.

HSE: From the two-way ANOVA F tests: main effect sex is significant, but main effect major and the interaction between major and sex are not significant.

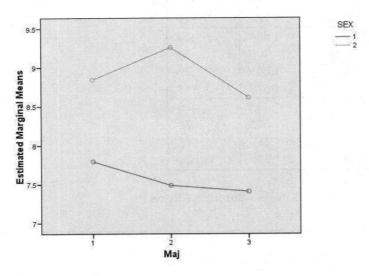

Descriptive Statistics

Dependent Variable: HSE

SEX	Maj	Mean	Std. Deviation	N
1	1	7.79	1.508	39
	2	7.49	2.151	39
	3	7.41	1.568	39
	Total	7.56	1.759	117
2	1	8.85	1.136	39
	2	9.26	.751	39
	3	8.62	1.161	39
	Total	8.91	1.058	117
Total	1	8.32	1.428	78
	2	8.37	1.831	78
	3	8.01	1.499	78
	Total	8.24	1.597	234

Tests of Between-Subjects Effects

Dependent Variable: HSE

Source	Type III Sum of Squares	df	Mean Square	F	Sig.
Corrected Model	116.791[a]	5	23.358	11.158	.000
Intercept	15868.927	1	15868.927	7580.665	.000
SEX	105.338	1	105.338	50.320	.000
Maj	5.880	2	2.940	1.405	.248
SEX * Maj	5.573	2	2.786	1.331	.266
Error	477.282	228	2.093		
Total	16463.000	234			
Corrected Total	594.073	233			

a. R Squared = .197 (Adjusted R Squared = .179)

Case Study 15.2

The side-by-side boxplots for species show Species 3 looks much higher than the others (except for some overlap with Species 1), and Species 4 looks much lower than the others. Species 2 is also much lower than Species 1 and 3.

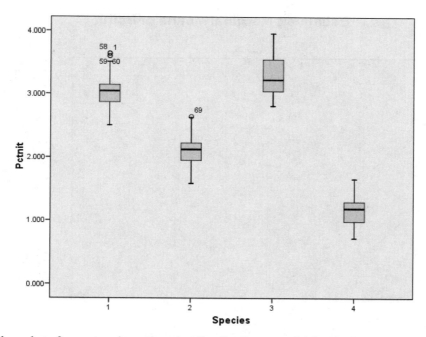

The side-by-side boxplots for water show that the distributions are fairly similar.

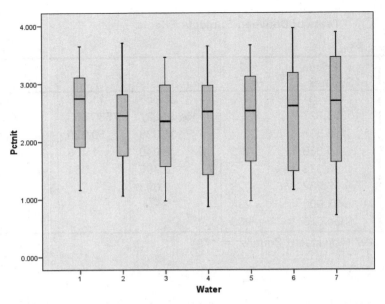

The means plot shows that Species 3 is the highest for almost all Water levels, followed closely by Species 1. Species 2 is much lower, and Species 4 is even lower. The lines are fairly parallel, but the lines for Species 3 and 1 do intersect.

Estimated Marginal Means of Pctnit

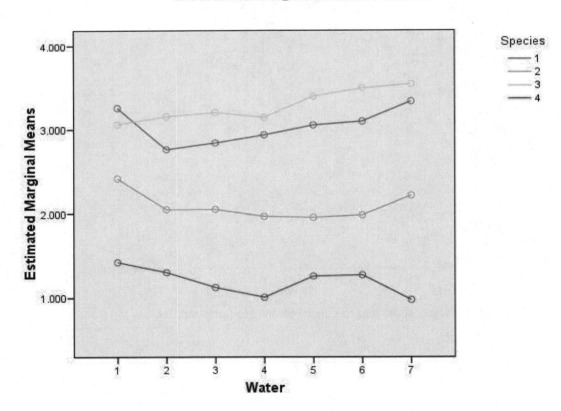

1. Species

Dependent Variable: Pctnit

Species	Mean	Std. Error	95% Confidence Interval	
			Lower Bound	Upper Bound
1	3.040	.026	2.988	3.092
2	2.093	.026	2.041	2.145
3	3.284	.026	3.232	3.337
4	1.196	.026	1.143	1.248

2. Water

Dependent Variable: Pctnit

Water	Mean	Std. Error	95% Confidence Interval	
			Lower Bound	Upper Bound
1	2.539	.035	2.470	2.608
2	2.318	.035	2.249	2.387
3	2.305	.035	2.236	2.374
4	2.264	.035	2.195	2.333
5	2.415	.035	2.346	2.484
6	2.462	.035	2.393	2.531
7	2.519	.035	2.450	2.588

The two-way ANOVA F tests show that Water, Species, and their interaction all are significant (with *P*-values close to 0). According to the Bonferroni multiple comparisons tests, all the Species are significantly different from each other. The results for Water are below (note that none of the confidence intervals in the Bonferroni output contain 0).

Multiple Comparisons

Dependent Variable: Pctnit

Bonferroni

(I) Species	(J) Species	Mean Difference (I-J)	Std. Error	Sig.	95% Confidence Interval	
					Lower Bound	Upper Bound
1	2	.94697*	.037441	.000	.84730	1.04663
	3	-.24456*	.037441	.000	-.34422	-.14489
	4	1.84422*	.037441	.000	1.74456	1.94389
2	1	-.94697*	.037441	.000	-1.04663	-.84730
	3	-1.19152*	.037441	.000	-1.29119	-1.09186
	4	.89725*	.037441	.000	.79759	.99692
3	1	.24456*	.037441	.000	.14489	.34422
	2	1.19152*	.037441	.000	1.09186	1.29119
	4	2.08878*	.037441	.000	1.98911	2.18844
4	1	-1.84422*	.037441	.000	-1.94389	-1.74456
	2	-.89725*	.037441	.000	-.99692	-.79759
	3	-2.08878*	.037441	.000	-2.18844	-1.98911

Based on observed means.

*. The mean difference is significant at the .05 level.

Multiple Comparisons

Dependent Variable: Pctnit

Bonferroni

(I) Water	(J) Water	Mean Difference (I-J)	Std. Error	Sig.	95% Confidence Interval Lower Bound	95% Confidence Interval Upper Bound
1	2	.22156*	.049530	.000	.06934	.37377
	3	.23419*	.049530	.000	.08198	.38641
	4	.27592*	.049530	.000	.12370	.42813
	5	.12397	.049530	.274	-.02824	.27618
	6	.07756	.049530	1.000	-.07466	.22977
	7	.02086	.049530	1.000	-.13135	.17307
2	1	-.22156*	.049530	.000	-.37377	-.06934
	3	.01264	.049530	1.000	-.13957	.16485
	4	.05436	.049530	1.000	-.09785	.20657
	5	-.09758	.049530	1.000	-.24980	.05463
	6	-.14400	.049530	.084	-.29621	.00821
	7	-.20069*	.049530	.001	-.35291	-.04848
3	1	-.23419*	.049530	.000	-.38641	-.08198
	2	-.01264	.049530	1.000	-.16485	.13957
	4	.04172	.049530	1.000	-.11049	.19393
	5	-.11022	.049530	.568	-.26243	.04199
	6	-.15664*	.049530	.037	-.30885	-.00443
	7	-.21333*	.049530	.001	-.36555	-.06112
4	1	-.27592*	.049530	.000	-.42813	-.12370
	2	-.05436	.049530	1.000	-.20657	.09785
	3	-.04172	.049530	1.000	-.19393	.11049
	5	-.15194	.049530	.051	-.30416	.00027
	6	-.19836*	.049530	.002	-.35057	-.04615
	7	-.25506*	.049530	.000	-.40727	-.10284
5	1	-.12397	.049530	.274	-.27618	.02824
	2	.09758	.049530	1.000	-.05463	.24980
	3	.11022	.049530	.568	-.04199	.26243
	4	.15194	.049530	.051	-.00027	.30416
	6	-.04642	.049530	1.000	-.19863	.10580
	7	-.10311	.049530	.808	-.25532	.04910
6	1	-.07756	.049530	1.000	-.22977	.07466
	2	.14400	.049530	.084	-.00821	.29621
	3	.15664*	.049530	.037	.00443	.30885
	4	.19836*	.049530	.002	.04615	.35057
	5	.04642	.049530	1.000	-.10580	.19863
	7	-.05669	.049530	1.000	-.20891	.09552
7	1	-.02086	.049530	1.000	-.17307	.13135
	2	.20069*	.049530	.001	.04848	.35291
	3	.21333*	.049530	.001	.06112	.36555
	4	.25506*	.049530	.000	.10284	.40727
	5	.10311	.049530	.808	-.04910	.25532
	6	.05669	.049530	1.000	-.09552	.20891

Based on observed means.

*. The mean difference is significant at the .05 level.

Case Study 15.3

Fbiomass

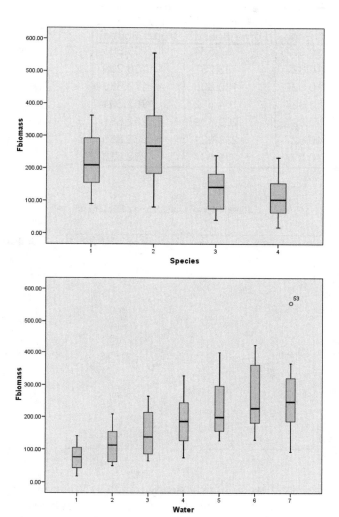

1. Species

Dependent Variable: Fbiomass

Species	Mean	Std. Error	95% Confidence Interval	
			Lower Bound	Upper Bound
1	219.978	8.185	203.702	236.254
2	268.896	8.185	252.620	285.172
3	134.716	8.185	118.441	150.992
4	110.256	8.185	93.980	126.531

2. Water

Dependent Variable: Fbiomass

Water	Mean	Std. Error	95% Confidence Interval	
			Lower Bound	Upper Bound
1	79.055	10.827	57.524	100.586
2	114.768	10.827	93.237	136.298
3	152.136	10.827	130.605	173.666
4	186.163	10.827	164.632	207.694
5	231.150	10.827	209.619	252.681
6	259.852	10.827	238.321	281.383
7	261.108	10.827	239.577	282.638

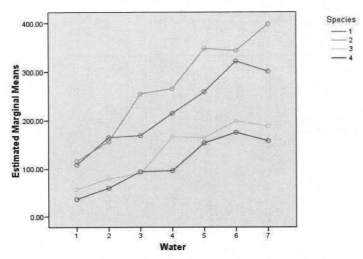

The means plot above shows that there is a fairly steady trend: as Water increases, the Fbiomass also increases. Species 2 is the highest, then Species 1, then Species 3, and then Species 4. There is little overlap of the lines. The two-way ANOVA F tests indicated that the main effect for Species, the main effect for Water, and their interaction are all significant. The Bonferroni multiple comparisons tests for Species show that only Species 3 and 4 are *not* significantly different—all the others are significantly different from each other. The Bonferroni output for Water follows below.

Tests of Between-Subjects Effects

Dependent Variable: Fbiomass

Source	Type III Sum of Squares	df	Mean Square	F	Sig.
Corrected Model	1010577.733[a]	27	37428.805	19.956	.000
Intercept	3769710.396	1	3769710.396	2009.858	.000
Species	458295.023	3	152765.008	81.448	.000
Water	491948.413	6	81991.402	43.715	.000
Species * Water	60334.297	18	3351.905	1.787	.040
Error	157551.234	84	1875.610		
Total	4937839.363	112			
Corrected Total	1168128.967	111			

a. R Squared = .865 (Adjusted R Squared = .822)

Multiple Comparisons

Dependent Variable: Fbiomass

Bonferroni

(I) Species	(J) Species	Mean Difference (I-J)	Std. Error	Sig.	95% Confidence Interval	
					Lower Bound	Upper Bound
1	2	-48.9182*	11.57463	.000	-80.1949	-17.6415
	3	85.2614*	11.57463	.000	53.9847	116.5381
	4	109.7221*	11.57463	.000	78.4455	140.9988
2	1	48.9182*	11.57463	.000	17.6415	80.1949
	3	134.1796*	11.57463	.000	102.9030	165.4563
	4	158.6404*	11.57463	.000	127.3637	189.9170
3	1	-85.2614*	11.57463	.000	-116.5381	-53.9847
	2	-134.1796*	11.57463	.000	-165.4563	-102.9030
	4	24.4607	11.57463	.225	-6.8160	55.7374
4	1	-109.7221*	11.57463	.000	-140.9988	-78.4455
	2	-158.6404*	11.57463	.000	-189.9170	-127.3637
	3	-24.4607	11.57463	.225	-55.7374	6.8160

Based on observed means.

*. The mean difference is significant at the .05 level.

Multiple Comparisons

Dependent Variable: Fbiomass

Bonferroni

(I) Water	(J) Water	Mean Difference (I-J)	Std. Error	Sig.	95% Confidence Interval Lower Bound	95% Confidence Interval Upper Bound
1	2	-35.7125	15.31180	.464	-83.6876	12.2626
	3	-73.0806*	15.31180	.000	-121.0558	-25.1055
	4	-107.1081*	15.31180	.000	-155.0833	-59.1330
	5	-152.0950*	15.31180	.000	-200.0701	-104.1199
	6	-180.7969*	15.31180	.000	-228.7720	-132.8217
	7	-182.0525*	15.31180	.000	-230.0276	-134.0774
2	1	35.7125	15.31180	.464	-12.2626	83.6876
	3	-37.3681	15.31180	.352	-85.3433	10.6070
	4	-71.3956*	15.31180	.000	-119.3708	-23.4205
	5	-116.3825*	15.31180	.000	-164.3576	-68.4074
	6	-145.0844*	15.31180	.000	-193.0595	-97.1092
	7	-146.3400*	15.31180	.000	-194.3151	-98.3649
3	1	73.0806*	15.31180	.000	25.1055	121.0558
	2	37.3681	15.31180	.352	-10.6070	85.3433
	4	-34.0275	15.31180	.608	-82.0026	13.9476
	5	-79.0144*	15.31180	.000	-126.9895	-31.0392
	6	-107.7163*	15.31180	.000	-155.6914	-59.7411
	7	-108.9719*	15.31180	.000	-156.9470	-60.9967
4	1	107.1081*	15.31180	.000	59.1330	155.0833
	2	71.3956*	15.31180	.000	23.4205	119.3708
	3	34.0275	15.31180	.608	-13.9476	82.0026
	5	-44.9869	15.31180	.090	-92.9620	2.9883
	6	-73.6888*	15.31180	.000	-121.6639	-25.7136
	7	-74.9444*	15.31180	.000	-122.9195	-26.9692
5	1	152.0950*	15.31180	.000	104.1199	200.0701
	2	116.3825*	15.31180	.000	68.4074	164.3576
	3	79.0144*	15.31180	.000	31.0392	126.9895
	4	44.9869	15.31180	.090	-2.9883	92.9620
	6	-28.7019	15.31180	1.000	-76.6770	19.2733
	7	-29.9575	15.31180	1.000	-77.9326	18.0176
6	1	180.7969*	15.31180	.000	132.8217	228.7720
	2	145.0844*	15.31180	.000	97.1092	193.0595
	3	107.7163*	15.31180	.000	59.7411	155.6914
	4	73.6888*	15.31180	.000	25.7136	121.6639
	5	28.7019	15.31180	1.000	-19.2733	76.6770
	7	-1.2556	15.31180	1.000	-49.2308	46.7195
7	1	182.0525*	15.31180	.000	134.0774	230.0276
	2	146.3400*	15.31180	.000	98.3649	194.3151
	3	108.9719*	15.31180	.000	60.9967	156.9470
	4	74.9444*	15.31180	.000	26.9692	122.9195
	5	29.9575	15.31180	1.000	-18.0176	77.9326
	6	1.2556	15.31180	1.000	-46.7195	49.2308

Based on observed means.

*. The mean difference is significant at the .05 level.

Dbiomass

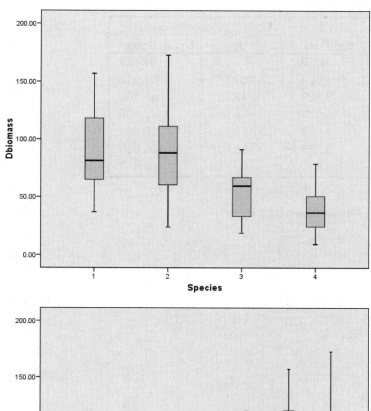

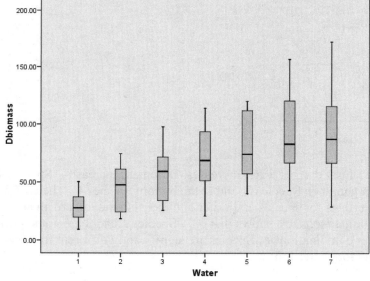

1. Species

Dependent Variable: Dbiomass

Species	Mean	Std. Error	95% Confidence Interval	
			Lower Bound	Upper Bound
1	88.862	2.743	83.407	94.317
2	85.168	2.743	79.713	90.623
3	52.204	2.743	46.749	57.659
4	39.085	2.743	33.630	44.540

2. Water

Dependent Variable: Dbiomass

Water	Mean	Std. Error	95% Confidence Interval	
			Lower Bound	Upper Bound
1	29.209	3.629	21.992	36.425
2	44.096	3.629	36.879	51.312
3	55.973	3.629	48.757	63.189
4	69.892	3.629	62.676	77.108
5	80.985	3.629	73.769	88.201
6	93.819	3.629	86.602	101.035
7	90.336	3.629	83.119	97.552

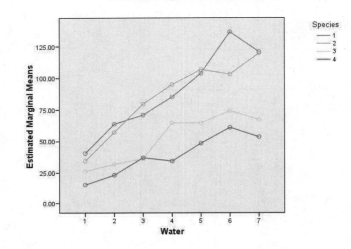

The means plot above shows that, as water increases, Dbiomass increases. Species 1 and 2 have plenty of overlap, then there is a gap, then Species 3, and at the bottom Species 4. The two-way ANOVA F tests indicate that the main effects for species and water and their interaction are all significant. The Bonferroni multiple comparisons test shows that only Species 1 and 2 are not significantly different from each other; all the other combinations of Species are significantly different from each other. The results for the Bonferroni tests for Water follow.

Tests of Between-Subjects Effects

Dependent Variable: Dbiomass

Source	Type III Sum of Squares	df	Mean Square	F	Sig.
Corrected Model	115566.245[a]	27	4280.231	20.315	.000
Intercept	492760.264	1	492760.264	2338.736	.000
Species	50523.790	3	16841.263	79.932	.000
Water	56623.630	6	9437.272	44.791	.000
Species * Water	8418.825	18	467.712	2.220	.008
Error	17698.388	84	210.695		
Total	626024.896	112			
Corrected Total	133264.632	111			

a. R Squared = .867 (Adjusted R Squared = .825)

Multiple Comparisons

Dependent Variable: Dbiomass

Bonferroni

(I) Species	(J) Species	Mean Difference (I-J)	Std. Error	Sig.	95% Confidence Interval	
					Lower Bound	Upper Bound
1	2	3.6939	3.87939	1.000	-6.7889	14.1767
	3	36.6579*	3.87939	.000	26.1751	47.1406
	4	49.7775*	3.87939	.000	39.2947	60.2603
2	1	-3.6939	3.87939	1.000	-14.1767	6.7889
	3	32.9639*	3.87939	.000	22.4811	43.4467
	4	46.0836*	3.87939	.000	35.6008	56.5664
3	1	-36.6579*	3.87939	.000	-47.1406	-26.1751
	2	-32.9639*	3.87939	.000	-43.4467	-22.4811
	4	13.1196*	3.87939	.007	2.6369	23.6024
4	1	-49.7775*	3.87939	.000	-60.2603	-39.2947
	2	-46.0836*	3.87939	.000	-56.5664	-35.6008
	3	-13.1196*	3.87939	.007	-23.6024	-2.6369

Based on observed means.

*. The mean difference is significant at the .05 level.

Multiple Comparisons

Dependent Variable: Dbiomass

Bonferroni

(I) Water	(J) Water	Mean Difference (I-J)	Std. Error	Sig.	95% Confidence Interval	
					Lower Bound	Upper Bound
1	2	-14.8869	5.13195	.100	-30.9664	1.1926
	3	-26.7644*	5.13195	.000	-42.8439	-10.6849
	4	-40.6831*	5.13195	.000	-56.7626	-24.6036
	5	-51.7763*	5.13195	.000	-67.8557	-35.6968
	6	-64.6100*	5.13195	.000	-80.6895	-48.5305
	7	-61.1269*	5.13195	.000	-77.2064	-45.0474
2	1	14.8869	5.13195	.100	-1.1926	30.9664
	3	-11.8775	5.13195	.485	-27.9570	4.2020
	4	-25.7963*	5.13195	.000	-41.8757	-9.7168
	5	-36.8894*	5.13195	.000	-52.9689	-20.8099
	6	-49.7231*	5.13195	.000	-65.8026	-33.6436
	7	-46.2400*	5.13195	.000	-62.3195	-30.1605
3	1	26.7644*	5.13195	.000	10.6849	42.8439
	2	11.8775	5.13195	.485	-4.2020	27.9570
	4	-13.9188	5.13195	.170	-29.9982	2.1607
	5	-25.0119*	5.13195	.000	-41.0914	-8.9324
	6	-37.8456*	5.13195	.000	-53.9251	-21.7661
	7	-34.3625*	5.13195	.000	-50.4420	-18.2830
4	1	40.6831*	5.13195	.000	24.6036	56.7626
	2	25.7963*	5.13195	.000	9.7168	41.8757
	3	13.9188	5.13195	.170	-2.1607	29.9982
	5	-11.0931	5.13195	.703	-27.1726	4.9864
	6	-23.9269*	5.13195	.000	-40.0064	-7.8474
	7	-20.4438*	5.13195	.003	-36.5232	-4.3643
5	1	51.7763*	5.13195	.000	35.6968	67.8557
	2	36.8894*	5.13195	.000	20.8099	52.9689
	3	25.0119*	5.13195	.000	8.9324	41.0914
	4	11.0931	5.13195	.703	-4.9864	27.1726
	6	-12.8338	5.13195	.301	-28.9132	3.2457
	7	-9.3506	5.13195	1.000	-25.4301	6.7289
6	1	64.6100*	5.13195	.000	48.5305	80.6895
	2	49.7231*	5.13195	.000	33.6436	65.8026
	3	37.8456*	5.13195	.000	21.7661	53.9251
	4	23.9269*	5.13195	.000	7.8474	40.0064
	5	12.8338	5.13195	.301	-3.2457	28.9132
	7	3.4831	5.13195	1.000	-12.5964	19.5626
7	1	61.1269*	5.13195	.000	45.0474	77.2064
	2	46.2400*	5.13195	.000	30.1605	62.3195
	3	34.3625*	5.13195	.000	18.2830	50.4420
	4	20.4438*	5.13195	.003	4.3643	36.5232
	5	9.3506	5.13195	1.000	-6.7289	25.4301
	6	-3.4831	5.13195	1.000	-19.5626	12.5964

Based on observed means.

*. The mean difference is significant at the .05 level.

Chapter 16: Nonparametric Tests

16.1 In the table below in the "Area" row, A = Asia and E = Eastern Europe.

Rank	1	2	3	4	5	6	7	8	9	10	11	12	13
Rate	-12.1	-5.2	-1.7	-1.5	-1.0	1.0	1.4	2.9	3.1	3.2	3.5	3.7	3.9
Area	E	E	E	E	E	E	E	A	A	E	E	E	A

Rank	14	15	16	17	18	19	20	21	22	23	24	25
Rate	4.1	4.4	4.6	4.7	4.9	5.2	5.4	6.0	6.2	7.0	7.2	9.4
Area	A	A	A	A	E	A	A	E	A	E	A	A

The European rates appear to have lower ranks than the Asian rates.

16.2 $W = 202$, $\mu_W = 156$, $\sigma_W = 18.385$. SPSS reports the test statistic $Z = 2.502$ and P-value $= 0.0055$ for a one-sided test. There is good evidence that the distribution of growth rates of private consumption in Asia is systematically higher than that in Eastern Europe.

16.3   Using the Normal approximation with the continuity correction for a one-tailed test, the test statistic is $Z = 2.48$, and the P-value $= 0.0066$. These results are close to the results from SPSS, and the same conclusion applies.

16.4   The rank sum for Europe is 123. $123 + 202 = 325$. The SPSS output is below (1 = Asia, 2 = Europe). Note that the P-value is the same as that in 16.2.

Ranks

1 = Asia, 2 =		N	Mean Rank	Sum of Ranks
rates	1	12	16.83	202.00
	2	13	9.46	123.00
	Total	25		

Test Statistics[b]

	rates
Mann-Whitney U	32.000
Wilcoxon W	123.000
Z	-2.502
Asymp. Sig. (2-tailed)	.012
Exact Sig. [2*(1-tailed Sig.)]	.011[a]

a. Not corrected for ties.

b. Grouping Variable: 1 = Asia, 2 = Eastern Europe

16.5 In the table below in the "brand" row, A = American brand and F = foreign brand. The brand labeling was not required in this exercise, but it is helpful for Exercise 16.6.

MPG	19	21	23	23	25	25	26	26	27	27	27	27	28	28	28	29
RANK	1	2	3.5	3.5	5.5	5.5	7.5	7.5	10.5	10.5	10.5	10.5	14	14	14	16
BRAND	F	F	F	F	A	A	F	F	F	A	F	F	F	F	A	F

MPG	30	30	30	30	30	30	30	32	32	32	32	34	34	34	37	51
RANK	20	20	20	20	20	20	20	25.5	25.5	25.5	25.5	29	29	29	31	32
BRAND	A	A	A	F	F	F	F	A	F	A	F	F	F	F	F	F

16.6 $W = 146.5$, P-value = 0.934 for a two-sided test using SPSS that does not correct for ties. No, there is not a significant difference between the mileages of domestic and foreign brands.

16.7 Yes, there is strong evidence that healthy firms have a higher ratio of assets to liabilities on the average. $W_{healthy} = 4299$, and $W_{failed} = 852$, $Z = -6.017$, and the P-value from SPSS for the one sided test is very close to 0.

16.8 **a)** The back-to-back stemplot shows that both types of apartments have fairly Normal distributions with no outliers. The two-bedroom apartments appear to have slightly higher rents overall, but there is quite a bit of overlap.

One-Bedroom	100s place	Two- Bedroom
8	3	
9 5	4	9
5 2 1 0	5	0 1 8
5 4 0	6	0 5 7 7 7
	7	5

b) There is evidence that two-bedroom apartments rent for significantly more than one-bedroom apartments. $Z = -1.818$, and the P-value for a one-sided test is 0.0375 using SPSS which does not correct for ties.

16.9 **a)** Yes, there appears to be strong evidence that the high fitness group has higher ego fitness as well. $Z = -4.503$, and the P-value for the one-sided test is close to 0 using SPSS that does not correct for ties. **b)** These results would probably not apply to the general population of middle-aged men. These executives are probably better educated and better paid than the majority of their age/gender group. Their fitness levels are attained by choice, as executives generally have sit-down desk jobs. **c)** No, we cannot prove causation here. This was not an experiment but an observational study. Perhaps people who are more self-confident choose to take better care of their bodies. Perhaps some other lurking variable (education or happiness with life in general) causes a person to choose to exercise more and to have higher ego fitness.

16.10 **a)** The men's and the women's SSHA scores are skewed right. There do not appear to be any outliers. Since the overall sample size is 38, we could probably use the two-sample comparison of means test anyway because the skewness is not extreme. **b)** Using the Wilcoxon rank sum test, $Z = -2.092$ and the P-value for a one-sided test is 0.0175 using SPSS that does not correct for ties. Yes, there is evidence that the distribution of SSHA scores for males is systematically higher than the distribution of SSHA scores for females. Using the two-sample comparison of means test, t = -2.223 and the *P*-value = 0.0165. There is evidence that the mean SSHA score is higher for males than for females.

16.11 **a)**

Price	2.92	2.92	2.93	2.93	2.97	3.57	3.58	3.59	3.6	3.62
Rank	1	2	3	4	5	6	7	8	9	10

b) $W = 40$, $\mu_W = 27.5$, $\sigma_W = 4.787$. **c)** *P*-value = 0.012.

16.12 **a)** The data primarily depart from Normality because they are integer valued. **b)** $W_{treatment} = 81$, $\mu_{treatment} = 156$, $\sigma_{treatment} = 18.385$. Yes, there is significant evidence (*P*-value = 0.0000) that Malathion significantly reduces larvae per stem.

16.13 **a)**

```
   8 | 09 |
     | 10 |
 0 0 | 11 | 8
   4 | 12 | 0 6  6 9
     | 13 |
   0 | 14 |
```

b) We do not have strong evidence that breaking strengths are lower for strips buried longer (*P* = 0.1467).

16.14 **a)** Answers may vary.
b) The mean difference for the treatment group is 11.4 and for the control group is 8.25. The control group is skewed to the right.

```
        | 0 |
      6 | 0 | 455
      7 | 0 | 78
   2110 | 1 | 12
    533 | 1 | 4
      6 | 1 |
```

c) Minitab calculated the *P*-value for a one-tailed test at 0.0494. This is significant at the 0.05 level.

16.15 **a)** Yes, there appears to be a difference in species counts.

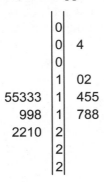

   b) H_0: There is no difference in the number of tree species in unlogged forests and logged forests. H_a: Logged forests have a significantly lower number of tree species.
   $W = 159$ with a *P*-value = 0.29. The results show a significantly lower number of tree species in logged forests.

16.16 The results are significant (*P*-value = 0.0000), and we can conclude that piano lessons increase spatial-temporal reasoning.

16.17 Yes, it appears that women are more concerned than men about food safety in restaurants. $W = 32267.5$ with a *P*-value = 0.0001.

16.18 The responses "srest" and "sfair" are not independent samples with different subjects. The responses are dependent on the subjects. We cannot conduct a two sample test using these results.

16.19 **a)** $\chi^2 = 3.955$, df = 4, *P*-value = 0.412. There is no strong evidence to indicate a relationship between income and city. **b)** No, there is no strong evidence to indicate a systematically higher income level in one city over the other. ($W = 56370$, *P*-value = 0.4949.)

16.20 Yes, there is strong evidence that Blue-B turns out darker than Blue-A. Every Blue-A value is higher than every Blue-B value. The test statistic is Z = 2.524 (Blue-A – Blue-B), and the one-sided *P*-value is 0.006.

16.21 **a)** Each day the air samples are measured in two locations. The unit here is the day. **b)** The test statistic for the Wilcoxon signed rank test is Z = 1.826, and the *P*-value is 0.034. There is statistical evidence that the kill room spore count distribution is systematically higher than the processing room spore count distribution, but the P-value is not as small as you might expect looking at the initial data.

16.22 **a)** The Normal quantile plot looks fairly good except for a slight deviation from the line at the top point (see the following page). However, since there are so few data points, even a small deviation from Normal is important. The t procedures would not be appropriate here. **b)** The Wilcoxon signed rank test gives a test statistic of Z = 1.825 and a *P*-value of 0.034 for a one-sided test using SPSS. There is statistical evidence to support the marketing claim that the distribution of new mobile phone software characters per second speed is systematically great than that of the old mobile phone software. (Matched pairs gives a test statistic of t = 2.111 and a *P*-value of 0.032 for a one-sided test.)

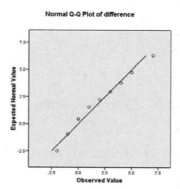

Normal Q-Q Plot of difference

16.23 Using SPSS, the test statistic is $Z = -0.595$, and the *P*-value is 0.552 for the two-sided test. There is not enough evidence to say that the distribution of battery life for MP3 players has a population median different from 6.5.

16.24 **a)** The differences (control − treatment) are: −0.01622, −0.01102, and −0.01607. Yes, it appears that the treated plots have faster growth. **b)** H_0: $\mu_D = 0$ and H_a: $\mu_D < 0$. $t = -8.45$ with df $= 2$ and *P*-value $= 0.007$. Yes, the mean difference between control and treatment is less than zero. **c)** Conducting a Wilcoxon signed rank test results in a *P*-value $= 0.091$. There is no strong evidence to indicate the difference is negative.

16.25 H_0: median increase$_{low} = 0$ H_a: median increase$_{low} > 0$. The Wilcoxon signed rank test results gives $\mu_{W+} = 5, \sigma_{W+} = 2.74$, $W^+ = 10$, *P*-value $= P(W^+ > 10) = P(Z > 1.642) \approx 0.05$. This test is just significant at the 0.05 level.

16.26 **a)** H_0: median$_{low}$ = median$_{medium}$ H_a: median$_{low}$ > median$_{medium}$, where the median is the difference resting − final. The proper test is the Wilcoxon rank sum test. **b)** $W = 39$ with *P*-value $= 0.0098$. There is significant evidence that the medium rate has a systematically higher difference than the low rate.

16.27 H_0: The distributions of the test scores are the same before and after a course. H_a: The scores are systematically higher after the course. $W^+ = 138.5$ with a *P*-value $= 0.002$. Conclude that the scores are higher after the course.

16.28

Score	1	1	2	2	2	3	3	3	3	3	3	6	6	6	6	6	**6**
Rank	1.5	1.5	4	4	4	8.5	8.5	8.5	8.5	8.5	8.5	15	15	15	15	15	**15**

$W^+ = 138.5$. The bold-faced column represents the one negative value.

16.29 Yes, there is evidence of a loss in vitamin C. $W^+ = 341$, *P*-value $= 0.000$.

16.30 $W^+ = 1552.5$ with a *P*-value $= 0.000$. The conclusion is that restaurant food is perceived to be safer than fair food.

16.31 *P*-value $= 0.206$. There is no strong evidence of a systematic difference between the perceived safety of fast food and fair food.

16.32 **a)** The data appears skewed to the right.

```
 9|  2578
10|  02455
11|  19
12|  2
```

b) $W^+ = 31$ with a *P*-value = 0.556. There is no strong evidence to indicate that the median $\neq$ 105.

16.33 $W^+ = 88$ with a *P*-value = 0.059. The evidence is not significant at the 0.05 level.

16.34 The 94.5% confidence level is (98.1, 110.5).

16.35 The 95% confidence level is (26.3, 38.6).

16.36 **a)** Graphical and numerical summaries are below. Nonfiction has the highest age of death in general, and poetry has the lowest age of death in general. Poetry is strongly left-skewed. Nonfiction is fairly symmetric except for a low outlier. Fiction is left-skewed. Fiction has a median of 73, poetry has a median of 68, and nonfiction has a median of 77.5. **b)** H_0: The age of death has the same distribution in all groups of writers, H_a: The age of death is systematically higher in some groups of writers than in others. SPSS gives a test statistic of $X^2 = 11.120$ and a *P*-value = 0.004. There is strong evidence that the age of death is systematically higher in some groups than in others.

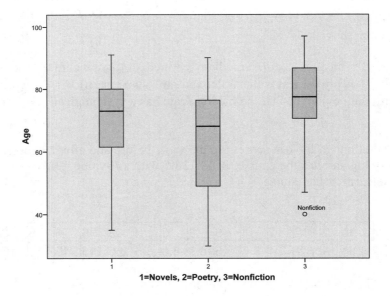

Descriptives

Age

	N	Mean	Std. Deviation	Std. Error	95% Confidence Interval for Mean Lower Bound	95% Confidence Interval for Mean Upper Bound	Minimum	Maximum
1	67	71.45	13.052	1.594	68.26	74.63	35	91
2	32	63.19	17.297	3.058	56.95	69.42	30	90
3	24	76.88	14.097	2.878	70.92	82.83	40	97
Total	123	70.36	15.104	1.362	67.66	73.05	30	97

16.37 **a)** See the graphical and numerical summaries below. The median for control is 0.219, the median for low dose is 0.216, and the median for high dose is 0.232. Control is right-skewed, low dose is fairly symmetric, and high dose is slightly right-skewed. The high dose distribution appears to be much higher than the other two distributions in general. There is quite a bit of overlap between the control and low dose distributions. **b)** H_0: The bone mineral densities have the same distribution in all treatment groups, H_a: The bone mineral densities are systematically higher in some treatment groups than in others. SPSS gives a test statistic of $X^2 = 9.116$ and a P-value $= 0.010$. There is evidence that the bone mineral densities are systematically higher in some treatment groups than in others.

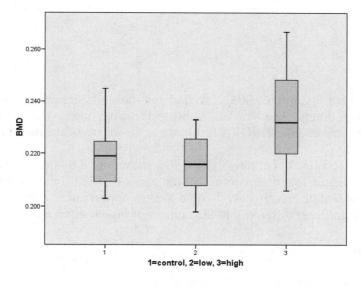

1=control, 2=low, 3=high

Descriptives

BMD

	N	Mean	Std. Deviation	Std. Error	95% Confidence Interval for Mean Lower Bound	95% Confidence Interval for Mean Upper Bound	Minimum	Maximum
1	15	.21887	.011587	.002992	.21245	.22528	.203	.245
2	15	.21593	.011511	.002972	.20956	.22231	.198	.233
3	15	.23507	.018771	.004847	.22467	.24546	.206	.267
Total	45	.22329	.016413	.002447	.21836	.22822	.198	.267

16.38 **b)** H_0: Consumer responses have the same distribution for each type of ad. H_a: Consumer responses are systematically higher in some groups than others. **c)** $H = 23.24$ (adjusted for ties) and *P*-value = 0.000. The conclusion is that the responses are higher for some of the ad types.

16.39 **a)** $H = 8.73$ with a *P*-value = 0.068. The results of this test are not significant at the 0.05 level. It appears that there is not a significant difference in vitamin C loss over time. **b)** Yes, the difference in *P*-values would lead to different conclusions.

16.40 **b)** Control   5 5
                              5 6
                              5 99
                              6 0011
                              6 2
                              6 5

Low jump   58 8
                              59 469
                              60 57
                              61
                              62
                              63 1258

High jump   62 2266
                              63 1
                              64 33
                              65 00
                              66
                              67 4

c) $H = 10.68$ with a *P*-value = 0.005. The findings show a systematically higher bone density in some groups over others. The Kruskal-Wallis tests the hypothesis that the distributions of bone density are the same and the ANOVA test looks at the means of the distributions.

16.41 **a)** The ANOVA tests the hypothesis that the four means are the same. The Kruskal-Wallis tests the hypothesis that the four distributions are the same. **b)** The Minitab output containing the medians and the *H* statistic is below. Lemon Yellow appears most effective. The results of the test indicate a significant difference in the number of insects attracted by each color.

Kruskal-Wallis Test

C9	N	Median	Ave Rank	Z
Blue	6	15.00	6.7	-2.33
Green	6	34.50	14.8	0.93
LYellow	6	46.50	21.2	3.47
White	6	15.50	7.3	-2.07
Overall	24		12.5	

H = 16.95 DF = 3 P = 0.001
H = 16.98 DF = 3 P = 0.001 (adjusted for ties)

16.42 Verify with above value of *H*.

16.43 **a)** 4.6, 6.54, 9.53, 16.09. **b)** 126, 126, 135, 110. The hypothesis tested is that the medians are all equal. **c)** $H = 5.63$ with a P-value = 0.131. The conclusion is that there is not a significant difference in the decay medians between the four lengths of time.

16.44 The responses for "srest" and "sfast" are dependent on the subject. They are not independent samples.

16.45 **a)** Unlogged

```
13 000
14
15 00
16
17
18 0
19 00
20 0
21 0
22 00
```

Logged(1)

```
0 2
0
0 7
0 8
1 11
1 23
1 4555
1
1 8
```

Logged(8)

```
0 4
0
0
1 0
1 2
1 455
1 7
1 88
```

The stemplots show many outliers for each of the distributions. The medians are 18.5, 12.5, and 15. **b)** $H = 9.44$ with a P-value = 0.009. The conclusion would be that there is a significant difference in medians between the three groups.

16.46 **a)** This relationship is shown in the data. 76% of those in the higher SES group have never smoked or are former smokers. Only 58% in the middle SES and 54% in the lower SES have never smoked or are former smokers. **b)** $\chi^2 = 18.51$ with df = 4 and P-value = 0.001. This indicates there is a significant relationship between SES groups and smoking status. **c)** $H = 6.88$ with a P-value = 0.032. Some SES classes smoke more heavily than others.

16.47 H_0: Right-handed people can turn knobs clockwise and counterclockwise at the same speed, H_a: Right-handed people turn knobs faster clockwise than counterclockwise. Use Wilcoxon signed rank test for matched pairs. P-value = 0.042. The results show a significant difference between the right-hand times and left-hand times. Right-hand times are faster than left-hand times

16.48 The 95% confidence interval for the median is (19, 24). Problem 7.13 gave the interval on μ as (19.98, 27.14).

16.49 **a)** A graph shows that the data are right-skewed with a large outlier. **b)** $W^+ = 378$ with P-value = 0.695. **c)** $t = 0.83$ with df = 49 and P-value = 0.41. The conclusions are the same. There is no reason to reject the hypothesis that the mean is equal to 20.

16.50 Yes, $W^+ = 154.5$ with a P-value = 0.034.

16.51 **a)**

Beef hot dogs	Meat hot dogs	Poultry hot dogs
8	8	8 67
9	9	9 49
10	10 7	10 226
11 1	11	11 3
12	12	12 9
13 1259	13 5689	13 25
14 1899	14 067	14 2346
15 2378	15 3	15 2
16	16	16
17 56	17 2359	17 0
18 146	18 2	18
19 00	19 015	19

The five-number summaries are:

Hot dog type	Minimum	Q_1	Median	Q_3	Maximum
Beef	111	139.5	152.5	179.8	190
Meat	107	138.5	153.0	180.5	195
Poultry	86	100.5	129.0	143.5	170

b) The distributions of the beef and meat hot dogs appear non-Normal. They are not symmetrical, have a gap in the data at 160 calories, and both have one low outlier. The poultry hot dogs have one high outlier. **c)** $H = 15.89$ with a P-value = 0.000. There is a systematically higher calorie content for the beef and meat hot dogs.

16.52 **a)** There is deviation from Normality both at the high end and at the low end. At the high end especially there are at least two outliers. The data looks very non-Normal.

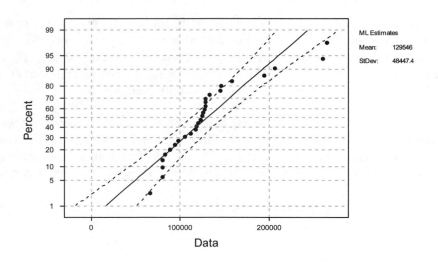

Normal Probability Plot for 3 Bedrooms

b) Use a two-sample t test. $H_0: \mu_1 = \mu_2$ and $H_a: \mu_1 \neq \mu_2$. $t = 3.08$ with df $= 12$ and P-value $= 0.0095$. There is a significant difference between the mean price of four-bedroom homes and the mean price of three-bedroom homes. **c)** H_o: The distribution of prices is the same. H_a: The distributions of prices are different. $H = 9.06$ with df $= 1$ and P-value $= 0.003$. There is a significant difference between the distribution of prices of four-bedroom homes and the distribution of prices of three bedroom homes.

16.53 a)

Beef hot dogs	Meat hot dogs	Poultry hot dogs
1	1 4	1
1	1	1
2	2	2
2 59	2	2
3 011223	3 3	3
3 778	3 67889	3 557889
4 024	4 002	4 23
4 7789	4 579	4
5	5 0014	5 112244
5 8	5	5 8
6 4	6	6

The five-number summaries are:

Hot dog type	Minimum	Q_1	Median	Q_3	Maximum
Beef	253	319.8	380.5	478.5	645
Meat	144	379.0	405.0	501.0	545
Poultry	357	379.0	430.0	535.0	588

b) The distributions all have outliers and the poultry sodium distribution appears to have two distinct groups of data. **c)** $H = 4.71$ with a P-value $= 0.095$. The evidence of systematically higher sodium content for some types of hot dogs is not strong.

16.54 a) With such small sample sizes, it is difficult to establish Normality; however, the sample standard deviations are all quite different. **b)** For meat: $H = 9.98$ with P-value $= 0.007$. For legumes: $H = 7.04$ with P-value $= 0.03$. For vegetables: $H = 5.6$ with P-value $= 0.061$. The median values show little difference in iron content between food cooked in aluminum pots and food cooked in clay pots.

16.55 The difference in iron content between food cooked in aluminum and clay pots was not significant for either meat or legumes. ($H = 1.32$ with P-value $= 0.251$ and $H = 2.08$ with P-value $= 0.149$, respectively.)

16.56 Yes, there appears to be a significant difference in iron content between the three food groups cooked in an iron pot. $H = 7.0$ with a P-value $= 0.03$.

Problems 16.57 through 16.60 cannot be done with the student version of Minitab because the data set is too large.

16.61 **a)** Let W_1 be the sum of the ranks from n_1. Let W_2 be the sum of the ranks from n_2.

$$W_1 + W_2 = \sum_{i=1}^{N} i.$$

$$\mu_{W_1} + \mu_{W_2} = \mu_{W_1 + W_2} = \mu_{\sum_{i=1}^{N} i} = \sum_{i=1}^{N} i. \quad \sum_{i=1}^{N} i = \frac{n_1(N+1)}{2} + \frac{n_2(N+1)}{2} = \frac{N(N+1)}{2}.$$

b) For N = 27, $(27 \times 28)/2 = 378$. **c)** $(62 \times 63)/2 = 1953$. $308 + 350 + 745 + 550 = 1953$.

Chapter 17: Logistic Regression

17.1 Exclusive territory: proportion = 0.7606, odds = 3.177. Non-exclusive territory: proportion = 0.536, odds = 1.155.

17.2 Men: proportion = 0.1076, odds = 0.1206. Women: proportion = 0.2128, odds = 0.2703.

17.3 1.156, 0.144.

17.4 Men: −2.1158, Women: −1.3082.

17.5 $b_0 = 0.143$, $b_1 = 1.013$. log(ODDS) = 0.143 + 1.013x. The odds ratio of exclusive territories to non-exclusive is 2.754.

17.6 $b_0 = -2.1158$, $b_1 = 0.8079$. log(ODDS) = −2.1158 + 0.8079x. The odds ratio of women label users to men label users is 2.243.

17.7 $$\frac{ODDS_{x+1}}{ODDS_x} = \frac{e^{-13.71}e^{2.25(x+1)}}{e^{-13.71}e^{2.25x}} = \frac{e^{2.25x}e^{2.25}}{e^{2.25x}} = e^{2.25} = 9.49.$$

17.8 β_0: −1.586, 0.0267. β_1: 0.3617, 0.0388. The estimate of the odds ratio of men to women is 1.436 with a 95% confidence interval of (1.33, 1.549).

17.9 log (ODDS) = 0.1431 + 1.0127x, where x = 1 if the franchise has an exclusive territory and x = 0 otherwise. The odds ratio of exclusive territories to nonexclusive territories is 2.75 with a 95% confidence interval of (1.19, 6.36).

17.10 log (ODDS) = −2.1158 + 0.8079x, where x = 1 for women and x = 0 for men. The odds ratio of female label users to male label users is 2.24 with a 95% confidence interval of (1.38, 3.65).

17.11 (2.3485, 3.8691).

17.12 Verify.

17.13 Verify.

17.14 **a)** The null hypothesis must have the parameter (the population slope), not the estimated slope: $H_0 : \beta_1 = 0$. **b)** There is no error term in our logistic regression model. **c)** The multiple logistic regression test would be $H_0 : \beta_1 = \beta_2 = \beta_3 = \beta_4 = \beta_5 = 0$ using a chi-square test statistic with 5 degrees of freedom.

17.15 **a)** The odds of an event is the probability of the event divided by one minus the probability of the event (or the probability of success divided by the probability of failure). **b)** No, the odds of the event is increased by $e^3 = 20.1$ when the explanatory variable increases by 1. **c)** The intercept corresponds to the odds of the event when x = 0.

17.16   **a)** Testing each variable, one at a time, we would use a null hypothesis of $H_0 : \beta_i = 0$ and
an alternative hypothesis of $H_a : \beta_i \neq 0$. **b)** The significance tests associated with the Wald
Z statistic here show that as long as $Z > 1.96$ (for a 5% significance level), we will reject the
null hypothesis. Therefore, the null hypothesis would be rejected for the coefficient for
reader age, model sex, and women's magazines. Only the coefficient for men's magazine
would not have the null hypothesis rejected. **c)** The ads are less likely to be sexual when
aimed at mature adults. Ads are less likely to be sexual when the model sex is male. Ads are
more likely to be sexual in men's magazines and less likely to be sexual in women's
magazines. (Note that the table is given in terms of ads being "not sexual," but this part of
the question is asking in terms of ads being "sexual.") **d)** (Including men's magazines in the
model even though its coefficient is not in the model) The model is:

$$\log\left(\frac{p}{1-p}\right) = -2.32 + 0.50x_{age} + 1.31x_{sex} - 0.05x_{men} + 0.45x_{women}$$

17.17   **a)** The confidence intervals for the odds ratios are related to testing the null hypothesis that
the odds ratio = 1 vs. the two-sided alternative. If the confidence interval contains 1, the null
hypothesis should not be rejected. **b)** For reader age, model sex, and women's magazines 1
is outside the confidence interval, and therefore the null hypothesis should be rejected. Only
the confidence interval for men's magazines contains 1, and therefore we would not reject the
null hypothesis for this odds ratio. **c)** The odds ratio confidence intervals show that men's
magazines has no effect on the probability that an ad will be not sexual. All the other
variables do have an effect on the probability that an ad will not be sexual. The confidence
interval for the odds ratio and the Wald test yield the same results. It is generally easier to
explain the results using odds ratios than the coefficients from the model though.

17.18   **a)** 0.60. **b)** 3 to 2. **c)** 0.40. **d)** 2 to 3. **e)** The results are reciprocals of each other.

17.19   **a)** 0.80, 4 to 1. **b)** 0.69, 2.23. **c)** 1.84.

17.20   **a)** 1.3863, 0.8020. **b)** 0.7911, 0.609. **c)** $e^{0.609} = 1.84$.

17.21   **a)** (−0.047, 1.265). **b)** (0.95, 3.54). **c)** There does not seem to be a difference in the
proportions of high tech companies and non-high tech companies that offer stock options.

17.22   The analysis stays the same for the estimates until we get to the inference portion. Because
the sample sizes increased, the standard error decreased. This results in the confidence
intervals for both β_1 and the odds show significant results. The 95% confidence interval for
β_1 is (0.1453, 1.0727) and for the odds ratio is (1.16, 2.92).

17.23   **a)** 0.32. **b)** 0.47 or approximately 1 to 2. **c)** 0.68. **d)** 2.13 or approximately 2 to 1. **e)** They are
reciprocals of each other.

17.24   **a)** log(ODDS) = −2.6293 + 2.6865x. **b)** The *P*-value for the significance test shows that there
is strong evidence that the slope is not equal to 0. **c)** (4.87, 44.27).

17.25   **a)** proportion = 0.0165, odds = 0.0168 or approximately 2 to 100. **b)** proportion = 0.0078,
odds = 0.0079. **c)** 2.12. Men with high-blood pressure are 2.12 times more likely to die of
cardiovascular disease than men with low-blood pressure.

17.26 **a)** (0.2452, 1.2558). **b)** $\chi^2 = 8.4681$. *P*-value = 0.004.

17.27 **a)** 2.12, (1.28, 3.51).

17.28 **a)** proportion = 0.80, odds = 4 to 1. **b)** proportion = 0.40, odds = 0.67. **c)** 5.97.

17.29 **a)** (1.0946, 2.5396). **b)** 24.30, *P*-value = 0.000. **c)** A female reference is 6.15 times more likely to a juvenile reference than a male reference is juvenile.

17.30 **a)** 6.15, (2.99, 12.67). **b)** The confidence interval shows that the odds are significantly greater than one.

17.31 **a)** log(ODDS) = –4.2767 + 1.3504*x*. **b)** For a binomial distribution, we would assume that each employee is an independent trial and each employee has the same chance of being terminated. This may not be realistic because the employee's performance is likely to play a role in their termination. **c)** 3.86, (1.72, 8.67). An employee that is over 40 years old is 3.86 times more likely to be terminated than an employee that is 40 or younger. The confidence interval on the odds estimate is shows that the odds are significantly greater than 1. **d)** You can also incorporate performance evaluations as an explanatory variable by creating a multiple logistic regression model.

17.32 The odds ratio of orders filled in 5 days or less before improvement and orders filled in 5 days or less after improvement are 47.25 with a 95% confidence interval of (26.01, 85.83). This is strong evidence that there is a true improvement.

17.33 log(ODDS) = –0.0282 + 0.6393*x*. $\chi^2 = 48.30$ with a *P*-value = 0.000. The odds ratio estimate is 1.90. There are significantly greater odds for a college graduate to use the Internet to make travel arrangements than a non-college graduate.

17.34 log(ODDS) = 0.033 + 0.604*x*. $\chi^2 = 5.56$ with a *P*-value = 0.000. The odds ratio estimate is 1.83. There are significantly greater odds for someone with an income greater than or equal to $50,000 to use the Internet to make travel arrangements than those who make less.

17.35 log(ODDS) = –1.804 + 1.136*x*. $\chi^2 = 5.29$ with a *P*-value = 0.000. The odds ratio estimate is 3.11. There are significantly greater odds for a male who died in a bicycle accident to test positive for alcohol than a female who died in a bicycle accident.

17.36 **a)** Logistic regression requires that each variable have only 2 options (0 or 1). **b)** In the results from the hypothesis testing in Exercise 17.16, we found that an ad is more likely to be "not sexual" in women's magazines than in general magazines and less likely to be "not sexual" in men's magazines. (Or phrased in terms of an ad being "sexual," more likely in men's magazines than in general magazines and less likely in women's magazines than in general magazines.) Therefore the data do support the idea that the sexual content expressed in the model dress varies by the magazine readership. **c)** The model (from Exercise 17.16) in general is:

$$\log\left(\frac{p}{1-p}\right) = -2.32 + 0.50x_{age} + 1.31x_{sex} - 0.05x_{men} + 0.45x_{women}$$

Magazine readership	x_{men}	x_{women}	$\log\left(\dfrac{p}{1-p}\right)$
Men	1	0	$-2.37 + 0.50x_{age} + 1.31x_{sex}$
Women	0	1	$-1.87 + 0.50x_{age} + 1.31x_{sex}$
General	0	0	$-2.32 + 0.50x_{age} + 1.31x_{sex}$

17.37   Verify.

17.38   **a)** See the table below.

Division	**I**	**II**	**III**
# who gamble	966	621	998
# who do not gamble	4653	2336	3091

b) Division I has coding $x_{II} = 0$ and $x_{III} = 0$, Division II has coding $x_{II} = 1$ and $x_{III} = 0$, and Division III has coding $x_{II} = 0$ and $x_{III} = 1$. **c)** The multiple logistic regression model is

$$\log\left(\frac{p}{1-p}\right) = -1.572 + 0.247x_{II} + 0.442x_{III}.$$ The test of $H_0 : \beta_{II} = \beta_{III} = 0$ has a chi-

square test statistic of 76.440 with 2 degrees of freedom and a *P*-value close to 0, so at least one of the division explanatory variables can be used to predict the odds of a student-athlete gambling. Both the variables' coefficients are significantly different from 0 (very small *P*-values for the Wald tests). (See the SPSS output below.)

Omnibus Tests of Model Coefficients

		Chi-square	df	Sig.
Step 1	Step	76.440	2	.000
	Block	76.440	2	.000
	Model	76.440	2	.000

Variables in the Equation

		B	S.E.	Wald	df	Sig.	Exp(B)	95.0% C.I.for EXP(B) Lower	Upper
Step 1a	xII	.247	.057	18.588	1	.000	1.280	1.144	1.433
	xIII	.442	.051	75.716	1	.000	1.555	1.408	1.718
	Constant	-1.572	.035	1977.031	1	.000	.208		

a. Variable(s) entered on step 1: xII, xIII.

17.39   **a)** See the table below. **b)** See the scatterplot on the next page. The trend is extremely linear. **c)** If simple linear regression is used, the fit is extremely good with an $R^2 = 99.5\%$. The equation of the line is $\hat{y} = -1.784 + 0.221x_{division}$.

Division	x_{II}	x_{III}	$\log\left(\dfrac{p}{1-p}\right)$	Estimated $\dfrac{p}{1-p}$
I	0	0	-1.572	0.208
II	1	0	-1.325	0.266
III	0	1	-1.130	0.323

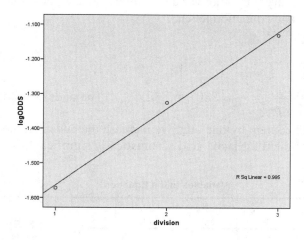

Model Summary

Model	R	R Square	Adjusted R Square	Std. Error of the Estimate
1	.998[a]	.995	.991	.021229

a. Predictors: (Constant), division

Coefficients[a]

Model		Unstandardized Coefficients		Standardized Coefficients	t	Sig.
		B	Std. Error	Beta		
1	(Constant)	-1.784	.032		-55.025	.012
	division	.221	.015	.998	14.722	.043

a. Dependent Variable: logODDS

17.40 **a)** The model is $\log\left(\dfrac{p}{1-p}\right) = -4.277 + 1.350 x_{over40}$ (with $x_{over40} = 0$ if not over 40, $x_{over40} = 1$ if over 40). The coefficient for x_{over40} is significantly different from 0. If a person is not over 40, $\log\left(\dfrac{p}{1-p}\right)$ is -4.277 with an estimated odds ratio of 0.0139. If a person is over 40, $\log\left(\dfrac{p}{1-p}\right)$ is -2.927 with an estimated odds ratio of 0.0536.

Variables in the Equation

		B	S.E.	Wald	df	Sig.	Exp(B)	95.0% C.I.for EXP(B) Lower	Upper
Step 1^a	over40	1.350	.413	10.692	1	.001	3.859	1.718	8.669
	Constant	-4.277	.381	126.275	1	.000	.014		

a. Variable(s) entered on step 1: over40.

b) Answers will vary, but other variables might include performance ratings, years of service to the company, and education level.

Case Study 17.1

Lactic: The model is $\log\left(\frac{p}{1-p}\right) = -10.780 + 6.332x_{lactic}$. The odds ratio for b_{lactic} is 562.278. If we increase the lactic acid content by one unit, we increase the odds that the cheese will be acceptable by 562.278. The coefficient for lactic acid is statistically significant.

Variables in the Equation

		B	S.E.	Wald	df	Sig.	Exp(B)	95.0% C.I.for EXP(B) Lower	Upper
Step 1^a	Lactic	6.332	2.453	6.662	1	.010	562.240	4.590	68874.866
	Constant	-10.780	3.975	7.353	1	.007	.000		

a. Variable(s) entered on step 1: Lactic.

H2S: The model is $\log\left(\frac{p}{1-p}\right) = -7.279 + 0.940x_{H2S}$. The odds ratio for b_{H2S} is 2.600. If we increase the H2S content by one unit, we increase the odds that the cheese will be acceptable by 2.600. The coefficient for H2S is statistically significant.

Variables in the Equation

		B	S.E.	Wald	df	Sig.	Exp(B)	95.0% C.I.for EXP(B) Lower	Upper
Step 1^a	H2S	.940	.344	7.451	1	.006	2.560	1.303	5.027
	Constant	-7.279	2.522	8.332	1	.004	.001		

a. Variable(s) entered on step 1: H2S.

Lactic and H2S: The model is $\log\left(\frac{p}{1-p}\right) = -11.718 + 3.777x_{lactic} + 0.735x_{H2S}$. The chi-square test for logistic regression has a test statistic of 16.192 with 2 degrees of freedom and a *P*-value close to zero, so at least one of these explanatory variables can be used to predict the odds that the cheese is acceptable. The tests for the individual coefficients at the 5% level shows that neither of these explanatory variables adds significant predictive ability once the other one is already in the model.

Omnibus Tests of Model Coefficients

		Chi-square	df	Sig.
Step 1	Step	16.192	2	.000
	Block	16.192	2	.000
	Model	16.192	2	.000

Variables in the Equation

		B	S.E.	Wald	df	Sig.	Exp(B)	95.0% C.I.for EXP(B)	
								Lower	Upper
Step 1a	Lactic	3.777	2.596	2.116	1	.146	43.679	.269	7084.337
	H2S	.735	.387	3.612	1	.057	2.085	.977	4.447
	Constant	-11.718	4.437	6.973	1	.008	.000		

a. Variable(s) entered on step 1: Lactic, H2S.

Lactic and Acetic: The model is $\log\left(\dfrac{p}{1-p}\right) = -16.558 + 5.257 x_{lactic} + 1.309 x_{acetic}$. The chi-square test for logistic regression has a test statistic of 12.877 with 2 degrees of freedom and a P-value of 0.002, so at least one of these explanatory variables can be used to predict the odds that the cheese is acceptable. The tests for the individual coefficients at the 5% level shows that lactic acid adds significant predictive ability when acetic acid is already in the model, but the same cannot be said of acetic acid when lactic acid is already in the model.

Omnibus Tests of Model Coefficients

		Chi-square	df	Sig.
Step 1	Step	12.877	2	.002
	Block	12.877	2	.002
	Model	12.877	2	.002

Variables in the Equation

		B	S.E.	Wald	df	Sig.	Exp(B)	95.0% C.I.for EXP(B)	
								Lower	Upper
Step 1a	Lactic	5.257	2.500	4.421	1	.036	191.939	1.428	25795.224
	Acetic	1.309	1.288	1.033	1	.309	3.702	.297	46.181
	Constant	-16.558	7.422	4.977	1	.026	.000		

a. Variable(s) entered on step 1: Lactic, Acetic.

H2S and Acetic: The model is $\log\left(\dfrac{p}{1-p}\right) = -12.847 + 1.096 x_{acetic} + 0.830 x_{H2S}$. The chi-square test for logistic regression has a test statistic of 14.226 with 2 degrees of freedom and a P-value of 0.001, so at least one of these explanatory variables can be used to predict the odds that the cheese is acceptable. The tests for the individual coefficients at the 5% level shows that H2S adds significant predictive ability when acetic acid is already in the model, but the same cannot be said of acetic acid when H2S is already in the model.

Omnibus Tests of Model Coefficients

		Chi-square	df	Sig.
Step 1	Step	14.226	2	.001
	Block	14.226	2	.001
	Model	14.226	2	.001

Variables in the Equation

		B	S.E.	Wald	df	Sig.	Exp(B)	95.0% C.I.for EXP(B)	
								Lower	Upper
Step 1[a]	Acetic	1.096	1.382	.629	1	.428	2.993	.199	44.926
	H2S	.830	.367	5.109	1	.024	2.294	1.117	4.712
	Constant	-12.847	7.868	2.666	1	.102	.000		

a. Variable(s) entered on step 1: Acetic, H2S.

Case Study 17.2

The chi-square test for multiple logistic regression has a test statistic of 37.197 with 5 degrees of freedom and a *P*-value close to 0, so we conclude that one or more of these explanatory variables can be used to predict the odds that the GPA will be at least 3.0. The model is

$$\log\left(\frac{p}{1-p}\right) = -7.373 + 0.343x_{HSM} + 0.225x_{HSS} + 0.019x_{HSE} + 0.001x_{SATM} + 0.003x_{SATV}$$

The tests for the individual coefficients shows that, at the 5% level, only HSM adds significant predictive ability once the other variables are already in the model. (At the 10% significance level, HSS would also add significant predictive ability.)

In Case 11.2, HSM had the only coefficient significantly different from 0. This agrees with the results from the multiple logistic regression.

Omnibus Tests of Model Coefficients

		Chi-square	df	Sig.
Step 1	Step	37.197	5	.000
	Block	37.197	5	.000
	Model	37.197	5	.000

Variables in the Equation

		B	S.E.	Wald	df	Sig.	Exp(B)	95.0% C.I.for EXP(B)	
								Lower	Upper
Step 1[a]	HSM	.343	.142	5.834	1	.016	1.409	1.067	1.861
	HSS	.225	.129	3.055	1	.080	1.252	.973	1.611
	HSE	.019	.129	.022	1	.883	1.019	.792	1.312
	SATM	.001	.002	.106	1	.745	1.001	.996	1.005
	SATV	.003	.002	2.280	1	.131	1.003	.999	1.007
	Constant	-7.373	1.477	24.926	1	.000	.001		

a. Variable(s) entered on step 1: HSM, HSS, HSE, SATM, SATV.

Case Study 17.3

For the combined data set (not separating out patients by condition and using Hospital A = 0, Hospital B = 1), the model is $\log\left(\dfrac{p}{1-p}\right) = -3.476 - 0.416 x_{hospital}$, and the coefficient for hospital is not significantly different from 0. The 95% confidence interval for the odds ratio for hospital is (0.379, 1.149).

Variables in the Equation

		B	S.E.	Wald	df	Sig.	Exp(B)	95.0% C.I.for EXP(B)	
								Lower	Upper
Step 1ᵃ	hospital	-.416	.283	2.157	1	.142	.660	.379	1.149
	Constant	-3.476	.128	738.408	1	.000	.031		

a. Variable(s) entered on step 1: hospital.

When the patient condition is also taken into account with hospital (using Poor Condition = 0, Good Condition = 1), the chi-square test for multiple logistic regression has a test statistic of 21.019 with 2 degrees of freedom and a *P*-value close to 0, so there is evidence that at least one of the explanatory variables can be used to predict the odds that a patient will die. The coefficient for hospital is not significantly different from 0, which means only condition adds significant predictive ability once hospital is already in the model.

The 95% confidence interval for the odds ratio for hospital is (0.624, 2.086) and for condition is (0.150, 0.530).

When only hospital is used, the coefficient for hospital is negative. When hospital and condition are used, the coefficient for hospital is positive. For the hospital-only results, switching from hospital A to hospital B decreases a patient's chance of survival. For the hospital and condition are used, switching from hospital A to hospital B increases a patient's chance of survival.

Omnibus Tests of Model Coefficients

		Chi-square	df	Sig.
Step 1	Step	21.019	2	.000
	Block	21.019	2	.000
	Model	21.019	2	.000

Variables in the Equation

		B	S.E.	Wald	df	Sig.	Exp(B)	95.0% C.I.for EXP(B)	
								Lower	Upper
Step 1ᵃ	hospital	.132	.308	.184	1	.668	1.141	.624	2.086
	condition	-1.266	.322	15.480	1	.000	.282	.150	.530
	Constant	-3.241	.133	596.304	1	.000	.039		

a. Variable(s) entered on step 1: hospital, condition.

Case Study 17.4

		Zip code	47904	47906
Price		Mean	94,900	194,158
		St.dev.	31,030.91	96,794.11
		Median	87,450	167,500
		Minimum	52,000	63,900
		Maximum	199,500	625,000
Square Feet		Mean	1308.48	2076.32
		St.dev.	428.903	671.730
		Median	1290	2000
		Minimum	698	936
		Maximum	2296	4840
Bedrooms		Mean	2.73	3.57
		St.dev.	0.694	0.611
		Median	3.00	4.00
		Minimum	1	2
		Maximum	5	5

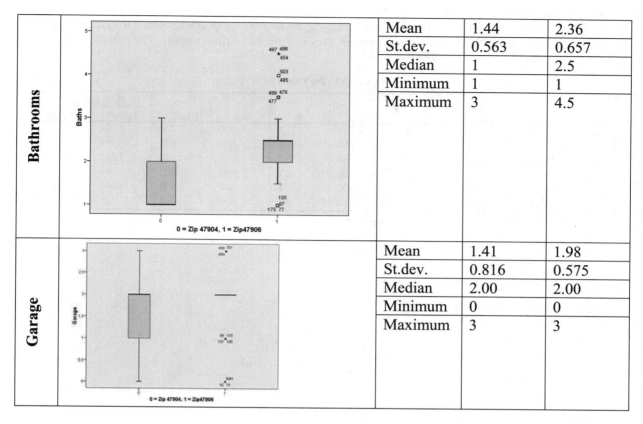

	Mean	1.44	2.36
Bathrooms	St.dev.	0.563	0.657
	Median	1	2.5
	Minimum	1	1
	Maximum	3	4.5
	Mean	1.41	1.98
Garage	St.dev.	0.816	0.575
	Median	2.00	2.00
	Minimum	0	0
	Maximum	3	3

Using all 5 explanatory variables, the chi-square test for the multiple logistic regression has a test statistic of 106.170, 5 degrees of freedom, and a P-value close to 0, so at least one of the explanatory variables can be used to predict the odds that a house is in the 47906 zip code instead of 47904.

Omnibus Tests of Model Coefficients

		Chi-square	df	Sig.
Step 1	Step	106.170	5	.000
	Block	106.170	5	.000
	Model	106.170	5	.000

The model is:

$$\log\left(\frac{p}{1-p}\right) = -11.750 + 6.56 \times 10^{-5} x_{price} - 0.003 x_{sqft} + 2.706 x_{bed} + 0.324 x_{bath} + 0.291 x_{garage}$$

When looking at the individual coefficients, price, square feet, and bedrooms have coefficients significantly different from 0, but bathrooms and garages do not. (The coefficient for Price is not actually 0 but is so small that SPSS doesn't show enough decimal places in this output. The actual coefficient is 6.56×10^{-5}.)

Variables in the Equation

		B	S.E.	Wald	df	Sig.	Exp(B)	95.0% C.I.for EXP(B)	
								Lower	Upper
Step 1[a]	Price	.000	.000	16.793	1	.000	1.000	1.000	1.000
	SqFt	-.003	.001	6.818	1	.009	.997	.995	.999
	BedRooms	2.706	.784	11.916	1	.001	14.976	3.221	69.628
	Baths	.324	.641	.256	1	.613	1.383	.394	4.854
	Garage	.291	.457	.406	1	.524	1.338	.546	3.275
	Constant	-11.750	2.636	19.876	1	.000	.000		

a. Variable(s) entered on step 1: Price, SqFt, BedRooms, Baths, Garage.

Chapter 18: Bootstrap Methods and Permutation Tests

Tim Hesterberg, with contributions from Michael Fligner and William Notz.

PREFACE

This chapter uses computionally demanding resampling procedures, for which the use of a computer is critical. We used S-PLUS while writing this chapter, and give commands below for performing the analyses in S-PLUS. Our goal is to make it as easy as possible for you, and students, to focus on the statistical aspects of this chapter. You may use S-PLUS for this chapter even if you use other software for other chapters.

To use S-PLUS you need:

a copy of S-PLUS: there is a free version for students, see `http://elms03.e-academy.com/splus`. Instructors see `http://www.insightful.com`

the S+Resample package: for this and the following items, see `http://www.insightful.com/bootstrap` and `http://www.whfreeman.com`

the PBS2data package, containing datasets and help documents.

In some cases exercises ask you to judge whether a particular procedure is appropriate, then to perform that procedure if appropriate. In the example code below, we show how to perform the procedure, whether or not it is appropriate.

Note to instructors:

Your answers to most questions in this chapter may differ slightly from ours due to random sampling. Here we specify random number seeds to make results reproducible, but we do not do that in materials we supply to students, because we want them to experience randomness.

```
> library(PBS2data)  # load the data
> library(resample)  # load the resample library
> trellis.settings <- trellis.settings # my copy, so I can modify colors
> trellis.settings$strip.background <- list(col = rep(0, 7))
> trellis.settings$plot.symbol$col <- 1
```

18.1

a and b Student answers will vary.

c Here is a stemplot for 200 resamples (students do 20):

```
 0 : 677889999
 1 : 000011111122223444444455555566678889999
 2 : 000001122236
 3 : 4678899
 4 : 000111111112222222233333344444444555555555555555566666777777888888888899
 5 : 001122455579
 6 : 899
 7 : 00112223334445566667777788899
 8 : 00001234
 9 :
10 : 122244467779
11 : 002
12 :
13 : 4
```

d The standard error for 1000 resamples is 2.8

This is normally done by hand, but the following commands would work:

```
> boot1 <- bootstrap(Exercise18.001, mean, B = 20, seed = 0)
> stem(boot1$replicates)

N = 20   Median = 4.5175
Quartiles = 3.758333, 4.995

Decimal point is at the colon

Low:  1.15

  1 : 4
  2 : 23
  3 : 789
  4 : 05555668
  5 : 2
  6 : 9
  7 : 1

High: 7.74167 7.85833

> boot1   # The standard error is the printed "SE"

Call:
bootstrap(data = Exercise18.001, statistic = mean, B = 20, seed = 0)

Number of Replications: 20

Summary Statistics:
     Observed  Mean      Bias     SE
mean    4.463  4.464  0.0006667  1.884
```

18.2

a It is approximately normal, but with some positive skewness. This amount of skewness would not be a concern in raw data, but here it occurs in a bootstrap distribution, after the central limit theorem has already acted.

b 986

c 19609.9, 23517

```
> boot2 <- bootstrap(Exercise18.002, mean, seed = 0)
> plot(boot2)
> qqnorm(boot2)
> boot2  # the SE is printed

Call:
bootstrap(data = Exercise18.002, statistic = mean, seed = 0)

Number of Replications: 1000

Summary Statistics:
      Observed  Mean   Bias    SE
mean     21485 21506  20.98 986.1

> limits.percentile(boot2)

         2.5%       5%      95%  97.5%
mean  19609.9 19870.11 23155.63 23517
```

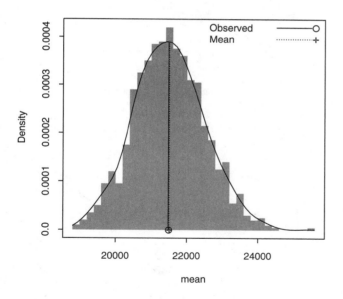

bootstrap : Exercise18.002 : mean

bootstrap : Exercise18.002 : mean

18.3

a See figures below.

b The distribution is symmetric and bell-shaped, and the quantile plot shows positive skewness. While positive skewness would not be a concern in raw data, here it occurs in a bootstrap distribution, after the central limit theorem has had a chance to work.

```
> Exercise18.003 # variable Spending
> hist(Exercise18.003$Spending)  # The usual way - specify which column
```

```
> hist(Exercise18.003)          # Shortcut - works if there is only one column
> qqnorm(Exercise18.003$Spending)# The usual way
> qqnorm(Exercise18.003)         # Shortcut - only works with library(PBS2data)
> boot3 <- bootstrap(Exercise18.003$Spending, mean, seed=0) # Usual
> boot3 <- bootstrap(Exercise18.003, mean, seed=0)          # Shortcut
> # The shortcuts work for some functions, but not others.
> plot(boot3)
> qqnorm(boot3)
```

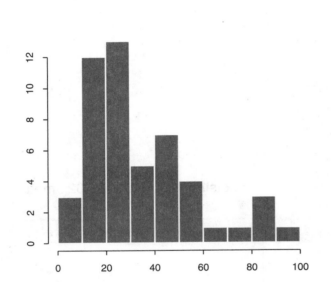

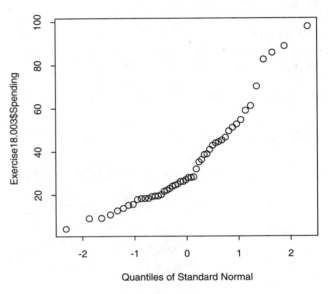

bootstrap : Exercise18.003 : mean

bootstrap : Exercise18.003 : mean

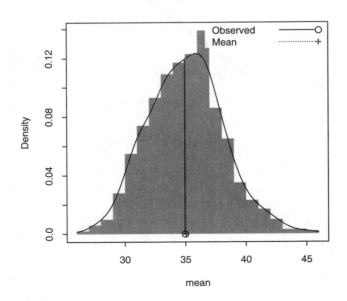

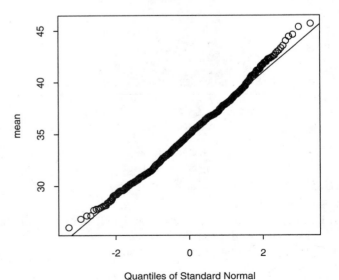

18.4

a See figures below.

b There is right skewness, but much less than for the data distribution.

```
> Exercise18.004 # variable Survival
> hist(Exercise18.004)
> qqnorm(Exercise18.004)
> boot4 <- bootstrap(Exercise18.004, mean, seed = 0)
> plot(boot4)
> qqnorm(boot4)
```

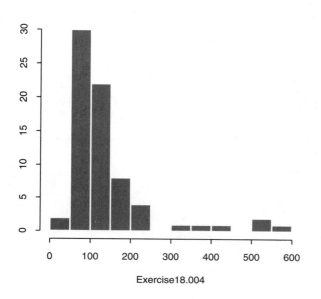

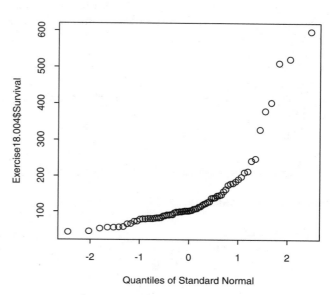

bootstrap : Exercise18.004 : mean

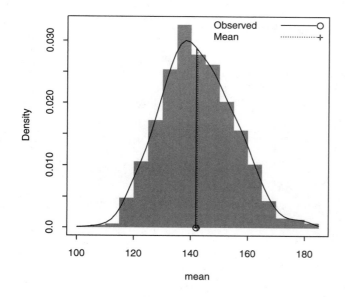

bootstrap : Exercise18.004 : mean

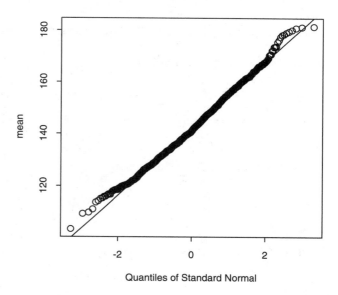

18.5

a The bootstrap distribution is roughly normal, but with positive skewness. The skewness is greater than for Exercise 18.3.

b The bootstrap standard error for Exercise 18.3 is 3.12, and for the data in this exercise the bootstrap standard error is 7.79. For a sample of size n, the standard error of the sample mean is $s/\sqrt{n}$, where s is the sample standard deviation. A smaller sample size will result in a larger standard error.

In addition, the standard deviation of the data is slightly larger in this Exercise (26.8) than in 18.3 (22.0).

```
> Exercise18.005 # Spending
> hist(Exercise18.005)
> qqnorm(Exercise18.005)
> boot5 <- bootstrap(Exercise18.005, mean, seed = 0)
> par(mfrow = c(2, 2))   # two rows and two columns of plots
> plot(boot5)
> qqnorm(boot5)
> plot(boot3)
> qqnorm(boot3)
> par(mfrow = c(1, 1))   # back to the usual single plot per page
> boot5


Call:
bootstrap(data = Exercise18.005, statistic = mean, seed = 0)

Number of Replications: 1000

Summary Statistics:
     Observed  Mean    Bias     SE
mean   34.06  33.64  -0.4208  7.791


> boot3


Call:
bootstrap(data = Exercise18.003, statistic = mean, seed = 0)

Number of Replications: 1000

Summary Statistics:
     Observed  Mean    Bias     SE
mean   34.94  35.02  0.07507  3.118


> stdev(Exercise18.005$Spending)


[1] 26.7727


> stdev(Exercise18.003$Spending)


[1] 22.02538
```

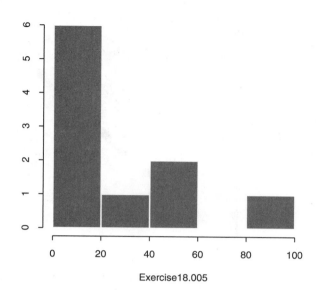

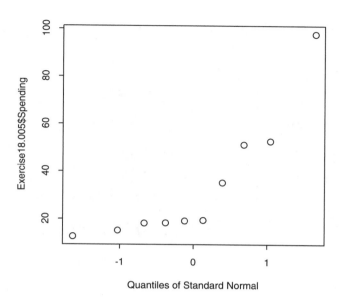

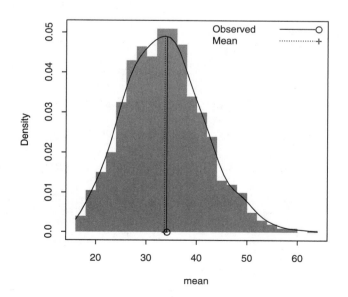

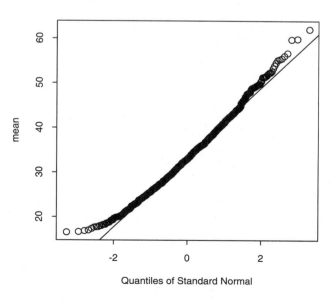

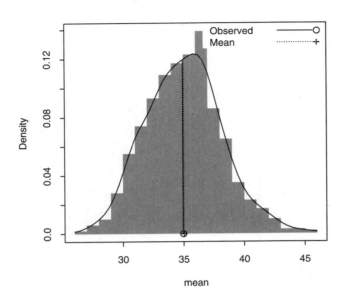

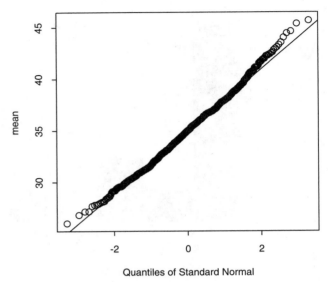

18.6

a This bootstrap distribution is less normal, with stronger right skewness.

b The bootstrap standard errors are 33.14 for these observations, and 12.82 for Exercise 18.4. For a sample of size n, the standard error of the sample mean is $s/\sqrt{n}$, where s is the sample standard deviation. A smaller sample size will result in a larger standard error.

In addition, the standard deviation of the data is larger in this Exercise (153) than in 18.4 (109).

```
> Exercise18.006 # Survival
> hist(Exercise18.006)
> qqnorm(Exercise18.006)
> boot6 <- bootstrap(Exercise18.006, mean, seed = 0)
> par(mfrow = c(2, 2))
> plot(boot6)
> qqnorm(boot6)
> plot(boot4)
> qqnorm(boot4)
> par(mfrow = c(1, 1))
> boot6

Call:
bootstrap(data = Exercise18.006, statistic = mean, seed = 0)

Number of Replications: 1000

Summary Statistics:
     Observed   Mean    Bias     SE
mean    169.3  168.9  -0.4205  33.14

> boot4

Call:
bootstrap(data = Exercise18.004, statistic = mean, seed = 0)
```

Number of Replications: 1000

Summary Statistics:
```
      Observed  Mean   Bias    SE
mean    141.8  142.3  0.4479  12.82
```

> *stdev(Exercise18.006$Survival)*

[1] 153.3702

> *stdev(Exercise18.004$Survival)*

[1] 109.2086

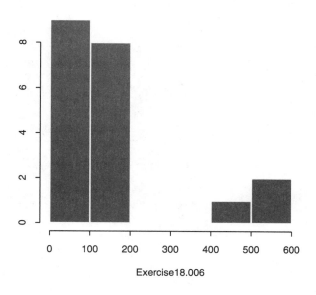

Exercise18.006

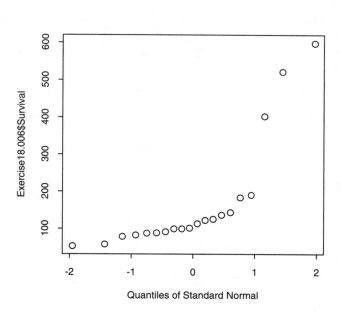

Quantiles of Standard Normal

bootstrap : Exercise18.006 : mean

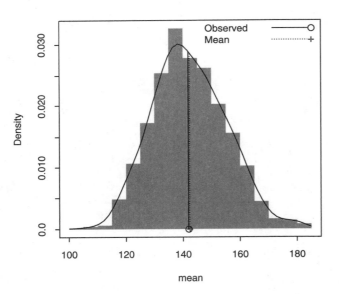

bootstrap : Exercise18.006 : mean

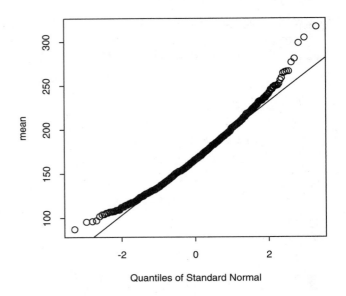

bootstrap : Exercise18.004 : mean

bootstrap : Exercise18.004 : mean

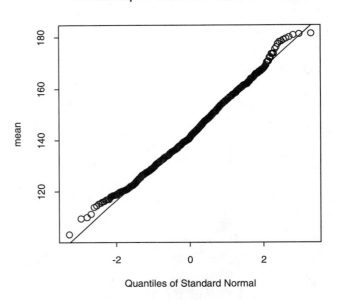

18.7

$s = 22.0$, so $s/\sqrt{n} = 3.11$. The bootstrap standard error in Exercise 18.3 is 3.12, which agrees with $s/\sqrt{n} = 3.11$.

```
> stdev(Exercise18.003$Spending)
```

```
[1] 22.02538
```

```
> stdev(Exercise18.003$Spending)/sqrt(50)
```

```
[1] 3.114859
```

```
> boot3
```

```
Call:
bootstrap(data = Exercise18.003, statistic = mean, seed = 0)
```

```
Number of Replications: 1000
```

```
Summary Statistics:
     Observed  Mean    Bias     SE
mean   34.94  35.02  0.07507  3.118
```

```
> stdev(boot3$replicates) # another way
```

```
[1] 3.118056
```

18.8

The estimated bias is 0.08 (this answer will vary randomly above or below zero, but should be close to zero). This is small compared to the standard error of 3.1. This indicates that the bias is small.

```
> boot3
```

```
Call:
bootstrap(data = Exercise18.003, statistic = mean, seed = 0)
```

```
Number of Replications: 1000
```

```
Summary Statistics:
     Observed  Mean    Bias     SE
mean   34.94  35.02  0.07507  3.118
```

```
> mean(boot3$replicates) - boot3$observed  # another way
```

```
     mean
 0.0750688
```

18.9

The estimated bias is 0.45 (this answer will vary randomly above or below zero, but should be close to zero). This is small compared to the standard error of 12.8. This indicates that the bias is small.

```
> boot4
```

```
Call:
bootstrap(data = Exercise18.004, statistic = mean, seed = 0)
```

```
Number of Replications: 1000
```

```
Summary Statistics:
     Observed  Mean   Bias     SE
mean   141.8  142.3  0.4479  12.82
```

```
> mean(boot4$replicates) - boot4$observed  # another way
```

```
     mean
 0.4479306
```

18.10

a c(28.7, 41.2)
b c(28.7, 41.2) The intervals are very similar.

```
> limits.t(boot3)


           2.5%        5%        95%     97.5%
mean 28.67125  29.71247  40.17753  41.21875


> t.test(Exercise18.003$Spending)


        One-sample t-Test

data:  Exercise18.003$Spending
t = 11.2188, df = 49, p-value = 0
alternative hypothesis:  mean is not equal to 0
95 percent confidence interval:
 28.68546 41.20454
sample estimates:
 mean of x
    34.945
```

18.11

a The 25% trimmed mean is 30.1, which is smaller than the sample mean of 34.9. If we examine the histogram of the data for the 50 we see that the data are right skewed. The trimmed mean eliminates much of the large right tail (i.e., the very large values that cause the sample mean to be large), and hence the trimmed mean is smaller than the sample mean.
b The 95% bootstrap t confidence interval for the 25% trimmed mean spending in the population of all shoppers is (23.7, 36.5)

```
> mean(Exercise18.003, trim = 0.25)


[1] 30.10385


> mean(Exercise18.003)


[1] 34.945


> hist(Exercise18.003)
> qqnorm(Exercise18.003)
> boot11 <- bootstrap(Exercise18.003, mean(Spending, trim = 0.25), seed = 0)
> limits.t(boot11)


            2.5%        5%       95%     97.5%
Param 23.73029  24.78808  35.41961  36.47741
```

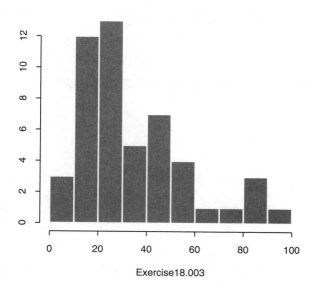

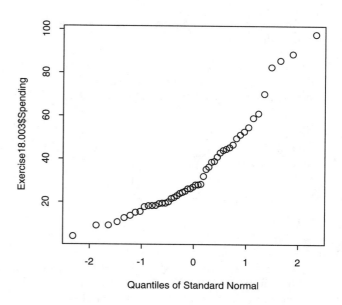

Exercise18.003

Quantiles of Standard Normal

18.12

The bootstrap distribution is not Normal; it has gaps, spikes, and a long right tail. The shape is not Normal so it is not appropriate to use a t interval which is based on Normal distributions.

```
> boot12 <- bootstrap(Exercise18.003, median, seed = 0)
> plot(boot12)
> qqnorm(boot12)
> qqnorm(boot12, pch = ".")=".") # this gives smaller points, easier to see duplicates
```

bootstrap : Exercise18.003 : median

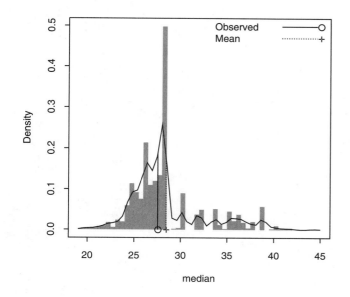

bootstrap : Exercise18.003 : median

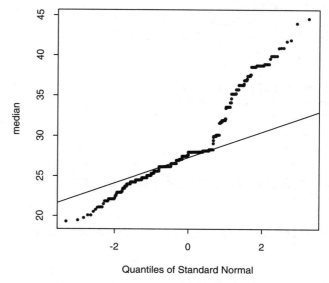

18.13

The formula-based standard error is 4.08. The bootstrap standard error in Example 18.7 is 4.052, which is close to the formula-based value.

```
> sqrt(stdev(ILEC$Time)^2/length(ILEC$Time) + stdev(CLEC$Time)^2/length(CLEC$Time))
```

```
[1] 4.08269
```

18.14

a 4.3

b Yes – the distribution appears to be very close to normal, with no appreciable bias.

c The bootstrap t interval calculated with the conservative rule for degrees of freedom is (1.01, 18.90), which is very
close to the formula t interval calculated with the conservative rule, (1.0, 18.9)

```
> Exercise18.014  # has columns score and group
> boot14 <- bootstrap2(Exercise18.014$score, mean, treatment = Exercise18.014$group,
+     seed = 0)
> boot14
```

```
Call:
bootstrap2(data = Exercise18.014$score, statistic = mean, treatment = Exercise18.014$group,
  seed = 0)

Number of Replications: 1000

Summary Statistics:
      Observed  Mean    Bias      SE
mean    9.954   9.979  0.02444  4.286
```

```
> plot(boot14, cex.main = 1)
> qqnorm(boot14, cex.main = 1)
> limits.t(boot14)
```

```
         2.5%       5%        95%     97.5%
mean 1.269243 2.722769 17.18613 18.63966
```

```
> boot14$observed + c(-1, 1) * qt(0.975, 20) * boot14$estimate$SE
```

```
[1]   1.012985 18.895917
```

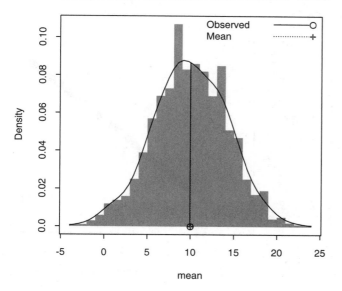

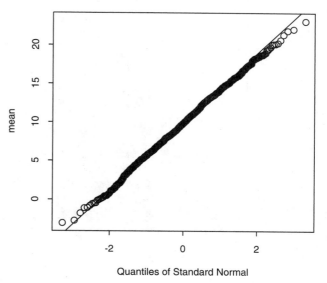

18.15

a Yes, the distribution appears to be quite close to Normal (the Normal quantile plot shows this better than the histogram does), with no appreciable bias.

b The observed difference is 0.902 and the standard error is SE = 0.113. The bootstrap t confidence interval is (0.67, 1.13).

c The two-sample t confidence interval reported on page 465 is (0.65, 1.15). This interval is just slightly wider than the bootstrap t confidence interval in part (b).

```
> Exercise18.015   # has columns status and ratio
> boot15 <- bootstrap2(Exercise18.015$ratio, mean, treatment = Exercise18.015$status,
+     seed = 0)
> plot(boot15, cex.main = 1)
> qqnorm(boot15, cex.main = 1)
> boot15

Call:
bootstrap2(data = Exercise18.015$ratio, statistic = mean, treatment = Exercise18.015$
  status, seed = 0)

Number of Replications: 1000

Summary Statistics:
      Observed   Mean      Bias       SE
mean     0.902  0.8997  -0.002224  0.1133


> limits.t(boot15)


           2.5%        5%      95%      97.5%
mean  0.6749981  0.7124441  1.09146  1.128906
```

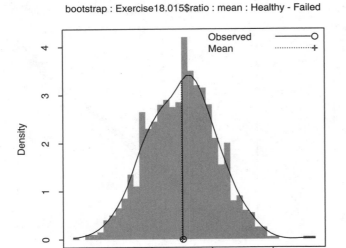

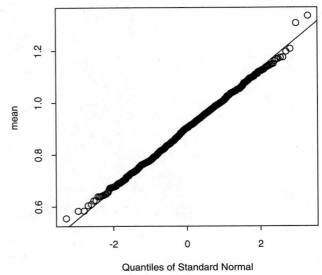

18.16

The standard deviation of a sample measures how spread a sample is. The standard error estimates how much a sample mean would vary, if you take the means of many samples from the same population. The standard error is smaller by a factor of $\sqrt{n}$.

18.17

a The two bootstrap distributions look similar.

b The bootstrap standard error of the mean is 45.0. In Example 18.5, the bootstrap standard error of the 25% trimmed mean is 16.83. We see that the bootstrap standard error of the mean is almost three times as large as the bootstrap standard error of the 25% trimmed mean. The bootstrap distribution for the mean has greater spread (the histogram covers a range from about 225 to 475) than the bootstrap distribution for the 25% trimmed mean (the histogram covers a range from about 200 to 300).

```
> boot17 <- bootstrap(Exercise18.017, mean, seed = 0)
> plot(boot17)
> qqnorm(boot17)
> boot17


Call:
bootstrap(data = Exercise18.017, statistic = mean, seed = 0)

Number of Replications: 1000

Summary Statistics:
     Observed Mean  Bias SE
mean    329.3  331 1.757 45
```

bootstrap : Exercise18.017 : mean

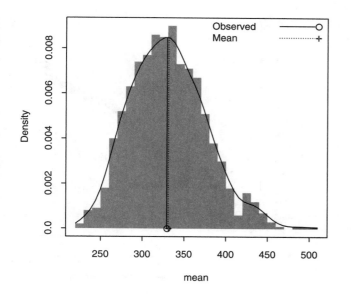

bootstrap : Exercise18.017 : mean

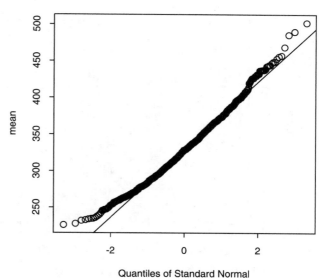

18.18

a 16.5

b The bootstrap distribution does not appear normal (it is bimodal, and has gaps).

```
> boot18 <- bootstrap(Exercise18.018, median, seed = 0)
> plot(boot18)
> qqnorm(boot18)
> boot18
```

```
Call:
bootstrap(data = Exercise18.018, statistic = median, seed = 0)

Number of Replications: 1000

Summary Statistics:
       Observed Mean   Bias    SE
median    244.9  242  -2.972 16.52
```

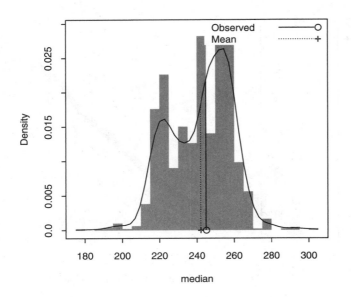

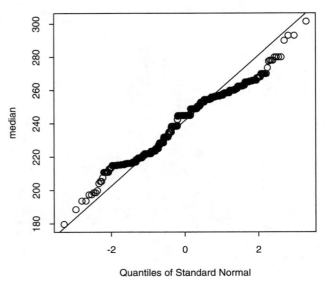

18.19

a There do not appear to be any significant departures from Normality. The histogram is centered at about 0 and the spread is approximately what we would expect for the N(0, 1) distribution.

b The standard error of the bootstrap mean is 0.128.

c Yes, the distribution appears very close to Normal, with no appreciable bias. The interval is (-0.129, 0.379).

```
> hist(Exercise18.019)
> qqnorm(Exercise18.019)
> boot19 <- bootstrap(Exercise18.019, mean, seed = 0)
> boot19


Call:
bootstrap(data = Exercise18.019, statistic = mean, seed = 0)

Number of Replications: 1000

Summary Statistics:
     Observed    Mean      Bias      SE
mean   0.1249  0.1234  -0.001474  0.1277


> plot(boot19)
> qqnorm(boot19)
> limits.t(boot19)


           2.5%          5%        95%       97.5%
mean  -0.1296459  -0.08786799  0.3376116  0.3793895
```

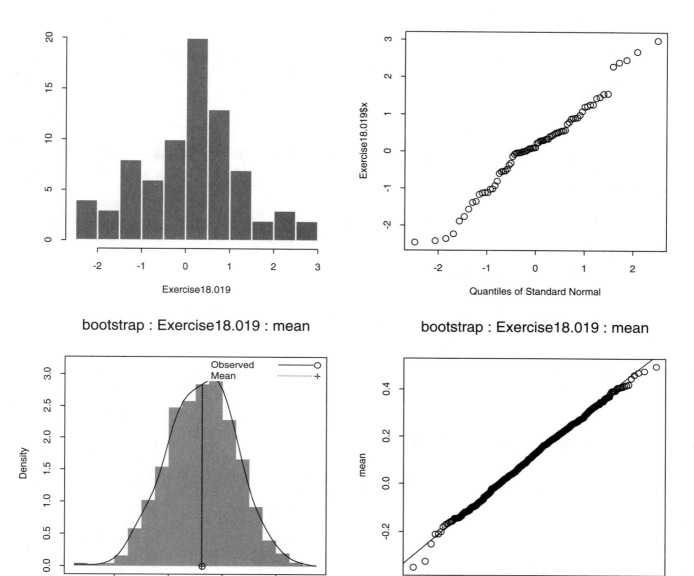

18.20

a The data have moderate right skewness, with median 350, mean 404, first and third quartiles 250 and 539, and range from 21 to 1103.

b For the trimmed mean – the bootstrap distribution shows substantial skewness. This amount of skewness would not be a worry in raw data, but here in a sampling distribution it translates directly into errors in coverage level or significance levels. (The example code shows how to call limits.t, even though it is not appropriate.)

For the median – not appropriate, distribution does not appear Normal.

```
> hist(Exercise18.020)
> qqnorm(Exercise18.020)
> summary(Exercise18.020)
```

```
        Salary
    Min.:   21.0
1st Qu.:  250.0
 Median:  350.0
   Mean:  404.2
3rd Qu.:  539.5
        Salary
   Max.:1103.0
```

```
> boot20 <- bootstrap(Exercise18.020, mean(Exercise18.020, trim = 0.25), seed = 0)
> plot(boot20)
> qqnorm(boot20)
> limits.t(boot20)
```

```
           2.5%        5%       95%      97.5%
Param  299.5907  309.7719  412.6797  422.8609
```

```
> boot20b <- bootstrap(Exercise18.020, median, seed = 0)
> plot(boot20b)
> qqnorm(boot20b)
> limits.t(boot20b)
```

```
            2.5%        5%       95%      97.5%
median  293.1456  302.5372  397.4628  406.8544
```

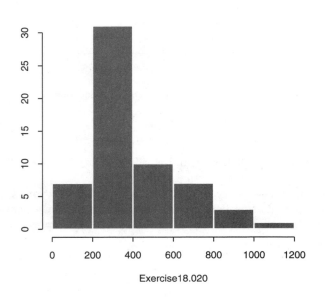

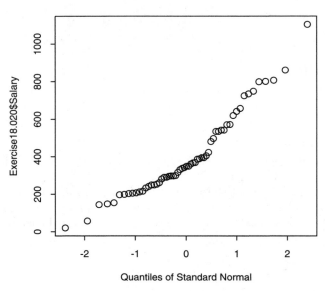

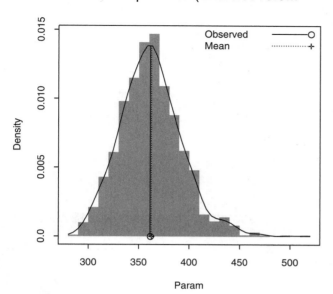

bootstrap : mean(Exercise18.0...

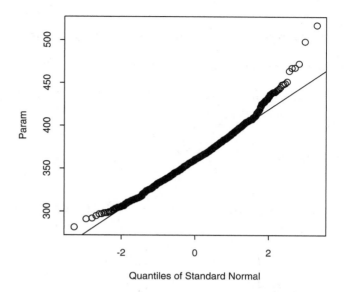

bootstrap : mean(Exercise18.0...

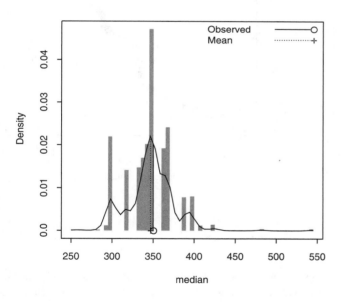

bootstrap : Exercise18.020 : median

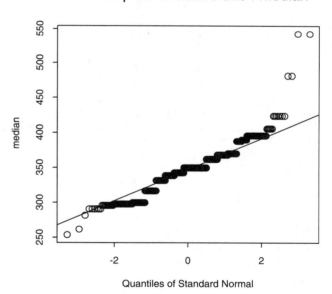

bootstrap : Exercise18.020 : median

18.21

a s = 7.72.

b The bootstrap standard error for s is SE = 2.21.

c The bootstrap standard error is almost one-third the value of the sample standard deviation. This suggests that the sample standard deviation is only moderately accurate as an estimate of the population standard deviation.

d The bootstrap distribution is not Normal. Thus, it would not be appropriate to give a bootstrap *t* interval for the population standard deviation.

```
> stdev(Exercise18.021$Weight)
```

```
[1] 7.724852
```

```
> boot21 <- bootstrap(Exercise18.021$Weight, stdev, seed = 0)
> boot21

Call:
bootstrap(data = Exercise18.021$Weight, statistic = stdev, seed = 0)

Number of Replications: 1000

Summary Statistics:
      Observed  Mean    Bias     SE
stdev    7.725 7.279  -0.4454  2.209

> plot(boot21)
> qqnorm(boot21)
```

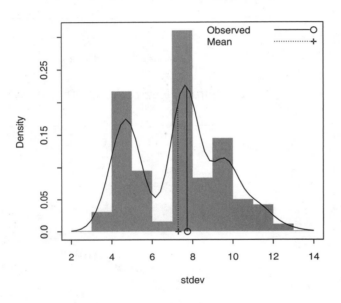

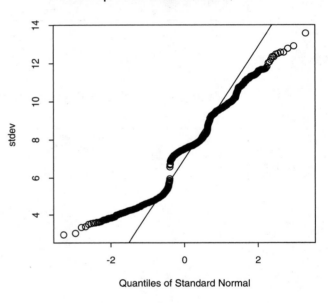

18.22

a The interquartile range is 6.7.

b The bootstrap standard error is 2.0.

c The bootstrap standard error is almost one-third the value of the sample interquartile range. This suggests that the sample interquartile range is only moderately accurate as an estimate of the population interquartile range.

d The bootstrap distribution has some positive skewness; it also has gaps and repeated values, which make the histogram appear very non-normal (a Normal quantile plot gives a better picture of the distribution).

While this amount of skewness would not be a concern in raw data, in a sampling distribution it results in errors in coverage level or significance level. Here the distribution is close enough to Normal that a bootstrap t interval would be acceptable for an application where only low accuracy is needed.

The bootstrap t interval is (2.48, 10.92).

```
> summary(Exercise18.021)

     Weight
   Min.:53.10
 1st Qu.:58.90
```

```
   Median:62.30
     Mean:63.08
 3rd Qu.:65.60
        Weight
     Max.:92.30
```

```
> quantile(Exercise18.021)
```

```
  0%   25%  50%  75%  100%
 53.1 58.9 62.3 65.6 92.3
```

```
> # simplify things by defining our own function
> interQuartile <- function(x)
+ {
+    a <- quantile(x)
+    a[4] - a[2]
+ }
> interQuartile(Exercise18.021)
```

```
 75%
 6.7
```

```
> boot22 <- bootstrap(Exercise18.021, interQuartile, seed = 0)
> boot22
```

```
Call:
bootstrap(data = Exercise18.021, statistic = interQuartile, seed = 0)

Number of Replications: 1000

Summary Statistics:
     Observed  Mean   Bias    SE
75%       6.7 7.048 0.3483 2.042
```

```
> plot(boot22)
> qqnorm(boot22)
> limits.t(boot22)
```

```
          2.5%       5%      95%     97.5%
75% 2.480315 3.203141 10.19686 10.91968
```

bootstrap : Exercise18.021 : interQuartile

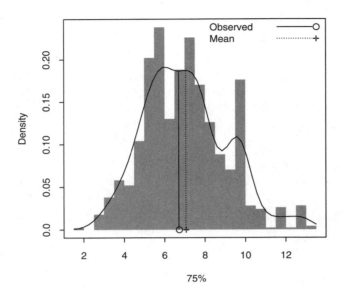

bootstrap : Exercise18.021 : interQuartile

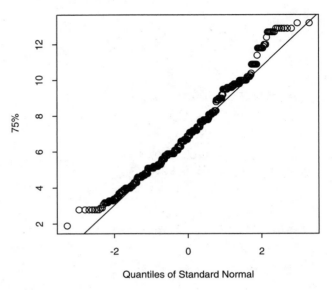

18.23

a The plots do not show any significant departures from Normality, so there is nothing in the plots to suggest that the difference in means might be non-Normal.

b A 95% paired t confidence interval for the difference in population means is (17.4, 25.1). The interval does not contain 0 and only includes positive values. This is evidence that the minority refusal rate is larger than the white refusal rate.

c The bootstrap distribution looks reasonably Normal. The bias is small. Thus, a bootstrap t confidence interval is appropriate here. A 95% bootstrap t confidence interval is (17.6, 24.9). This is close to the formula-based interval that we calculated in (b).

```
> Exercise18.023  # columns Minority and White
> par(mfrow=c(2, 2))  # two rows and two columns of plots
> hist(Exercise18.023$Minority)
> qqnorm(Exercise18.023$Minority)
> hist(Exercise18.023$White)
> qqnorm(Exercise18.023$White)
> par(mfrow = c(1, 1))
> t.test(Exercise18.023$Minority, Exercise18.023$White, paired = T)


        Paired t-Test

data:  Exercise18.023$Minority and Exercise18.023$White
t = 11.4579, df = 19, p-value = 0
alternative hypothesis:  mean of differences is not equal to 0
95 percent confidence interval:
 17.37232 25.13768
sample estimates:
 mean of x - y
        21.255


> difference23 <- Exercise18.023$Minority - Exercise18.023$White
> t.test(difference23)
```

```
        One-sample t-Test

data:  difference23
t = 11.4579, df = 19, p-value = 0
alternative hypothesis:  mean is not equal to 0
95 percent confidence interval:
 17.37232 25.13768
sample estimates:
 mean of x
    21.255
```

```
> boot23 <- bootstrap(difference23, mean, seed = 0)
> # another way:
> # boot23 <- bootstrap(Exercise18.023, mean(Minority) - mean(White), seed=0)
> plot(boot23)
> qqnorm(boot23)
> limits.t(boot23)
```

```
          2.5%        5%       95%     97.5%
mean   17.56804  18.21001  24.29999  24.94196
```

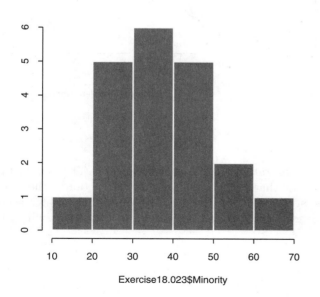

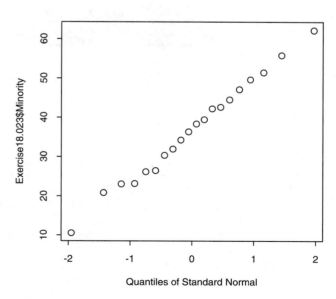

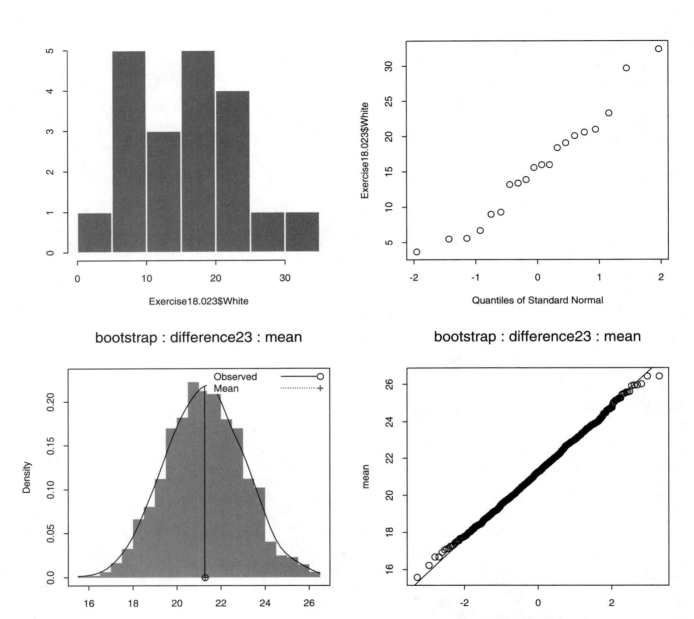

bootstrap : difference23 : mean

bootstrap : difference23 : mean

18.24

The distribution has a long tail, so we will use a trimmed mean rather than an ordinary mean. The trimmed mean is 1.95, standard error is 0.37, and estimated bias is 0.08 – note that the bias is a substantial fraction of the standard error. The bootstrap distribution is very skewed, so a bootstrap t interval would not be appropriate if high accuracy is important. For now we will do one anyway in order to get a rough idea; it gives a 95% confidence limit of (1.17, 2.72) for the average wealth of the middle 50% of billionaires.

```
> sort(Exercise18.024$NetWorth)
```

```
[1] 1.0 1.0 1.1 1.2 1.3 1.4 1.4 1.5 1.7 1.8 2.0 2.1 2.4 2.5 2.7 3.0 5.0 5.0 5.2 8.6
```

```
> hist(Exercise18.024)
> qqnorm(Exercise18.024)
> boot24 <- bootstrap(Exercise18.024, mean(Exercise18.024, trim = 0.25), seed = 0)
> plot(boot24)
> qqnorm(boot24)
> boot24
```

```
Call:
bootstrap(data = Exercise18.024, statistic = mean(Exercise18.024, trim = 0.25), seed = 0
  )

Number of Replications: 1000

Summary Statistics:
      Observed  Mean    Bias      SE
Param     1.95 2.026 0.07566  0.3688
```

```
> limits.t(boot24)
```

```
            2.5%       5%      95%    97.5%
Param 1.177113 1.311687 2.588313 2.722887
```

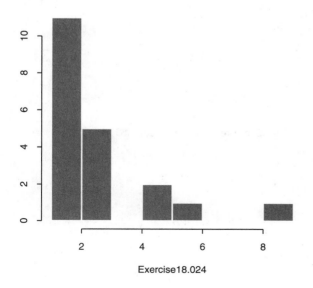

Exercise18.024

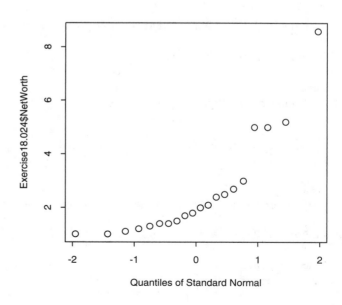

Quantiles of Standard Normal

bootstrap : mean(Exercise18.0...   bootstrap : mean(Exercise18.0...

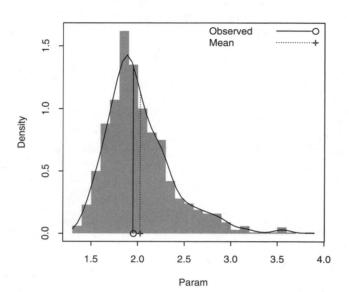

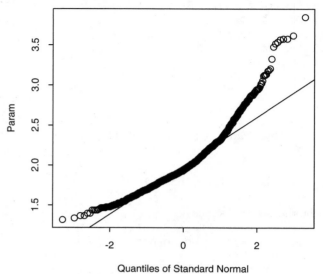

18.25

a This bootstrap distribution is right-skewed. The bootstrap distribution of the Verizon repair times appears to be approximately Normal. The standard error for the CLEC mean is 4.1, much larger than the standard error for the Verizon mean, 0.37.

b Because the Verizon bootstrap means vary so little, what really matters when you take (ILEC mean) − (CLEC mean) is the CLEC mean. Because of the "−" sign, the right skewness of the CLEC means makes the difference have less skewness.

```
> boot25 <- bootstrap(CLEC, mean, seed = 0)
> plot(boot25)
> qqnorm(boot25)
> boot25

Call:
bootstrap(data = CLEC, statistic = mean, seed = 0)

Number of Replications: 1000

Summary Statistics:
     Observed  Mean   Bias    SE
mean    16.51 16.65 0.1394 4.092

> boot25b <- bootstrap(ILEC, mean, seed = 36)  # This was used for Figure 18.3
> boot25b

Call:
bootstrap(data = ILEC, statistic = mean, seed = 36)

Number of Replications: 1000

Summary Statistics:
     Observed  Mean     Bias    SE
mean    8.412 8.395 -0.01698 0.3672
```

```
> plot(boot25b)
> qqnorm(boot25b)
> # CLEC is more skewed, and much larger standard error
```

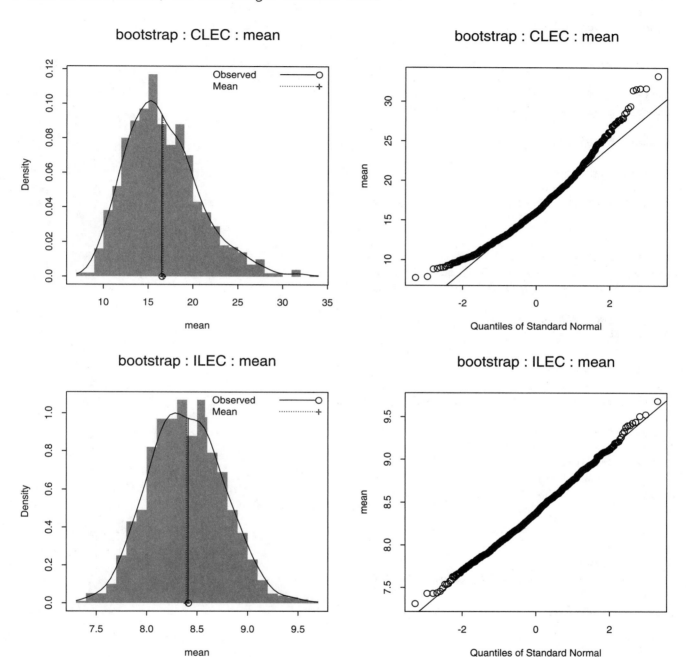

18.26

a Normal with mean 8.4 and standard deviation $14.7/\sqrt{n}$.

b and c See figures.

d Students' answers may vary, depending on their samples. They may see some skewness for smaller samples. They should have almost no bias, and standard deviation decreasing by a factor of 2 each time the sample size increases by a factor of 4.

```
> set.seed(1))  # So can reproduce results (but do not use seed 0, use that below)
> x10 <- rnorm(10, mean = 8.4, sd = 14.7)
> boot26a <- bootstrap(x10, mean, seed = 0)
> plot(boot26a)
> qqnorm(boot26a)
> boot26a
```

Call:
bootstrap(data = x10, statistic = mean, seed = 0)

Number of Replications: 1000

Summary Statistics:
        Observed Mean   Bias   SE
mean   12.79   12.76 -0.03282 4.057

```
> set.seed(1)
> x40 <- rnorm(40, mean = 8.4, sd = 14.7)
> boot26b <- bootstrap(x40, mean, seed = 0)
> plot(boot26b)
> qqnorm(boot26b)
> boot26b
```

Call:
bootstrap(data = x40, statistic = mean, seed = 0)

Number of Replications: 1000

Summary Statistics:
        Observed Mean   Bias   SE
mean   8.36   8.355 -0.005727 2.356

```
> set.seed(1)
> x160 <- rnorm(160, mean = 8.4, sd = 14.7)
> boot26c <- bootstrap(x160, mean, seed = 0)
> plot(boot26c)
> qqnorm(boot26c)
> boot26c
```

Call:
bootstrap(data = x160, statistic = mean, seed = 0)

Number of Replications: 1000

Summary Statistics:
        Observed Mean   Bias   SE
mean   7.455   7.44 -0.01506 1.181

bootstrap : x10 : mean

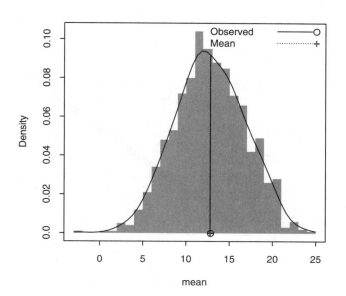

bootstrap : x10 : mean

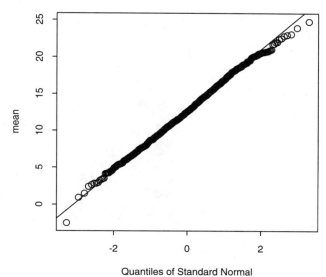

bootstrap : x40 : mean

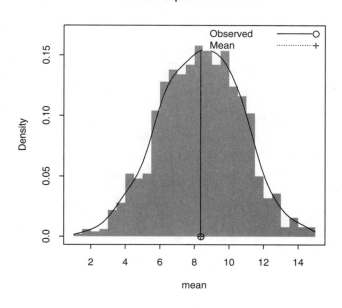

bootstrap : x40 : mean

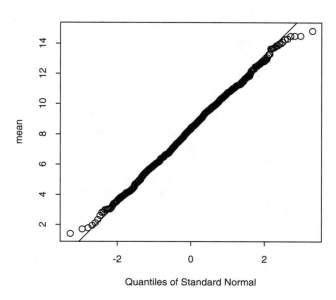

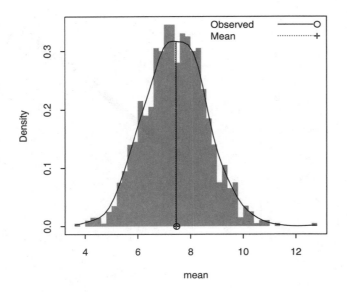

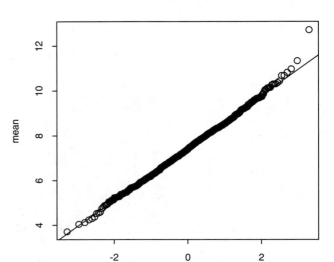

18.27

a mean is 8.4, standard deviation is $14.7/\sqrt{n}$.

b and c See figures.

d Students' answers may vary, depending on their samples. They should see substantial right skewness for smaller samples, closer to Normal for large samples. There should be almost no bias, and the standard deviation should decrease by a factor of 2 each time the sample size increases by a factor of 4.

```
> set.seed(1))  # different seed than zero
> y10 <- sample(ILEC, size = 10)
> boot27a <- bootstrap(y10, mean, seed = 0)
> plot(boot27a)
> qqnorm(boot27a)
> boot27a

Call:
bootstrap(data = y10, statistic = mean, seed = 0)


Number of Replications: 1000


Summary Statistics:
      Observed   Mean      Bias     SE
mean     6.703  6.677  -0.02602  2.238

> set.seed(1))  # different seed than zero
> y40 <- sample(ILEC, size = 40)
> boot27b <- bootstrap(y40, mean, seed = 0)
> plot(boot27b)
> qqnorm(boot27b)
> boot27b

Call:
bootstrap(data = y40, statistic = mean, seed = 0)
```

```
Number of Replications: 1000

Summary Statistics:
     Observed  Mean    Bias     SE
mean    7.524  7.586  0.06176  1.487
```

```
> set.seed(1))  # different seed than zero
> y160 <- sample(ILEC, size = 160)
> boot27c <- bootstrap(y160, mean, seed = 0)
> plot(boot27c)
> qqnorm(boot27c)
> boot27c
```

```
Call:
bootstrap(data = y160, statistic = mean, seed = 0)

Number of Replications: 1000

Summary Statistics:
     Observed  Mean    Bias      SE
mean    8.469  8.482  0.01334  0.9382
```

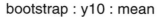

bootstrap : y10 : mean

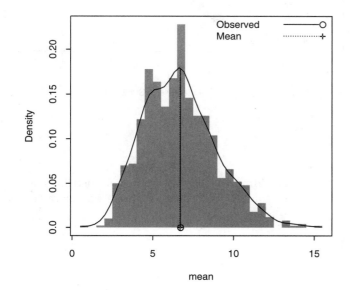

bootstrap : y10 : mean

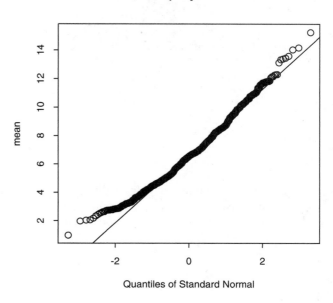

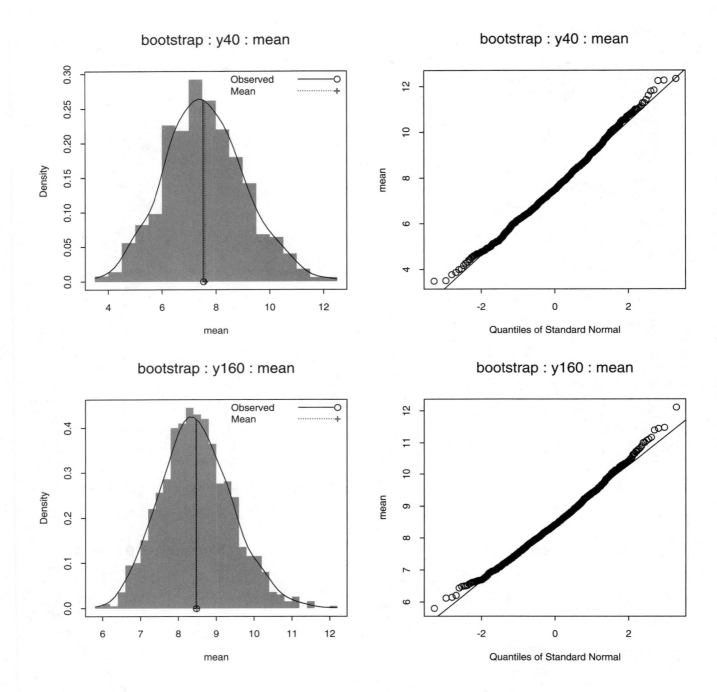

18.28

Students' answers should vary depending on their samples. They should notice that the bootstrap distributions are approximately Normal for larger sample sizes; for small samples, the sample could be skewed one way or the other, and that would be reflected in the bootstrap distribution.

18.29

5% and 95%.

18.30

a Yes, approximately Normal. There is a small amount of left skewness.

b 1.49, (106.0, 111.9).

c See figures. The distribution appears very close to Normal, with no appreciable bias. The standard error is 1.46, and the 95% bootstrap t confidence interval is (106.0, 111.8).

d (105.9, 111.7). All three intervals agree quite closely. The formula confidence interval is good enough.

```
> qqnorm(Exercise18.030)
> stdev(Exercise18.030$IQ)/sqrt(length(Exercise18.030$IQ))


[1] 1.491319


> t.test(Exercise18.030$IQ)


        One-sample t-Test

data:  Exercise18.030$IQ
t = 73.0381, df = 77, p-value = 0
alternative hypothesis:  mean is not equal to 0
95 percent confidence interval:
 105.9535 111.8927
sample estimates:
 mean of x
  108.9231


> boot30 <- bootstrap(Exercise18.030, mean, seed = 0)
> plot(boot30)
> qqnorm(boot30)
> boot30


Call:
bootstrap(data = Exercise18.030, statistic = mean, seed = 0)

Number of Replications: 1000

Summary Statistics:
      Observed Mean    Bias    SE
mean     108.9  109 0.09292 1.456


> limits.t(boot30)


          2.5%       5%      95%    97.5%
mean 106.0207 106.4971 111.349 111.8255


> limits.percentile(boot30)


          2.5%       5%      95%    97.5%
mean 105.9372 106.6032 111.3455 111.717
```

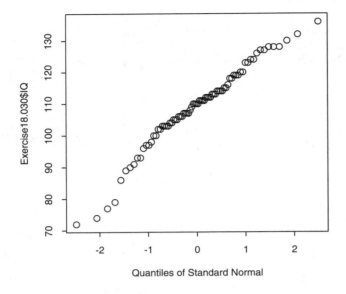

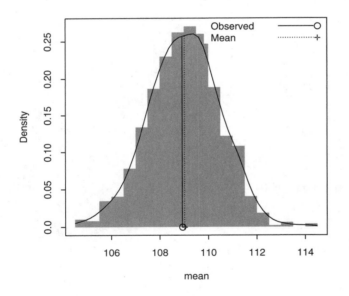

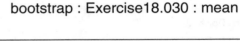

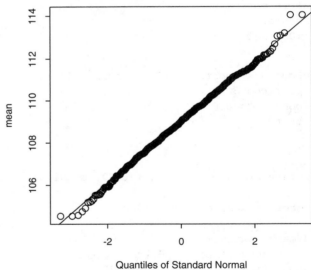

18.31

The 95% bootstrap t interval is (-0.159, 0.373) and the bootstrap percentile interval is (-0.143, 0.381). There is very close agreement between the upper endpoints of both intervals. However, the lower endpoints differ somewhat and this may indicate skewness, or just randomness in the bootstrap distribution.

18.32

The bootstrap t interval is (0.12, 0.59) and the percentile interval is (0.11, 0.57). These are reasonably close, and the bootstrap distribution appears approximately normal, so these intervals appear trustworthy.

```
> Exercise18.032  # columns Wages LOS Size
> boot32 <- bootstrap(Exercise18.032, cor(Wages, LOS), seed = 0)
> boot32

Call:
bootstrap(data = Exercise18.032, statistic = cor(Wages, LOS), seed = 0)

Number of Replications: 1000

Summary Statistics:
      Observed  Mean      Bias      SE
Param   0.3535  0.347  -0.006469  0.1157

> plot(boot32)
> qqnorm(boot32)
> limits.t(boot32)

            2.5%        5%        95%      97.5%
Param  0.1215831  0.1598873  0.5470484  0.5853526

> limits.percentile(boot32)

            2.5%        5%        95%      97.5%
Param  0.1096636  0.1565661  0.5276105  0.5725484
```

bootstrap : Exercise18.032 : cor(Wages, LOS)

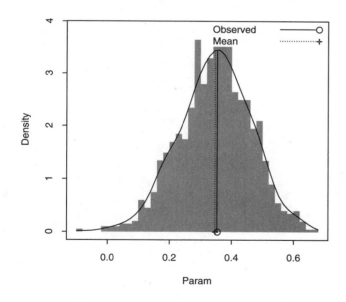

bootstrap : Exercise18.032 : cor(Wages, LOS)

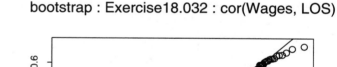

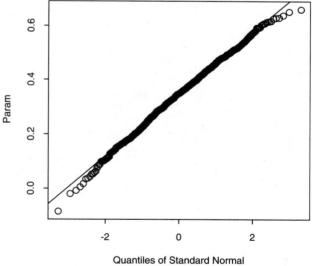

18.33

The 95% bootstrap t confidence interval is (241.1, 417.5). The 95% percentile confidence interval is (252.5, 433.1). The 95% formula-based one-sample t confidence interval is (239.2, 419.3). The BCa 95% confidence interval is (270, 455.7) The 95% tilting confidence interval is (265.0, 458.7). Students should draw a picture. The bootstrap t and traditional intervals are centered at the sample mean. The bootstrap percentile interval is shifted to the right of these two. BCa and tilting intervals are shifted even further to the right. The latter two better reflect the skewed nature of the data. Using a t interval or the bootstap percentile interval, we get a biased picture of what the value of the population mean is likely to be. In particular, we would underestimate its value. Any policy decisions based on these data, such as tax rates, would reflect this underestimate.

```
> 329.3 + qt(c(0.025, 0.975), 49) * 43.9
```

```
[1]  241.0796 417.5204
```

```
> t.test(Seattle2002$Price)
```

```
        One-sample t-Test
```

```
data:  Seattle2002$Price
t = 7.3484, df = 49, p-value = 0
alternative hypothesis:  mean is not equal to 0
95 percent confidence interval:
 239.2150 419.2992
sample estimates:
 mean of x
  329.2571
```

```
> boot33 <- bootstrap(Seattle2002, mean, B = 1000, seed = 0)
> plotWithIntervals(boot33, usualT = c(241.1, 417.5))
```

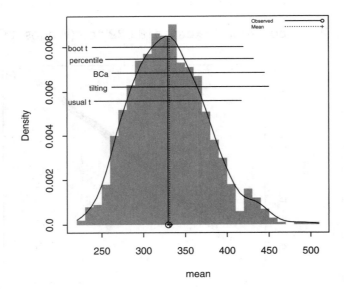

18.34

The intervals are:

```
bootstrap t:  (209.3, 278.7)
percentile:   (212.3, 280.3)
BCa:          (212.3, 280.7)
Tilting:      (212.9, 279.7)
```

The intervals are very similar. The percentile and BCa intervals have endpoints slightly to the right of the bootstrap *t* interval.

```
> boot34 <- bootstrap(Seattle2002, mean(Seattle2002, trim = 0.25), seed = 0)
> limits.t(boot34)
```

```
            2.5%        5%       95%      97.5%
Param 209.2208  214.9933  273.0106  278.783

> limits.percentile(boot34)

            2.5%        5%       95%      97.5%
Param 212.2583  218.0675  274.6219  280.3038

> limits.bca(boot34)

            2.5%        5%       95%      97.5%
Param 212.2645  218.0482  274.4862  280.6842

> limits.tilt(boot34)

            2.5%        5%       95%      97.5%
Param 212.8527  217.1022  273.4106  279.7388

> plotWithIntervals(boot34)
```

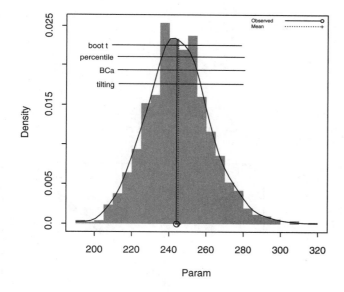

18.35

The bootstrap t confidence interval is (0.122, 0.585). The bootstrap percentile interval is (0.110, 0.573). The 95% BCa: interval is (0.133, 0.594). The tilting interval is (0.118, 0.555). The percentile and tilting intervals are lower than the bootstrap t and BCa intervals. These intervals should differ slightly from Exercise 18.32 because they use different random bootstrap samples.

```
> boot35 <- bootstrap(Exercise18.032, cor(Wages, LOS), seed = 0)
> boot35

Call:
bootstrap(data = Exercise18.032, statistic = cor(Wages, LOS), seed = 0)

Number of Replications: 1000
```

```
Summary Statistics:
       Observed  Mean     Bias      SE
Param   0.3535  0.347  -0.006469  0.1157

> plot(boot35)
> qqnorm(boot35)
> limits.t(boot35)

             2.5%       5%        95%      97.5%
Param 0.1215831 0.1598873 0.5470484 0.5853526

> limits.percentile(boot35)

             2.5%       5%        95%      97.5%
Param 0.1096636 0.1565661 0.5276105 0.5725484

> limits.bca(boot35)

             2.5%       5%        95%      97.5%
Param 0.1331635 0.1667363 0.5417794 0.5938335

> limits.tilt(boot35)

             2.5%       5%        95%      97.5%
Param 0.1178957 0.1565829 0.5278238 0.5550835

> plotWithIntervals(boot35)
```

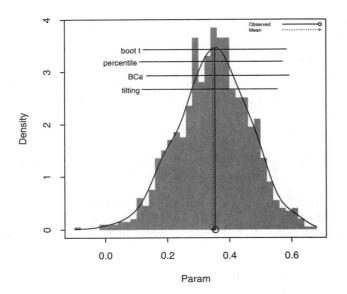

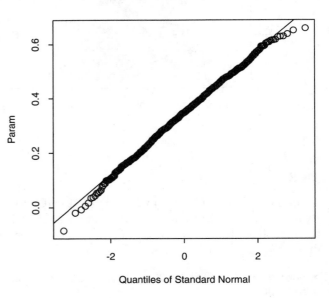

18.36

a The sample mean is 16.5; the histogram and Normal quantile plot show strong right skewness, with one large observation.

b The bootstrap distribution shows strong right skewness. The formula t, bootstrap t, and (to a lesser extent) the percentile intervals would not be accurate. The BCa and tilting intervals adjust for skewness so should be accurate.

c The standard error is 4.1, the bootstrap *t* interval is (8.0, 25.0).

d The percentile interval is (10.1, 26.2). The BCa interval is (11.4, 31.7). The tilting interval is (10.7, 29.1).

e The tilting and BCa interval have both endpoints substantially to the right of the bootstrap *t* interval, because they adjust for skewness. The percentile interval is in the middle; it partially adjusts for skewness.

f You would tend to underestimate the requirements.

```
> hist(CLEC)
> qqnorm(CLEC)
> mean(CLEC)
```

```
[1] 16.50913
```

```
> boot36 <- bootstrap(CLEC, mean, seed = 0)
> plot(boot36)
> qqnorm(boot36)
> boot36
```

```
Call:
bootstrap(data = CLEC, statistic = mean, seed = 0)

Number of Replications: 1000

Summary Statistics:
     Observed  Mean   Bias     SE
mean    16.51  16.65  0.1394  4.092
```

```
> limits.t(boot36)
```

```
          2.5%       5%       95%      97.5%
mean 8.011573 9.475426 23.54284 25.00669
```

```
> limits.percentile(boot36)
```

```
          2.5%       5%       95%      97.5%
mean 10.10785 10.74915 24.62728 26.15751
```

```
> limits.bca(boot36)
```

```
          2.5%       5%       95%      97.5%
mean 11.37387 12.04885 27.80038 31.69748
```

```
> limits.tilt(boot36)
```

```
          2.5%       5%       95%      97.5%
mean 10.68218 11.59409 26.66405 29.13644
```

```
> plotWithIntervals(boot36)
```

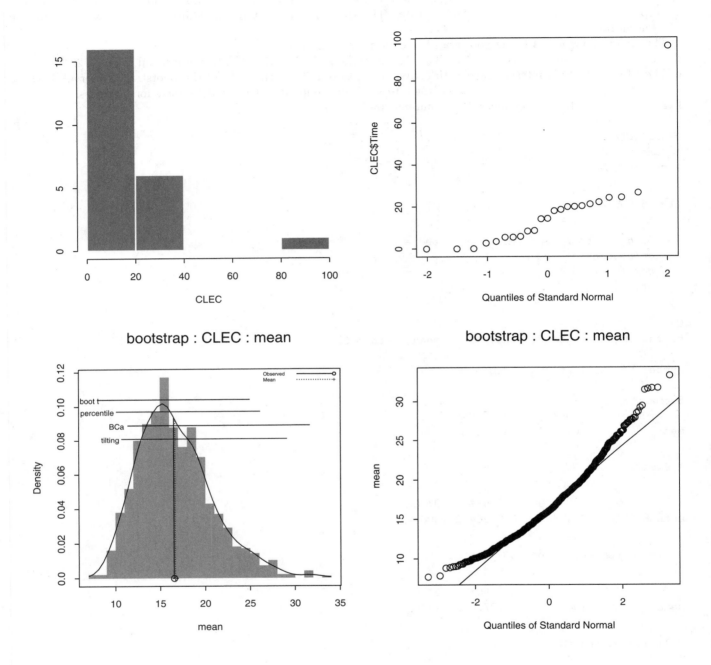

18.37

a and b The 95% BCa confidence interval is (-17.3, -2.1), the tilting interval is (-20.6, -2.1). The tilting interval reaches much farther to the left. Neither interval includes 0, so we would conclude that the mean repair time for ILEC customers is lower than the mean repair time for CLEC customers.

```
> # boot37 <- bootstrap2(Verizon, mean(Time), treatment = Group, seed=0)
> # Previous works, but the BCa calculations below are much slower
> boot37 <- bootstrap2(Verizon$Time, mean, treatment = Verizon$Group, seed = 0)
> limits.bca(boot37)
```

```
          2.5%       5%        95%       97.5%
mean -17.29894 -16.1745 -2.901759 -2.095697
```

```
> limits.tilt(boot37)
```

```
          2.5%       5%         95%       97.5%
mean -20.63503 -18.16698 -3.042819 -2.101872
```

```
> plotWithIntervals(boot37)
```

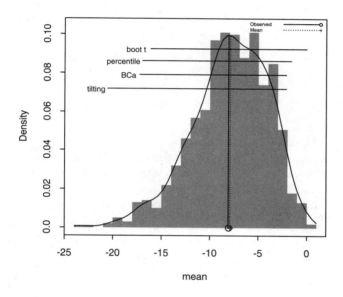

bootstrap : Verizon\$Time : mean : ILEC - CLEC

18.38

See figures for Exercise 18.19.

a The bootstrap distribution appears very normal with no bias, so a *t* interval is appropriate.
b (-0.13, 0.37). This interval does include zero.

```
> plot(boot19)   # boot19 was created in Exercise 19.
> qqnorm(boot19)
> limits.percentile(boot19)
```

```
           2.5%          5%         95%       97.5%
mean -0.1276154 -0.09408974 0.3321154 0.3679391
```

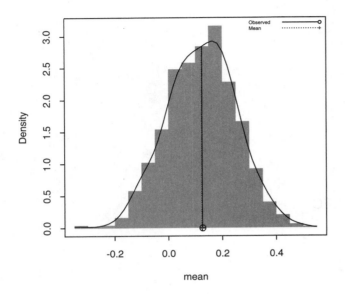

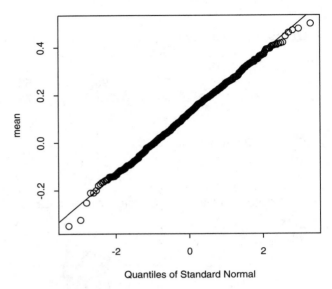

18.39

a A 95% traditional one-sample t confidence interval is (59.89, 66.27).

b The value 92.3 is an outlier and might strongly influence the confidence interval.

c The 95% percentile interval is (60.48, 66.45). Both ends are to the right of the interval in (a), due to skewness in the sampling distribution (which in turn is due to the outlier. This interval is influenced even more by the outlier.

d A 95% confidence interval for the mean weights of male runners (in kilograms) is (60.48, 66.45).

Should we throw out the outlier? No, unless there is reason to believe the point is faulty. Otherwise, an outlier indicates that the distribution has a long tail. And in fact, maybe the sample underrepresented that tail of the distribution; other samples could have even more outliers on that side. Hence a good confidence interval will reach farther to that side.

```
> t.test(Exercise18.021$Weight)

        One-sample t-Test

data:  Exercise18.021$Weight
t = 40.8293, df = 24, p-value = 0
alternative hypothesis:  mean is not equal to 0
95 percent confidence interval:
 59.89134 66.26866
sample estimates:
 mean of x
     63.08

> hist(Exercise18.021)
> qqnorm(Exercise18.021)
> boot39 <- bootstrap(Exercise18.021, mean, seed = 0)
> limits.percentile(boot39)

        2.5%      5%      95%    97.5%
mean 60.4777 60.7962 65.7718 66.4546
```

```
> plot(boot39)
> qqnorm(boot39)
> plotWithIntervals(boot39)
```

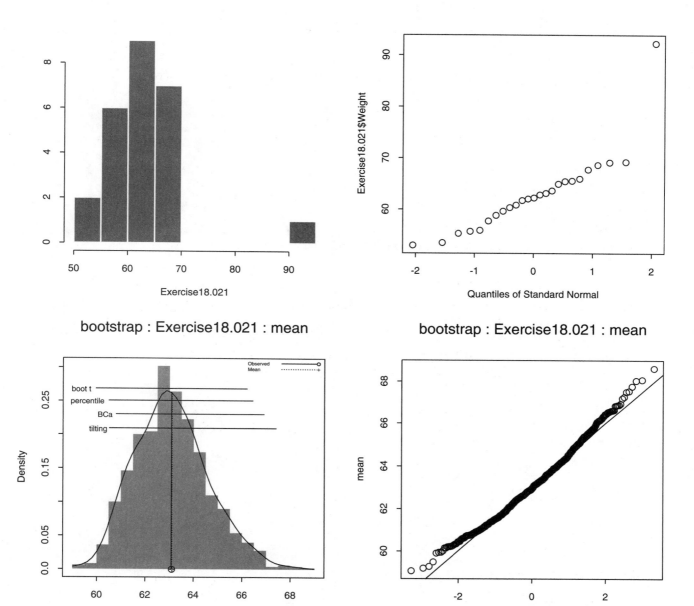

18.40

a The data are right skewed. A robust statistic like a trimmed mean would be more representative of the bulk of the data than a simple mean would be.

b The standard error for the trimmed mean is 1031. (The standard error for the mean is only slightly larger, 1074).

c Students should pick a statistic and report an interval. Both bootstrap distributions are skewed, so they should report a BCa or tilting interval. Some intervals for the trimmed mean: BCa (17321, 21321), tilting (17368,

21391), bootstrap t (16343, 20880), percentile (17221, 21071). For the simple mean: BCa (18251, 22920), tilting (18243, 22612), bootstrap t (17440, 22168), percentile (17862, 22070). The intervals for the mean lie above those for the trimmed mean (the observed mean is larger than the trimmed mean).

```
> hist(Exercise18.040)
> qqnorm(Exercise18.040)
> boot40 <- bootstrap(Exercise18.040, mean(Exercise18.040, trim = 0.25), seed = 0)
> boot40

Call:
bootstrap(data = Exercise18.040, statistic = mean(Exercise18.040, trim = 0.25), seed = 0
  )

Number of Replications: 1000

Summary Statistics:
      Observed Mean  Bias    SE
Param    18612 18778 166.3 1031

> plot(boot40)
> qqnorm(boot40)
> boot40b <- bootstrap(Exercise18.040, mean, seed = 0)
> boot40b

Call:
bootstrap(data = Exercise18.040, statistic = mean, seed = 0)

Number of Replications: 1000

Summary Statistics:
     Observed Mean  Bias    SE
mean    19804 19765 -39.3 1074

> plot(boot40b)
> qqnorm(boot40b)
> limits.bca(boot40)

          2.5%       5%       95%      97.5%
Param 17321.41 17424.83 20925.27 21321.61

> limits.tilt(boot40)

          2.5%       5%       95%      97.5%
Param 17368.32 17495.76 20847.01 21390.55

> limits.t(boot40)

          2.5%       5%       95%      97.5%
Param 16339.84 16758.57 20464.43 20883.16

> limits.percentile(boot40)

          2.5%       5%       95%      97.5%
Param 17221.17 17408.17 20741.01 21071.02

> limits.bca(boot40b)
```

```
        2.5%        5%        95%     97.5%
mean 18251.3  18477.71  22313.77  22920.3
```

```
> limits.tilt(boot40b)
```

```
        2.5%        5%        95%     97.5%
mean 18243.17  18465.91  22107.75  22611.93
```

```
> limits.t(boot40b)
```

```
        2.5%        5%        95%     97.5%
mean 17437.21  17873.51  21734.82  22171.12
```

```
> limits.percentile(boot40b)
```

```
        2.5%        5%       95%  97.5%
mean 17861.74  18099.51  21651.93  22070
```

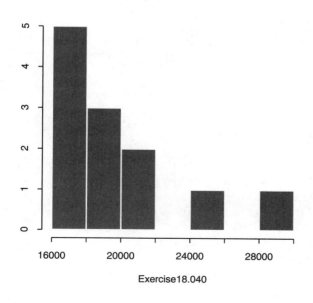

Exercise18.040

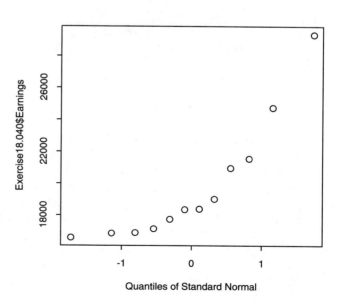

Quantiles of Standard Normal

bootstrap : mean(Exercise18.0...

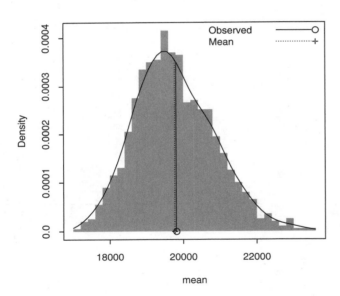

bootstrap : mean(Exercise18.0...

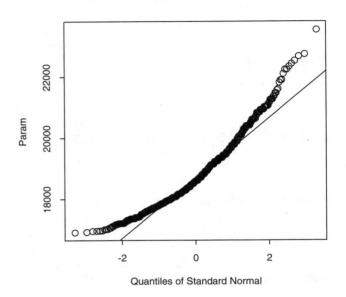

bootstrap : Exercise18.040 : mean

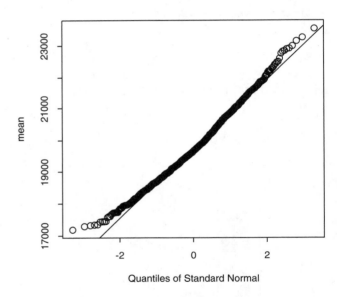

bootstrap : Exercise18.040 : mean

18.41

a There are two large outliers present. t procedures can be used even for clearly skewed distributions when the sample size is large. In this example, n = 43, which may not be enough given this skewness.

b A 95% traditional one-sample t confidence interval is (116.3, 124.8).

c The bootstrap distribution shows moderate skewness to the right, so a bootstrap t interval should be moderately accurate.

d The 95% percentile interval is (116.9, 124.4), and bootstrap t interval is (116.6, 124.5). These agrees closely with the interval found in (b), so we conclude that the one-sample t interval is reasonably accurate here.

```
> hist(Exercise18.041)
> qqnorm(Exercise18.041)
```

```
> t.test(Exercise18.041$x)
```

```
        One-sample t-Test
```

```
data:  Exercise18.041$x
t = 57.4992, df = 42, p-value = 0
alternative hypothesis:  mean is not equal to 0
95 percent confidence interval:
 116.3493 124.8135
sample estimates:
 mean of x
  120.5814
```

```
> boot41 <- bootstrap(Exercise18.041, mean, seed = 0)
> plot(boot41)
> qqnorm(boot41)
> limits.t(boot41)
```

```
        2.5%       5%       95%     97.5%
mean 116.6251  117.285  123.8777  124.5377
```

```
> limits.percentile(boot41)
```

```
        2.5%        5%       95%     97.5%
mean 116.8843  117.3256  123.7442  124.4407
```

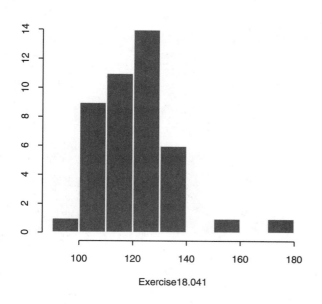

Exercise18.041

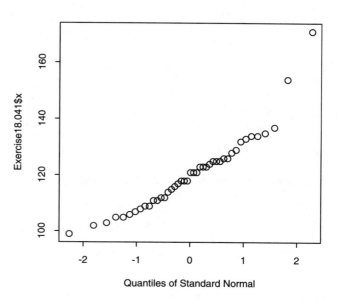

Quantiles of Standard Normal

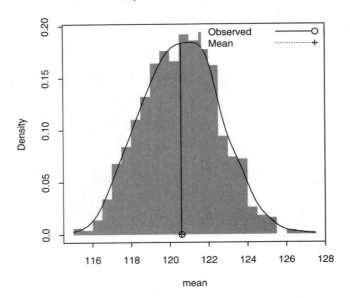

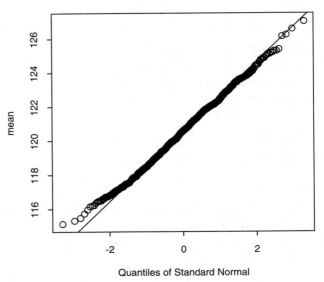

18.42

a The BCa limit is (117.0, 124.7) and the tilting interval is (116.7, 125.6).

b These intervals are similar to the percentile interval. However, if we look more closely, we notice that these intervals extend farther to the right than to the left of the observed value (-3.5, 4.0) and (-3.8, 5.0). The percentile interval captured only part of this asymmetry, (-3.7, 3.9). These new intervals suggest that the *t* interval is not as good here as we thought.

c We would generally use the percentile interval as a quick check, or the BCa or tilting interval as a more accurate check.

```
> limits.bca(boot41)

          2.5%       5%      95%      97.5%
mean  117.0448  117.449  123.8198  124.6515

> limits.bca(boot41) - boot41$observed

          2.5%        5%       95%      97.5%
mean  -3.536609  -3.132381  3.238436  4.070107

> limits.tilt(boot41)

          2.5%       5%      95%      97.5%
mean  116.7525  117.351  124.6197  125.5953

> limits.tilt(boot41) - boot41$observed

          2.5%        5%       95%      97.5%
mean  -3.828874  -3.230429  4.03826  5.013887

> limits.percentile(boot41) - boot41$observed

          2.5%        5%       95%      97.5%
mean  -3.697093  -3.255814  3.162791  3.859302
```

```
> plotWithIntervals(boot41)
```

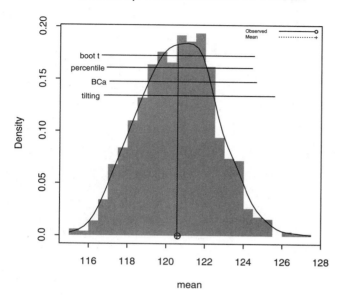

bootstrap : Exercise18.041 : mean

18.43

a The data are clearly right-skewed. The mean would not be a useful measure of the price of a typical house in Ames. The trimmed mean or median might be more useful. We examine the trimmed mean.

b The standard error of our bootstrap statistic is SE = 6797.

c The distribution looks approximately normal and the bias is relatively small. The 95% bootstrap t interval or the 95% bootstrap percentile interval are reasonable choices. The 95% percentile interval is (119,677, 144,161). For comparison, the 95% BCa interval is (120,484, 147,562), the 95% maximum-likelihood tilting interval is (120,496, 146,665), and the 95% bootstrap t interval is (119,058, 146,375).

d We are 95% confident that the mean selling price of all homes sold in Ames for the period represented by these data is in the interval ($119,677, $144,161).

```
> Exercise18.043  # variables Price, SquareFootage, Age
> hist(Exercise18.043$Price)
> qqnorm(Exercise18.043$Price)
> boot43 <- bootstrap(Exercise18.043, mean(Price, trim = 0.25), seed = 0)
> boot43

Call:
bootstrap(data = Exercise18.043, statistic = mean(Price, trim = 0.25), seed = 0)

Number of Replications: 1000

Summary Statistics:
      Observed   Mean   Bias     SE
Param   132717  132671  -45.73  6797

> plot(boot43)
> qqnorm(boot43)
> limits.percentile(boot43)

          2.5%       5%       95%      97.5%
Param  119677.5  121796.6  144161.8  147018.7
```

```
> limits.bca(boot43)
```

```
              2.5%       5%       95%       97.5%
Param   120484.3  122725.7  145350.5  147562.1
```

```
> limits.tilt(boot43)
```

```
              2.5%       5%       95%       97.5%
Param   120495.6  122260.4  144351.1  146664.7
```

```
> limits.t(boot43)
```

```
              2.5%       5%       95%       97.5%
Param   119041.8  121311.5  144122.8  146392.4
```

```
> plotWithIntervals(boot43)
```

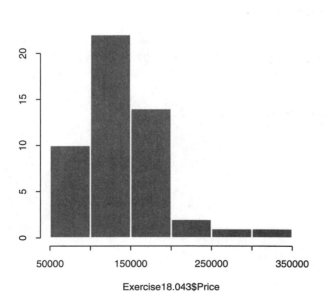

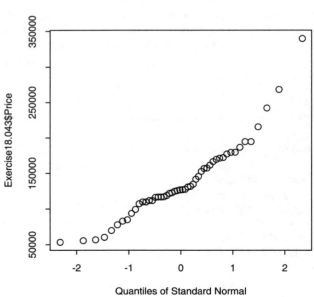

bootstrap : Exercise18.043 : mean(Price, trim ...   bootstrap : Exercise18.043 : mean(Price, trim ...

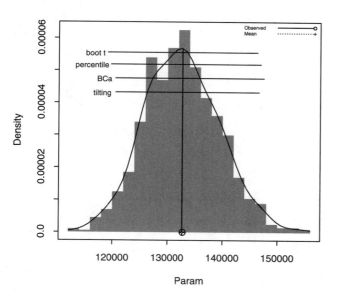

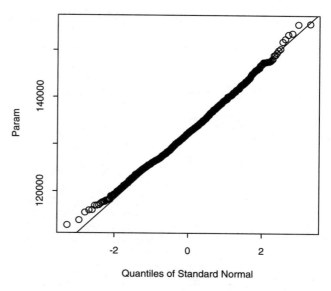

18.44

The bootstrap distribution is clearly non-normal; a t or percentile interval would not be accurate. The 95% BCa interval is (0.70, 0.90), and tilting interval is (0.71, 0.90). In contrast, the bootstrap t interval is (0.73, 0.93); the t interval is symmetric about the observed correlation, while the BCa interval extends to the left and right (-0.13, 0.07) (more than twice as far to the left, before rounding).

```
> boot44 <- bootstrap(Exercise18.044, cor(Price, SquareFootage), seed = 0)
> plot(boot44)
> qqnorm(boot44)
> limits.t(boot44))  # should not use this as final answer, only as check

            2.5%        5%       95%       97.5%
Param 0.7341165 0.7507795 0.9182545 0.9349175

> limits.percentile(boot44)) # ditto

            2.5%        5%       95%       97.5%
Param 0.7063105 0.7359897 0.8956225 0.9045518

> limits.bca(boot44)

            2.5%        5%       95%       97.5%
Param 0.6999152 0.7288067 0.8932955 0.901099

> limits.tilt(boot44)

            2.5%        5%       95%       97.5%
Param 0.7085679 0.7319598 0.8917389 0.9004622

> limits.bca(boot44) - boot44$observed

            2.5%         5%        95%        97.5%
Param -0.1346018 -0.1057103 0.05877851 0.06658198
```

```
> plotWithIntervals(boot44)
```

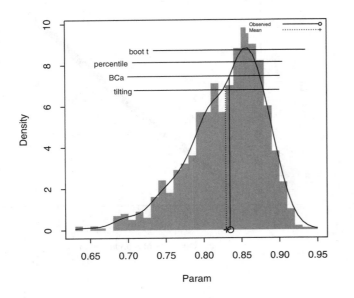

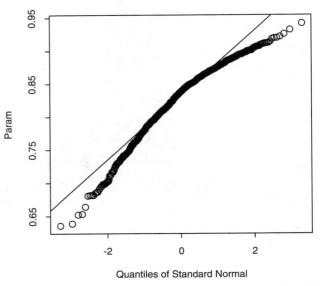

Regression problems follow. Here is command-line code, but it would be more natural to do this using menus, under: Statistics/Regression/LinearBootstrap

18.45

a The relationship appears linear and the association is negative. r = -0.848.

b The 95% BCa interval is (-0.898, -0.769) and the 95% tilting interval is (-0.900, -0.776). They provide a 95% confidence interval for the population correlation between weight and gas mileage in miles per gallon for all 1990 model year cars.

c The least-squares regression line to predict gas mileage from weight is Mileage = 48.35 -0.0082(Weight). The traditional 95% t confidence interval for the slope is (-0.0096, -0.0068)

d The bootstrap percentile interval is (-0.0095, -0.0068).

```
> Exercise18.045 # variables Weight, Mileage
> plot(Exercise18.045$Weight, Exercise18.045$Mileage)
> cor(Exercise18.045)

          Weight    Mileage
 Weight  1.0000000 -0.8478541
Mileage -0.8478541  1.0000000

> boot45a <- bootstrap(Exercise18.045, cor(Weight, Mileage), seed = 0)
> limits.bca(boot45a)

            2.5%        5%        95%       97.5%
Param -0.8976598 -0.8895653 -0.7830701 -0.7692549

> limits.tilt(boot45a)

            2.5%        5%        95%       97.5%
Param -0.8997292 -0.8922958 -0.7881989 -0.7759033
```

```
> lm45 <- lm(Mileage ~ Weight, data = Exercise18.045)
> abline(lm45))  # add regression line to the plot
> lm45           # short summary of numerical results

Call:
lm(formula = Mileage ~ Weight, data = Exercise18.045)

Coefficients:
 (Intercept)        Weight
    48.34935 -0.008192823

Degrees of freedom: 60 total; 58 residual
Residual standard error: 2.562435

> summary(lm45) # longer summary, including standard error

Call: lm(formula = Mileage ~ Weight, data = Exercise18.045)
Residuals:
    Min    1Q  Median    3Q    Max
 -4.696 -1.74 -0.1733 1.898 5.624

Coefficients:
             Value Std. Error  t value Pr(>|t|)
(Intercept) 48.3493   1.9794   24.4261   0.0000
    Weight  -0.0082   0.0007  -12.1779   0.0000

Residual standard error: 2.562 on 58 degrees of freedom
Multiple R-Squared: 0.7189
F-statistic: 148.3 on 1 and 58 degrees of freedom, the p-value is 0

> -0.0082 + qt(c(0.025, 0.975), df = 58) * 0.0007

[1] -0.009601202 -0.006798798

> boot45b <- bootstrap(lm45, coef, seed = 0)
> limits.percentile(boot45b)

                  2.5%           5%          95%          97.5%
(Intercept)  43.840470283 44.747487826 51.672095244 52.276598515
    Weight   -0.009542733 -0.009301473 -0.007025862 -0.006755601

> # The problem doesn't ask for this, but it is interesting to put
> # regression lines on the plot.  Not too many or it gets busy.
> bootstrap(lm45, abline(lm45, col = 2), B = 20, seed = 2)

Call:
bootstrap(data = lm(formula = Mileage ~ Weight, data = Exercise18.045, method =
   "model.list"), statistic = abline(lm(data), col = 2), B = 20, seed = 2)

Other calls used in creating the object:
bootstrap(data = lm45, statistic = abline(lm45, col = 2), B = 20, seed = 2)

Number of Replications: 20

Summary Statistics:
(None - statistic had length 0.)
```

```
> abline(lm45, lwd = 2)  # Add the original line with a wider line

Call:
bootstrap(data = lm(formula = Mileage ~ Weight, data = Exercise18.045, method =
  "model.list"), statistic = abline(lm(data), col = 2), B = 20, seed = 2)

Other calls used in creating the object:
bootstrap(data = lm45, statistic = abline(lm45, col = 2), B = 20, seed = 2)

Number of Replications: 20

Summary Statistics:
(None - statistic had length 0.)
```

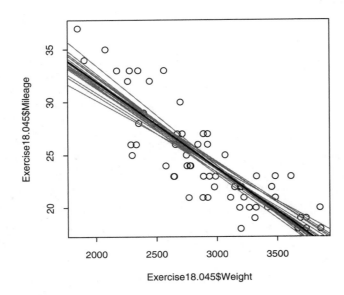

18.46

a The line is (predicted salary in \$1M) = 0.812 + 7.717(Average). Each increase of .001 in batting average results in an increase in predicted salary of \$7,717.

b The bootstrap distribution (for slope) suggests that any of the intervals would be reasonably accurate. The 95% intervals are bootstrap t: (-12.1, 27.5), percentile (-10.7, 28.6), BCa (-11.9, 27.1), tilting (-9.0, 26.7).

c This agrees; all intervals include zero, which corresponds to no (linear) relationship between batting average and salary.

```
> Exercise18.046 # variables Name, Salary, Average
> plot(Exercise18.046$Average, Exercise18.046$Salary/10^6)
> lm46 <- lm(I(Salary/10^6) ~ Average, data=Exercise18.046)
> abline(lm46)
> lm46

Call:
lm(formula = I(Salary/10^6) ~ Average, data = Exercise18.046)

Coefficients:
```

```
(Intercept)  Average
 0.8124751 7.716975

Degrees of freedom: 50 total; 48 residual
Residual standard error: 2.718337

> boot46 <- bootstrap(lm46, coef, seed = 0)
> plot(boot46)
> qqnorm(boot46)
> limits.t(boot46)

                  2.5%       5%       95%     97.5%
(Intercept)  -4.195893 -3.364677  4.989627  5.820843
    Average -12.070738 -8.786659 24.220610 27.504688

> limits.percentile(boot46)

                  2.5%       5%       95%     97.5%
(Intercept)  -4.184901 -3.449656  4.632944  5.536679
    Average -10.662592 -7.423219 24.981379 28.637785

> limits.bca(boot46)

                  2.5%       5%       95%     97.5%
(Intercept)  -3.733074 -3.060384  5.045409  6.181114
    Average -11.874154 -8.102628 24.215260 27.136212

> limits.tilt(boot46)

                  2.5%       5%       95%     97.5%
(Intercept)  -3.764150 -3.043560  4.583589  5.229703
    Average  -9.018227 -6.671867 23.711326 26.737958
```

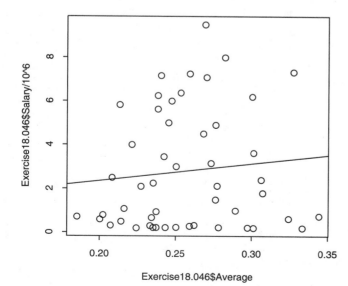

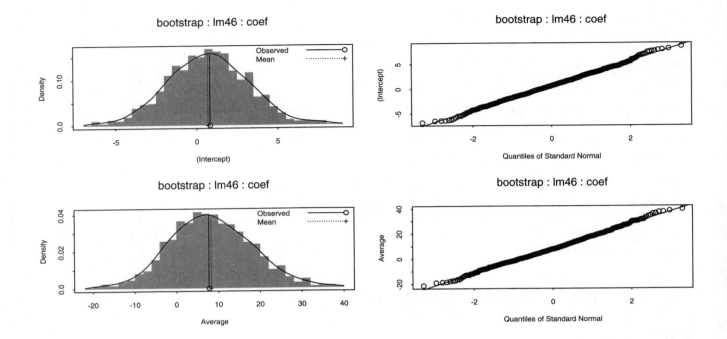

18.47

a Examining the plots, we see that the bootstrap distribution with the outlier excluded is shifted significantly to the right (centered at a larger value), compared to the bootstrap distribution with all the data. Also, the bootstrap distribution with the outlier included appears to be slightly left-skewed. There is little bias in either case (in fact, any apparent bias is due to random resampling, because the sample mean has no true bias).

b A 95% BCa interval for the mean based on all data included is (16504, 18322). A 95% BCa interval for the mean with the outlier removed is (17241, 18614). The outlier brings the lower end of the condidence interval down by about 740; it brings the upper end down by about 290.

```
> hist(Exercise18.047)
> qqnorm(Exercise18.047)
> stem(Exercise18.047)

Removed

N = 15    Median = 17516
Quartiles = 16555, 19090

Decimal point is 3 places to the right of the colon

   12 : 6
   13 :
   14 :
   15 :
   16 : 0069
   17 : 1358
   18 : 24
   19 : 133
   20 : 8

> which(Exercise18.047 < 14000) # observation 10

[1] 10
```

```
> Exercise18.047[-10,  ] # omit observation 10
```

```
[1] 16015 17516 17274 16555 20788 19312 17124 18405 19090 17813 18206 19338 15953 16904
```

```
> boot47a <- bootstrap(Exercise18.047, mean, seed = 0)
> boot47b <- bootstrap(Exercise18.047[-10,  ], mean, seed = 0)
> par(mfrow = c(2, 2))
> plot(boot47a)
> qqnorm(boot47a)
> plot(boot47b, main="bootstrap : 18.047[omit obs 10] : mean")
> qqnorm(boot47b, main="bootstrap : 18.047[omit obs 10] : mean")
> par(mfrow = c(1, 1))
> boot47a
```

```
Call:
bootstrap(data = Exercise18.047, statistic = mean, seed = 0)

Number of Replications: 1000

Summary Statistics:
      Observed  Mean    Bias    SE
mean     17529  17525  -3.695  454.5
```

```
> boot47b
```

```
Call:
bootstrap(data = Exercise18.047[-10,  ], statistic = mean, seed = 0)

Number of Replications: 1000

Summary Statistics:
      Observed  Mean    Bias    SE
mean     17878  17878  -0.2643  351.9
```

```
> limits.bca(boot47a)
```

```
          2.5%      5%      95%     97.5%
mean  16503.65  16705.61  18191.66  18321.91
```

```
> limits.bca(boot47b)
```

```
          2.5%      5%      95%     97.5%
mean  17240.81  17331.64  18479.95  18614.15
```

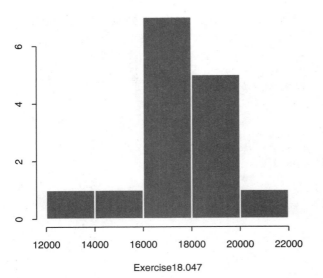

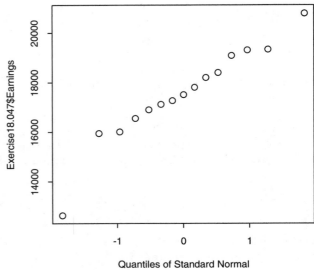

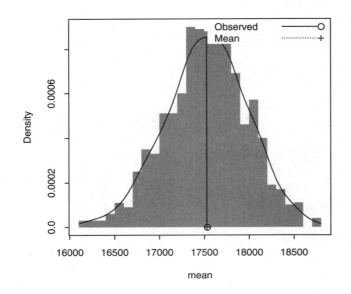

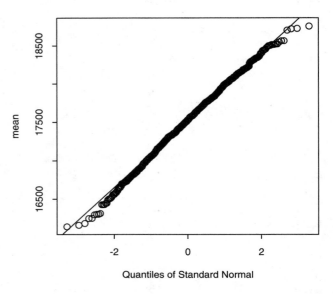

bootstrap : 18.047[omit obs 10] : mean

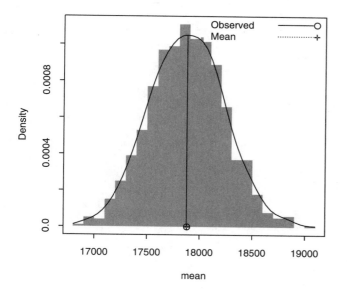

bootstrap : 18.047[omit obs 10] : mean

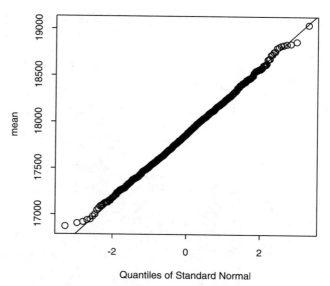

18.48

a 3.

b, c, and d Answers will vary. In this example there are only 15 possible combinations, which give differences in means equal to (-18.00, -15.00, -11.25, -8.25, -8.25, -4.50, -1.50, -1.50, 1.50, 3.00, 5.25, 9.75, 12.75, 16.50, 19.50), and the exact P-value is 0.4.

This should be done by hand; the following is for reference.

```
> mean(c(24, 61)) - mean(c(42, 33, 46, 37))

[1] 3

> perm48 <- permutationTestMeans(c(24, 61), data2 = c(42, 33, 46, 37), seed = 0,
+     alternative = "greater", B = 20)
> perm48

Call:
permutationTestMeans(data = c(24, 61), data2 = c(42, 33, 46, 37), B = 20, alternative =
  "greater", seed = 0)

Number of Replications: 20

Summary Statistics:
    Observed Mean    SE alternative p.value
Var        3 -0.3 11.16      greater  0.4762

> hist(perm48, cex.main = 1)
```

Instructor only:

```
> indices = samp.combinations(n = 6, B = 15, k = 2)
> values = (indexMeans(c(24, 61, 42, 33, 46, 37), indices[1:2,  ]) - indexMeans(c(24, 61,
+     42, 33, 46, 37), indices[3:6,  ]))
> sort(values)
```

```
[1] -18.00 -15.00 -11.25  -8.25  -8.25  -4.50  -1.50  -1.50   1.50   3.00   5.25   9.75
[13]  12.75  16.50  19.50
```

```
> mean(values >= perm48$observed) # exact one-sided P-value
```

```
[1] 0.4
```

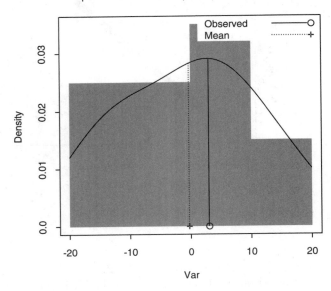

permutation : mean : c(24, 61) - c(42, 33, 46, 37)

18.49

a Let μ_1 denote the mean selling price for all Seattle real estate transactions in 2001, and μ_2 the mean selling price for all Seattle real estate transactions in 2002. We test $H_0 : \mu_1 = \mu_2$, $H_a : \mu_1 \neq \mu_2$.

b 0.423 (not pooling variances).

c The P-value is 0.462. This is consistent with the P-value we computed in (b). We conclude that there is little evidence that the population means μ_1 and μ_2 differ.

d A BCa 95% confidence interval for the change from 2001 to 2002 is (-40.1, 164.8). This interval includes 0 and suggests that the two means are not significantly different at the 0.05 level. This is consistent with the conclusions in (c).

```
> Exercise18.049 # variables Price and Year
> t.test(Exercise18.049$Price[Exercise18.049$Year == 2002], y = Exercise18.049$Price[
+    Exercise18.049$Year == 2001], var.equal = F)

        Welch Modified Two-Sample t-Test

data:  Exercise18.049$Price[Exercise18.049$Year == 2002] and Exercise18.049$Price[Exercise18.049$Year
t = 0.8057, df = 71.8952170780399, p-value = 0.4231
alternative hypothesis:  difference in means is not equal to 0
95 percent confidence interval:
 -59.45468  140.11588
sample estimates:
 mean of x mean of y
  329.2571  288.9265

> perm49 <- permutationTestMeans(Exercise18.049, treatment = Year, seed = 0)
> perm49
```

```
Call:
permutationTestMeans(data = Exercise18.049, treatment = Year, seed = 0)

Number of Replications: 999

Summary Statistics:
        Observed    Mean    SE alternative p.value
Price    40.33  -0.03134 50.66   two.sided    0.462

> plot(perm49, cex.main = 1)
> # boot49 <- bootstrap2(Exercise18.049, mean(Price), treatment=Year, seed=0)
> boot49 <- bootstrap2(Exercise18.049$Price, mean, treatment = Exercise18.049$Year,
+     seed = 0)
> plot(boot49, cex.main = 1)
> limits.bca(boot49)

          2.5%       5%      95%     97.5%
mean -40.08891 -30.48446 136.062 164.8292

> limits.tilt(boot49)

          2.5%       5%      95%     97.5%
mean -43.1708 -30.16752 142.5903 167.5817

> plotWithIntervals(boot49, Par=list(cex.main = 1))
```

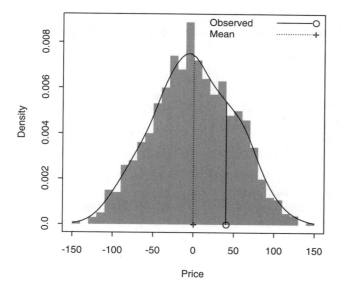

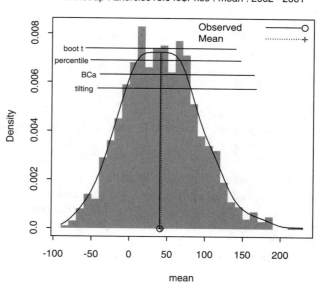

18.50

a $H_0 : \mu_1 = \mu_2$, $H_a : \mu_1 > \mu_2$, where μ_1 is the mean ratio among healthy firms.

b The t statistic is 7.9, and the P-value is about $6 \cdot 10^{-12}$.

c The estimated P-value is 0.001, which is the smallest possible value with 1000 replications. This result is consistent with the formula-based t test.

d A 95% BCa confidence interval is (0.67, 1.11). The interval does not include zero, so this agrees with the conclusion from the significance tests, that the data are not consistent with the hypothesis that the difference in means is zero.

```
> Exercise18.050  # variables status and ratio
> result <- t.test(Exercise18.050$ratio[Exercise18.050$status == "Healthy"],
+   Exercise18.050$ratio[Exercise18.050$status == "Failed"], alternative = "greater",
+   var.equal = F)
> result


        Welch Modified Two-Sample t-Test

data:  Exercise18.050$ratio[Exercise18.050$status == "Healthy"] and Exercise18.050$ratio[Exercise18.050
t = 7.9037, df = 81.6919596062767, p-value = 0
alternative hypothesis:  difference in means is greater than 0
95 percent confidence interval:
 0.7120916          NA
sample estimates:
 mean of x mean of y
  1.725588 0.8236364


> result$p.value


[1] 5.536238e-012


> perm50 <- permutationTestMeans(Exercise18.050, treatment = status, alternative =
+     "greater", seed = 0)
> perm50


Call:
permutationTestMeans(data = Exercise18.050, treatment = status, alternative = "greater",
  seed = 0)


Number of Replications: 999


Summary Statistics:
      Observed     Mean      SE alternative p.value
ratio    0.902 0.001664  0.1529      greater   0.001


> plot(perm50, cex.main = 1)
> # observed value is far outside the range of chance variation
> boot50 <- bootstrap2(Exercise18.050$ratio, mean, treatment = Exercise18.050$status,
+     seed = 0)
> plot(boot50, cex.main = 1)
> limits.bca(boot50)


          2.5%        5%       95%     97.5%
mean 0.6748105 0.7021837  1.077596  1.111262


> limits.tilt(boot50)


          2.5%        5%       95%     97.5%
mean 0.6685845 0.7070728  1.081596  1.117711


> plotWithIntervals(boot50, Par=list(cex.main = 1))
```

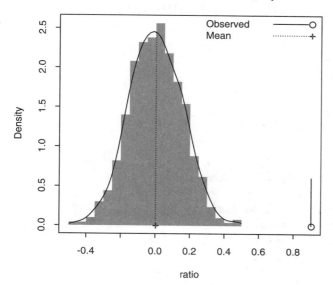

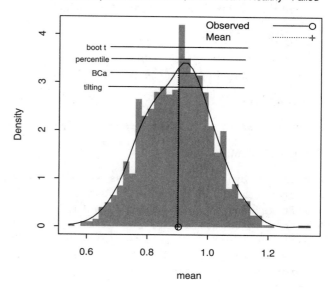

18.51

The standard deviation for the estimated P-value of 0.015 for the DRP study, based on B = 999 resamples is 0.00385. The standard deviation for the estimated P-value of 0.0183 based on the 500,000 resamples in the Verizon study is 0.000190.

```
> sqrt((0.015 * (1 - 0.015))/999)

[1] 0.00384575

> sqrt((0.0183 * (1 - 0.0183))/500000)

[1] 0.0001895527
```

18.52

a The two populations should be the same, but may be skewed (or differ otherwise from Normality).
b The two populations are the same, and are normal.
c Two normal populations with the same mean but different variances.

18.53

a Let p_1 denote the probability of success of new franchise firms with exclusive territory clauses and p_2 the probability of success of new franchise firms without exclusive territory clause. We test the hypotheses $H_0 : p_1 = p_2$, $H_a : p_1 > p_2$.
b The z statistic is z = 2.43. The P-value for the test is 0.0075.
c Under the null hypothesis, all 170 firms are equally likely to be a success. In this case, successes occur for reasons that have nothing to do with whether the firm has an exclusive territory clause. We can resample in a way consistent with the null hypothesis by choosing an ordinary SRS of 142 of the firms without replacement and assigning them to the exclusive territory clause group. The P-value for the permutation test is 0.018. This P-value is larger than that found in part (b), largely because the z-test fails to take ties into account.
d There is evidence at the 0.05 level, that exclusive territory clauses increase the chance of success. There is not evidence that exclusive territory clauses increase the chance of success at the 0.01 level.

e A 95% BCa confidence interval for the difference between the two population proportions is (0.039, 0.424). This interval does not include 0 and lies to the positive side of 0. This is consistent with is consistent with the results of the permutation test in part (d), which rejected the null hypothesis at the 0.05 level.

```
> p1 <- 108/142
> p2 <- 15/28
> p <- (108 + 15)/(142 + 28)
> (p1 - p2)/sqrt((p * (1 - p))/142 + (p * (1 - p))/28)

[1] 2.431293

> 1 - pnorm((p1 - p2)/sqrt((p * (1 - p))/142 + (p * (1 - p))/28))

[1] 0.00752252

> # Note - by recording success and failure as 1 and 0, we can compute
> # proportions by calculating means
> # It is easiest to do this from the GUI.  From the command line,
> # need to create a data set with one row per observation:
> Exercise18.053 <- data.frame(Exclusive = rep(c("Exclusive", "No"), c(142, 28)), Success
+    = rep(c(1, 0, 1, 0), c(108, 142 - 108, 15, 28 - 15)))
> perm53 <- permutationTestMeans(Exercise18.053, treatment = Exclusive, seed = 0,
+    alternative = "greater")
> perm53

Call:
permutationTestMeans(data = Exercise18.053, treatment = Exclusive, alternative =
  "greater", seed = 0)


Number of Replications: 999


Summary Statistics:
        Observed      Mean      SE alternative p.value
Success   0.2248 -0.001517 0.08993      greater   0.018

> # increase number of replications for greater accuracy:
> permutationTestMeans(Exercise18.053, treatment = Exclusive, seed = 0, alternative =
+    "greater", B = 99999)

Call:
permutationTestMeans(data = Exercise18.053, treatment = Exclusive, B = 99999,
  alternative = "greater", seed = 0)


Number of Replications: 99999


Summary Statistics:
        Observed       Mean      SE alternative p.value
Success   0.2248 -0.0004553 0.09316      greater 0.01667

> # Note - z-test fails to take ties into account.
> plot(perm53, cex.main = 1)
> boot53 <- bootstrap2(Exercise18.053$Success, mean, treatment = Exercise18.053$
+    Exclusive, seed = 0)
> plot(boot53)
> limits.bca(boot53)

          2.5%         5%        95%      97.5%
mean 0.03923541 0.06086519  0.388833  0.4244194
```

```
> limits.tilt(boot53)
```

```
              2.5%          5%         95%       97.5%
mean  0.03203727  0.06135004  0.3923254  0.4227374
```

```
> plotWithIntervals(boot53, Par=list(cex.main = 1))
```

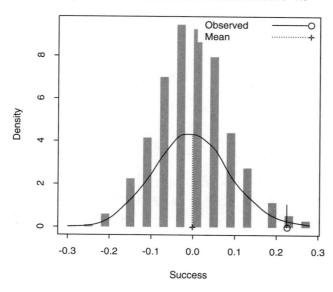

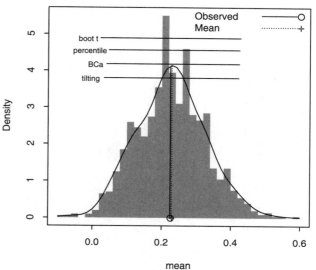

18.54

a $H_0 : \mu_1 = \mu_2$, $H_a : \mu_1 < \mu_2$, where μ_1 is the mean resposne time for turning the knob clockwise (to the right). (A two-sided alternative would also be reasonable.)

b P-value = 0.0043.

c See figure; the area to the left of the verical line segment on the left side of the figure.

```
> Exercise18.054 # variables Right and Left
> perm54 <- permutationTestMeans(Exercise18.054$Right, data2 = Exercise18.054$Left,
+     paired = T, seed = 0, alternative = "less")
> perm54
```

```
Call:
permutationTestMeans(data = Exercise18.054$Right, data2 = Exercise18.054$Left,
  alternative = "less", paired = T, seed = 0)

Number of Replications: 999

Summary Statistics:
     Observed    Mean     SE alternative p.value
Var    -13.32  0.05602  5.019         less   0.005
```

```
> # more samples for higher accuracy:
> permutationTestMeans(Exercise18.054$Right, data2 = Exercise18.054$Left, B = 99999,
+     paired = T, seed = 0, alternative = "less")
```

```
Call:
permutationTestMeans(data = Exercise18.054$Right, data2 = Exercise18.054$Left, B = 99999,
  alternative = "less", paired = T, seed = 0)

Number of Replications: 99999

Summary Statistics:
     Observed      Mean    SE alternative p.value
Var    -13.32 -0.006327 5.224          less 0.00434

> plot(perm54, cex.main = 1)
```

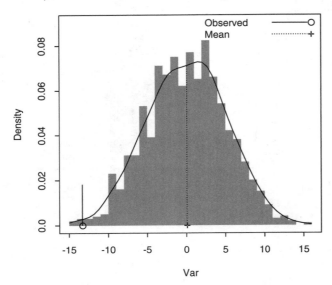

permutation : mean : Exercise18.054$Right - Exercise18.054$Left

18.55

a Let r denote the correlation between the salaries and batting averages of all major league baseball players. We test the hypotheses $H_0 : r = 0$, $H_a : r > 0$.

b The P-value is 0.257. We conclude that there is not strong evidence that salaries and batting averages are correlated in the population of all major league players.

```
> Exercise18.055 # variables Name, Salary and Average
> Must permute only one of the variables:
> perm55 <- permutationTest(Exercise18.055, resampleColumns = "Salary", seed = 0,
+     cor(Salary, Average), alternative = "greater")
> perm55

Call:
permutationTest(data = Exercise18.055, statistic = cor(Salary, Average), alternative =
  "greater", resampleColumns = "Salary", seed = 0)

Number of Replications: 999

Summary Statistics:
       Observed     Mean     SE alternative p-value
Param    0.1068 0.007398 0.1442      greater   0.257
```

```
> plot(perm55, cex.main = 1)
```

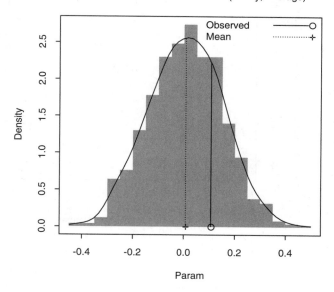

permutation : Exercise18.055 : cor(Salary, Average)

18.56

$H_0 : \mu_2 > \mu_1$, where μ_1 = mean for one-bedroom and μ_2 = mean for two-bedroom apartments. The P-value is 0.032; we conclude there is significant evidence that the mean rent for 2-bedroom apartments is higher.

```
> Exercise18.056 # variable Apartment Bedrooms Rent
> qqnorm(Exercise18.056$Rent[Exercise18.056$Bedrooms == 2])
> qqnorm(Exercise18.056$Rent[Exercise18.056$Bedrooms == 1])
> perm56 <- permutationTestMeans(Exercise18.056$Rent, seed = 0, treatment =
+     Exercise18.056$Bedrooms, alternative = "greater")
> perm56


Call:
permutationTestMeans(data = Exercise18.056$Rent, treatment = Exercise18.056$Bedrooms,
  alternative = "greater", seed = 0)

Number of Replications: 999

Summary Statistics:
    Observed    Mean     SE alternative p.value
Var       80 -0.5516  41.57      greater   0.032


> plot(perm56, cex.main = 1)
```

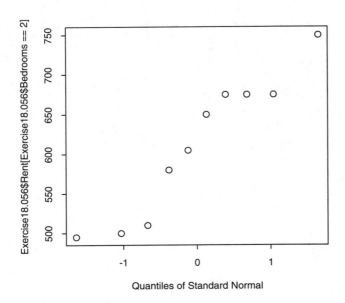

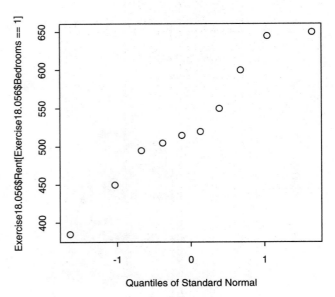

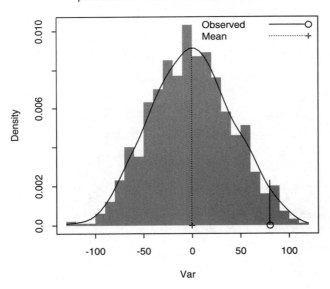

18.57

$H_0 : m_2 > m_1$, where m_1 = median for one-bedroom and m_2 = median for two-bedroom apartments. The P-value is 0.097; we conclude there is not significant evidence that the median rent for 2-bedroom apartments is higher.

Note—for normal or short-tailed data, comparing means has higher power than comparing medians.

```
> perm57 <- permutationTest2(Exercise18.056, median(Rent), seed = 0, treatment =
+     Bedrooms, alternative = "greater")
> perm57

Call:
permutationTest2(data = Exercise18.056, statistic = median(Rent), treatment = Bedrooms,
```

```
      alternative = "greater", seed = 0)

Number of Replications: 999

Summary Statistics:
        Observed  Mean     SE alternative p.value
Param        110 2.362  76.09      greater   0.097

> plot(perm57, cex.main = 1)
```

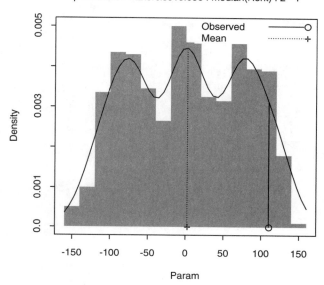

permutation : Exercise18.056 : median(Rent) : 2 - 1

18.58

a The averages of the two groups appear about the same; the heights of the forwards are a bit more spread out.

b $H_0 : \mu_1 = \mu_2$, $H_a : \mu_1 < \mu_2$, where μ_1 is the mean height of forwards. (Could also do a two-sided test.)

c The P-value is 0.35. We conclude that there is not significant evidence that the mean height of forwards is less than that of centers.

```
     Forwards         Centers
           45 : 6 :
       666677 : 6 : 6
      8888999 : 6 : 888889
000000011111 : 7 : 000111
       222223 : 7 : 222333
        44555 : 7 : 5
            6 : 7
```

```
> Exercise18.058 # variables Height and Position
> # Stem plots; put these together back-to-back by hand:
> stem(Exercise18.058$Height[Exercise18.058$Position == "Forward"], scale = -1, nl = 2)

N = 39   Median = 70
Quartiles = 68, 72

Decimal point is 1 place to the right of the colon
```

```
6 : 45
6 : 666677
6 : 8888999
7 : 000000011111
7 : 222223
7 : 44555
7 : 6
```

```
> stem(Exercise18.058$Height[Exercise18.058$Position == "Center"], scale = -1, nl = 2)
```

```
N = 20    Median = 70.5
Quartiles = 68, 72

Decimal point is 1 place to the right of the colon

   6 : 6
   6 : 888889
   7 : 000111
   7 : 222333
   7 : 5
```

```
> perm58 <- permutationTestMeans(Exercise18.058, treatment = Position, seed = 0,
+     alternative = "less")
> perm58
```

```
Call:
permutationTestMeans(data = Exercise18.058, treatment = Position, alternative = "less",
  seed = 0)

Number of Replications: 999

Summary Statistics:
       Observed     Mean      SE alternative p.value
Height  -0.3231 0.008714  0.7748        less    0.35
```

```
> plot(perm58, cex.main = 1)
```

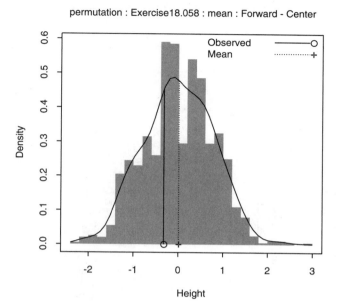

permutation : Exercise18.058 : mean : Forward - Center

18.59

a For the median we test the hypotheses $H_0 : m_1 = m_2$, $H_a : m_1 \neq m_2$, where m_1 and m_2 are median response times for the right and left hands, respectively. For the 25% trimmed mean we test the hypotheses $H_0 : M_1 = M_2$, $H_a : M_1 \neq M_2$, where M_1 and M_2 are the 25% trimmed means for the right and left hands, respectively.

b The permutation distribution is clearly not Normal. The P-value = 0.002 for the permutation test for the difference in medians.

c The permutation distribution looks much more like a Normal distribution than the permutation distribution in (b) for the difference in medians. The P-value = 0.002 for the permutation test for the difference in 25% trimmed means.

d There is strong evidence that there is a difference in the population median times when using the right hand versus when using the left hand. There is strong evidence that there is a difference in the population 25% trimmed mean times when using the right hand versus when using the left hand.

```
> Exercise18.059 # variables Time, Distance, Hand; latter "right" or "left"
> perm59a <- permutationTest2(Exercise18.059, median(Time), treatment = Hand, seed
+      = 0)
> plot(perm59a, cex.main = 1)
> perm59a

Call:
permutationTest2(data = Exercise18.059, statistic = median(Time), treatment = Hand, seed
   = 0)

Number of Replications: 999

Summary Statistics:
      Observed   Mean    SE alternative p.value
Param    -101.5 0.1271 35.77   two.sided   0.002

> perm59b <- permutationTest2(Exercise18.059, mean(Time, trim = 0.25), treatment =
+     Hand, seed = 0)
> plot(perm59b, cex.main = 1)
> perm59b
```

```
Call:
permutationTest2(data = Exercise18.059, statistic = mean(Time, trim = 0.25), treatment
   = Hand, seed = 0)

Number of Replications: 999

Summary Statistics:
        Observed      Mean     SE alternative p.value
Param        -99  -0.05586  26.27    two.sided    0.002
```

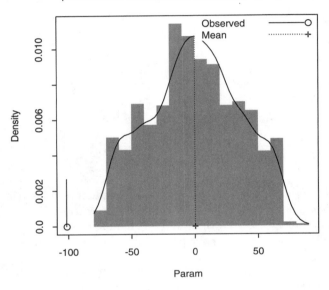

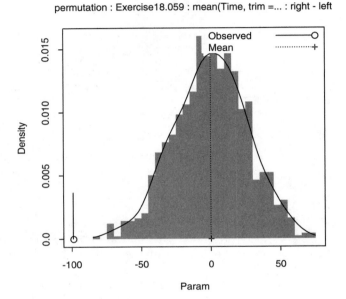

18.60

a It appears that the weights are somewhat larger for the younger customers.

```
        Age < 60       Age >= 60
              9 : 6 : 8
             34 : 7 : 1234
          55678 : 7 : 5778
             01 : 8 : 0
```

b greater, because the goal of this significance test is to test the hypothesis that the weight given to younger customers is greater than given to older customers.

c The P-value is 0.223. This does not provide signficant evidence against the null hypothesis. We would fail to reject the null hypothesis of equality. However, it is possible that there is an effect, just not large enough to easily detect with a sample of this size.

```
> Exercise18.060 # variables Weight and Age, either "< 60" or ">= 60"
> # Stem plots; do back-to-back by hand:
> stem(Exercise18.060$Weight[Exercise18.060$Age == "< 60"])

N = 10   Median = 75.5
Quartiles = 74, 78

Decimal point is 1 place to the right of the colon
```

```
    6 : 9
    7 : 34
    7 : 55678
    8 : 01

> stem(Exercise18.060$Weight[Exercise18.060$Age == ">= 60"])

N = 10   Median = 74.5
Quartiles = 72, 77

Decimal point is 1 place to the right of the colon

    6 : 8
    7 : 1234
    7 : 5778
    8 : 0

> perm60 <- permutationTestMeans(Exercise18.060, treatment = Age, alternative =
+     "greater", seed = 0)
> plot(perm60)
> perm60

Call:
permutationTestMeans(data = Exercise18.060, treatment = Age, alternative = "greater",
  seed = 0)

Number of Replications: 999

Summary Statistics:
        Observed      Mean    SE alternative p.value
Weight       1.3 -0.004505 1.554      greater   0.223
```

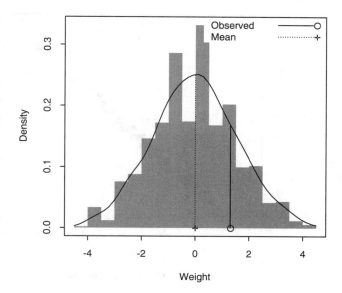

permutation : Exercise18.060 : mean : < 60 - >= 6

18.61

a Let p_1 denote the proportion of women in the population who pay attention to a "No Sweat" label when buying a garment and p_2 denote the proportion of men in the population who pay attention to a "No Sweat" label when buying a garment. We test the hypotheses. $H_0 : p_1 = p_2$, $H_a : p_1 \neq p_2$.

b The P-value for the permutation test is 0.002.

c The permutation distribution is approximately Normal (except that it is discrete; you can see this using a normal quantile plot or by observing spikes in the histogram) and thus it is not surprising that the permutation test agrees closely with the z test in Example 8.6.

```
> 63/296 # women

[1] 0.2128378

> 27/251 # men

[1] 0.1075697

> Exercise18.061 <- data.frame(Sex = rep(c("Women", "Men"), c(296, 251)), User = rep(c(1,
+   0, 1, 0), c(63, 296 - 63, 27, 251 - 27)))
> perm61 <- permutationTestMeans(Exercise18.061, treatment = Sex, seed = 0)
> perm61

Call:
permutationTestMeans(data = Exercise18.061, treatment = Sex, seed = 0)

Number of Replications: 999

Summary Statistics:
      Observed       Mean      SE alternative p.value
User    0.1053  0.0003515  0.03049   two.sided    0.002

> plot(perm61, cex.main = 1)
> qqnorm(perm61, cex.main = 1)
```

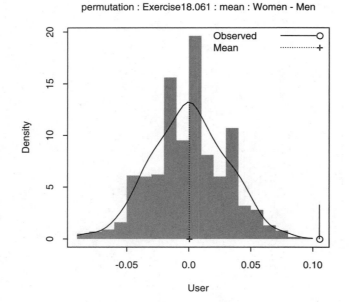

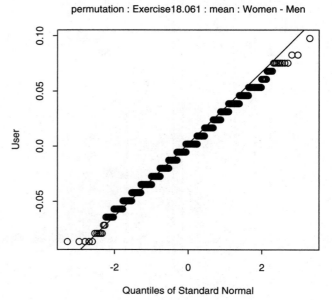

18.62

The observed difference in medians is -15.88; 2002 is lower. The P-value for the two-sided alternative is 0.608; we conclude that there is not signficant evidence of a change in price.

```
> names(Exercise18.062)  # Price and Year

[1] "Price" "Year"

> tapply(Exercise18.062$Price, Exercise18.062$Year, median)

  2001    2002
260.8 244.925

> perm62 <- permutationTest2(Exercise18.062, median(Price), treatment = Year, seed
+      = 0)
> plot(perm62, cex.main = 1)
> perm62

Call:
permutationTest2(data = Exercise18.062, statistic = median(Price), treatment = Year,
  seed = 0)

Number of Replications: 999

Summary Statistics:
       Observed   Mean    SE alternative p.value
Param    -15.88 0.2518 26.69   two.sided   0.608
```

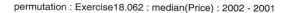

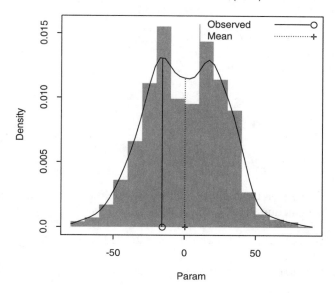

18.63

A two-sided permutation test of the hypothesis has P-value = 0.004, and we conclude that there is strong evidence that there is a correlation between square footage and age of a house in Ames, Iowa.

```
> names(Exercise18.063) # variables Price, SquareFootage, Age
```

```
[1] "Price"          "SquareFootage" "Age"

> perm63 <- permutationTest(Exercise18.063, resampleColumns = "SquareFootage", cor(
+     Age, SquareFootage), seed = 0)
> plot(perm63, cex.main = 1)
> perm63

Call:
permutationTest(data = Exercise18.063, statistic = cor(Age, SquareFootage),
  resampleColumns = "SquareFootage", seed = 0)

Number of Replications: 999

Summary Statistics:
      Observed    Mean      SE alternative p-value
Param   -0.4065 0.002224 0.1424    two.sided   0.004
```

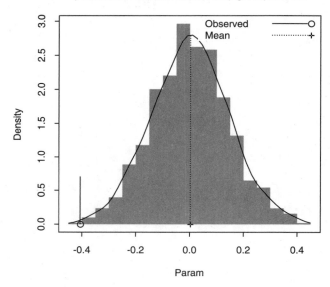

permutation : Exercise18.063 : cor(Age, SquareFo...

18.64

For the one-sided alternative that the success probability is greater for subjects receiving calcium, the P-value is 0.273. We conclude that there is not significant evidence that calcium gives an improvement.

```
> Exercise18.064 <- data.frame(Treatment = rep(c("Calcium", "Placebo"), c(10, 11)),
+     Success = rep(c(1, 0, 1, 0), c(6, 10 - 6, 4, 11 - 4)))
> perm64 <- permutationTestMeans(Exercise18.064, treatment = Treatment, alternative
+     = "greater", seed = 0)
> plot(perm64, cex.main = 1)
> perm64

Call:
permutationTestMeans(data = Exercise18.064, treatment = Treatment, alternative =
  "greater", seed = 0)
```

Number of Replications: 999

Summary Statistics:
```
          Observed    Mean      SE alternative p.value
Success     0.2364 0.01125  0.2249      greater   0.273
```

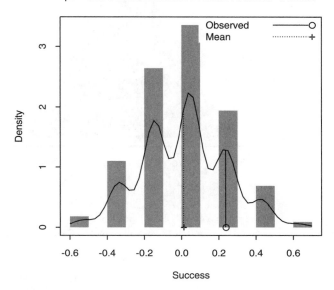

permutation : Exercise18.064 : mean : Calcium - Placebo

18.65

A 95% bootstrap z interval using the observed difference in proportions (0.2364) and the bootstrap standard error (SE = 0.208) is (-0.171, 0.643).

```
> boot65 <- bootstrap2(Exercise18.064$Success, mean, treatment = Exercise18.064$
+       Treatment, seed = 0)
> plot(boot65) # unusual plot -- high-low pattern.  This is because
>                # histograms are sensitive to the width of bins.
> plot(boot65, nclass = 10)  # more reasonable
> plot(boot65, nclass = 40)  # shows gaps
> qqnorm(boot65) # note the bunching & gaps, explains the high-low pattern
> boot65

Call:
bootstrap2(data = Exercise18.064$Success, statistic = mean, treatment = Exercise18.064$
  Treatment, seed = 0)

Number of Replications: 1000

Summary Statistics:
      Observed    Mean     Bias      SE
mean    0.2364  0.2442 0.007873  0.2076

> limits.t(boot65, z = T)

            2.5%         5%        95%       97.5%
mean  -0.1705423 -0.1051226  0.5778499  0.6432696
```

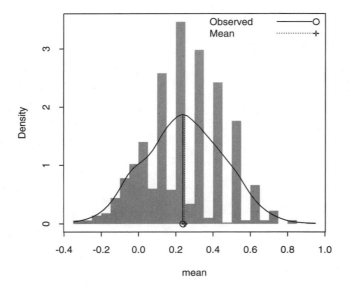

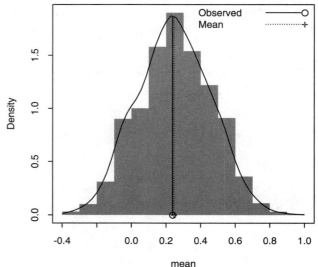

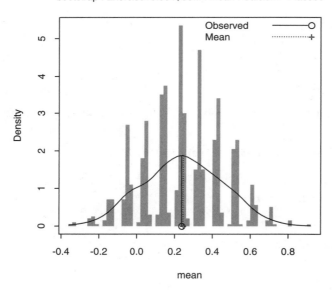

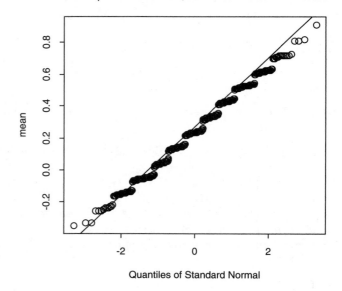

18.66

a The ILEC set is strongly right-skewed. The CLEC set is bimodal, with about a third "1" and two-thirds "5".

b The null hypothesis is that the mean of the two groups is the same; the alternative is that the mean of the CLEC group is larger. The t-statistic is -3.25, and the P-value is 0.004 for the one-sided test.

c The P-value is 0.0073. The permutation test does not require normal distributions, and gives more accurate answers in the caes of skewness.

d The difference is significant at both the 5% and 1% levels.

```
> Exercise18.066 # variables Time and Group (ILEC or CLEC)
> histogram( ~ Time | Group, data = Exercise18.066)
> qqmath( ~ Time | Group, data = Exercise18.066)
```

```
> t.test(Exercise18.066$Time[Exercise18.066$Group == "ILEC"], Exercise18.066$Time[
+    Exercise18.066$Group == "CLEC"], alternative = "less", var.equal = F)

        Welch Modified Two-Sample t-Test

data:  Exercise18.066$Time[Exercise18.066$Group == "ILEC"] and Exercise18.066$Time[Exercise18.066$Group ==
t = -3.2486, df = 10.712802219295, p-value = 0.004
alternative hypothesis:  difference in means is less than 0
95 percent confidence interval:
        NA -0.9244845
sample estimates:
 mean of x mean of y
  1.726316      3.8


> # Easy to do perm test for difference in means:
> perm66a <- permutationTestMeans(Exercise18.066, treatment = Group, alternative =
+    "less", seed = 0)
> perm66a

Call:
permutationTestMeans(data = Exercise18.066, treatment = Group, alternative = "less",
  seed = 0)


Number of Replications: 999


Summary Statistics:
      Observed       Mean     SE alternative p.value
Time    -2.074 -0.0001264 0.6373        less   0.009


> permutationTestMeans(Exercise18.066, treatment = Group, B = 99999, alternative = "less",
+    seed = 0)

Call:
permutationTestMeans(data = Exercise18.066, treatment = Group, B = 99999, alternative =
  "less", seed = 0)


Number of Replications: 99999


Summary Statistics:
      Observed      Mean     SE alternative p.value
Time    -2.074 0.001671 0.6325        less 0.00729

> plot(perm66a, cex.main = 1)
> # Very skewed left
>
> # It is possible but harder to do a perm test where the test
> # statistics is a pooled-variance t; need to ensure that only one
> # variable is permuted.
> # As a side note, there is a one-to-one relationship between the difference
> # in means and the pooled-variance to, so tests based on these statistics
> # are equivalent; hence we usually test based on the simpler statistic.
> perm66b <- permutationTest(Exercise18.066, resampleColumns = "Time", alternative
+    = "less", seed = 0, t.test(Time[Group == "ILEC"], Time[Group == "CLEC"],
+    alternative = "less", var.equal = T)$statistic)
> perm66b
```

```
Call:
permutationTest(data = Exercise18.066, statistic = t.test(Time[Group == "ILEC"], Time[
  Group == "CLEC"], alternative = "less", var.equal = T)$statistic, alternative = "less",
  resampleColumns = "Time", seed = 0)

Number of Replications: 999

Summary Statistics:
  Observed     Mean     SE alternative p-value
t   -3.441 -0.03155  1.012          less   0.008
```

```
> # The answer may differ from from permutationTestMeans, because random
> # permutations are done differently.
> plot(perm66b, cex.main = 1)
```

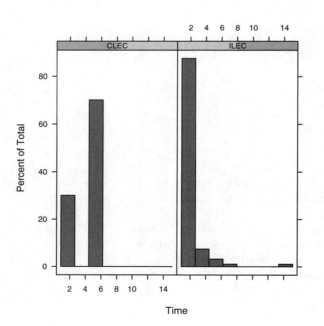

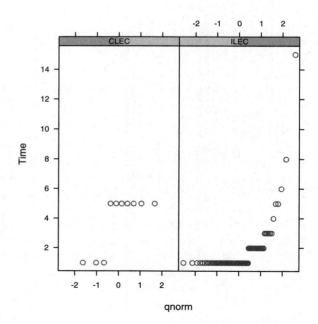

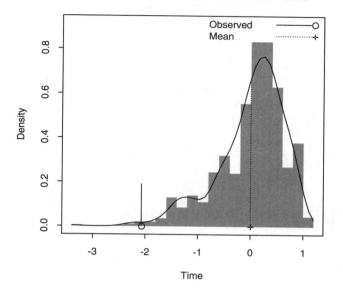

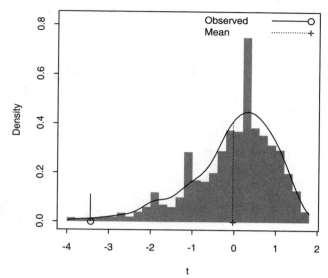

18.67

a We performed a two-sided permutation test on the ratio of standard deviations (using variances would have been equivalent). Some of the ratios were infinite because the permutation test produced a standard deviation of 0 in the denominator. The mean and SE of the permutation distribution are undefined, but we can still obtain the P-value = 0.366 based on the permutation distribution. This P-value tells us that there is not strong evidence that the variability in the repair times for ILEC and CLEC customers differs.

b The P-value for the permutation test differs from that obtained by the F statistic. This suggests that the test based on the F statistic is not very accurate.

```
> perm67 <- permutationTest2(Exercise18.066, stdev(Time), ratio = T, treatment =
+     Group, seed = 0)
> perm67


Call:
permutationTest2(data = Exercise18.066, statistic = stdev(Time), treatment = Group,
  ratio = T, seed = 0)

Number of Replications: 999

Summary Statistics:
      Observed Mean SE alternative p.value
Param   0.9321  Inf NA   two.sided    0.366


> plot(perm67, cex.main = 1)
```

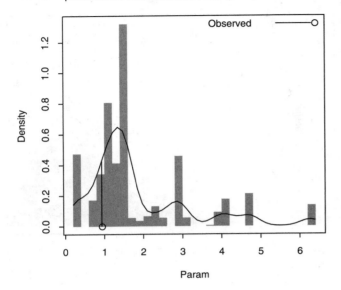

permutation : Exercise18.066 : stdev(Time) : ILEC / CLEC

18.68

a $H_0 : \sigma_1^2 = \sigma_2^2$, $H_a : \sigma_1^2 \neq \sigma_2^2$, or $H_0 : \sigma_1^2/\sigma_2^2 = 1$, $H_a : \sigma_1^2/\sigma_2^2 \neq 1$.

b The P-value is 0.048. This is marginally significant at the 5% level. However, it would be better to take more permutations, to reduce random variability in borderline cases like this.

c The P-value there is 0.0792. The permutation test P-value is lower, because the "Failed" group appears slightly non-Normal, with a left tail that is shorter Normal.

```
> Exercise18.068 # variables status (Healthy or Failed) and ratio
> qqmath( ~ ratio | status, data = Exercise18.068)
> perm68 <- permutationTest2(Exercise18.068, var(ratio), ratio = T, treatment =
+     status, seed = 0)
> perm68
```

```
Call:
permutationTest2(data = Exercise18.068, statistic = var(ratio), treatment = status,
  ratio = T, seed = 0)


Number of Replications: 999


Summary Statistics:
      Observed  Mean     SE alternative p.value
Param    1.766 1.053 0.2945   two.sided   0.048
```

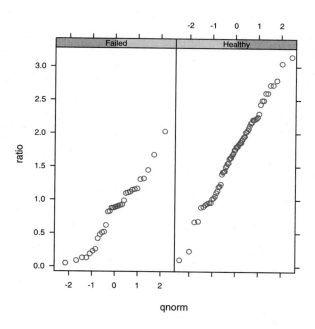

18.69

a We test the hypotheses $H_0 : \mu = 0$, $H_a : \mu > 0$, where μ is the mean change (Posttest $-$ Pretest). Note that positive values of μ indicate that mean posttest scores are higher than mean pretest scores, and hence that test scores have improved.

b The P-value is 0.026, so there is evidence (significant at the 0.05 level but not at the 0.01 level) that the mean change (Posttest - Pretest) is positive.

c The area to the right of 1.45 is the P-value.

```
> Exercise18.069 # variables Pretest and Posttest
> perm69 <- permutationTestMeans(Exercise18.069$Posttest, data2 = Exercise18.069$
+     Pretest, paired = T, alternative = "greater", seed = 0)
> perm69


Call:
permutationTestMeans(data = Exercise18.069$Posttest, data2 = Exercise18.069$Pretest,
  alternative = "greater", paired = T, seed = 0)

Number of Replications: 999

Summary Statistics:
     Observed      Mean     SE alternative p.value
Var       1.45 -0.003654 0.7492      greater   0.026


> plot(perm69, cex.main = 1)
```

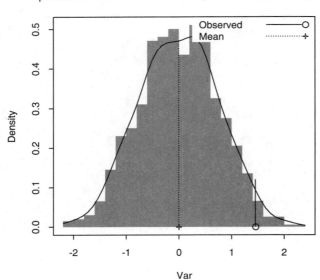

permutation : mean : Exercise18.069$Po... - Exercise18.069$Pr...

18.70

There is strong evidence that fitness and ego strength are related; the observed difference in ego strength lies substantially outside the range of normal chance variation, with an estimated P-value of 0.002 (the smallest possible for a two-sided test with 999 replications. Additional note—in this case, where there is complete separation between groups, the exact permutation test P-value is $1/\mathrm{choose}(n,n1) = 1/40116600$.

```
> Exercise07.087 # variables Subject Fitness Group   Ego
> qqmath( ~ Ego | Fitness, data = Exercise07.087)
> perm70 <- permutationTestMeans(Exercise07.087$Ego, treatment = Exercise07.087$
+     Fitness, seed = 0)
> perm70
```

```
Call:
permutationTestMeans(data = Exercise07.087$Ego, treatment = Exercise07.087$Fitness, seed
   = 0)

Number of Replications: 999

Summary Statistics:
    Observed      Mean      SE alternative p.value
Var   -1.789 -0.009287  0.4175   two.sided    0.002


> plot(perm70, cex.main = 1)
```

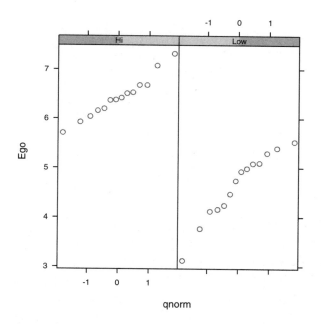

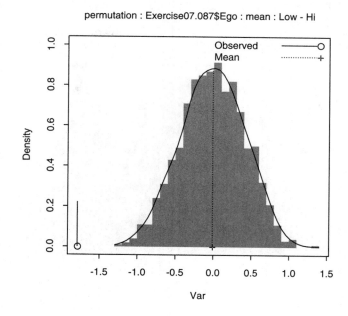

18.71

There is strong evidence that fitness and ego strength are related; the observed difference in ego strength lies substantially outside the range of normal chance variation, with an estimated P-value of 0.002 (the smallest possible for a two-sided test with 999 replications. In this cae the observed difference is not as far from the limits of observed chance variation.

```
> perm71 <- permutationTest2(Exercise07.087$Ego, median, treatment = Exercise07.087$
+     Fitness, seed = 0)
> perm71


Call:
permutationTest2(data = Exercise07.087$Ego, statistic = median, treatment =
  Exercise07.087$Fitness, seed = 0)

Number of Replications: 999

Summary Statistics:
        Observed    Mean     SE alternative p.value
median    -1.565 0.01948  0.678    two.sided   0.002


> plot(perm71)
```

permutation : Exercise07.087$Ego : median : Low

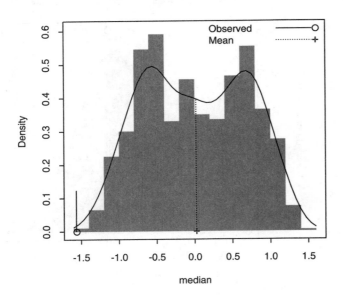

18.72

a The distribution is approximately Normal, aside from being discrete.
b The mean is 3.62, and formula standard error is 0.52.
c The bootstrap standard error is 0.51. This is close to the formula standard error.

```
> Exercise18.072 # variable Change
> hist(Exercise18.072)
> qqnorm(Exercise18.072)
> mean(Exercise18.072)


[1] 3.617647


> stdev(Exercise18.072$Change)/sqrt(length(Exercise18.072$Change))


[1] 0.5239618


> boot72 <- bootstrap(Exercise18.072, mean, seed = 0)
> boot72


Call:
bootstrap(data = Exercise18.072, statistic = mean, seed = 0)

Number of Replications: 1000

Summary Statistics:
     Observed  Mean    Bias      SE
mean    3.618  3.643  0.02521  0.5085
```

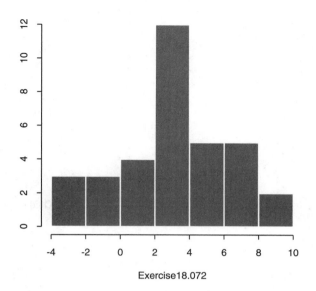

Exercise18.072

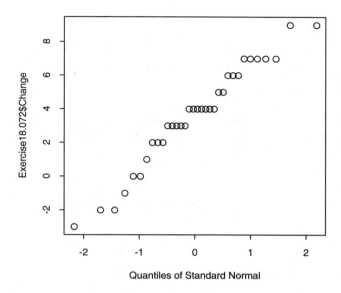

Quantiles of Standard Normal

18.73

In this problem, the answers will depend strongly on the random sample drawn.

a For a Uniform distribution on 0 to 1, the population median is 0.5. The shape of the bootstrap distribution will depend on the sample drawn.

b The bootstrap standard error is 0.072. A 95% bootstrap *t* confidence interval is (0.337, 0.572). (Both depend heavily on the sample drawn.)

c The bootstrap BCa 95% confidence interval is (0.369, 0.620). A tilting 95% interval is (0.373, 0.572). The bootstrap *t* 95% confidence interval is the same as the 95% tilting interval, slightly narrower than the 95% BCa interval. How close the bootstrap *t* is to the other intervals will depend on your sample; in general it is not reliable in this example, though it may appear so.

```
> set.seed(1)
> x73 <- runif(50)
> median(x73)

[1] 0.4818099

> boot73 <- bootstrap(x73, median, seed = 0)
> plot(boot73)
> qqnorm(boot73)
> boot73

Call:
bootstrap(data = x73, statistic = median, seed = 0)

Number of Replications: 1000

Summary Statistics:
        Observed    Mean       Bias      SE
median    0.4818   0.4802   -0.001635   0.07217

> limits.t(boot73)
```

```
              2.5%        5%        95%      97.5%
median  0.3365956  0.3606961  0.6029237  0.6270243

> limits.bca(boot73)

              2.5%        5%        95%      97.5%
median  0.3694765  0.3838869  0.6115975  0.6198372

> limits.tilt(boot73)

              2.5%        5%        95%      97.5%
median  0.3731141  0.3838869  0.5720608  0.5720608

> plotWithIntervals(boot73)
```

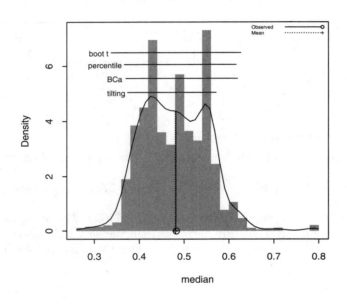

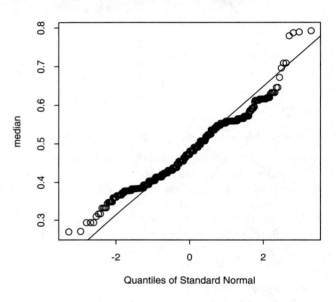

18.74

a The difference appears quite significant.

```
        : 1 : 9
        : 2 : 01
    3 : 2 : 2233
    5 : 2 : 4
    6 : 2 :
  899 : 2 :
   01 : 3 :
   22 : 3 :
    5 : 3 :
```

b The P-value is about 0.00056 (based on 99,999 resamples). For 999 resamples, the answer will usually be either 0.002 or 0.004 (because the estimated P-value is twice 1/1000 or 2/1000).

c We conclude that there is significant evidence that the mean ages differ. Note—with a large enough number of resamples we see that the permutation test P-value is consistent with the answer form a *t* test, but students doing only 1000 resamples may get an answer that indicates that the *t* test P-value is too small.

```
> Exercise18.074 # variables Age and Sex (male or female)
> stem(Exercise18.074$Age[Exercise18.074$Sex == "male"], scale = -1, nl = 2)


N = 11   Median = 29
Quartiles = 26, 32


Decimal point is 1 place to the right of the colon


   2 : 3
   2 : 5
   2 : 6
   2 : 899
   3 : 01
   3 : 22
   3 : 5


> stem(Exercise18.074$Age[Exercise18.074$Sex == "female"], scale = -1, nl = 2)


N = 9   Median = 22
Quartiles = 21, 23


Decimal point is 1 place to the right of the colon


   1 : 9
   2 : 01
   2 : 2233
   2 : 4


High:  29


> perm74 <- permutationTestMeans(Exercise18.074, treatment = Sex, seed = 0)
> perm74


Call:
permutationTestMeans(data = Exercise18.074, treatment = Sex, seed = 0)


Number of Replications: 999


Summary Statistics:
    Observed    Mean    SE alternative p.value
Age    6.535 -0.0753 2.044   two.sided   0.002


> permutationTestMeans(Exercise18.074, treatment = Sex, seed = 0, B = 99999)


Call:
permutationTestMeans(data = Exercise18.074, treatment = Sex, B = 99999, seed = 0)


Number of Replications: 99999


Summary Statistics:
    Observed     Mean    SE alternative p.value
Age    6.535 0.0007791 2.056   two.sided 0.00056


> plot(perm74, cex.main = 1)
```

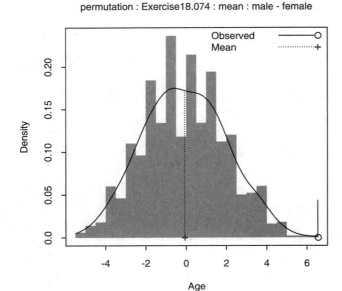

permutation : Exercise18.074 : mean : male - female

18.75

a The bootstrap distribution is left-skewed and does not appear to be approximately Normal. The bootstrap standard error is 0.134.

b The bootstrap t confidence interval is not appropriate here because the bootstrap distribution is not approximately normal.

c A 95% BCa confidence interval is (0.179, 0.710) and a 95% tilting interval is (0.218, 0.698).

```
> Table02.006 # variables Year, "Overseas...return", "US...return"
> boot75 <- bootstrap(Table02.006, cor(Overseas...return, US...return), seed = 0)
> boot75$defaultLabel = "bootstrap : cor(Overseas, US)"
> plot(boot75)
> boot75

Call:
bootstrap(data = Table02.006, statistic = cor(Overseas...return, US...return), seed = 0)

Number of Replications: 1000

Summary Statistics:
      Observed    Mean       Bias      SE
Param   0.5034  0.4998  -0.003626  0.1336

> limits.bca(boot75)

            2.5%        5%        95%      97.5%
Param  0.1792823  0.2272457  0.6777648  0.7095517

> limits.tilt(boot75)

            2.5%        5%        95%      97.5%
Param  0.218003  0.2642474  0.6720276  0.6980628

> plotWithIntervals(boot75)
```

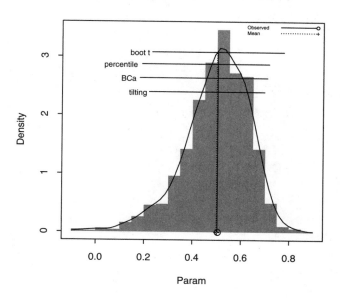

bootstrap : cor(Overseas, US)

18.76

a The standard deviation of daily changes is 2.21

b The bootstrap standard error is 0.31

c The bootstrap t interval is (1.56, 2.87)

d BCa (1.69, 2.96), tilting (1.65, 2.89). The two more accurate intervals reach farther to the right than the left, e.g. (-0.52, 0.75) for the BCa and (-0.56, 0.68) for tilting. This asymmetry suggests that t intervals would not be accurate.

Note—the big reason for the difference between t and more accurate intervals is bias. The percentile interval is even worse than the t—it does exactly the wrong thing in the case of bias.

```
> Exercise18.076 # variables Day, Close, Change
> x76 <- (100 * Exercise18.076$Change)/Exercise18.076$Close # percent change
> # There we divided by the close, because it was easy.  Really should divide
> # by the previous day's close:
> x76b <- (100 * Exercise18.076$Change)/(Exercise18.076$Close - Exercise18.076$Change)
> stdev(x76)

[1] 2.211902

> stdev(x76b)

[1] 2.214922

> boot76 <- bootstrap(x76, stdev, seed = 0)
> boot76

Call:
bootstrap(data = x76, statistic = stdev, seed = 0)

Number of Replications: 1000

Summary Statistics:
      Observed  Mean     Bias      SE
stdev    2.212 2.146  -0.06615  0.3131
```

```
> plot(boot76)
> limits.t(boot76)

            2.5%        5%       95%      97.5%
stdev  1.555653  1.669918  2.753887  2.868152

> limits.bca(boot76)

            2.5%        5%       95%      97.5%
stdev  1.693609  1.771606  2.838994  2.961138

> limits.bca(boot76) - boot76$observed

             2.5%         5%        95%       97.5%
stdev  -0.5182935  -0.4402961  0.6270912  0.7492353

> limits.tilt(boot76)

            2.5%       5%       95%     97.5%
stdev  1.650036  1.73455  2.783021  2.890715

> limits.tilt(boot76) - boot76$observed

             2.5%         5%        95%       97.5%
stdev  -0.5618669  -0.4773521  0.5711181  0.6788122

> plotWithIntervals(boot76)
```

bootstrap : x76 : stdev

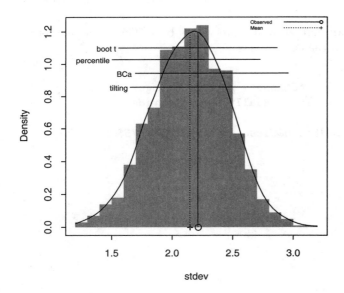

18.77

a The histogram of the 2000 data is strongly right-skewed with two outliers, one of which is extreme. This violates the guideline for using the t procedure given in Section 17.1, namely for a sample size of at least 15, t procedures can be used except in the presence of outliers or strong skewness. The histogram of the 2001 is right-skewed, but less strongly than that of the 2000 data.

b The P-value for the permutation test for the difference in means is 0.292. We conclude that there is not strong evidence that the mean selling prices for all Seattle real estate in 2000 and in 2001 are different.

```
> Exercise18.077 # Price
> par(mfrow = c(2, 2))
> hist(Seattle2001)
> qqnorm(Seattle2001)
> hist(Exercise18.077)
> qqnorm(Exercise18.077)
> par(mfrow = c(1, 1))
> perm77 <- permutationTestMeans(Seattle2001, data2 = Exercise18.077, seed = 0)
> perm77
```

```
Call:
permutationTestMeans(data = Seattle2001, data2 = Exercise18.077, seed = 0)

Number of Replications: 999

Summary Statistics:
        Observed   Mean    SE alternative p.value
Price    -80.02  -2.42 66.64    two.sided   0.292
```

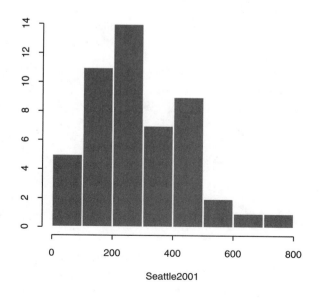

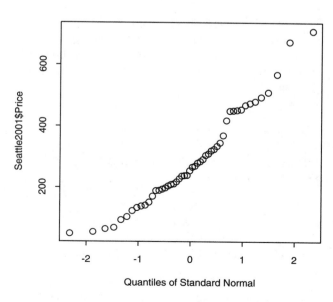

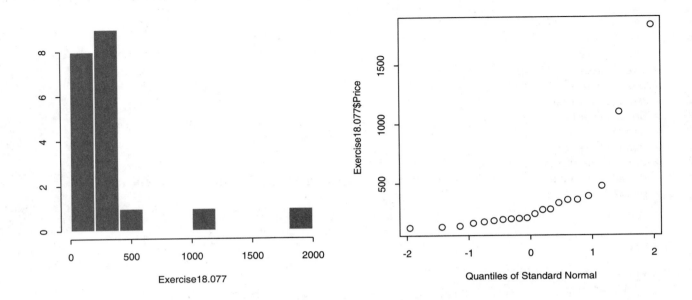

18.78

a The formula-based t-interval is (78.8, 115.7).

b The tilting interval is (72.4, 108.1), or observed value plus (-24.9, 10.9).

c The bootstrap distribution shows strong left skewness (compared to what we expect to see for a sampling distribution, as opposed to the distribution of a dataset).

d The *t* interval is not robust in this case. It indicates that the value 105 is well within the range of the interval, while a more accurate interval suggests that it is barely within the range of the interval.

```
> Exercise18.078 # variable Radon
> t.test(Exercise18.078$Radon)

        One-sample t-Test

data:  Exercise18.078$Radon
t = 11.6062, df = 11, p-value = 0
alternative hypothesis:  mean is not equal to 0
95 percent confidence interval:
  78.80025 115.68142
sample estimates:
 mean of x
  97.24083

> boot78 <- bootstrap(Exercise18.078, mean, seed = 0)
> limits.tilt(boot78)

         2.5%       5%       95%     97.5%
mean 72.386 77.01686 106.4936 108.1253

> limits.tilt(boot78) - boot78$observed

          2.5%        5%       95%      97.5%
mean -24.85483 -20.22398 9.252753 10.88451
```

```
> plot(boot78)
> qqnorm(boot78)
```

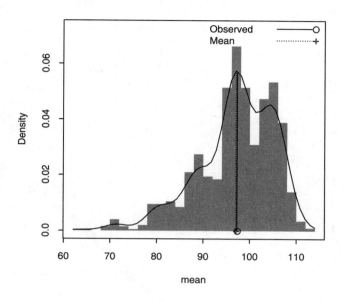

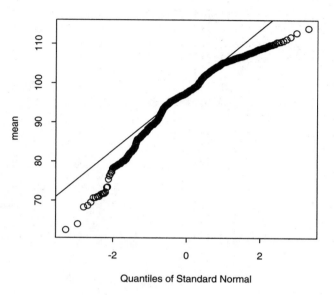

18.79

The study described in Exercise 18.78 is a one-sample problem. We have no methods for carrying out a permutation test in such one-sample problems (there is no obvious way to resample that is consistent with a one-sample test for a mean). If we permute the observations we get exactly the same mean every time!

18.80

a We are interested in whether the presentation causes an improvement in glove use. We must used a matched pairs method, because the same nurses were recorded both times.

b The P-value is 0.002 (the smallest possible for a two-sided test with 1000 resamples). This provides significant evidence that the presentation was helpful.

```
> Exercise18.080 # variables Before and After
> perm80 <- permutationTestMeans(Exercise18.080$Before, data2 = Exercise18.080$After,
+     paired = T, alternative = "less", seed = 0)
> perm80

Call:
permutationTestMeans(data = Exercise18.080$Before, data2 = Exercise18.080$After,
  alternative = "less", paired = T, seed = 0)

Number of Replications: 999

Summary Statistics:
    Observed    Mean      SE alternative p.value
Var  -0.6386 0.004548 0.1942        less   0.002
```

18.81

A 95% bootstrap t confidence interval for the mean change (after-before) is (0.41, 0.86). Zero is outside this interval, so the result is significant at the 0.05 level. We conclude that there is strong evidence that the mean change is different from 0, i.e. positive.

```
> boot81 <- bootstrap(Exercise18.080, mean(After) - mean(Before), seed = 0)
> plot(boot81, cex.main = 1)
> qqnorm(boot81, cex.main = 1)
> limits.t(boot81)

              2.5%        5%        95%      97.5%
Param  0.4118964  0.4528185  0.8243243  0.8652465
```

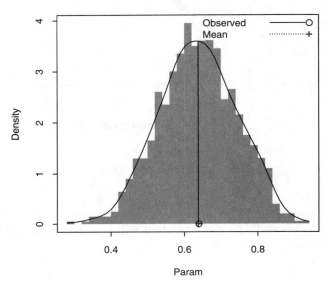

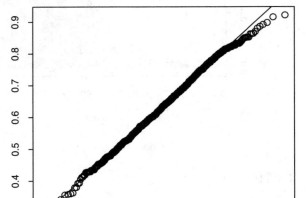

18.82

a Both distributions look approximately Normal (look at the quantile plots, not the histograms).

b The t-test P-value for the two-sided alternative is 0.0001.

c The permutation test P-value for the two-sided permutatino test is 0.002 (the smallest possible for a two-sided test with 1000 replications). The average unemployment rate has increased, and the change is statististically significant.

```
> Exercise18.082 # variables Y2001 and Y2002
> par(mfrow = c(2, 2))
> hist(Exercise18.082$Y2001, main = "2001")
> qqnorm(Exercise18.082$Y2001, main = "2001")
> hist(Exercise18.082$Y2002, main = "2002")
> qqnorm(Exercise18.082$Y2002, main = "2002")
> par(mfrow = c(1, 1))
> t.test(Exercise18.082$Y2001, Exercise18.082$Y2002, paired = T)

        Paired t-Test

data:  Exercise18.082$Y2001 and Exercise18.082$Y2002
```

```
t = -5.228, df = 18, p-value = 0.0001
alternative hypothesis:  mean of differences is not equal to 0
95 percent confidence interval:
 -1.2985662 -0.5540654
sample estimates:
 mean of x - y
    -0.9263158
```

```
> perm82 <- permutationTestMeans(Exercise18.082$Y2002, data2 = Exercise18.082$Y2001,
+     paired = T, seed = 0)
> perm82
```

```
Call:
permutationTestMeans(data = Exercise18.082$Y2002, data2 = Exercise18.082$Y2001, paired
   = T, seed = 0)

Number of Replications: 999

Summary Statistics:
     Observed      Mean      SE alternative p.value
Var    0.9263  0.004963  0.2655    two.sided   0.002
```

```
> permutationTestMeans(Exercise18.082$Y2002, B = 99999, data2 = Exercise18.082$Y2001,
+     paired = T, seed = 0)
```

```
Call:
permutationTestMeans(data = Exercise18.082$Y2002, data2 = Exercise18.082$Y2001, B =
   99999, paired = T, seed = 0)

Number of Replications: 99999

Summary Statistics:
     Observed      Mean      SE alternative p.value
Var    0.9263  0.001571  0.2746    two.sided   6e-005
```

```
> plot(perm82, main = "permutation : mean : 18.082 2002-2001")
```

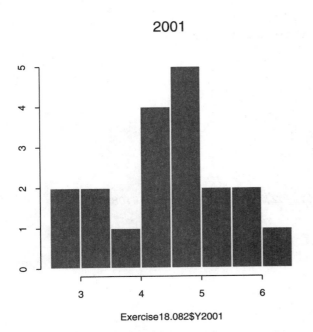

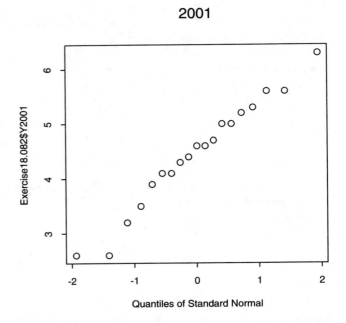

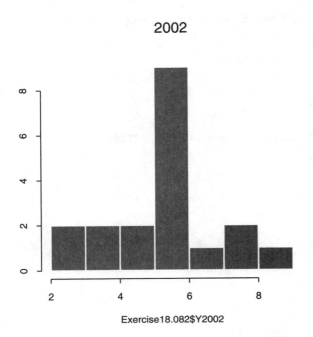

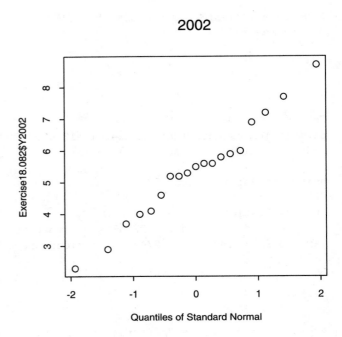

permutation : mean : 18.082 2002-2001

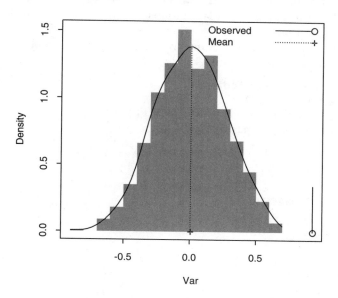

18.83

a 80% for girls, and 66% for boys.
b The P-value for a two-sided permutation test is 0.198. There is not strong evidence that there is a difference in the proportion of boys and girls who like chocolate ice cream.

```
> 40/50

[1] 0.8

> 30/45

[1] 0.6666667

> Exercise18.83 <- data.frame(Sex = rep(c("Girls", "Boys"), c(50, 45)), Like = rep(c(1, 0,
+   1, 0), c(40, 10, 30, 15)))
> perm83 <- permutationTestMeans(Exercise18.83, treatment = Sex, seed = 0)
> perm83

Call:
permutationTestMeans(data = Exercise18.83, treatment = Sex, seed = 0)

Number of Replications: 999

Summary Statistics:
     Observed      Mean     SE alternative p.value
Like   0.1333 0.0003693 0.0905   two.sided   0.198
```

18.84

a Both sets of data could come from Normal distributions. There are gaps and bunches, but that is normal.
b The bootstrap standard errors are 17.0 and 14.7 for the High and Medium groups, respectively.
c The bootstrap distributions are very Normal.

d The percentile limits are (106.4, 173.7) and (93.3, 150.1), and the tilting intervals are (106.8, 171.1) and (94.6, 150.9). Using either confidence interval methods, the intervals for the two groups overlap. This suggests that there may not be a statistically-significant difference between the two groups. However, we should do a confidence interval for the difference to answer that question.

e The 95% percentile confidence interval for the difference is (-26, 62). This interval includes zero. The observed data do not provide strong evidence of a difference in mean word counts.

```
> Exercise18.084 # variables WordCount and Education (High, Medium)
> histogram( ~ WordCount | Education, data = Exercise18.084)
> qqmath( ~ WordCount | Education, data = Exercise18.084)
> groupMeans(Exercise18.084$WordCount, group = Exercise18.084$Education)

 High   Medium
  140  121.3889

> x84 <- split(Exercise18.084$WordCount, Exercise18.084$Education)
> boot84a <- bootstrap(x84$High, mean, seed = 0)
> boot84b <- bootstrap(x84$Medium, mean, seed = 0)
> boot84a

Call:
bootstrap(data = x84$High, statistic = mean, seed = 0)


Number of Replications: 1000


Summary Statistics:
      Observed  Mean    Bias    SE
mean       140  140.1  0.07589  17.04


> boot84b

Call:
bootstrap(data = x84$Medium, statistic = mean, seed = 0)


Number of Replications: 1000


Summary Statistics:
      Observed  Mean    Bias    SE
mean     121.4  121.6  0.2308  14.7

> par(mfrow = c(2, 2))
> plot(boot84a)
> qqnorm(boot84a)
> plot(boot84b)
> qqnorm(boot84b)
> par(mfrow = c(1, 1))
> limits.percentile(boot84a)

          2.5%       5%       95%     97.5%
mean 106.4486 110.7833 167.6389 173.7056

> limits.percentile(boot84b)

          2.5%       5%       95%     97.5%
mean 93.34028 97.11389 146.5889 150.1639

> limits.tilt(boot84a)
```

```
          2.5%       5%      95%     97.5%
mean  106.7554  111.9811  166.3616  171.1016
```

```
> limits.tilt(boot84b)
```

```
         2.5%       5%      95%     97.5%
mean  94.57862  98.63603  146.1044  150.9024
```

```
> boot84c <- bootstrap2(Exercise18.084$WordCount, mean, treatment = Exercise18.084$
+     Education, seed = 0)
> limits.percentile(boot84c)
```

```
          2.5%        5%       95%     97.5%
mean  -26.27639  -19.20278  55.83333  62.44306
```

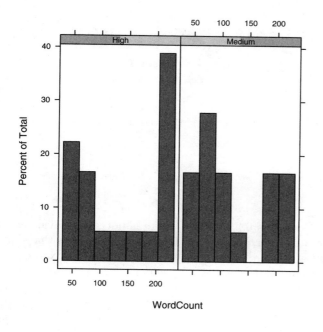

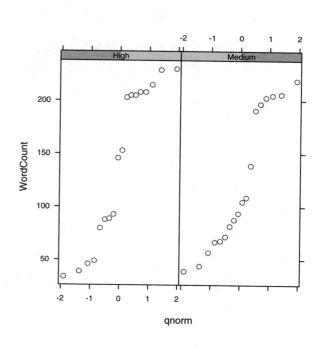

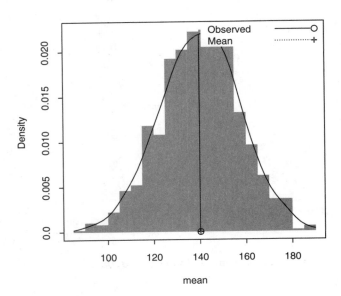

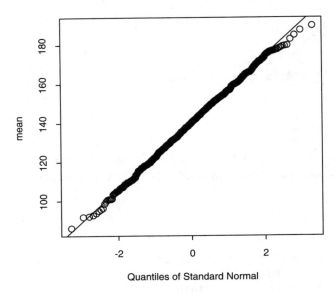

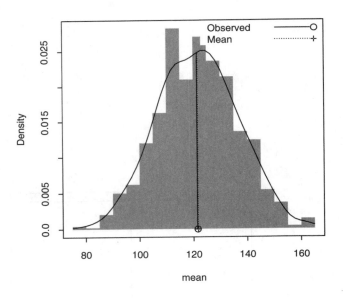

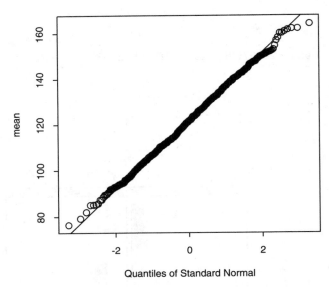

18.85

We test the hypotheses $H_0 : \mu_1 = \mu_2$, $H_a : \mu_1 > \mu_2$. The P-value is 0.212. Thus, there is not strong evidence that the mean word count is higher for ads placed in magazines aimed at people with high education levels than for ads placed in magazines aimed at people with medium education levels. The 95% confidence interval in Exercise 18.84 (d) for the difference in means contained 0. This suggests that there is not strong evidence of a difference in mean word counts. Here we conclude that there is not strong evidence that the mean word counts is higher for ads placed in magazines aimed at people with high education levels than for ads placed in magazines aimed at people with medium education levels.

```
> perm85 <- permutationTestMeans(Exercise18.084, treatment = Education, seed = 0,
+      alternative = "greater")
> perm85

Call:
permutationTestMeans(data = Exercise18.084, treatment = Education, alternative =
   "greater", seed = 0)


Number of Replications: 999


Summary Statistics:
            Observed    Mean    SE alternative p.value
WordCount     18.61  0.9411 22.42     greater   0.212
```

18.86

a Both datasets appear approximately Normal. The average number of burglaries was 64.3 before and 60.6 after the program began.

b A one-sided test, because we wish to test whether the program made an improvement. The P-value for the two-sample t test is 0.22.

c The P-value for the permutation test is 0.22. This is the same (after rounding) as the formula t test. The bootstrap distribution is very normal with no bias, suggesting that t intervals should work fine.

d The P-value is 0.788. This is testing whether the data provide strong evidence that burglaries have increased. We do not perform this test, because our goal is to determine whether the program has *reduced* burglaries. The P-value is more than 50% because the actual change was negative rather than positive; there is greater than a 50% chance that random chance would yield an increase greater than -3.7 (i.e. a decrease less than 3.7).

```
> Exercise18.086 # variables Burglaries, When (Before and After)
> groupMeans(Exercise18.086$Burglaries, Exercise18.086$When)

    After   Before
 60.64706 64.31707


> histogram( ~ Burglaries | When, data = Exercise18.086)
> qqmath( ~ Burglaries | When, data = Exercise18.086)
> x86 <- split(Exercise18.086$Burglaries, Exercise18.086$When)
> t.test(x86$Before, x86$After, alternative = "greater", var.equal = F)

        Welch Modified Two-Sample t-Test

data:  x86$Before and x86$After
t = 0.7856, df = 31.4879856371815, p-value = 0.219
alternative hypothesis:  difference in means is greater than 0
95 percent confidence interval:
 -4.246831         NA
sample estimates:
 mean of x mean of y
  64.31707   60.64706


> perm86a <- permutationTestMeans(Exercise18.086, treatment = When, alternative =
+      "greater", seed = 0)
> perm86a

Call:
permutationTestMeans(data = Exercise18.086, treatment = When, alternative = "greater",
   seed = 0)
```

```
Number of Replications: 999

Summary Statistics:
           Observed    Mean    SE alternative p.value
Burglaries     3.67 0.05042 4.722      greater   0.222
```

```
> plot(perm86a, cex.main = 1)
> qqnorm(perm86a, cex.main = 1)
> perm86b <- permutationTestMeans(Exercise18.086, treatment = When, alternative =
+     "less", seed = 0)
> perm86b
```

```
Call:
permutationTestMeans(data = Exercise18.086, treatment = When, alternative = "less", seed
  = 0)

Number of Replications: 999

Summary Statistics:
           Observed    Mean    SE alternative p.value
Burglaries     3.67 0.05042 4.722         less   0.788
```

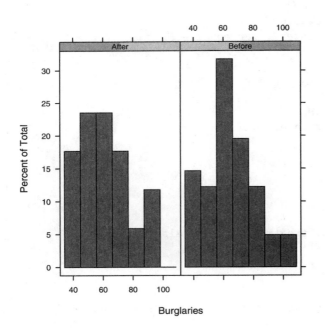

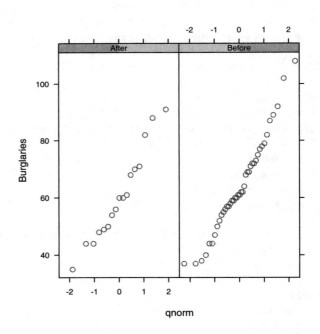

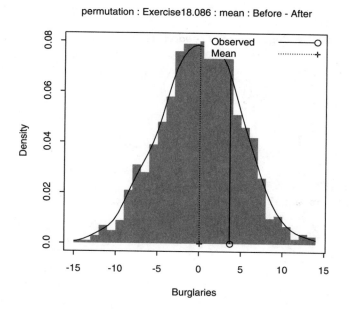

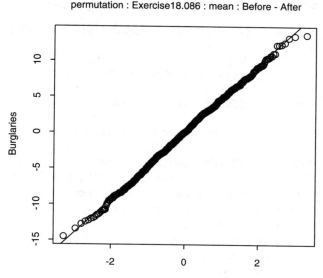

18.87

a The bootstrap distribution appears to be approximately Normal.

b The bootstrap standard error is 4.603. A 95% bootstrap t confidence interval for the difference in means, $\mu_{\text{After}} - \mu_{\text{Before}}$, using the conservative method for the degrees of freedom, is (-13.4, 6.1). Using(n1+n2-2) degrees of freedom gives a narrower interval (-12.9, 5.6).

c A 95% percentile interval is (-12.5, 5.6). This agrees closely with the second interval found in (b), so we conclude that the intervals are reasonably accurate. These intervals include 0 and so we would conclude that there is not strong evidence (at the 0.05 level) of a difference in the mean monthly burglary counts. The tests in Exercise 18.86 were one-sided tests and showed no strong evidence of a decrease in mean monthly burglaries (or of an increase in the case of part (d) of Exercise 18.86).

```
> boot87 <- bootstrap2(Exercise18.086$Burglaries, mean, treatment = Exercise18.086$
+    When, seed = 0)
> plot(boot87)
> qqnorm(boot87, cex.main = 1)
> boot87

Call:
bootstrap2(data = Exercise18.086$Burglaries, statistic = mean, treatment =
  Exercise18.086$When, seed = 0)

Number of Replications: 1000

Summary Statistics:
     Observed Mean    Bias    SE
mean      3.67 3.72 0.04981 4.603

# # The bootstrap function uses the difference:
# #  (mean of first sample) - (mean of second sample)
# # That is the opposite of what is desired here, so reverse
# # all intervals (by hand).
> limits.t(boot87)
```

```
            2.5%       5%       95%       97.5%
mean -5.873277 -4.232305 11.57233  13.21331

> limits.t(boot87, df = (nrow(Exercise18.086) - 2)) # degrees of freedom if pooling

            2.5%       5%       95%       97.5%
mean -5.562449 -4.035977 11.37601  12.90248

> t.test(x86$Before, x86$After)

        Welch Modified Two-Sample t-Test

data:  x86$Before and x86$After
t = 0.7856, df = 31.4879856371815, p-value = 0.438
alternative hypothesis:  difference in means is not equal to 0
95 percent confidence interval:
 -5.85160  13.19163
sample estimates:
 mean of x mean of y
  64.31707  60.64706

> limits.percentile(boot87)

            2.5%       5%      95%      97.5%
mean -5.556958 -3.465997 11.2599  12.47636

> plotWithIntervals(boot87, Par=list(cex.main = 1))
```

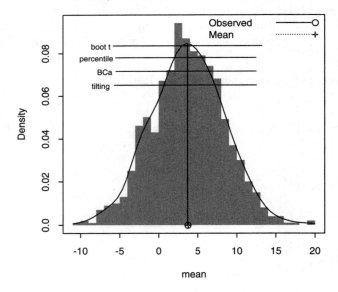

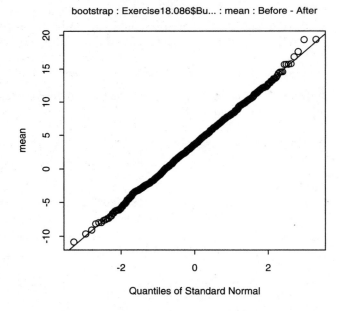